KT-420-941

BTEC Level 4 HNC and Level 5 HND in Engineering

Compiled from:

Mechanical Engineering Science
Third Edition
by J. Hannah and M. J. Hillier

Applied Mechanics
Third Edition
by J. Hannah and M. J. Hillier

Electrical and Electronic Technology
Tenth Edition
by John Hiley, Keith Brown and Ian McKenzie Smith

Control Engineering
Second Edition
by W. Bolton

Statics and Mechanics of Materials
Second Edition
by R. C. Hibbeler

Mechanical Power Transmission
by William J. Patton

Mathematics for Engineers: A Modern Interactive Approach
Third Edition
by Anthony Croft and Robert Davison

PEARSON
Custom
Publishing

Pearson Education Limited
Edinburgh Gate
Harlow
Essex CM20 2JE

And associated companies throughout the world

Visit us on the World Wide Web at:
www.pearsoned.co.uk

First published 2011

This Custom Book Edition © 2011 Published by Pearson Education Limited

Compiled from:

Mechanical Engineering Science Third Edition
by J. Hannah and M. J. Hillier
ISBN 978 0 582 32675 0
Copyright © John Hannah & MJ Hiller 1962
Copyright © John Hannah 1991, 1999

Applied Mechanics Third Edition
by J. Hannah and M. J. Hillier
ISBN 978 0 582 25632 3
Copyright © J. Hannah and m. J. Hillier 1971, 1988, 1995

Electrical and Electronic Technology Tenth Edition
by John Hiley, Keith Brown and Ian McKenzie Smith
ISBN 978 0 13 206011 0
Copyright © Pearson Education Limited 1960, 2005, 2008

Control Engineering Second Edition
by W. Bolton
ISBN 978 0 582 32773 3
Copyright © Addison Wesley Longman Limite 1998

Statics and Mechanics of Materials Second Edition
by R. C. Hibbeler
ISBN 978 0 13 1290011 2
Copyright © 2004 by R. C. Hibbeler

Mechanical Power Transmission
by William J. Patton
ISBN 978 0 13 569905 4
Copyright © 1980 by Prentice-Hall, Inc., Englewood Cliffs, N. J. 07632

Mathematics for Engineers: A Modern Interactive Approach Third Edition
by Anthony Croft and Robert Davison
ISBN 978 0 13 205156 9
Copyright © Pearson Education Limited 2004, 2008

ISBN 978 0 85776 008 1

Printed and bound in Great Britain by Henry Ling Limited at the Dorset Press,
Dorchester DT1 1HD

BTEC Level 4 HNC and Level 5 HND in Engineering

Contents

CHAPTER 1
Engineering Science

Unit 2:   Engineering Science

Unit code: L/601/1404

QCF level: 4

Credit value: 15

Aim

This unit aims to provide learners with an understanding of the mechanical and electrical principles that underpin mechanical and electrically focused engineering systems.

Unit abstract

Engineers, from no matter what discipline, need to acquire a fundamental understanding of the mechanical and electrical principles that underpin the design and operation of a large range of engineering equipment and systems.

This unit will develop learners' understanding of the key mechanical and electrical concepts that relate to all aspects of engineering.

In particular, learners will study elements of engineering statics including the analysis of beams, columns and shafts. They will then be introduced to elements of engineering dynamics, including the behavioural analysis of mechanical systems subject to uniform acceleration, the effects of energy transfer in systems and to natural and forced oscillatory motion.

The electrical system principles in learning outcome 3 begin by refreshing learners' understanding of resistors connected in series/parallel and then developing the use of Ohm's law and Kirchhoff's law to solve problems involving at least two power sources. Circuit theorems are also considered for resistive networks only, together with a study of the characteristics of growth and decay of current/voltage in series C-R and L-R circuits.

The final learning outcome develops learners' understanding of the characteristics of various AC circuits and finishes by considering an important application – the transformer.

Learning outcomes

On successful completion of this unit a learner will:

1 Be able to determine the behavioural characteristics of elements of static engineering systems
2 Be able to determine the behavioural characteristics of elements of dynamic engineering systems
3 Be able to apply DC theory to solve electrical and electronic engineering problems
4 Be able to apply single phase AC theory to solve electrical and electronic engineering problems

Unit content

1 Be able to determine the behavioural characteristics of elements of static engineering systems

Simply supported beams: determination of shear force; bending moment and stress due to bending; radius of curvature in simply supported beams subjected to concentrated and uniformly distributed loads; eccentric loading of columns; stress distribution; middle third rule

Beams and columns: elastic section modulus for beams; standard section tables for rolled steel beams; selection of standard sections eg slenderness ratio for compression members, standard section and allowable stress tables for rolled steel columns, selection of standard sections

Torsion in circular shafts: theory of torsion and its assumptions eg determination of shear stress, shear strain, shear modulus; distribution of shear stress and angle of twist in solid and hollow circular section shafts

2 Be able to determine the behavioural characteristics of elements of dynamic engineering systems

Uniform acceleration: linear and angular acceleration; Newton's laws of motion; mass moment of inertia and radius of gyration of rotating components; combined linear and angular motion; effects of friction

Energy transfer: gravitational potential energy; linear and angular kinetic energy; strain energy; principle of conservation of energy; work–energy transfer in systems with combine linear and angular motion; effects of impact loading

Oscillating mechanical systems: simple harmonic motion; linear and transverse systems; qualitative description of the effects of forcing and damping

3 Be able to apply DC theory to solve electrical and electronic engineering problems

DC electrical principles: refresh idea of resistors in series and parallel; use of Ohm's and Kirchhoff's laws; voltage and current dividers; review of motor and generator principles eg series, shunt; circuit theorems eg superposition, Thévenin, Norton and maximum power transfer for resistive circuits only; fundamental relationships eg resistance, inductance, capacitance, series C–R circuit, time constant, charge and discharge curves of capacitors, L–R circuits

4 Be able to apply single phase AC theory to solve electrical and electronic engineering problems

AC electrical principles: features of AC sinusoidal wave form for voltages and currents; explanation of how other more complex wave forms are produced from sinusoidal wave forms; R, L, C circuits eg reactance of R, L and C components, equivalent impedance and admittance for R–L and R–C circuits; high or low pass filters; power factor; true and apparent power; resonance for circuits containing a coil and capacitor connected either in series or parallel; resonant frequency; Q-factor of resonant circuit; transformer fundamentals: construction eg double wound; transformation ratio; equivalent circuit; unloaded transformer; resistance (impedance) matching; transformer losses; applications eg current transformers, voltage transformers

Learning outcomes and assessment criteria

Learning outcomes On successful completion of this unit a learner will:	Assessment criteria for pass The learner can:
LO1 Be able to determine the behavioural characteristics of elements of static engineering systems	1.1 determine distribution of shear force, bending moment and stress due to bending in simply supported beams 1.2 select standard rolled steel sections for beams and columns to satisfy given specifications 1.3 determine the distribution of shear stress and the angular deflection due to torsion in circular shafts
LO2 Be able to determine the behavioural characteristics of elements of dynamic engineering systems	2.1 determine the behaviour of dynamic mechanical systems in which uniform acceleration is present 2.2 determine the effects of energy transfer in mechanical systems 2.3 determine the behaviour of oscillating mechanical systems
LO3 Be able to apply DC theory to solve electrical and electronic engineering problems	3.1 solve problems using Kirchhoff's laws to calculate currents and voltages in circuits 3.2 solve problems using circuit theorems to calculate currents and voltages in circuits 3.3 solve problems involving current growth/decay in an L-R circuit and voltage growth/decay in a C-R circuit
LO4 Be able to apply single phase AC theory to solve electrical and electronic engineering problems	4.1 recognise a variety of complex waveforms and explain how they are produced from sinusoidal waveforms 4.2 apply AC theory to solve problems on R, L, C circuits and components 4.3 apply AC theory to solve problems involving transformers

Guidance

Links

This unit may be linked with *Unit 1: Analytical Methods for Engineers.*

Successful completion of this unit would enable learners to meet, in part, the Incorporated Engineer (IEng) requirements laid down in the UK Engineering Council Standard for Professional Engineering Competence (UK-SPEC) Competence A2, 'Use appropriate scientific, technical or engineering principles'.

Essential requirements

Learners will need access to suitable mechanical and electrical laboratory equipment.

Employer engagement and vocational contexts

Liaison with employers would prove of benefit to centres, especially if they are able to offer help with the provision of suitable mechanical or electrical systems/equipment that demonstrate applications of the principles.

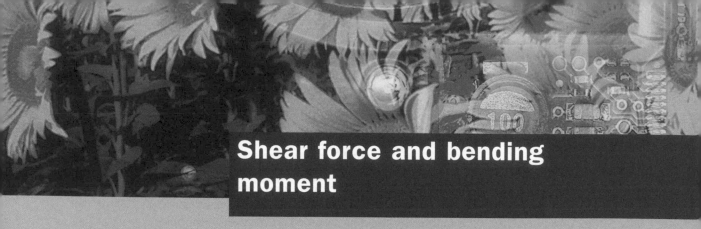

Shear force and bending moment

Introduction

The effects of shearing and bending due to the forces produced by the load-ing on a structure will be considered in this section. Shear force and bending moment are defined and several standard cases of beams of various types, supports and loading are described. The shear force and bending moment are found for a number of points on the beam in each case, leading to the construction of diagrams showing the variation in values along the beam.

The cantilever beam

Consider the horizontal beam shown in Fig. 1.1. The end A is rigidly *built-in* to the wall and the end B is free. Such a beam is called a *cantilever*.

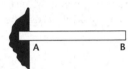

Fig. 1.1   Cantilever beam

The simply supported beam

The beam shown in Fig. 1.2(a) is supported on a pair of knife edges and is said to be *simply* or *freely* supported. Other forms of support that may be often considered as *simple* are shown in Figs. 1.2(b) and (c).

The reaction exerted by a simple support on a beam is assumed to act at a point.

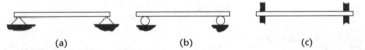

(a)   (b)   (c)

Fig. 1.2   Simply supported beams: (a) knife edge; (b) roller supports; (c) short bearings

Calculations of reactions

When a beam is fixed at some point or supported by props, the fixings and props exert reaction forces on the beam. To calculate these reactions the procedure is

• to equate the net transverse force to zero;
• to equate the total moment about any convenient point to zero.

For a horizontal cantilever beam, the fixed end is supported by a vertical reaction together with a moment about the same point, exerted by the fixing.

For a simply supported horizontal beam, the reactions may be found by taking moments about each support in turn and then checking that the net vertical force is zero.

Shear force

The cantilever beam shown in Fig. 1.3 carries a vertical transverse load of magnitude W at the free end. It will be assumed that the load is concentrated at a single point. Such a load is then called a *concentrated* or *point load*. For equilibrium of vertical forces acting on the beam AB the downward load W must be balanced by an equal and opposite vertical reaction W at the built-in end A (the weight of the beam is neglected here).

Consider now the effect of a transverse saw-cut at any section X of the beam. The effect of the load W would be to move the portion XB downwards. Before the saw-cut was made, therefore, there must have been an upward vertical force, equal and opposite to W, opposing the tendency of the load to move the portion XB downwards. This force must be exerted by the material of the beam itself at the section X. The effect of the applied load at any section therefore is to tend to *shear* the beam across at that section.

We now define the *shear force* at any section as the force transverse to the beam tending to cause it to shear across the section.

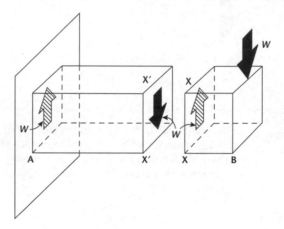

Fig. 1.3

Sign convention

The shear force at any section is taken *positive* if the portion of the beam to the *right* of the section tends to slide downwards relative to the left-hand portion, Fig. 1.4(a).

A *negative* shear force tends to cause the right-hand portion to slide *upwards* relative to the left-hand portion at the section considered, Fig. 1.4(b).

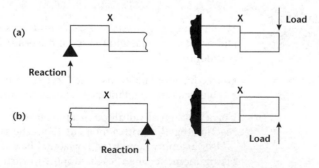

Fig. 1.4   (a) Positive shear force; (b) negative shear force

Resultant shear force

If several loads act on a beam, the *total, net* or *resultant* shear force at any section is equal in magnitude to the resultant of the transverse loads *on one side* of the section, due account being taken of sign. Thus

the resultant shear force at any section of a loaded beam is the algebraic sum of the loads to one side of the section.

It does not matter which side of the section is considered provided that all loads on that side of the section are taken into account, including reactions exerted by fixings and supports. (The algebraic sum of the loads to the left-hand side of the section is, of course, equal to the algebraic sum of the loads to the right-hand side of the section.) Note that shear is caused only by loads *transverse* to the section of the beam.

Shear force diagram

The *shear force diagram* is a graph plotted along the axis of the beam showing the variation of shear force along the beam. For the beam shown in Fig. 1.5(a), the shear force is $+W$, and is uniform along the beam. Figure 1.5(b) shows the shear force diagram for this beam, the line O–O being the axis of zero shear force.

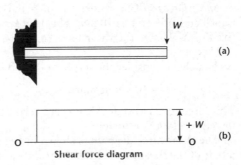

Fig. 1.5

Where the load W is a 'dead' load it may be given in units of mass, i.e. kilograms or tonnes, and it is necessary to calculate the *weight* of such loads in force units (newtons) before carrying out calculations.

Example 1.1

Draw the shear force diagram for the loaded cantilever beam shown in Fig. 1.6(a).

Solution

We first calculate the reaction at the built-in end A.

Net applied downward load on beam = $10 - 6 = 4$ kN

The fixing reaction at A is equal and opposite to this and is therefore 4 kN upwards, Fig. 1.6(b).

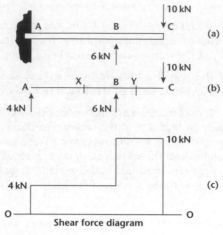

Fig. 1.6

Shear force in AB: consider the force acting on the left-hand portion of any section X in AB. The only force *on* the beam to the left of X is the 4 kN reaction and this tends to slide AX upward relative to XC. The shear force in AB is therefore +4 kN and is uniform along AB.

Shear force in BC: consider section Y in BC. The force on the beam to the right-hand side of Y is 10 kN. This load tends to shear YC downward relative to AY. Hence the shear force in BC is uniform, positive, and equal to +10 kN.

As a check consider the forces to the left of Y. Their resultant is

$$4 + 6 = 10 \text{ kN, upward}$$

This force tends to slide AY upward relative to YC. The shear force at Y is therefore +10 kN, as before.

The shear force diagram is shown in Fig. 1.6(c). It is seen that the magnitude of the shear force changes abruptly at each concentrated load and that the shear force is uniform on unloaded portions of the beam. The shear force diagram for a beam carrying only concentrated loads therefore consists of straight horizontal lines.

Example 1.2

Draw the shear force diagram for the simply supported beam shown in Fig. 1.7(a). State the magnitude of the greatest shear force. What is the change of shear force at B?

Solution

We first calculate the reactions L and R of the simple supports at A and C respectively.

Taking moments about A,

$$R \times 10 = 6 \times 6$$

therefore

$$R = 3.6 \text{ kN}$$

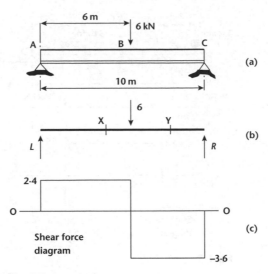

Fig. 1.7

Taking moments about C,

$$L \times 10 = 6 \times 4$$

therefore

$$L = 2.4 \text{ kN}$$

Shear force in AB: the portion of beam to the left of section X in AB, Fig. 1.7(b), is subject to an upward force $L = 2.4$ kN. This force tends to slide AX upward relative to XC. Therefore, the shear force in AB = +2.4 kN.

Shear force in BC: the portion of beam to the right of section Y in BC is subject to an upward force $R = 3.6$ kN. This force tends to slide YC upward relative to AY. Therefore, shear force in BC = −3.6 kN. The shear force diagram is as shown in Fig. 1.7(c). The greatest shear force is **3.6 kN** at every section between B and C.

The change in shear force at B = 2.4 − (−3.6)

$$= \mathbf{6 \text{ kN}} \ (= \text{load at B})$$

Example 1.3   **The beam shown in Fig. 1.8 is simply supported at B and D and carries at A and C concentrated masses of 1 tonne and 3 tonnes respectively. Determine the reactions L and R at B and D and draw the shear force diagram.**

Solution

The reaction at D is found by taking moments about B for *all* the loads on the beam, i.e. equating clockwise and anticlockwise moments about B. The weight of the 1 tonne mass is 9.8 kN and the weight of the 3 tonne mass is 29.4 kN. Thus

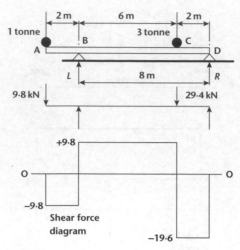

Fig. 1.8

$$(9.8 \times 2) + (R \times 8) = 29.4 \times 6$$

Therefore

$$R = \mathbf{19.6 \ kN}$$

Similarly, taking moments about D,

$$L \times 8 = (29.4 \times 2) + (9.8 \times 10)$$

Therefore

$$L = \mathbf{19.6 \ kN}$$

Alternatively, equating the net vertical force to zero,

$$L + R = 29.4 + 9.8$$

so that

$$L = 39.2 - 19.6$$

$$= 19.6 \ kN, \text{ as before}$$

Shear force diagram   The diagram is drawn by remembering that

- the shear force changes abruptly at a concentrated load;
- the shear force is uniform on an unloaded portion of the beam.

Using the given sign convention, we may start at the *left-hand end* and draw the diagram by following the arrows representing the loads and reactions; thus we draw

- at A, 9.8 kN down, then a horizontal line to B;
- at B, 19.6 kN up, then a horizontal line to C;
- at C, 29.4 kN down, then a horizontal line to D;
- at D, 19.6 kN up to the zero line again.

Note that in this method we have followed the *changes* in shear force along the beam.

Problems

1.1 Calculate, for the cantilever beam loaded as shown in Fig. 1.9(a), the shear force at A and the reaction at the built-in end. Draw the shear force diagram for the beam.   (+2 kN; 3 kN; upward)

1.2 A cantilever, Fig. 1.9(b), is loaded as shown and supported by a vertical prop. Calculate the load P in the prop for the reaction at the built-in end to be zero. Draw the shear force diagram for the beam.
(9 kN)

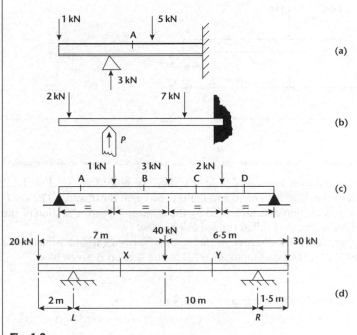

(a)

(b)

(c)

(d)

Fig. 1.9

1.3 A simply supported beam of span 10 m between supports carries a mass of 5 t at a point 6 m from the left-hand support. Calculate (a) the shear force just to the right-hand side of the load, and (b) the change in shear force under the load.   (−29.4 kN; 49 kN)

1.4 A horizontal cantilever beam forming part of a wall crane carries the crane and its load totalling 3 t at the free end 3 m from the built-in end, and a vertical load of 1 t at 1 m from the wall. A tie-bar supports the beam and exerts an upward vertical force of 15 kN at the free end. Draw to scale the shear force diagram for the beam and state (a) the reaction at the built-in end and (b) the greatest shear force in the beam.   (24.2 kN upward; 24.2 kN)

1.5 Draw the shear force diagram for the simply supported beam shown in Fig. 1.9(c). State the value of the shear force at the points A, B, C and D.   (+2.75, +1.75, −1.25, −3.25 kN)

1.6 A beam is simply supported over a span of 6 m and carries a vertical concentrated load of 80 kN at a distance of 1.5 m from the left-hand support. The beam also carries a load of 100 kN at distance x from the right-hand support. Calculate the greatest value of x if the greatest shear force near the left-hand end is to be not greater than 80 kN.   (1.2 m)

1.7 An 0–6–0 diesel shunting locomotive has three axles, spaced 1.8 m apart. The mass of the locomotive is distributed as follows: front axle, 12 t; centre axle, 14 t; rear axle, 16 t. The locomotive rests on a bridge of 9 m span with the front axle 2.4 m from the left-hand support. If the bridge is simply supported, calculate the shear force at the midpoint of the span and draw the shear force diagram for the bridge.   (−43.1 kN)

1.8 The beam shown in Fig. 1.9(d) is simply supported but overhangs both supports. For the loading shown, calculate the reactions L and R at the supports and state the shear force at points X and Y.

(L, 39.5 kN; R, 50.5 kN; +19.5, −20.5 kN)

1.9 Draw to scale the shear force diagram for the simply supported beam loaded as shown in Fig. 1.10. State the magnitude of the reactions L and R and of the greatest and least shear forces on the beam.

($L = 6.3$ kN; $R = 3.7$ kN; 6.3 kN along AB; 0.3 kN along CD)

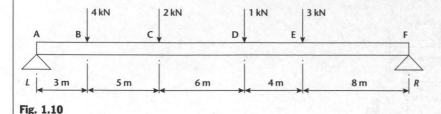

Fig. 1.10

Bending moment

Consider a cantilever beam loaded by a transverse point load W, Fig. 1.11. The effect of this load is to bend and deflect the beam downward. The *bending effect* at any section X is measured by the *moment* about the section of the load W. This moment is called the *bending moment*.

If the perpendicular distance of the section X from the line of action of the load at B is x, the bending moment M at the section is given by

$$M = W \times x$$

The units of bending moment are N m, kN m, MN m.

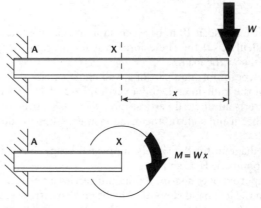

Fig. 1.11

Sign convention

A bending moment is *positive* if its effect is to tend to make the beam *sag* at the section considered, Fig. 1.12. If the moment tends to make the beam bend upward at the section, or *hog*, it is *negative*.

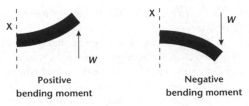

Positive
bending moment

Negative
bending moment

Fig. 1.12

Resultant bending moment

When more than one load acts on a beam, *the bending moment at any section is the algebraic sum of the moments due to all the forces on one side of the section.*

The moments of *all* the forces on *one side* of the section must be considered, including any moments exerted by end fixings and reactions. It does not matter which side of the section is considered, since the algebraic sum of the moments of all forces to the left of the section is equal to the sum of moments of all forces to the right of the section.

We must distinguish carefully between 'taking moments' and calculating a 'bending moment':

1. *The principle of moments* states that for equilibrium the algebraic sum of the moments of all the forces about any point is zero, i.e. when forces on *both* sides of a beam section are considered.
2. *The bending moment* is the algebraic sum of the moments of forces on *one* side of the section about that section.

Bending moment diagram

The *bending moment diagram* is a graph showing the variation along the axis of the beam of the applied bending moment.

For the beam shown in Fig. 1.13, the bending moment at section X is negative, since the beam tends to hog. Hence the bending moment M at section X is

$$M = -Wx$$

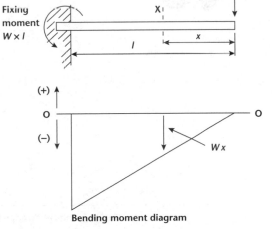

Bending moment diagram

Fig. 1.13

This expression for the bending moment applies to the whole length of the beam.

The moment M is proportional to x; hence the graph is a straight line. It is seen that the bending moment is zero at the free end where $x = 0$, and takes its greatest value at the built-in end where $x = l$. The bending moment diagram is therefore as shown in Fig. 1.13 and is everywhere negative.

The greatest bending moment is $-Wl$ and occurs at the built-in end. The fixing moment exerted by the wall on the beam at the built-in end is equal and opposite to the applied moment, therefore;

$$\text{fixing moment} = Wl, \textit{anticlockwise}$$

Example 1.4   **Draw the bending moment diagram for the simply supported beam shown in Fig. 1.14(a).**

Solution

Reactions: we first calculate the reactions L and R at the simple supports A and C respectively. Taking moments about A,

$$R \times 10 = 5 \times 7$$

therefore

$$R = 3.5 \text{ kN}$$

Equating upward and downward forces,

$$L + R = 5 \text{ kN}$$

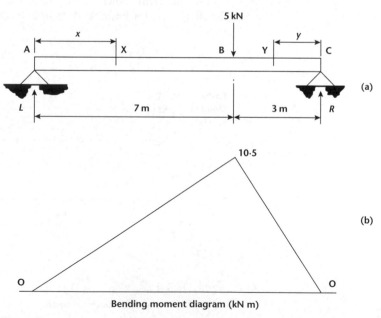

Bending moment diagram (kN m)

Fig. 1.14

Hence

$$L = 1.5 \text{ kN}$$

Consider section X, distance x from A.

Bending moment at X, $M_x = +L \times x$

$$= +1.5x \text{ kN m}$$

This moment is positive since it tends to make the beam sag at X. Since the moment M_x is proportional to x, the bending moment diagram for length AB is therefore a *straight line*. At point A, where $x = 0$, $M_x = 0$. At point B, where $x = 7$ m, $M_x = 10.5$ kN m.

Consider now section Y, distant y from C. The bending moment at Y is $+R \times y = +3.5y$. This moment is proportional to y; hence the bending moment graph is a straight line between C and B. At C, where $y = 0$, the bending moment is zero, and at B, where $y = 3$ m, the bending moment is $+10.5$ kN m, as already found.

To draw the bending moment diagram we plot the values of the moments at A, B and C and join the plotted points by straight lines, Fig. 1.14(b).

Note. This example shows that the bending moment diagram for a beam loaded only with concentrated point loads will consist of a series of straight lines. The slope of the diagram changes at each load. At the free end of a beam, the bending moment must be zero. Therefore, to draw the bending moment diagram for a beam carrying only point loads, it is only necessary to calculate the bending moment at each load, plot these values, and join the plotted points by straight lines. This method assumes that the weight of the beam itself is negligible.

Example 1.5 Draw the bending moment diagram for the propped cantilever loaded as shown in Fig. 1.15(a). The prop exerts an upward force of 6 kN. State the magnitude of the greatest bending moment and the fixing moment at the built-in end.

Solution

The bending moment diagram is made up of straight lines between the points A, B and C. It is sufficient, therefore, to calculate the moment at each of these points.

Bending moment at A due to load at $C = -4 \times 8 = -32$ kN m

(negative, since it tends to make the beam hog at A)

Bending moment at A due to load at $B = +6 \times 5 = +30$ kN m

(positive, since it tends to make the beam sag at A)

Resultant bending moment at $A = -32 + 30 = -2$ kN m

(the resultant bending is negative and therefore tends to make the beam hog at A)

The fixing moment exerted at the built-in end is equal and opposite to the resultant bending moment exerted by the applied loads. The fixing moment is therefore **2 kN m, anticlockwise**, Fig. 1.15(b).

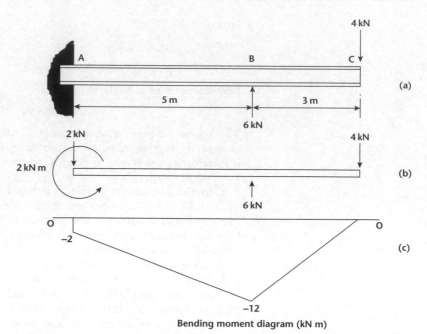

Fig. 1.15

To find the bending moment at B, consider the portion of beam to the right of B; then

bending moment at B $= -4 \times 3 = -12$ kN m

Alternatively, considering the portion of beam to the left of B,

vertical reaction at A $= 6 - 4 = 2$ kN, downward

Therefore, bending moment at B

$=$ moment of vertical reaction at A $+$ fixing moment at A

$= -2 \times 5 - 2$

$= -12$ kN m, as before

The bending moment at the free end C is zero.

The bending moment diagram is shown in Fig. 1.15(c). The greatest bending moment occurs at B and has magnitude **12 kN m**.

Example 1.6   **Draw to scale the bending moment diagram for the simply supported beam loaded as shown in Fig. 1.16(a).**

Solution

We first calculate the magnitude of the reactions L and R at A and E respectively. Taking moments about A and E in turn we obtain

$R = 4.286$ kN

$L = 3.714$ kN

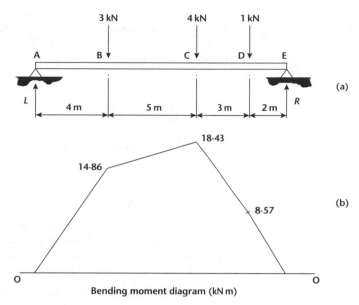

Fig. 1.16

The bending moment is zero at the free ends A and E.

Bending moment at B = +3.714 × 4 (considering loads on AB)

= +14.86 kN m

Bending moment at C = +3.714 × 9 − 3 × 5 (considering loads on AC)

= +18.43 kN m

Bending moment at D = +4.286 × 2 (considering loads on DE)

= +8.57 kN m

The bending moment diagram is drawn by plotting the moments at A, B, C, D and E and joining the plotted points by straight lines, Fig. 1.16(b). The greatest bending moment occurs at C and is of magnitude **18.4 kN m**.

Example 1.7

A horizontal joist carrying a travelling crane is simply supported over a span of 4 m. The mass of the crane is 150 kg. Determine the maximum load that the crane can support in kg, if the bending moment on the beam is not to exceed 5000 N m and the shear force is not to exceed 3 kN when the crane is positioned at midspan.

Solution

Let W newtons be the total weight of the crane and its load. The bending moment diagram is a triangle with its apex at the midpoint of the beam. The greatest bending moment occurs at the midpoint and is $Wl/4$, where $l = 4$ m is the span. Thus

$$\text{greatest bending moment} = \frac{Wl}{4} = 5000 \text{ N m}$$

Therefore

$$W = 5000 \text{ N}$$

The shear force is constant in magnitude along the beam and is equal to $W/2$; therefore

$$\frac{W}{2} = 3 \times 1000 \text{ N}$$

and

$$W = 6000 \text{ N}$$

The maximum permissible value of W is therefore 5000 N or 5 kN. For this value of W, both the bending moment and the shear force are kept within the given limiting values. This load is equivalent to the weight of a mass of 5000/9.8, or 510 kg. Therefore

$$\text{maximum load (mass) crane can carry} = 510 - \text{mass of crane}$$

$$= 510 - 150$$

$$= \mathbf{360 \text{ kg}}$$

Problems

1.10 Draw the bending moment diagram for the cantilever beam shown in Fig. 1.17(a) and state the magnitude of the fixing moment at the built-in end.   (90 kN m)

1.11 For the cantilever beam loaded as shown in Fig. 1.17(b), calculate the vertical load P in the prop if the fixing moment at the built-in end is to be zero. For this value of P, draw the shear force and bending moment diagrams and state the values of the bending moment and shearing force at a point 1 m from the built-in end.   (75 kN; 25 kN m; 25 kN)

1.12 Draw the shear force and bending moment diagrams for the loaded cantilever shown in Fig. 1.17(c). State the greatest value of shear force and bending moment.   (3000 N; −14 000 N m)

1.13 Draw the shear force and bending moment diagrams for the simply supported beam shown in Fig. 1.17(d). State the value of the bending moment at each load. What is the shear force at a section between the 20 kN and 10 kN loads?   (82.5, 105, 97.5 kN m; 7.5 kN)

1.14 Draw the shear force and bending moment diagrams for the simply supported beam shown in Fig. 1.17(e). State (a) the reactions at the supports, (b) the bending moment at midspan and (c) the least and greatest shear forces.
          (Left-hand reaction, 46.875 kN, right-hand, 43.125 kN; 195 kN m, 13.125 kN, 46.875 kN)

1.15 Draw the bending moment diagram for the beam shown in Fig. 1.17(f). The beam overhangs its supports at each end. State the magnitude of the reactions at the supports and the bending moment at points A, B and C.
          (Left-hand reaction, 2.1 kN, right-hand, 3.9 kN; A, −0.8 kN m; B, −0.75 kN m; C, −1.2 kN m)

1.16 A wall crane is constructed from a horizontal cantilever beam. The crane mechanism has a mass of 180 kg and is mounted 2.5 m from the built-in end. Calculate the greatest mass which can be lifted if the maximum bending moment in the cantilever is not to exceed 90 kN m.   (3.5 tonnes)

1.17 A four-wheel motor lorry has an unladen mass of $1\frac{1}{2}$ t (excluding wheels and axles) and its centre of gravity lies 1 m behind the front axle. The wheel base is 4 m. The lorry carries a load of 4 t having a centre of gravity midway between the axles. Calculate the load on the front axle and the bending moment on the chassis at a point midway between the axles.   (30.7 kN; 46.6 kN m)

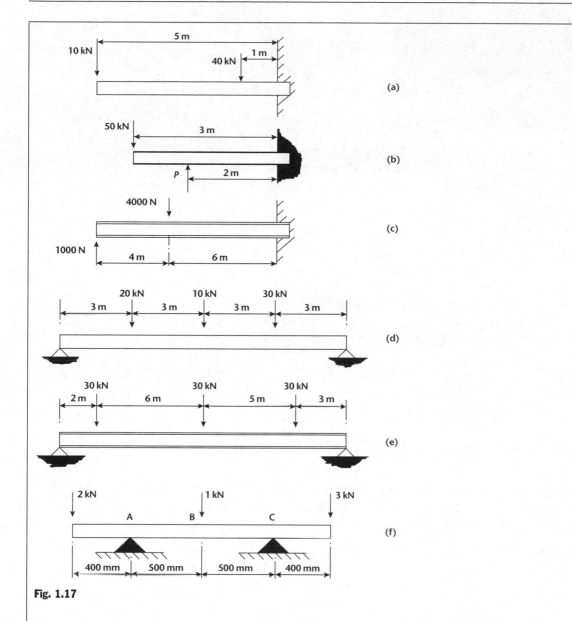

Fig. 1.17

1.18 A motor vehicle has a wheel base of 3 m. The load on the front axle is 12 kN and that on the rear axle is 16 kN. The vehicle rests on a simply supported bridge of span 8 m, the front axle being 2 m from one support. Calculate the reactions of the bridge supports and the bending moment under each axle.
(13, 15 kN; 39, 30 kN m)

1.19 A horizontal beam of span 6 m supports two equal masses M kg, one at midspan, the other at a point 2 m from one support. If the greatest shear force is limited to 10 kN and the greatest bending moment to 20 kN m, find the safe value for M.
(818 kg)

Motion; velocity and acceleration

Introduction

In this section the linear motion of a body that has a change in its speed and direction is considered, irrespective of the forces involved. The equations of linear motion are derived, connecting time with the vector quantities of displacement, velocity and acceleration: these quantities can be treated in the same manner as forces in terms of resolution and combination. The speed–time graph, relative velocity, triangle of velocities and the equations of motion are applied to problems involving the motion of ships and aircraft, etc., freely falling bodies and the flight of projectiles.

Displacement and motion

When a body moves in a straight path in one plane, its displacement alters in magnitude but its direction remains constant. The body is said to have *plane rectilinear motion*. If the body moves in a curved path, both the magnitude and direction of its displacement alter and the motion is said to be *curvilinear*.

Speed

The *average speed* of a body, a car for example, is defined as the distance travelled along the path of its motion divided by the time taken. Thus if the distance travelled along any curved path PQ, Fig. 1.18, is denoted by s, and the time taken is denoted by t, the average speed v_{av} is given by

$$v_{av} = \frac{s}{t}$$

Speed is a derived quantity since it is defined in terms of the two fundamental quantities, length and time. In metre second units the unit of speed is the *metre per second* (m/s). This is the derived SI unit. Other units used are the kilometre per second and the kilometre per hour. A non-SI unit in use for navigation work is the *knot*, equal to one nautical mile per hour and equivalent to 0.514 m/s or 1.85 km/h.

If the distance travelled is the same in successive intervals of time then the speed is said to be *constant*. For constant speed v, we have

$$v = \frac{s}{t} \qquad\qquad [1.1]$$

In practice the speed of a car or other body is not always constant but may change from instant to instant. As shown, the average speed may always be calculated if both the total distance and the time taken are known. This tells

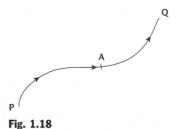

Fig. 1.18

us nothing, however, of the *speed at a point*. Suppose therefore that at some point A on the path PQ the speed is said to be of amount v. This merely means that if that speed were to be maintained from the point A onwards the body would travel a distance v in unit time. The speed at a point is often described as a *rate of change* of distance with time. A precise definition of this idea requires the use of the calculus.

Acceleration

If the speed of a body increases from one instant to the next it is said to *accelerate*, and the change of motion is termed *acceleration*. If the speed decreases the body is said to *decelerate* or *retard*, and the change of motion is said to be *deceleration* or *retardation*.

The *average* acceleration is defined as the increase in speed divided by the time taken. Thus, if t is the time taken for the speed to increase from an amount u to an amount v, the average acceleration is

$$a_{\text{av}} = \frac{\text{increase in speed } (v - u)}{\text{time taken } (t)}$$

$$= \frac{v - u}{t}$$

A deceleration may be considered as a negative acceleration. For example, if the speed of a vehicle decreases from $u = 60$ m/s, to $v = 36$ m/s in a time $t = 12$ s, the average acceleration is

$$a_{\text{av}} = \frac{36 - 60}{12} \left(\frac{\text{metres per second}}{\text{seconds}} \right)$$

$$= -2 \text{ m/s}^2 \text{ (metres per second per second)}$$

This is negative; hence the change in speed is a deceleration. If the deceleration is constant, this means that the speed of the body falls by an amount 2 m/s in every second.

If the speed of a body increases by equal amounts in equal times the acceleration is said to be *constant*. Thus a constant acceleration of +2 m/s^2 means that the speed of the body increases by an amount 2 m/s in every second. The term *uniform acceleration* is sometimes used to mean constant acceleration.

Note that the only recommended unit of acceleration is the *metre per second per second*. Multiples and sub-multiples should not be used.

The formula for constant acceleration is identical with that for average acceleration. Thus constant acceleration a is given by

$$a = \frac{v - u}{t}$$

or

$$at = v - u$$

i.e. $$v = u + at$$ [1.2]

The speed–time graph

The relation between speed and time expressed by the equation $v = u + at$ is shown in the speed–time graph, Fig. 1.19. For a constant speed u, the graph is a horizontal line CB and OC = u. For constant acceleration a, the graph is a straight line CD and AD = v, OA = t. Hence

$$a = \frac{v - u}{t}$$

$$= \frac{AD - OC}{OA}$$

$$= \frac{AD - AB}{OA}$$

$$= \frac{BD}{CB}$$

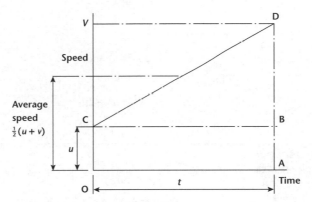

Fig. 1.19

Thus the acceleration a is given by the gradient BD/CB of the graph.

When the acceleration is *constant*, the average speed is given by the mean height, i.e.

$$\text{average speed} = \tfrac{1}{2}(u + v)$$

But average speed = s/t, hence

$$v_{av} = \frac{s}{t} = \tfrac{1}{2}(u + v)$$

Therefore

$$s = \tfrac{1}{2}(u + v)t \qquad\qquad [1.3]$$

Also, we have

$$v = u + at$$

Hence, substituting for v,

$$s = \tfrac{1}{2}[u + (u + at)]t$$

or

$$s = ut + \tfrac{1}{2}at^2 \qquad\qquad [1.4]$$

This gives the distance s travelled in time t.

Alternatively the distance can be expressed by an equation which does not involve the time. Thus, from equation [1.3],

$$\text{distance, } s = \tfrac{1}{2}(u + v)t$$

Also,

$$\text{time, } t = \frac{v - u}{a}$$

Therefore

$$s = \tfrac{1}{2}(v + u)\frac{(v - u)}{a}$$

$$= \frac{v^2 - u^2}{2a}$$

or

$$2as = v^2 - u^2$$

Thus

$$v^2 = u^2 + 2as \qquad\qquad [1.5]$$

Summary of equations for constant acceleration

$$v = u + at$$
$$s = \tfrac{1}{2}(u + v)t$$
$$s = ut + \tfrac{1}{2}at^2$$
$$v^2 = u^2 + 2as$$

Note that these equations are *not* valid if the acceleration is not constant. The first equation only may be used, however, for a varying acceleration if a is replaced by the average acceleration a_{av}. *Finally, it should be remembered that a is negative for a retardation.*

Example 1.8   Calculate the time taken for a train to travel 1000 m if its initial speed is 30 m/s and it has a constant acceleration of 0.1 m/s².

Solution

Since

$$s = 1000 \text{ m}$$

$$u = 30 \text{ m/s}$$

$$a = 0.1 \text{ m/s}^2$$

and
$$s = ut + \tfrac{1}{2}at^2$$

then
$$1000 = 30t + \tfrac{1}{2} \times 0.1 \times t^2$$

i.e. $0.05t^2 + 30t - 1000 = 0$

$$t^2 + 600t - 20\,000 = 0$$

Hence
$$t = -300 \pm 332$$

Since the negative answer has no meaning here,
$$t = -300 + 332$$
$$t = 32 \text{ s}$$

Example 1.9   **Find the deceleration of a car that is brought to rest in 60 m from a speed of 45 km/h. What is the time taken?**

Solution

The following factor for converting kilometres per hour to metres per second is useful and should be memorized:

$$1 \text{ km/h} = \frac{1 \times 1000}{3600} = \frac{1}{3.6} \text{ m/s}$$

Hence, to convert km/h to m/s divide by 3.6. Thus

$$u = 45 \text{ km/h} = \frac{45}{3.6} = 12.5 \text{ m/s}$$

$$v = 0$$

$$s = 60 \text{ m}$$

Since
$$v^2 = u^2 + 2as$$
$$0 = 12.5^2 + (2 \times a \times 60)$$
$$a = -1.3 \text{ m/s}^2$$

This is negative since the car is being retarded.
    Again, to find the time t, from

$$v = u + at$$
$$0 = 12.5 - 1.3t$$

Therefore

$$t = 9.6 \text{ s}$$

Problems

1.20 A car travelling at 80 km/h is brought to rest with constant retardation in a distance of 60 m. Calculate the retardation. (4.12 m/s^2)

1.21 A piston moves from rest to a speed of 5 m/s in one twenty-fifth of a second. What are the average acceleration and the distance travelled? $(125 \text{ m/s}^2; 100 \text{ mm})$

1.22 The constant acceleration of a train is 1 m/s². Calculate the time taken to increase its speed from 10 to 40 km/h and the distance travelled in this time. $(8.3 \text{ s}; 57.8 \text{ m})$

1.23 Calculate the time taken for a car to cover a distance of 100 m if the initial speed is 10 km/h and it has a constant acceleration of 1.5 m/s². (9.9 s)

1.24 The maximum retardation of a lift is 3 m/s². Calculate the shortest time required to bring it to rest from a speed of 9 m/s. What is the distance travelled in this time? $(3 \text{ s}; 13.5 \text{ m})$

1.25 A planing machine table comes to rest from a speed of 27 m/min in a distance of 8 cm. If the retardation is constant, calculate its value. (1.27 m/s^2)

1.26 A train moves with constant acceleration from a speed of 20 km/h to a final speed of 150 km/h. What is its average speed? If the time taken is 6 min, calculate the distance travelled in this period.
$(85 \text{ km/h}; 8.5 \text{ km})$

1.27 An aircraft increases its speed from 160 km/h to 960 km/h in one minute. If the acceleration is constant, calculate its value and the distance travelled in this time. $(3.7 \text{ m/s}^2; 9.34 \text{ km})$

1.28 A motor boat is travelling at 16 knots in calm water when the engine cuts out. The boat slows to 10 knots in 15 s. Assuming constant deceleration, find its value and the distance travelled in kilometres in this time. What further time elapses before the boat comes to rest? 1 knot = 0.514 m/s.
$(0.21 \text{ m/s}^2; 0.1 \text{ km}; 25 \text{ s})$

1.29 An airliner is required to have a speed of 370 km/h along the ground on a level runway before it can take off. The initial acceleration is limited to 3 m/s². Assuming constant acceleration during the run-up, find the minimum length of runway needed. (1.76 km)

1.30 An aeroplane lands on the deck of a stationary aircraft carrier at a horizontal speed of 30 m/s and is brought to rest by the arrestor gear in a distance of 60 m. Find the deceleration of the plane, assuming it to be constant, and the time taken to halt the plane. $(7.5 \text{ m/s}^2; 4 \text{ s})$

Use of the speed–time graph

Many problems are conveniently solved by making use of the fact that *the area under the speed–time graph is equal to the distance travelled*. This is proved as follows.

In Fig. 1.20 the line CD represents the v–t graph for motion with constant acceleration.

$$\text{Area under } v\text{–}t \text{ graph} = \text{area OADC}$$
$$= \text{area OABC} + \text{area CBD}$$
$$= \text{OC} \times \text{OA} + \tfrac{1}{2}\text{CB} \times \text{BD}$$
$$= ut + \tfrac{1}{2}t(v - u)$$

But

$$v - u = at$$

Hence

$$\text{area} = ut + \tfrac{1}{2}at \times t$$
$$= ut + \tfrac{1}{2}at^2$$
$$= s \quad \text{from equation [1.4], p. 26}$$

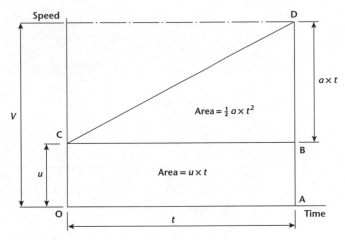

Fig. 1.20

Thus

$$\text{average speed} = \frac{s}{t}$$

$$= \frac{\text{area under } v\text{–}t \text{ graph}}{\text{total time taken}}$$

Example 1.10 A cycle accelerates with a constant acceleration of 0.2 m/s² from rest for a period of 7 s and continues at this speed for 30 s before coming to rest in 5 s. The deceleration is constant. Sketch the v–t diagram and determine the time taken to travel the first 15 m and the total distance travelled.

Solution

In the v–t diagram, Fig. 1.21, OA represents the period of constant accelera-tion, AB the period of constant speed and BC the retardation. Since at O the velocity $u = 0$, the velocity at the end of the acceleration is

$$v = at$$

$$= 0.2 \times 7 = 1.4 \text{ m/s}$$

Distance travelled during acceleration

$$= \text{area OAE}$$

$$= \tfrac{1}{2} \times 1.4 \times 7$$

$$= 4.9 \text{ m}$$

In order to cover a distance of 15 m, the additional distance to be travelled at a constant speed of 1.4 m/s

$$= 15 - 4.9$$

$$= 10.1 \text{ m}$$

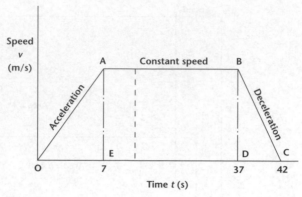

Fig. 1.21

Time taken to travel this additional distance at constant speed

$$= \frac{\text{distance}}{\text{speed}}$$

$$= \frac{10.1}{1.4}$$

$$= 7.2 \text{ s}$$

Total time to travel 15 m

$$= 7 + 7.2 = \mathbf{14.2 \text{ s}}$$

Total distance travelled at constant speed

$$= \text{area ABDE}$$

$$= 1.4 \times 30$$

$$= 42 \text{ m}$$

Distance travelled in coming to rest

$$= \text{area BCD}$$

$$= \tfrac{1}{2} \times 1.4 \times 5$$

$$= 3.5 \text{ m}$$

Total distance travelled in coming to rest

$$= 4.9 + 42 + 3.5$$

$$= \mathbf{50.4 \text{ m}}$$

Example 1.11   An electric train starting from rest is uniformly accelerated during the first 0.4 km, runs 1.2 km at the maximum speed attained and is afterwards brought to rest in 0.2 km.

If the time for the whole journey is 5 min, find the uniform acceleration at the start.

Solution

The v–t diagram is shown in Fig. 1.22. Let v = maximum speed attained (km/h), x (h) the time for the acceleration, y the time at constant speed, z the time to come to rest.

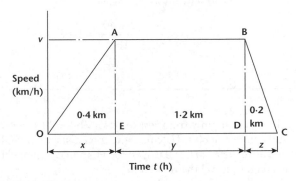

Fig. 1.22

$$\text{Area OAE} = 0.4 \text{ km}$$

i.e. $\frac{1}{2}vx = 0.4$

or

$$vx = 0.8$$
$$\text{Area ABDE} = 1.2 \text{ km}$$

therefore

$$vy = 1.2$$
$$\text{Area BDC} = 0.2 \text{ km}$$

therefore

$$\tfrac{1}{2}vz = 0.2$$
$$vz = 0.4$$

Hence

$$v = \frac{0.8}{x} = \frac{1.2}{y} = \frac{0.4}{z} \text{ km/h}$$

therefore

$$y = \frac{3x}{2} \text{ h and } z = \tfrac{1}{2}x \text{ h}$$

Also

$$x + y + z = \text{total time taken} = 5 \text{ min} = \tfrac{1}{12} \text{ h}$$

i.e. $x + \tfrac{3}{2}x + \tfrac{1}{2}x = \tfrac{1}{12}$ h

Therefore

$$x = \tfrac{1}{36} \text{ h} = 100 \text{ s}$$

For the first stage of the journey,

$$s = 0.4 \text{ km} = 400 \text{ m}$$

$$t = 100 \text{ s}$$

From $s = \frac{1}{2}at^2$, we have

$$a = \frac{2s}{t^2} = \frac{2 \times 400}{100^2} = \textbf{0.08 m/s}^2$$

Problems

1.31 A diesel train accelerates uniformly from rest to 70 km/h for 30 s, continues at this speed for 60 s and decelerates uniformly to rest in 60 s. Calculate the total distance travelled.   (2.04 km)

1.32 A car accelerates uniformly from rest at 0.6 m/s^2 for 11 s and continues at the maximum speed attained. Calculate the time taken to travel the first 75 m.   (16.9 s)

1.33 An electric train is uniformly accelerated from rest for 700 m, runs 1000 m at the maximum speed attained and is then brought to rest at the next station. The distance between stations is 3.2 km and the total time taken is 3 min. Calculate the maximum speed attained.   (30 m/s)

1.34 A hoist is accelerated uniformly from rest to 4.5 m/s and then retarded uniformly to rest. The distance travelled in the accelerated portion of its motion is double that in the second part. Calculate the total time taken if the initial acceleration is 1.5 m/s^2.   (4.5 s)

1.35 A planing machine accelerates from rest to its maximum speed of 80 mm/s over a distance of 8 cm, continuing at this speed for a distance of 48 cm and then comes to rest in 8 cm. Assuming the acceleration and retardation each to be constant, calculate the total time taken for the stroke.   (10 s)

Variable acceleration

When the acceleration is not constant, the increase or decrease in speed varies from instant to instant; the v–t diagram is no longer made up of straight lines, but may be as in Fig. 1.23. For example, if the accelerator pedal of a car is held at a constant position then, all other things being equal, the acceleration is constant. When the pedal is being moved, the acceleration is variable.

It may be proved that the distance travelled is given by the area under the v–t diagram, as before. This area is found by *Simpson's rule*, or any other suitable rule for irregular areas.

The *average speed* is that constant speed at which the same distance would be covered in the same time. Thus

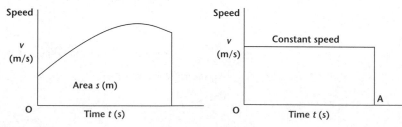

Fig. 1.23

$$\text{Average speed} = \frac{s}{t} = \frac{\text{area of } v\text{–}t \text{ graph}}{\text{total time taken}}$$

Example 1.12   The following table gives the speed v of a car at various times t. Calculate the distance travelled and the average speed.

t (s)	0	1	2	3	4	5	6	7	8
v (km/h)	17	19	20	21	21	20	19	15	10

Solution

The distance travelled in 8 s is the area under the v–t diagram. There are an odd number of equally spaced ordinates, hence Simpson's rule may be used. If

s = area under graph

F = first ordinate (17)

L = last ordinate (10)

E = sum of all even ordinates (75)

O = sum of all odd ordinates, excepting the first and last (60)

$$D - \text{spacing between ordinates} = 1 \times \frac{1}{60} \times \frac{1}{60} = \frac{1}{3600} \text{ h}$$

then Simpson's rule states that

$$s = \frac{D}{3}(F + L + 4E + 2O)$$

Therefore $$s = \frac{1}{3 \times 3600}[17 + 10 + (4 \times 75) + (2 \times 60)]$$

$$= 0.0114 \text{ km} = \mathbf{41.4 \text{ m}}$$

Average speed,

$$\frac{s}{t} = \frac{41.4}{8} = 5.17 \text{ m/s} = \mathbf{18.6 \text{ km/h}}$$

Problems

1.36   The following table gives the speed of a train at intervals of 1 min. Sketch the v–t diagram and calculate the total distance travelled.

Speed (km/h)	0	15	45	60	90	100	100	80	62	20	0
Time (min)	0	1	2	3	4	5	6	7	8	9	10

(9.4 km)

1.37   The following table gives the speed of a car at intervals of 1 s when braking. Calculate the distance travelled in coming to rest and the average speed.

Speed (m/s)	30	29	25	20	15	10	5	2	0
Time (s)		0	1	2	3	4	5	6	7	8

(121 m; 54.6 km/h)

Displacement

Consider the translation of a body from its initial position at the point P, Fig 1.24(a), to a final position at Q. The distance travelled, s, is measured along the curved path actually traversed. The *displacement*, on the other hand, is measured by the straight line joining the initial and final positions P and Q respectively.

The *magnitude* of the displacement is the length $x = $ PQ; the *direction* is along the line PQ, and the *sense* is from P to Q. Displacement is a quantity which possesses magnitude, direction and sense. It is therefore a *vector quantity*.

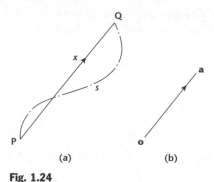

(a)   **(b)**

Fig. 1.24

Velocity

Suppose a body moves from P to Q in time t, Fig. 1.24(a). The distance travelled, measured along the curved path, is s. Hence the average speed is of amount $v_{av} = s/t$. The displacement PQ, on the other hand, is of amount x, measured along the straight line PQ.

We define the *average velocity* of the motion between P and Q as a vector of length x/t, direction along PQ and sense from P to Q. The *velocity vector* may be represented in a velocity diagram, Fig. 1.24(b), by a line **oa** drawn from the point **o** representing zero velocity, parallel to PQ, and of length x/t.

The velocity is said to be *uniform* if the motion is along the straight line PQ and the speed is constant. The magnitude (length) of the velocity vector then represents the speed.

Vector change of velocity

Consider the motion of a body at constant speed along the curved path PQ, Fig. 1.25(a). Although the speed may be constant, the velocity is changing continuously, for the direction of motion, and therefore the direction of the velocity vector, is everywhere tangential to the path of the motion.

If at some instant the body is at point A then its velocity may be represented to some scale by the vector **oa** in the velocity diagram Fig. 1.25(b). Its direction is tangential to the path of motion at A. At some later instant the body will be at A′ and its speed may have changed. The velocity at A′ may be represented by the vector **oa′**, parallel to the tangent to the path at A′. (The point **o** is the point of zero velocity in the velocity diagram and is therefore the same for both vectors.)

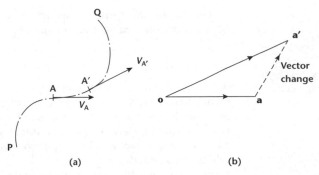

Fig. 1.25

The *vector change in velocity* in going from A to A' is defined as the vector **aa'**. The vector change is itself a vector, of magnitude equal to the length of **aa'**, direction along **aa'**, and sense from **a** to **a'**.

Acceleration vector

The average acceleration between points A and A', Fig. 1.25(a), may now be defined as a vector of magnitude (length) given by

$$\frac{\text{magnitude of vector change of velocity (aa')}}{\text{time taken (t)}} = \frac{\mathbf{aa'}}{t}$$

where t is the time taken for the body to move from A to A'. The direction of the acceleration vector is along **aa'** and its sense from **a** to **a'**.

Uniform acceleration is motion along a straight line with constant acceleration.

The *acceleration at a point* is identical with the vector representing the average acceleration if the two points A and A' are very close together. The acceleration due to motion in a circle is a special case of acceleration arising from a vector change in velocity (a change in direction).

Resultant displacement

Consider the points **o**, **a** and **b**, Fig. 1.26. They may be regarded as points on a map. The straight lines **oa**, **ab** and **ob** are distances or vector displacements on the map. Evidently it is possible to go from **o** to **b** either

- directly along the straight line **ob**, or
- indirectly by going first from **o** to **a** and then from **a** to **b**.

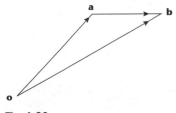

Fig. 1.26

The displacement **ob** is equivalent to the two displacements **oa** and **ab** *taken in turn*; **ob** is called the *resultant* of **oa** and **ab**.

Resultant velocity

A body may have several different velocities simultaneously, as, for example, when a person walks across a moving ship or an aircraft flies in a crosswind. Suppose that in Fig. 1.26 the three displacements **ob**, **oa** and **ab** take place *simultaneously* in a given time. The three vectors now represent *velocities*, each to the same scale. The vector **ob** represents the *resultant* of the two velocities **oa** and **ab**.

Velocities can therefore be compounded to give a resultant, in the same way as forces are compounded.

Example 1.13

A car travelling forwards at 50 km/h starts to skid sideways at 20 km/h. How far will it travel in the direction of the resultant motion in 3 s?

Solution

Figure 1.27 shows the velocity triangle for the car's motion. The car has two speeds – its forward speed, represented by vector **oa**, and its sideways speed, represented by **ab**; these two vectors are drawn head to tail. The resultant speed is

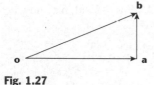

Fig. 1.27

$$\mathbf{ob} = \sqrt{(50^2 + 20^2)}$$

$$= 53.85 \text{ km/h}$$

$$= 15 \text{ m/s}$$

In 3 s the car travels $3 \times 15 = $ **45 m**, in the direction of its resultant motion.

Problems

1.38 A lathe tool is traversed at 1.5 mm/s and its rate of feed into the work is 0.55 mm/s. What is its resultant velocity? (1.6 mm/s)

1.39 A train travels due S at 60 km/h in a 45 km/h wind which is blowing due E. In what direction does the smoke travel? (37°E of S)

1.40 A pin on the mechanism of a shaping machine is moving vertically at 1.8 m/s and horizontally at 1.2 m/s. What are its resultant velocity and direction of motion? (2.17 m/s; 33.7° to vertical)

1.41 A sleeve is moved axially at 0.8 m/s along a rotating shaft. If the surface speed of the shaft is 1 m/s, what is the resultant rubbing velocity between the shaft and sleeve surfaces? (1.3 m/s)

Momentum and energy

Introduction

Newton's laws of motion are stated, together with the principles of conservation of momentum and energy to which they lead; these are the fundamental laws forming the basis of engineering dynamics and they relate to the effects produced when forces change the motion of bodies. We have already used the simple $F = ma$ equation but the momentum principle is particularly useful when collisions, explosions or reaction propulsion are involved. We are concerned here only with *linear* momentum for which the relationship between impulse and change of momentum is derived. Examples are given of impulsive forces; jet aircraft and rockets are used to illustrate reaction propulsion. Energy, the capacity to do work, the various forms of energy and the application of the principle of conservation of energy follow on from the work on momentum. Many problems in dynamics may be solved by employing the two important laws of conservation but care must be taken with the energy principle to ensure that all forms of energy are accounted for, including heat energy.

Momentum

It is found experimentally that the average force required to bring to rest a small, quickly moving mass may be as great as that to bring to rest a large, slowly moving mass, the time being the same in each case.

The 'quantity of motion' possessed by either body is called its *momentum* and is measured by the product of its mass m and its velocity v. Thus

$$\text{Momentum} = mv$$

The unit of mass is the kilogram (kg) and the unit of velocity is the metre per second (m/s). Hence, the unit of momentum is the *kilogram metre per second* (**kg m/s**) or *newton second* (**N s**). However, numerically it may be more convenient to work in tonnes and kilometres per hour.

Momentum has magnitude, and its direction and sense correspond to that of the velocity. Momentum is therefore a vector quantity. A change of momentum may be produced in a body:

- by a change in mass, as in a rocket ejecting burnt fuel;
- by a change in the *direction* of the velocity, as in a body rotating in a circular path;
- by a change in the *magnitude* of the velocity, as in an accelerated body;
- by a change in both mass and velocity.

Laws of motion

First law of motion

Consider a body projected with an initial velocity along a horizontal path. Experience suggests that it is slowed down and eventually comes to rest due to friction forces opposing the motion. Galileo (1564–1642) showed, however, that as the resistance to motion is reduced, so the distance travelled by the projected body before stopping increases. It is possible to imagine a perfectly smooth path offering no resistance to motion; once started, motion would continue indefinitely. This is an instance of Newton's *first law of motion*, which states that

Every body continues in a state of rest, or of uniform motion in a straight line, except when compelled by impressed forces to change that state.

A rocket ship far out in empty space, with its motor shut off and remote from the gravitational pull of the earth or sun, will continue in its motion at constant velocity. Evidently there is negligible force available to change the motion it already has.

Prior to Galileo, it was thought that, in order for a body to continue to move with a uniform velocity, a force was required. It can now be seen that this idea is correct if the force is applied to overcome only the resistance to motion. There is then no resultant out-of-balance force and no acceleration.

Second law of motion

A resultant out-of-balance force F causes an acceleration a according to the relation

$$F = ma$$

If the acceleration a is uniform, and the mass m is *constant*, then

$$a = \frac{v - u}{t}$$

where u and v are the initial and final velocities respectively and t is the time taken for the change. Hence

$$F = \frac{m(v - u)}{t}$$

$$= \frac{mv - mu}{t}$$

$$= \frac{\text{change of momentum}}{\text{time taken}}$$

i.e. **the applied force is equal to the rate of change of momentum.**

This is a special case of Newton's *second law of motion* which states that

The rate of change of momentum is proportional to the resultant out-of-balance force and takes place in the direction of that force

if no force acts on the body, $F = 0$, and there is, therefore, no change of momentum. This agrees with the first law of motion, since if there is no change of momentum the body continues with uniform motion in a straight line.

When the acceleration a is not uniform, equation (1) gives the *average* force F acting for time t, i.e.

$$\text{Average force} = \frac{\text{change of momentum}}{\text{time taken}}$$

Example 1.14

A planing machine has moving parts of mass 1.5 t and is brought to rest from a speed of 0.12 m/s in 0.8 s. Calculate the average retarding force.

Solution

$$\text{Change in momentum} = m(v - u)$$

$$= 1.5 \times 10^3 \times (0.12 - 0)$$

$$= 180 \text{ kg m/s}$$

$$\text{Average force exerted} = \frac{\text{change of momentum}}{\text{time taken}}$$

$$= \frac{180}{0.8}$$

$$= 225 \text{ N}$$

Example 1.15

A 400 t train attains 120 km/h from rest on a gradient of 1 in 100. The constant tractive effort is 240 kN and the average track resistance is 110 N/t. Find the momentum of the train at its maximum speed and the time taken to reach it.

Solution

$$\text{Momentum of train at } 120 \text{ km/h} = mv$$

$$= 400 \times 10^3 \times \frac{120}{3.6}$$

$$= 13.3 \times 10^6 \text{ kg m/s}$$

The student should sketch the train ascending the gradient showing the forces acting on it, i.e. the tractive effort, track resistance and the weight component down the slope.

Average accelerating force on train up the slope is given by

$$F = \text{tractive effort} - \text{track resistance} - \text{weight component}$$

$$= 240 \times 10^3 - 110 \times 400 - 400 \times 10^3 \times 9.8 \times \frac{1}{100}$$

$$= 157 \times 10^3 \text{ N}$$

Average force × time taken = change in momentum

$$157 \times 10^3 \times t = 13.3 \times 10^6 - 0$$

$$\therefore \qquad\qquad t = 85 \text{ s}$$

This problem has been solved using 'momentum'. The student should rework the solution using the equation of motion $F = ma$.

Problems

1.42 A train of total mass 100 t is travelling at 90 km/h. Find the total resisting force required to stop the train in one minute. If the rolling resistance to motion is 100 N/t, what is the braking effort required? (41.7 kN; 31.7 kN)

1.43 A train of total mass 700 t reaches a steady speed of 90 km/h from rest when the net tractive force exerted by the locomotive is 34.5 kN. Find the time taken. (8.45 min)

1.44 A machine tool table is driven by a constant force of 250 N. The table, of mass 2070 kg, reaches a speed of 0.1 m/s from rest. What is the time taken? (0.83 s)

1.45 A shunting locomotive jolts a stationary 12 t wagon which moves off freely at 4 m/s. After 18 s the wagon slows down to 2.9 m/s, Find the change in momentum of the wagon and the average track resistance per tonne of wagon. (13.2×10^3 kg m/s; 61.1 N/t)

1.46 A 20 t truck reaches a speed of 54 km/h in 94 s when climbing a gradient from rest. Find its momentum at this speed and hence the average net force on the truck. If the gradient is 1 in 20 and the tractive effort is 18 kN, what is the average track and air resistance per tonne of vehicle? (3×10^5 kg m/s; 3.19 kN; 250 N/t)

1.47 An aircraft of mass 68.5 Mg touches down at 210 km/h on a level runway with a negligible vertical component of velocity and takes 47 s to come to rest. Find the momentum of the aircraft at touchdown and the average retarding force (due to braking, rolling friction and air drag). What is the minimum length of runway required? (4×10^6 kg m/s; 85.1 kN; 1.37 km)

Third law of motion

It is known from statics that a single force cannot exist alone. For equilibrium, forces come in pairs. This is an oversimplification of Newton's *third law of motion*, which states that

action and reaction are equal and opposite.

For example, the pull of gravity on a body (its weight) is the *action* of the earth's pull. By the third law of motion, there is an equal and opposite pull exerted by the body on the earth. This is termed a *reaction*. Examples of 'action and reaction' are rocket and jet aircraft propulsion, the recoil of a gun when fired and the recoil of a fire-hose.

An *active* force is one that can cause an acceleration. For example, the weight of a load hung from a crane hook is an active force exerted by the earth on the body, for if the load were removed from the hook, it would accelerate downwards.

A *reactive* force is one that cannot *of itself* cause acceleration. The force exerted by a crane hook which supports a load is a reactive force. (The force exerted by the crane hook produces an upward acceleration ($-g$) to cancel the downward acceleration ($+g$) due to the gravitational pull.)

Note that active and reactive forces are two equal and opposite forces on the *same* body. Action and reaction are two equal and opposite forces exerted between two *separate* bodies.

We are now in a position to define *force* as *that which produces or tends to produce an acceleration in a body*.

The first two laws of motion appear to have been known to Galileo, but the first formal statement of the three laws as forming the basis of mechanics was made by Newton in 1687.

Reaction propulsion

An example of 'action and reaction' is rocket propulsion. A rocket carries its own oxygen and fuel (the *propellants*) which burn in a chamber open at one end. A high-speed jet of exhaust gases is ejected from the opening via an exit convergent-divergent nozzle, Fig. 1.28(a), and the rocket is accelerated by the action of the gases. To accelerate the gases and eject them requires that a force be exerted by the rocket on the gases. By Newton's third law, there is an equal and opposite force exerted by the gases on the rocket and it is this reaction or *thrust* which propels the rocket forward. This is the principle of *reaction propulsion*. The same principle applies to the working of propeller and jet-driven aircraft and ships, helicopters and rocket thrusters for satellite control. Apart from the mechanical aspects and body structure, each type of vehicle differs greatly in regard to the mass of fluid dealt with and the speed of the jet formed.

The engine of a turbo–jet aircraft is distinguished from a rocket motor by requiring air to burn its fuel. The forward flight of the aircraft forces air into the engine where it mixes with fuel, followed by combustion and expulsion of a high-speed jet through a nozzle, Fig. 1.28(b). The force on the jet is equal to the rate of change of momentum of the air (and fuel) passing through the engine. The equal and opposite force, i.e. the force propelling the plane forward, is the pressure of the combustion gases on the inside surfaces of the combustion chamber.

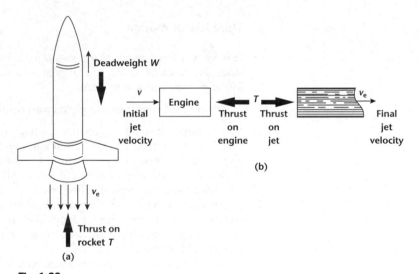

Fig. 1.28

Thrust of a jet

Let v, v_e be the fluid velocities relative to the engine, at entry and exit respectively, Fig. 1.28(b). Then, *relative to the engine* the initial momentum of m kg of fluid is mv, the final momentum mv_e and the change in momentum $m(v_e - v)$. If $\dot{m}$ is the mass of fluid passing through the engine per second, the force on the jet is equal to its change in momentum per second, i.e.

$$\text{Force} = \dot{m}(v_e - v)$$

The thrust T on the engine is equal and opposite to the force on the jet, hence the propulsive force on the vehicle is

engine thrust = (mass of fluid/second)
× (change in fluid velocity in passing through the engine)

i.e.
$$T = \dot{m}(v_e - v)$$

If the mass flow rate $\dot{m}$ is in kg/s, v and v_e in m/s, then T is in newtons. This formula applies to any vehicle which uses a jet of fluid for propulsion. Note that the exhaust jets of aircraft and rockets may have speeds well above the speed of sound (340 m/s at sea-level).

Rockets

The propellants are initially at rest relative to the rocket since they are carried with the rocket, i.e. $v = 0$, and the thrust is

$$T = \dot{m}\, v_e$$

The mass flow rate $\dot{m}$ is the mass of propellants consumed divided by the time taken, assuming a steady rate of burning. The thrust for any propulsion stage is fairly constant.

A rocket does not require surrounding air in order to operate and works more efficiently where there is no atmosphere since any air present would resist and slow down the exhaust jet and the motion of the rocket. This makes them the ideal vehicles for high-altitude and space travel. Enormous thrusts can be generated by giving large quantities of propellants a very high speed relative to the rocket in the shortest possible time. The initial thrust of a Saturn V rocket system, for example, was 34 MN for a burning time of 160 s, and the total rated thrust of a Shuttle's three main engines, 5 MN, boosted at lift-off by two rockets, each giving 3 MN of thrust for two minutes of flight. Again, on a different scale, the rockets used for the precise adjustment of the motion of the Orbiter craft give a thrust as low as 100 N.

Jet aircraft

The gas turbine engine takes in a large quantity of air and utilizes a high air-to-fuel ratio. The velocity of the air changes from v at intake to v_e in the jet at exit, both velocities being *relative to the engine*. The fuel (already in the engine) changes in speed from zero to v_e, relative to the engine. Since the air:fuel ratio is very large (a typical figure for a turbo-jet is 70:1), the thrust due to the fuel in the jet is small in comparison with that due to the airflow and may be neglected with little error. The value of $\dot{m}$ may therefore be taken as the mass flow rate of air at intake or gas in the jet.

When an aeroplane flies through *still air*, the velocity of the intake air relative to the engine, v, is also the forward speed of the plane relative to the ground (otherwise the effect of wind velocity has to be taken into account). Thus the thrust for a jet aircraft in still air is

$$T = \dot{m}(v_e - v)$$

where v is the *forward speed* of the plane.

Example 1.16   A rocket in level flight ejects 100 kg of burnt fuel in 8 s at a velocity of 500 m/s relative to the rocket. Calculate (a) the change in momentum of the burnt fuel and (b) the average thrust on the rocket due to the ejection.

Solution

(a) The burnt fuel is originally moving with the rocket at some unknown speed and therefore has some unknown momentum. Its change in velocity is 500 m/s, therefore the change in momentum

$$= 100 \times 500$$

$$= 50\ 000\ \text{kg m/s}$$

(b) The average force required to produce this change in momentum

$$= \frac{\text{change in momentum}}{\text{time taken}}$$

$$= \frac{50\ 000}{8}$$

$$= 6250\ \text{N} = \textbf{6.25 kN}$$

The average thrust on the rocket is equal and opposite to this.
  Alternatively, using the formula devised above, then

$$T = \dot{m}\, v_e$$

$$= \frac{100}{8} \times 500$$

$$= 6250\ \text{N}$$

Example 1.17   A rocket has a weight of 27 MN at lift-off from its launch pad. The propellants are burned steadily at the rate of 12 t/s and the initial acceleration is to be 2.4 m/s². Find the thrust and the velocity of the exhaust jet relative to the rocket.

Solution

Refer to Fig. 1.28(a). At lift-off the thrust must overcome the deadweight and accelerate the vehicle. The accelerating force is

$$F = ma$$

i.e. $$T - W = \frac{W}{g}a$$

i.e. $$T - 27 \times 10^6 = \frac{27 \times 10^6}{9.8} \times 2.4$$

Therefore

$$T = 33.6 \times 10^6\ \text{N}$$

$$= \textbf{33.6 MN}$$

and

$$T = \dot{m}\,v_e$$

i.e. $\quad 33.6 \times 10^6 = 12 \times 10^3 \times v_e$

Therefore

$$v_e = 2.8 \times 10^3\ \text{m/s} \quad \text{or} \quad \textbf{2.8 km/s}$$

Example 1.18 A turbo-jet aircraft cruises at 270 m/s in still air when the jet issues from the engine at 650 m/s relative to the engine, with a mass flow rate of 99 kg/s. Find the thrust.

Solution

$$v = 270\ \text{m/s};\ v_e = 650\ \text{m/s};\ \dot{m} = 99\ \text{kg/s}$$

Thrust $T = \dot{m}(v_e - v)$

$$= 99(650 - 270) \times \frac{1}{1000}\ \text{kN}$$

$$= \textbf{37.6 kN}$$

Example 1.19 A 5 t jet-plane approaches a runway at 30 m/s horizontal speed, Fig. 1.29. Fuel consumption is 0.4 kg/s and the exhaust jet issues at 400 m/s relative to the engine. If the thrust is 8 kN find the air/fuel ratio.

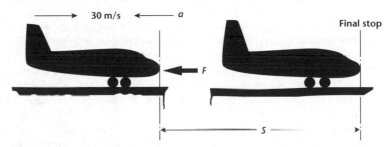

Fig. 1.29

The jet is deflected immediately on touch-down to produce a constant braking thrust of 40 per cent of the forward thrust on approach. Find the minimum runway required, assuming no other resisting forces to be acting.

Solution

$$T = 8000\ \text{N};\ v = 30\ \text{m/s};\ v_e = 400\ \text{m/s}$$

$$T = \dot{m}(v_e - v)$$

i.e. $8000 = \dot{m}(400 - 30)$

i.e. $\dot{m} = 21.6 \text{ kg/s}$

$$\frac{\text{air}}{\text{fuel}} = \frac{21.6}{0.4} = 54$$

The braking force is 40 per cent of forward thrust, thus

$$F = 0.4 \times 8 \times 10^3 = 3.2 \times 10^3 \text{ N}$$

and

$$F = ma$$

i.e. $3.2 \times 10^3 = 5 \times 10^3 \times a$

Therefore

$$a = 0.64 \text{ m/s}^2$$

Using the equation $v^2 = u^2 + 2as$ where s is the length of runway required, v the final velocity is zero, and *a the deceleration* is 0.64 m/s². Thus

$$0 = 30^2 - 2 \times 0.64 \times s$$

Therefore

$$s = 703 \text{ m}$$

Problems

1.48 A rocket ejects 2000 kg of burnt gases at a velocity of 2000 m/s relative to the rocket. Calculate the average force on the rocket if the time taken is 100 s.   (40 kN)

1.49 A rocket of mass 10 t is mounted vertically on its test bed and ejects exhaust gases at a uniform rate of 0.1 t/s with a velocity of 300 m/s. If the rocket does not move during the test, calculate (a) the force exerted on the rocket by the exhaust gases and (b) the load on the test bed foundation at the start of the test (assume that the exhaust gases do not impinge on the foundation).   (30 kN; 68 kN)

1.50 An Ariane rocket burns propellants at the rate of 1300 kg/s and lifts off from rest with an all-up mass of 210 t. The speed of the exhaust jet relative to the rocket is 2 km/s. Find the thrust and acceleration at lift-off.   (2.6 MN; 2.6 m/s²)

1.51 A spacecraft has an all-up mass of 3000 t on the launch pad. The propellants in the rockets which fire at lift-off represent 62 per cent of the total mass and they burn out in 155 s. If the lift-off acceleration is to be 2.2 m/s², what is the thrust required and the minimum velocity of the exhaust jet relative to the craft?   (36 MN; 3 km/s)

1.52 A communications satellite has a mass of 180 kg and orbits the earth. Its four adjuster rockets fire in the line of flight for 5 s to slow it down. Each rocket discharges a jet at the rate of 0.25 kg/s with a velocity of 360 m/s relative to the satellite. What is the reduction in speed achieved?   (10 m/s)

1.53 A space vehicle leaves its launching pad with an all-up mass of 2800 t. At a point in its vertical flight the burn-rate is 12 t/s and the mass of the vehicle is reduced by 1885 t from burning of propellants, jettisoning of rocket casings and other debris. The jet issues at a speed of 2.5 km/s relative to the vehicle. Find the thrust and acceleration at this instant.   (30 MN; 23 m/s²)

1.54 A four-engined jet airliner is cruising in straight, level flight at 300 m/s. Each engine takes in air at the rate of 45 kg/s and its jet issues at 900 m/s relative to the engine. What is the resisting force due to the air, i.e. the drag force?   (108 kN)

1.55 A turbo-jet engine is tested on a stationary rig. Air is supplied at the rate of 27 kg/s and velocity 80 m/s to the combustion chamber and the speed of the exhaust jet is 665 m/s. What is the thrust on the supports? (15.8 kN)

1.56 A twin-engined aircraft of mass 8.5 Mg is cruising in straight, level flight at 185 m/s in still air and draws air into each engine at the rate of 40 kg/s. The jets leave the engines at 500 m/s relative to the aircraft. Find the thrust. What is the additional thrust needed (i) to give the aircraft an acceleration of 1.5 m/s^2 while maintaining straight, level flight and (ii) to enable the craft to climb at a steady speed of 185 m/s at 20° to the horizontal? Assume the drag force to remain constant.

(25.2 kN; 12.8 kN; 28.5 kN)

1.57 A jet-plane of mass 8 t flies in straight level flight in still air at 972 km/h and the exhaust jet issues at the rate of 30 kg/s with a velocity of 950 m/s relative to the plane. The drag force is 5 kN. Find the thrust and acceleration. (20.4 kN; 1.93 m/s^2)

1.58 A jet-plane travels at 864 km/h in still air with the exhaust jet issuing at 900 m/s relative to the engine at the rate of 80 kg/s. Find the thrust.

If the mass of the plane is 30 t and the acceleration is 1.5 m/s^2 whilst maintaining straight level flight with this thrust, estimate the drag force. (52.8 kN; 7.8 kN)

1.59 A ramjet missile takes in a large amount of air at its front end, burns it with a small amount of fuel and ejects a high-speed jet. If the air is drawn in at the rate of 70 kg/s when the flight speed is 250 m/s, what must be the exit velocity of the jet for a thrust of 24 kN? (593 m/s relative to missile)

1.60 A four-engined jet-plane of mass 155 t has to reach a take-off speed of 252 km/h. On the run-up, each engine takes in air at the rate of 74 kg/s and the jetspeed at the exit nozzle is 700 m/s relative to the plane. Find the total thrust.

Assuming the thrust to be constant from the beginning of the run-up and a track and wind resistance of 40 kN, find the minimum runway required. (187 kN; 2.6 km)

| **Conservation of momentum** | In principle, all problems in mechanics can be solved using the three laws of motion. In practice the solution may be very difficult. For example, in the case of an impact between two bodies, the forces involved are unknown, may be very large and may act for a very short time. A further principle, based on the first law of motion, which simplifies the solution of such problems is the *principle of conservation of momentum*. |

Momentum can be destroyed only by a force and can be created only by the action of a force. If no *external* force acts on a body or system of bodies then the momentum remains constant, i.e. constant in both magnitude and direction. This is termed the *principle of conservation of momentum.*

| **Application of conservation of momentum to collision of two bodies** | A body of mass m_1 moving with velocity u_1 collides with a second body of mass m_2 and velocity u_2, as shown in Fig. 1.30. Both bodies are moving in the same straight line. |

During the collision, the only forces acting are the equal and opposite forces between the two bodies. There is no *external* force acting on the *two-body system* immediately before, during or after impact. Hence *the total momentum of the system remains constant*, i.e.

momentum before impact = momentum after impact

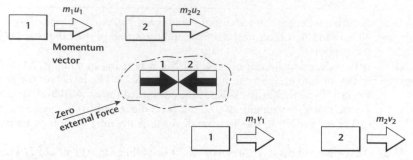

Fig. 1.30

If the bodies move off after impact with velocities v_1, v_2 respectively, then

$$\text{total initial momentum} = m_1u_1 + m_2u_2$$

$$\text{total final momentum} = m_1v_1 + m_2v_2$$

Therefore

$$m_1u_1 + m_2u_2 = m_1v_1 + m_2v_2$$

or

$$-m_1(v_1 - u_1) = m_2(v_2 - u_2)$$

That is, the magnitude of the change in momentum of each body is the same, or the gain in momentum of one body is equal to the loss in momentum of the other body.

If the bodies lock together after impact and move off with a common velocity V, then

$$v_1 = v_2 = V$$

and

$$m_1u_1 + m_2u_2 = (m_1 + m_2)V$$

If the bodies are moving initially *towards* each other then, since the total initial momentum is the vector sum of the separate momenta, one of the quantities must be considered negative. The final direction of motion then depends on which body has the greater momentum.

It should be noted that the assumption that the bodies move after impact with a common velocity is a special case, as for example in the coupling together of railway wagons. Otherwise the two bodies will in general have different final velocities. Further information is then necessary since the momentum equation alone cannot give both these velocities. In the questions set here, this information will be given.

Example 1.20   A railway wagon of mass 35 t travels along a level track at 15 km/h and collides with another wagon of mass 15 t travelling in the opposite direction at 20 km/h. After impact, the first is seen to travel in the same direction as before with a speed of 3 km/h. Find the speed of the second wagon.

Solution

It will be convenient to use the tonne (1000 kg) as the unit of mass and the kilometre per hour as the unit of velocity.

$$\text{Initial momentum of first wagon} = 35 \times 15$$

$$\text{Initial momentum of second wagon} = -15 \times 20$$

$$\text{Total initial momentum of system} = (35 \times 15) - (15 \times 20)$$

$$= 225$$

$$\text{Final momentum of first wagon} = 35 \times 3$$

$$\text{Final momentum of second wagon} = 15 \times V$$

where V is the velocity of the second wagon after impact. The second wagon must move in the same direction as the first in this case.

$$\text{Final total momentum} = 225 = (35 \times 3) + (15 \times V)$$

Hence

$$15V = 225 - 105$$

so that

$$V = 8 \text{ km/h}$$

Example 1.21   A 10 t wagon is set moving at 6 m/s and travels against a track resistance of 90 N/t over a distance of 100 m. It then strikes a 5 t wagon moving at 3 m/s in the same direction. What is the velocity of the smaller wagon immediately after impact if the 10 t wagon moves on immediately at 2 m/s?

Solution

For the 10 t wagon the initial velocity $u = 6$ m/s, the distance travelled $s = 100$ m, and the decelerating force F is $90 \times 10 = 900$ N, Fig. 1.31. Then

$$F = ma$$

$$900 = 10 \times 10^3 \times a$$

$$a = 0.09 \text{ m/s}^2$$

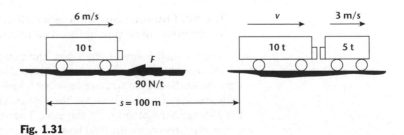

Fig. 1.31

Using $v^2 = u^2 + 2as$, where $a = -0.09 \ \text{m/s}^2$,

$$v^2 = 6^2 - 2 \times 0.09 \times 100$$

$$v = 4.24 \ \text{m/s}$$

The 10 t wagon therefore has a velocity of 4.24 m/s on impact. Let V be the velocity of the 5 t wagon immediately after impact. Equating the momentum before and after impact, working in tonne, metre, second units:

$$(10 \times 4.24) + (5 \times 3) = (10 \times 2) + 5V$$

$$V = 7.5 \ \text{m/s}$$

Problems

1.61 A railway wagon of mass 12 t and travelling at 15 km/h collides with a second similar wagon at rest. If both wagons travel on coupled together, calculate their common velocity. If the second wagon were moving at 15 km/h in the opposite direction to the first, what would then be their common velocity?

(7.5 km/h; 0)

1.62 A truck of mass 8 t travelling due E with velocity 10 km/h collides with a second truck of mass 12 t travelling due W at 1 km/h, both trucks moving on the same straight line. (a) Find the magnitude and direction of their common velocity if they are locked together after impact. (b) If the resistance to motion is 90 N/t, find how far the trucks will move before coming to rest.   (3.4 km/h due E; 5 m)

1.63 A 10 t wagon moving at 4 m/s strikes a 20 t wagon moving at 2.5 m/s in the same direction on the same track. After the collision the 10 t wagon travels backwards at 3.6 m/s. Find the velocity of the 20 t wagon immediately after impact.   (6.3 m/s)

1.64 A rail wagon of mass 7 t is checked at rest on a slope inclined at 2° to level ground. It starts to roll freely down the slope against a track resistance of 50 N/t. After 5 s it strikes a stationary 12 t wagon held in check until the moment of impact when it immediately moves off down the slope at 0.5 m/s. Find the velocity of the 7 t wagon immediately after impact.   (0.6 m/s)

1.65 A shunting locomotive strikes a wagon of mass 10 t and sets it in motion with an initial speed of 4 m/s. The wagon travels freely along a level track against a track resistance of 60 N/t. After 10 s it collides with a second wagon of mass 12 t moving in the opposite direction at 0.5 m/s. If the wagons move off immediately coupled together, find their common speed and the time taken for the coupled wagons to come to rest.   (1.3 m/s; 21 s)

Explosions: recoil

When a body explodes freely and instantaneously, as, for example, a shell from a gun, a payload ejecting from a rocket, or simply a body fragmenting, then the initial momentum is redistributed among the parts. The momentum principle may be applied since there are no external forces acting except for gravity which can be neglected, as an explosion is over before it can have any effect.

The total momentum, although redistributed, remains unchanged in any given direction before and immediately after an explosion.

When a shell is fired from a gun, the gun kicks back due to the force of recoil. Equal and opposite forces are exerted on the shell and gun during the time the shell takes to traverse the barrel, hence both shell and gun have the same change of momentum, i.e. the *forward* momentum of the shell equals the *backwards* momentum of the gun. The initial momentum of shell and gun is zero, therefore the final momentum immediately after firing is zero.

A rocket in flight may be separated from its payload, such as a communications satellite, by a small explosion or spring-release mechanism. If the rocket and satellite continue along the line of flight then the sum of their momenta along the line of flight after the explosion must equal the initial momentum of rocket and satellite. The average force and time of separation, i.e. time during which the force acts, is the same for both rocket and satellite. For each body, therefore

average force × time of separation = change of momentum

Note that when the time of action of a very large force is extremely short, as in an explosion, the force is called an *impulsive force* and the change in momentum, i.e. *force × time*, is called an *impulse*, the units being N s, the same as momentum.

See also the sections 'Change of kinetic energy' and 'Potential energy' (p. 55 and p. 57) but note here that an explosion adds energy to the system.

Example 1.22

A shell is fired from a gun at 600 m/s at an angle of 30° to the horizontal. If the shell's mass is 10 kg and the velocity of recoil of the gun is to be limited to 1.2 m/s, calculate the minimum mass of gun required.

Solution

Before firing, the total momentum is zero.

$$\text{After firing, the momentum of shell} = 10 \times 600$$
$$= 6000 \text{ kg m/s}$$
$$\text{Horizontal component of this momentum} = 6000 \times \cos 30°$$
$$= 5196 \text{ kg m/s}$$

Let m = mass of gun in kg.

Horizontal momentum of gun at recoil = $-m \times 1.2$ kg m/s, Fig. 1.32. For gun and shell together.

$$\text{initial (horizontal) momentum} = \text{final (horizontal) momentum}$$
$$0 = 5196 - (m \times 1.2)$$

i.e. $m = 4330$ kg

$$= 4.33 \text{ Mg}$$

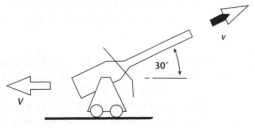

Fig. 1.32

Example 1.23 A satellite is released to the rear of its host rocket in the line of flight by triggering off a small explosion when the rocket is coasting in orbit. The separating force is 480 N acting for 1.2 s. The mass of satellite is 960 kg and the mass of rocket after separation is 240 kg. Find the speed of recession.

Solution

Let x_1 (m/s) be the *reduction* in speed of the satellite and x_2 (m/s) the *gain* in speed of the rocket, Fig. 1.33. The speed of recession is the relative velocity of the two parts, i.e. the velocity of the satellite assuming the rocket to be at rest.

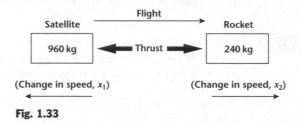

Fig. 1.33

For the satellite,

$$\text{average force} \times \text{time of separation} = \text{change of momentum}$$
$$= \text{mass} \times \text{change in speed}$$

i.e. $480 \times 1.2 = 960 \times x_1$

therefore

$$x_1 = 0.6 \text{ m/s (reduction)}$$

For the rocket,

$$480 \times 1.2 = 240 \times x_2$$

$$x_2 = 2.4 \text{ m/s (gain)}$$

The speed of recession is $x_2 + x_1$, i.e.

$$(2.4 + 0.6) = 3 \text{ m/s}$$

Note that the initial speed of the rocket with satellite is not required since we are dealing here with *changes* in momentum.

Example 1.24 A satellite-carrying rocket of total mass 1280 kg coasts in space at 8 km/s. An explosion ejects the satellite (320 kg) rearwards in the line of flight and its speed falls by 18 m/s immediately after separation. Find the final speed of the rocket and the speed of recession.

If the duration of the explosion is 1.5 s, what is the force of the explosion?

Solution

The mass of the rocket remaining after separation is $(1280 - 320)$ kg, i.e. 960 kg. Let v be the velocity of the rocket immediately after the explosion. Equating the initial and final momenta (noting that rocket and satellite continue in the *same* direction, the final speed of the satellite is 7982 m/s and momentum is *mass × speed*):

$$1280 \times 8000 = (320 \times 7982) + 960v$$

therefore

$$v = \mathbf{8006 \ m/s}$$

The rocket gains in speed by 6 m/s, and the speed of recession is therefore $6 + 18 = \mathbf{24 \ m/s}$.

For the satellite,

$$\text{average force} \times \text{time} = \text{change of momentum}$$

i.e. $\text{average force} \times 1.5 = 320 \times 18$

∴ $\text{average force} = \mathbf{3840 \ N}$

Checks

1. Equate the change of momentum of satellite to change of momentum of rocket to confirm that change in speed of rocket is 6 m/s.
2. For the rocket,

$$\text{average force} \times 1.5 = 960 \times 6$$

∴ $\text{average force} = \mathbf{3840 \ N}$

Problems

1.66 A gun fires a shell of mass 5 kg in a horizontal direction. The gun recoils at 0.5 m/s and its mass is 3 t. Calculate the velocity of the shell.   (300 m/s)

1.67 A gun fires a 12 kg shell at 20° to the horizontal with a velocity of 300 m/s. If the gun's mass is 4 t and it recoils in the horizontal direction, find (a) the velocity of recoil and (b) the resistance to motion if the gun comes to rest in 150 mm.   (0.85 m/s; 9.52 kN)

1.68 A gun of mass 10 t fires a 50 kg projectile with a horizontal velocity of 750 m/s. Calculate the initial recoil velocity of the gun and if the shell takes 0.01 s to leave the barrel, find the average force on the gun.   (3.75 m/s; 3.75 MN)

1.69 A bullet, mass 17 g, strikes a wood-block target of mass 16 kg and remains embedded in the wood after impact. The target is suspended by a light string and at the moment of impact it is moving towards the bullet at 0.6 m/s. Target and bullet then move along the line of flight of the bullet at 0.4 m/s. What is the striking speed of the bullet?   (942 m/s)

1.70 A rocket travelling in a horizontal straight line at 1 km/s explodes and breaks up into two parts of mass, 800 kg and 200 kg respectively. Both parts travel on in the same direction as before but the lighter section is moving 100 m/s faster than the heavier part. Calculate the velocity of each section.   (980; 1080 m/s)

1.71 A projectile of mass 42 kg is travelling at constant speed 25 m/s when it explodes into two parts. One part of mass 28 kg is immediately at rest. Find the speed of the second part if it continues along the line of flight.   (75 m/s)

1.72 If the projectile of problem 9.30 explodes into three parts such that a 28 kg fragment is immediately at rest, a second fragment of 8 kg continues upwards at 30° to the line of flight with a speed of 40 m/s, find the speed and direction of the third part.   (132 m/s at 11.7° to line of flight; downwards)

1.73 A 56 kg projectile is moving at constant speed 8 m/s when it explodes into three pieces, A, B and C. Figure 1.34 shows the masses, speed and direction of A, B and C, immediately after the explosion. Confirm that the total momentum along the line of flight remains at 448 kg m/s and that the momentum at right angles to the line of flight remains zero immediately after the explosion.

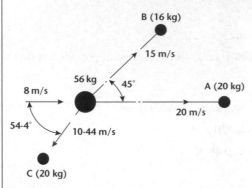

Fig. 1.34

1.74 A rocket is coasting in space when a small explosion discharges a satellite of mass 180 kg in the line of flight. The separating thrust is 1200 N and the satellite's speed increases by 10 m/s after the thrust period of duration t s. Find t.   (1.5 s)

1.75 A satellite is launched from a spacecraft by firing a duster of small rockets to give a total separating thrust of 4.8 kN, acting for 1 s. The mass of the satellite is 1200 kg and the mass of the craft remaining after separation is 800 kg. Find the speed of recession.   (10 m/s)

1.76 An astronaut of mass 90 kg floats in space attached by a cord to the craft, and carries a piece of rocket debris of mass 8 kg. He is at rest relative to the craft and hurls the debris away from him. If the debris travels at 45 m/s relative to the craft, what is the speed of recession of astronaut and debris?   (49 m/s)

1.77 A rocketcraft of mass 1800 kg including a payload is coasting in space when holding bolts are broken by an explosion to release the payload rearwards in the line of flight. The speed of the payload falls by 24 m/s and the craft gains by 6 m/s. Find the mass of the payload.   (360 kg)

1.78 A spacecraft of total mass 1000 kg travelling at 10 km/s releases a cargo of mass 200 kg using a powerful spring-loaded tilt table. The cargo recedes rearwards in the line of flight at a speed of 1 km/s relative to the craft. Find the final speeds of craft and cargo immediately after separation.   (10.2 km/s; 9.2 km/s)

Principle of conservation of energy

Energy is defined as the capacity to do work. *The principle of conservation of energy states that energy can be neither created nor destroyed.* This principle enables us to obtain directly the answer to certain complex problems where the use of the laws of motion would be tedious. Before discussing in detail the nature of energy, it is convenient to study the connexion between work and energy, using as a starting point the second law of motion.

Energy and work

Consider the work done in uniformly accelerating a body of mass m from rest to speed v over a distance s along a horizontal straight line, Fig. 1.35. The acceleration required is given by

$$v^2 = 2as$$

or

$$a = \frac{v^2}{2s}$$

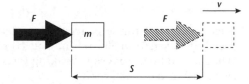

Fig. 1.35

By the second law of motion the *average* force required is

$$F = ma$$

$$= m \times \frac{v^2}{2s}$$

The work done by the force F in distance s is

$$F \times s = m \times \frac{v^2}{2s} \times s$$

$$= \tfrac{1}{2}mv^2$$

The expression on the right-hand side is known as the *kinetic energy* (KE), or *energy of motion* of the body at velocity v; it is the energy possessed by the body by virtue of its mass and velocity. The units of KE are the same as those of work, i.e. *newton metre* (N m) or *joule* (J). (Nm is normally reserved for 'torque').

Change of kinetic energy

The work done in accelerating a body from velocity u *to velocity* v *is equal to the change in its kinetic energy.*

Thus the acceleration required is given by:

$$v^2 - u^2 = 2as$$

or

$$a = \frac{v^2 - u^2}{2s}$$

The uniform (or average) force required is

$$F = ma$$

$$= m \times \frac{v^2 - u^2}{2s}$$

and the work done over distance s is

$$F \times s = m \times \frac{v^2 - u^2}{2s} \times s$$

$$= \tfrac{1}{2}mv^2 - \tfrac{1}{2}mu^2$$

which is the change in kinetic energy.

Example 1.25

A car of mass 1 tonne is accelerated from a speed of 24 km/h to a speed of 48 km/h in 50 m. Find the average tractive effort required. What would be the average braking force required to bring the car to rest in 50 m from 48 km/h?

Solution

$$u = 6.67 \text{ m/s}; \, v = 13.33 \text{ m/s}$$

Let E be the tractive effort; then the work done $= E \times 50$ J.

$$\text{Change in kinetic energy} = \tfrac{1}{2}m(v^2 - u^2)$$

$$= \tfrac{1}{2} \times 1 \times 10^3 \times (13.33^2 - 6.67^2)$$

$$= 66\,600 \text{ J}$$

Since work done = change of kinetic energy

$$E \times 50 = 66\,600$$

so that

$$E = 1333 \text{ N} = \textbf{1.33 kN}$$

Let F be the braking force, then the work done in bringing the car to rest is $F \times 50$ J.
Therefore

$$F \times 50 = \tfrac{1}{2} \times 1 \times 10^3 \times (13.3^2 - 0)$$

i.e. $$F = 1780 \text{ N} = \textbf{1.78 kN}$$

Example 1.26

An aircraft carrier is cruising at 18 knots while heading into a wind of 10 knots when a 4.5 t aircraft touches down on deck against the wind with an airspeed of 84 knots. It is brought to a halt in a distance of 70 m by the arrestor gear, a reverse engine thrust of 8 kN and wheel braking force of 10 kN. Find (a) the speed of the aircraft relative to the ship, (b) the kinetic energy to be absorbed in halting the aircraft and (c) the average force needed from the arrestor gear. 1 knot = 0.514 m/s.

Solution

(a) *Airspeed* is the speed of a body relative to the speed of the surrounding air:

$$\text{airspeed at carrier deck} = 18 + 10 = 28 \text{ knots}$$

$$\text{airspeed of aircraft} = 84 \text{ knots}$$

Therefore,

$$\text{speed of aircraft relative to ship} = 84 - 28 = \textbf{56 knots}$$

(b) The kinetic energy to be absorbed is $\frac{1}{2}mv^2$ where v is the speed of the aircraft relative to the ship. Thus

$$\text{kinetic energy} = \tfrac{1}{2} \times 4.5 \times (56 \times 0.514)^2$$

$$= 1864 \text{ kJ} \quad \text{or} \quad \textbf{1.86 MJ}$$

(c) If the average force exerted by the arrestor gear is P kN then the total retarding force is

$$F = P + 8 + 10 = P + 18 \text{ kN}$$

The work done by the force F in a distance of 70 m is equal to the loss of KE of the aircraft, therefore

$$F \times 70 = 1864$$

i.e. $\quad (P + 18) \times 70 = 1864$

i.e. $\quad\quad\quad\quad P = \textbf{8.6 kN}$

Potential energy

The work done in lifting a body of weight W through a vertical height h is $W \times h$. This quantity is known as the *potential energy* (PE) of the body referred to its original position. The body possesses this energy by virtue of its weight and position (height). Potential energy is a relative quantity since the original position is chosen arbitrarily for convenience in solving a given problem, i.e. we calculate *changes* in potential energy.

If m is the mass of the body in kg and h is the height in metres then the potential energy is mgh joules.

More correctly, we are dealing here with the gravitational potential energy of a body in the particular gravitational field caused by the earth. Near the surface of the earth its gravity field force is fairly uniform and the variation in g can be ignored.

Example 1.27   A drop hammer is lifted a height 6 m above the ground and then allowed to fall from rest on to a forging at ground level. Calculate the downward velocity of the hammer when it strikes the forging.

Solution

Let the mass of the hammer be m kg; then the work done in raising it h m is mgh J. This is then its potential energy above ground level.

In falling h m the earth-pull does an equal amount of work in accelerating the hammer to a velocity v m/s from rest. In effect the potential energy of the hammer is converted into kinetic energy of motion (principle of conservation of energy).

Thus

kinetic energy at ground level = initial potential energy

i.e.
$$\tfrac{1}{2}mv^2 = mgh$$

or
$$v = \sqrt{(2gh)} = \sqrt{(2 \times 9.8 \times 6)}$$

Hence
$$v = \textbf{10.9 m/s}$$

Example 1.28

In a stamping machine the die has a mass of 35 kg and falls from a height of 2 m on to a metal block. If the depth of indentation is 10 mm find the average stamping force assuming the die does not rebound.

Solution

Loss of potential energy of die $= mgh$
$$= 35 \times 9.8 \times (2 + 0.01)$$
$$= 689 \text{ J}$$

The average stamping force is equal to the average resisting force of the metal against which the die moves through 10 mm.

Work done against resisting force = loss of potential energy of die

i.e.

$$\text{average resisting force} \times 0.01 = 689$$

so that

$$\text{average resisting force} = 68\ 900 \text{ N}$$

or

$$\text{average stamping force} = \textbf{69 kN}$$

Problems

1.79 A mass of 18 kg moving at 20 m/s is acted on by a constant force for 5 s as it covers a distance of 125 m. What is the gain in its kinetic energy and the force? (4.5 kJ; 36 N)

1.80 A railway truck of mass 12 t moving at 2 m/s strikes a second truck of mass 18 t moving in the same direction at 1.2 m/s and they move off, coupled together, with a common velocity of 1.1 m/s. What is the loss of kinetic energy to the system? (18.8 kJ)

1.81 A ship moves through the water at 4 knots and when its engines are stopped, it travels a distance of 60 m before coming to rest. What is the kinetic energy per unit mass of the ship at 4 knots and the average water resistance in kN/t? 1 knot = 0.514 m/s.   (2.1 kJ/t; 0.035 kN/t)

1.82 Calculate by an energy method the braking force required to stop a car in 15 m when travelling at 100 km/h. The car has a mass of 1 tonne.   (25.7 kN)

1.83 An aircraft of mass 2000 kg is to be catapulted from the deck of a stationary aircraft carrier with a speed of v m/s in a distance of 70 m. The engine propelling force on the plane during take-off is 20 kN; the estimated forces exerted by the catapult and drag resistance are 8 kN and 4 kN respectively. Find the speed v and the kinetic energy of the plane when launched.   (41 m/s; 1.68 MJ)

1.84 An aircraft of mass 3000 kg lands on the deck of a carrier against the wind with an airspeed of 110 knots. The ship is cruising at 26 knots into a head wind of 28 knots. The aircraft is brought to rest on the deck by the combined action of wheel brakes, reverse thrusters and arrestor gear. Find (i) the speed of the aircraft relative to the ship, (ii) the kinetic energy to be absorbed in halting the aircraft and (iii) the total braking force necessary and the time taken to bring the aircraft to rest in a distance of 60 m. 1 knot = 0.514 m/s.   (56 knots; 1.24 MJ; 20.7 kN; 4.2 s)

Notes on conservation of energy

We recall that energy is the capacity to do work. In dynamics we deal only with kinetic and (gravitational) potential energy which are the two forms of mechanical energy. Kinetic energy is the energy possessed by a body by virtue of its mass and velocity. Potential energy is the energy possessed by a body by virtue of its weight and its position (height). Another form of 'potential' energy is *strain energy*, when the work done in stretching or compressing a bar or spring is stored and available as energy, i.e. there is no permanent deformation of the bar or spring. All forms of energy are transferable; that is, the work done in accelerating a body reappears as kinetic energy; similarly the potential energy lost by a falling body reappears as kinetic energy as its velocity increases. For all practical purposes energy cannot be destroyed. However, it is sometimes converted into a form which may be of no further practical use. For example, work done against friction is converted into heat, which may be of no further value but which is nevertheless a form of energy. In such a case, the energy may be considered 'lost', for it may not always be recovered to do useful work, as can potential energy or work done against gravity.

Similarly, in a collision, kinetic energy is generally 'lost'. Hence it is not ever possible to write that the kinetic energy after impact is equal to the kinetic energy before impact. The initial kinetic energy of two bodies before a collision occurs is recoverable only if both are perfectly elastic. This is not ever the case, the energy reappearing partly as heat, sound and mechanical vibration, none of which is recoverable.

The principle of conservation of energy has been illustrated by using the second law of motion to obtain a relation between kinetic energy and work. However, the principle is independent of the laws of motion. It stands alone and for bodies of constant mass no exception has ever been found.

Example 1.29

A train of mass 200 t is moving up an incline of 1 in 100 at 60 km/h. The resistance to motion is 50 N/t. If power is shut off calculate the distance travelled along the incline before the train comes to rest.

Solution

No collision is involved; hence the energy principle may be used provided that allowance is made for work done in overcoming resistance to motion. Let s metres be the distance travelled after power is shut off.

$$\text{Gain in height} = \frac{s}{100}$$

$$\text{Work done against gravity} = 200 \times 10^3 \times 9.8 \times \frac{s}{100}$$

$$= 19\ 600\ s\ \text{J}$$

$$\text{Total resistance to motion} = 50 \times 200\ \text{N}$$

$$= 10\ 000\ \text{N}$$

$$\text{Work done against resistance} = 10\ 000 \times s\ \text{J}$$

$$\text{Initial velocity} = 60\ \text{km/h} = 16.7\ \text{m/}s$$

$$\text{Initial kinetic energy} = \tfrac{1}{2} \times 200 \times 10^3 \times 16.7^2$$

$$= 2.79 \times 10^7\ \text{J}$$

Initial kinetic energy = work done against gravity + work done in overcoming resistance

i.e. $2.79 \times 10^7 = 19\ 600\ s + 10\ 000\ s$

so that

$$s = \frac{2.79 \times 10^7}{2.96 \times 10^4}$$

$$= 943\ \text{m}$$

Momentum and energy

It has been seen that, in addition to the second and third laws of motion, two further principles are available to solve problems in mechanics:

- *The principle of conservation of momentum.*
- *The principle of conservation of energy.*

For their correct application it must be realized that:

- Momentum is not conserved if an external force acts.
- Mechanical energy is not conserved if work is done against a resistance, or energy is put into the system, as in the burning of a fuel. Nevertheless, when the work done against a resistance is known, it may be allowed for and the energy equation used.

In the recoil of a gun total momentum is conserved, since no external forces act upon the system of gun and shell during the explosion. The propelling force on the shell is equal and opposite to the recoil force of the gun. These equal and opposite forces are internal forces. They act for the same *time*; hence the momentum given to the shell is equal and oppositely directed to the momentum given to the gun. The mechanical energy is not constant, since firing of the charge converts chemical energy into heat, sound, and mechanical vibration together with useful kinetic energy of motion.

The velocity of the shell is greater than that of the gun since it is of smaller mass. The time for which the propelling force acts is the same for both; hence the distance travelled by the shell is greater than the distance travelled by the gun in the same time. Since the forces on shell and gun are of equal magnitude, the work done on the shell is greater than the work done on the gun. Hence the kinetic energy given to the shell is greater than that given to the gun.

Similarly a rocket which loses the greater part of its mass in burnt fuel will receive as kinetic energy a greater proportion of the chemical energy liberated than will the ejected burnt gases.

Example 1.30   A hammer (or 'monkey') of mass 100 kg falls 4 m on to a pile of mass 300 kg and drives it 80 mm into the ground, Fig. 1.36. Calculate (a) the loss of energy on impact, (b) the work done by the resistance of the ground and (c) the average resistance to penetration. Assume the hammer does not rebound on impact.

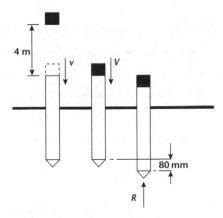

Fig. 1.36

Solution

(a) Initial potential energy of hammer = mgh. Let v be velocity of hammer just before impact; then kinetic energy of hammer

$$= \tfrac{1}{2}mv^2 = \tfrac{1}{2} \times 100v^2 = 50v^2 \text{ J}$$

Equating kinetic energy gained to potential energy lost by the hammer,

$$50v^2 = mgh = 100 \times 9.8 \times 4 = 3920 \text{ J}$$

so that

$$v = 8.86 \text{ m/s}$$

In collisions between perfectly elastic bodies, both momentum and energy are conserved. This gives sufficient information for such a problem to be solved. In general, however, for bodies in collision energy is *always* lost on impact, as in this problem, so that energy is never conserved. It is necessary in this case therefore to use the momentum principle to find the common velocity after impact.

Let V be the common velocity of hammer and pile after impact. The total mass moving at velocity V is therefore $(100 + 300)$ kg, i.e. 400 kg.

Momentum before impact = momentum after impact

i.e. $\qquad\qquad 100 \times 8.86 = 400 \times V$

so that

$$V = 2.22 \text{ m/s}$$

Kinetic energy after impact $= \frac{1}{2} \times 400 \times 2.22^2$

$$= 986 \text{ J}$$

Kinetic energy before impact = initial potential energy

$$= 3920 \text{ J}$$

Loss of kinetic energy on impact

$$= 3920 - 986 = 2934 \text{ J}$$

$$= 2.93 \text{ kJ}$$

(b) Work done by resistance of ground in bringing pile and hammer to rest

= total energy of pile and hammer *after impact*

= kinetic energy of pile and hammer + potential energy of pile *and* hammer

$= 986 + (400 \times 9.8 \times 0.08) = 1300 \text{ J}$

$$= 1.3 \text{ kJ}$$

(c) Let average resistance to penetration be R newtons; then work done $= R \times 0.08$ newtons. Therefore

$$R \times 0.08 = 1300$$

and

$$R = 16.3 \text{ kN}$$

Motion in a circle

When a body moves in a circular path, it is accelerated even although its speed round the circle may be constant. This is because its velocity is changing since the direction of motion is changing. This vector change in velocity gives rise to a special acceleration of the body called **centripetal acceleration**, directed radially inwards towards the centre of motion, A further acceleration occurs if the speed is not constant, i.e. a *linear acceleration* tangential to the circle of motion. This acceleration can be related to the motion of a radial line joining the body to the centre of motion. The angle swept out in unit time by this radial line is the *angular velocity* of the line and a change in this angular velocity is the **angular acceleration** of the line. These accelerations, the relationship between them and the forces involved will now be dealt with in detail.

| **Centripetal acceleration** | A linear acceleration can be caused by a change in direction without a change in speed, that is, by a *vector* change in velocity. |

Consider a point A moving in a circular path of radius r with constant angular velocity ω about a fixed point O (Fig. 1.37(a)). Let the line OA move to OA′ in a small time dt, and let angle AOA′ = dθ rad. The initial vector velocity of A perpendicular to the line OA (Fig. 1.37(b)):

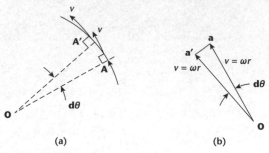

(a)   (b)

Fig. 1.37

$$v = \mathbf{oa}$$
$$= \omega \times \text{OA}$$
$$= \omega r$$

After time dt the vector velocity of A perpendicular to OA′:

$$v = \mathbf{oa'}$$
$$= \omega r$$

The vector *change* in velocity of A in time dt since dθ is small:

$$\text{change} = \mathbf{aa'}$$
$$= \omega r \times \mathrm{d}\theta$$

Therefore the acceleration of A is

$$a = \text{rate of vector change in velocity}$$
$$= \frac{\mathbf{aa'}}{\mathrm{d}t}$$
$$= \frac{\omega r \, \mathrm{d}\theta}{\mathrm{d}t}$$
$$= \omega^2 r \ [\text{since } \mathrm{d}\theta/\mathrm{d}t = \omega]$$

Also, since

$$\omega = \frac{v}{r}$$

then $$a = \left(\frac{v}{r}\right)^2 \times r$$

$$= \frac{v^2}{r}$$

The direction of the change **aa′** is in the sense **a** to **a′**, that is, along the line AO. Thus the acceleration of A due to its rotation is directed radially inward from A to O and is of amount

$$a = \omega^2 r = \frac{v^2}{r}$$

This acceleration is called the *centripetal acceleration*.

Centripetal force

Consider now a body of mass m at A, rotating about O. The centripetal acceleration a can only take place if there is a force acting in the direction A to O. The magnitude of this force F is given by

$$F = ma$$

$$= m \times \omega^2 r$$

$$= \frac{mv^2}{r}$$

and its direction is that of a, i.e. radially *inwards*. It is an active force since it is the force causing the body to move in a circular path and is known as the *cemtripetal force*. For example, a body whirled in a horizontal circle at the end of a light cord is maintained in its circular path by the tension in the cord acting radially inwards at its connection with the body at A, Fig. 1.38(a).

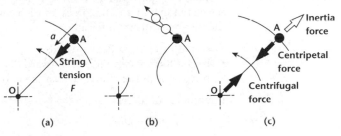

Fig. 1.38

The inertia force in rotation

For balance of forces at the body A, the centripetal force F may be considered as being in equilibrium with an equal and opposite inertia force of magnitude $m\omega^2 r$, Fig. 1.38(c). This inertia force is a reactive force, since it cannot of itself cause motion. If the cord is cut the active force F disappears and the body A moves in a straight line tangential to the circular path, Fig. 1.38(b). It does not fly radially outwards.

Centrifugal force

Now consider the tension in the cord at O. This is equal and opposite to the centripetal force at A and therefore acts radially outwards. This force at O is called the *centrifugal force* and may be thought of as due to the cord tension required to provide the motion in a circle, or the action of A upon the point O due to the rotation of the mass.

Example 1.31

A centrifugal clutch is shown at the rest position with its axis mounted vertically, Fig. 1.39. The rotating bobs are each of mass 225 g and the spring strength is 7.5 kN/m. The centre of mass of each bob is at 150 mm radius in the rest position. Calculate the radial force on the clutch face at 720 rev/min.

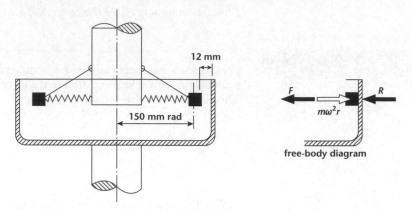

Fig. 1.39

Solution

As the shaft speed rises, the bobs fly out until they engage the inside face of the clutch cylinder. The forces on each rotating mass are then as shown on the free-body diagram for a bob:

- spring force F, radially inwards
- inertia force $m\omega^2 r$, radially outwards
- reaction R of the clutch face on the bob, radially inwards

For balance of forces:

$$F + R = m\omega^2 r$$

At engagement, the spring force

$$F = \text{stiffness} \times \text{extension}$$
$$= 7.5 \times 1000 \times 0.012$$
$$= 90 \text{ N}$$

Radius of rotation

$$r = 150 + 12 = 162 \text{ mm} = 0.162 \text{ m}$$

$$\text{Inertia force} = m\omega^2 r = 0.225 \left(\frac{2\pi \times 720}{60} \right)^2 \times 0.162$$

$$= 207 \text{ N}$$

hence $\qquad 90 + R = 207$

therefore $\qquad R = 117 \text{ N}$

The force *on* the clutch face is equal and opposite to this.

Note: As the speed rises from rest, there is a particular speed at which engagement just commences. At this speed the spring force is equal to the inertia force. As the speed rises above the engagement speed the spring force remains constant but the inertia force increases in value, thus increasing R. The value of R governs the friction force between bob and rim surfaces and hence determines the power transmitted.

Example 1.32   A body of mass 0.5 kg slides in smooth guides when whirled in a horizontal circle at the end of a spring. The spring stiffness, S = 1.5 kN/m. The natural unstretched length of the spring is l = 150 mm. Calculate the radius of rotation of the weight and the stretch in the spring when the speed of rotation is 360 rev/min.

Solution

The radial forces acting on the body A are: the spring force F inwards and the inertia force $m\omega^2 r$ outwards. Hence

$$F = m\omega^2 r$$

$$= 0.5 \left(\frac{2\pi \times 360}{60} \right)^2 \times r$$

$$= 711r \text{ N}$$

where r is in metres.

Let spring extension equal x m, then the spring force

$$F = S \times x$$

$$= 1.5 \times 1000 \times x \text{ N}$$

but $\qquad\qquad x = r - \text{initial length of spring}$

$$= r \times 0.15 \text{ m}$$

therefore $\qquad F = 1500(r - 0.15) \text{ N}$

i.e. $\qquad\qquad F = 711r = 1500(r - 0.15)$

hence $\qquad\qquad r = 0.285 \text{ mm}$

thus   extension $x = 285 - 150 = $ **135 mm**

Dynamic instability

When the body A in the above example is displaced along the spring axis it will tend to return to its original position providing the spring is not

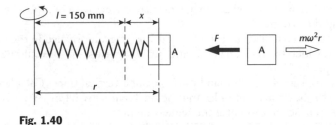

Fig. 1.40

'overstretched'. The example showed there will be a definite radius of rotation corresponding to the particular speed of rotation. However, there is a critical value of the speed at which the body will not return to its original position but will fly radially outwards. At this speed the radius tends to become *indefinitely* large and the body is then *unstable*. To find this *critical speed*, we must find an expression for the radius of rotation r in terms of the other variables. Thus, for equilibrium, referring to Fig. 1.40

$$F = m\omega^2 r$$

and $$F = S \times x$$

$$= S(r - l)$$

Therefore $\quad S(r - l) = m\omega^2 r$

Hence $$r = \frac{Sl}{S - m\omega^2}$$

Now r tends to infinity as the denominator tends to zero, i.e. the condition for instability is

$$S - m\omega^2 = 0$$

i.e. $$\omega^2 = \frac{S}{m}$$

Using the figures from the above example

$$\omega^2 = \frac{1.5 \times 1000}{0.5}$$

Hence the critical speed is

$$\omega = 54.8 \text{ rad/s}$$

$$= 523 \text{ rev/min}$$

Such problems of dynamic instability are of great importance in rotating and other machinery in motion. A machine running at a critical speed may suffer considerable damage and an effort must be made to avoid such speeds by correct design.

Problems

1.85 What is the maximum speed at which a car may travel over a humpbacked bridge of radius 15 m without leaving the ground? (43.7 km/h)

1.86 A 2 kg mass is attached at the end of a cord 1 m long and whirled in the vertical plane. Find the greatest speed at which the tension in the cord just disappears. What would he the maximum tension in the cord at a speed of 3 rev/s? (0.5 rev/s; 732 N)

1.87 A trolley travels at 30 km/h round the inside of a vertical track. Calculate the maximum force on the track if the trolley's mass is 14 kg and the track radius is 2.4 m. What is the least velocity the trolley must have in order not to fall at the highest point? (543 N; 17.5 km/h)

1.88 A rotor in a gyro instrument consists essentially of a flat disc of 100 mm diameter and 25 mm thick. It is mounted accurately on a spindle so that the central axis of the spindle coincides with the centre of the disc. What is the maximum out-of-balance force on the spindle at a gyro speed of 12 000 rev/min if the centre of mass of the disc is 0.025 mm out of alignment? Steel has a density of 7.8 Mg/m³. (60.6 N)

1.89 A centrifugal clutch is designed just to engage when the centres of gravity of the rotating weights are 200 mm from the centre of rotation. The speed at engagement is 1440 rev/min. If the revolving masses are each 0.5 kg, calculate the spring stiffness required for an extension of 20 mm when the masses move from the rest to the engaged position. (113.5 kN/m)

1.90 The centrifugal clutch shown at rest in Fig. 1.41 has springs of stiffness 15 kN/m and is designed to just engage at 10 rev/s. Calculate the required value of the revolving mass. What is the force on the clutch rim at 16 rev/s? (0.345 kg; 234 N)

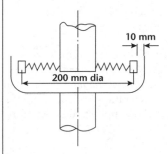

Fig. 1.41

1.91 A control mechanism is to he actuated by a mass of 4.5 kg rotating at the end of a spring at 300 rev/min. Calculate the minimum stiffness of spring required if the control is to be just stable at this speed. (4.45 kN/m)

1.92 A body of mass 1.8 kg is whirled round at the end of a spring of stiffness 1.8 kN/m extension at a speed of 60 rev/min. Calculate the radius of the path of the body if the unstretched length of the spring is 150 mm. At what speed would the radius tend to be indefinitely great? (156 mm; 302 rev/min)

| Vehicle rounding a curve | Figure 1.42 shows a two-wheeled vehicle (e.g. a cycle) rounding a curve of radius r at constant speed v. The cycle has mass m; A and B are the points of contact of the front and rear wheels, respectively, with the ground; O is the centre of rotation. For simplicity assume the rolling resistance to motion negligible. Hence there is no friction or other resisting force at A or B tangential to the path. Radial forces are necessary in order that the vehicle shall move in a curved path and not a straight line, and these are provided by radially inward friction forces F_1 and F_2 at A and B, respectively. |

Owing to rotation, every particle of mass dm of which the vehicle is composed has an inertia force d$m(v^2/r)$ acting upon it radially outward. The net radial effect of all these forces is equivalent to a force acting at the centre of mass (i.e. the centre of gravity G). The forces F_1, F_2 and the inertia force are in equilibrium and are represented in the force diagram, Fig. 1.42, by **ab**, **bc** and **ca**, respectively.

In practice the angle ∠AOB is often small and the forces F_1, F_2 approximately in the same straight line. The total friction force $F = F_1 + F_2$ is then, for an unbanked flat track, equal and opposite to the inertia force, or

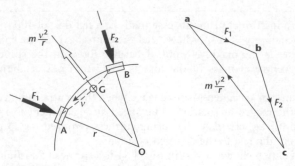

Fig. 1.42

$$F = \frac{m\upsilon^2}{r}$$

The friction force is here an active force in that it causes the vehicle to deviate from a straight line. A vehicle on a perfectly smooth sheet of ice, for example, could not move except in a straight line. When the limiting friction force is insufficient to provide the centripetal acceleration (radially inward), the vehicle tends to move in a straight line. It then appears to be skidding 'outwards'.

Superelevation of tracks: elimination of side thrust

The superelevation of a railway track is the amount by which the outer rail is raised above the level of the inner rail. The wheels of a train are flanged, the flanges being on the inside of the rails. As the train rounds a curved track, the centripetal force required to provide the circular motion is provided by the inward thrust of the outer rail. To reduce the magnitude of this lateral load, a second rail may sometimes be provided on the inside curve so that the inner wheel flange is contained between two rails. This second rail then takes some of the side thrust. More generally, the side thrust may be eliminated completely at a particular speed by suitable banking of the track. The amount of banking or *cant* depends on the tightness of the curve and the speed of the trains using the track. In practice the amount of superelevation is limited to about 150 mm, i.e. about 6° of cant since 25 mm of superelevation on a standard gauge line is equal to 1° of cant. The speed chosen is the average speed at which a train (usually a freight train) may be expected to take the curve. At any speed higher than the one suitable for that angle of banking, there will be a side thrust on the outer rail, so that fast passenger trains have some lateral force; at lower speeds than the design value there will be a side thrust in all cases on the inner rail. The amount of *extra* banking needed at a given speed to remove this side thrust altogether is called the 'cant deficiency' and this is normally limited to about 110 mm of superelevation.

The banking of a car race track serves a similar purpose to the superelevation of a rail track, i.e. to eliminate side thrust on the tyres. To serve its purpose for cars of different speed, the gradient of the banking is increased towards the outside of the curve. There is a correct angle of banking for any particular speed and this angle is independent of the weight of the vehicle (see Example 1.36). Most racing tracks are now unbanked (except in the

USA) so that means have had to be found to provide an increase in side thrust to allow high speeds round corners. Large, wide tyres give extra adhesive force but cause extra drag. In order to increase the downward force on the vehicle without affecting the weight, aerodynamic devices are used.

Example 1.33

A car of mass 2 t rounds an unbanked curve of 60 m radius at 72 km/h. Calculate the side thrust on the tyres.

Solution

The radial forces acting on the car are: (*a*) the outward inertia force, mv^2/r; (*b*) the inward force F exerted by the road on the tyres, i.e. the *side thrust* (Fig. 1.43). These two forces are in balance, therefore

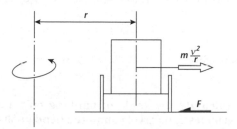

Fig. 1.43

$$F = \frac{mv^2}{r}$$

$$= 2 \times 1000 \times \frac{20^2}{60} \text{ since } 72 \text{ km/h} = 20 \text{ m/s}$$

$$= 13\,330 \text{ N}$$

(Note that F is *not* equal to the limiting friction force which is μmg)

Example 1.34

A racing car travels at 180 km/h on a track banked at 30° to the horizontal. The limiting coefficient of friction between tyres and track is 0.7. Calculate the minimum radius of curvature of the track if the car is not to slide outwards.

Solution

The *total* reaction R of the track on the car acts at an angle ϕ to the normal, where $\tan \phi = \mu = 0.7$. This reaction is in balance with the inertia force and the weight of the car. These three forces act at a point and can be represented by the triangle of forces, **oab**, Fig. 1.44. From the triangle of forces,

$$\tan (30° + \phi) = \frac{mv^2}{r} \div mg = \frac{v^2}{gr}$$

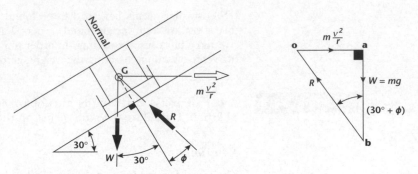

Fig. 1.44

But $\tan \phi = 0.7$, thus $\phi = 35°$ and $\upsilon = 180$ km/h $= 50$ m/s. Hence

$$\tan (30° + 35°) = \frac{50^2}{9.8 \times r}$$

therefore $\qquad\qquad r = 119$ m

Example 1.35   **Calculate the angle of banking on a bend of 100 m radius so that vehicles can travel round the bend at 50 km/h without side thrust on the tyres. For this angle of banking, what would be the value of the coefficient of friction if skidding outwards commences for a car travelling at 120 km/h?**

Solution

If the angle of banking is θ, Fig. 1.45, then the forces on the vehicle parallel to the slope are (i) the component of the weight $mg \sin \theta$ acting inwards; (ii) the component of the inertia force $(m\upsilon^2/r) \cos \theta$ acting outwards; (iii) the side thrust F acting inwards.

The equation of forces parallel to the slope is therefore

$$F + mg \sin \theta = \frac{m\upsilon^2}{r} \cos \theta$$

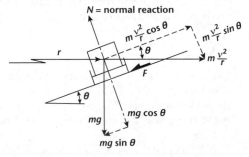

Fig. 1.45

If there is to be no side thrust, $F = 0$, hence

$$\tan \theta = \frac{v^2}{gr} = \frac{(50/3.6)^2}{9.8 \times 100} = 0.198$$

and $\theta = 11°12'$

Note that the angle of banking is independent of the weight of the car.
When skidding outwards commences, limiting conditions exist so that

$$F = \mu \times N$$

$$= \mu \left(\frac{mv^2}{r} \sin \theta + mg \cos \theta \right)$$

where $v = 120$ km/h $= 33.3$ m/s. The equation of forces parallel to the slope becomes

$$\mu \left(\frac{mv^2}{r} \sin \theta + mg \cos \theta \right) + mg \sin \theta = \frac{mv^2}{r} \cos \theta$$

hence $\mu = \dfrac{(v^2/gr) - \tan \theta}{(v^2/gr) \tan \theta + 1}$

i.e. $\dfrac{v^2}{gr} = \dfrac{(120/3.6)^2}{9.8 \times 100} = 1.135$

therefore $\mu = \dfrac{1.135 - 0.198}{1.135 \times 0.198 + 1} = 0.765$

The student should rework this problem using the method of the previous example.

Example 1.36 Calculate the superelevation of the outside rail of a curved track if a train is to traverse the curve without side thrust on the rails at 50 km/h. The radius of the curve is 180 m and the track gauge is 1440 mm.

Solution

If the superelevation is h and the track width x, the angle of banking θ is given by:

$$\sin \theta = \frac{h}{x}$$

The forces acting on the vehicle are shown in the free-body diagram, Fig. 1.46, i.e. the weight W, the total reaction R and the inertia force mv^2/r. Since there is no side thrust, the reaction R exerted by the track on the vehicle must be normal to the track incline. From the triangle of forces (Fig. 1.46):

$$\tan \theta = \frac{ab}{oa} \quad \text{where} \quad oa = W = mg$$

$$ab = \frac{mv^2}{r} = m \times \frac{(50/3.6)^2}{180} = 1.075 \text{ m}$$

Hence $\tan \theta = \dfrac{m \times 1.075}{m \times 9.8} = 0.1095$

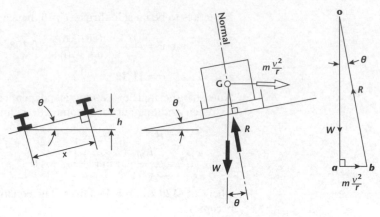

Fig. 1.46

But since tan θ is small, tan θ = sin θ approximately, so that

$$\tan \theta = \frac{h}{1.44}$$

thus $\qquad h = 1.44 \tan \theta = 1.44 \times 0.1095 = 0.158 \text{ m} = \textbf{158 mm}$

Passenger comfort – the pendulum car

Anyone who has been thrown outwards while in a vehicle travelling round a curve at speed will be familiar with the reality of the radial inertia force. Of course, what is experienced by a passenger is the tendency to move in a straight line while the vehicle turns. Experiments have shown that an uncompensated radial acceleration (v^2/r) in excess of about 0.1 g (0.98 m/s^2) is definitely unpleasant. This acceleration would be attained at about 100 km/h on an 800 m radius curve. One solution already exists, apart from straightening out the track system – superelevation of the track.

In addition to reducing the side thrust on the rails, superelevation tends to ensure that the resultant force due to weight and inertia force is normal to the seat. Then if the superelevation is sufficient, there is no side force tending to slide the passenger across the seat. However, if a train moves slowly or stops on a curve, the inside rail is subject to considerable thrust.

A second solution to the problem is to allow the body of the carriage to swing like a pendulum about a longitudinal axis O, placed above its centre of gravity G, Fig. 1.47(a). The train in effect leans into the bend, passengers feel more comfortable and bends can be taken faster. This is *passive* tilting, limited in practice to about 6° of tilt at a maximum speed of 120 km/h. The disadvantage is the slow response time when entering and leaving a bend. In an *active* system the carriage is tilted by hydraulic jacks, electronically controlled. In practice there is a combination of banked track and tilting carriage. Speeds above 200 km/h are possible with a pendulum car subject to restrictions for other reasons such as braking requirements.

The forces acting on the swinging carriage are: its weight W, the inertia force mv^2/r radially outward and the reaction R at the pivot. The three forces are in equilibrium, hence all three forces pass through G. The line of

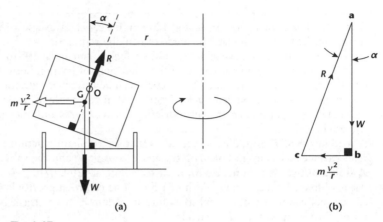

Fig. 1.47

action of R is therefore from G to O. The resultant force is always normal to the carriage floor; a similar argument applies also to any passenger seated in the swinging carriage.

The triangle of forces **abc** is shown in Fig. 1.47(b). If there is no superelevation of the track, the angle between the vertical and the reaction R is the angle α through which the carriage swings about O. From the triangle of forces:

$$\tan \alpha = \frac{\mathbf{bc}}{\mathbf{ab}}$$

$$= \frac{mv^2}{r} \div W$$

$$= \frac{v^2}{gr} \text{ since } W = mg$$

For example, at 120 km/h on a 1200 m radius curve, $v = 33.3$ m/s, and

$$\tan \alpha = \frac{33.3^2}{9.8 \times 1200} = 0.095$$

thus $\alpha = 5.4°$

and the pendulum car swings outwards nearly 6°. It should be noted, however, that allowing the carriage to pivot does not affect the side thrust on the track. In this case, since there is no superelevation, the side thrust would be equal to the inertia force.

Problems

1.93   Calculate the minimum limiting coefficient of friction between tyres and road in order that a car shall negotiate an unbanked curve of 120 m radius at 100 km/h.   (0.66)
1.94   Calculate the minimum radius of unbanked track which a motor cycle may traverse at 130 km/h without skidding outwards if the coefficient of sliding friction is 0.6.   (222 m)
1.95   A vehicle travels at 72 km/h round a track banked at 20° to the horizontal. The coefficient of sliding friction between tyres and road is 0.5. Calculate the radius at which skidding would occur.
                                                                                                (38.7 m)

1.96 A race track is to be banked so that at 120 km/h a car can traverse a 180 m radius curve without side thrust on the tyres. Calculate the angle of banking required. (32°13′)

1.97 A car travels round a curve of 60 m radius which is banked at 10° to the horizontal, the slope being *away* from the inside of the curve. If the coefficient of friction between tyres and road is 0.7 calculate the maximum speed at which the curve can be traversed without skidding. (60 km/h)

1.98 A vehicle traverses a banked track of radius 90 m and angle of banking 60°. If its speed is 12 m/s, calculate the minimum coefficient of friction between tyres and track if the vehicle is not to slip *down* the track. (1.22)

1.99 A road curve of 75 m radius is banked so that the resultant reaction for any vehicle is normal to the road surface at 72 km/h. Calculate the angle of banking and the value of the coefficient of friction if skidding outwards commences for a car travelling at 120 km/h. (28°30′; 0.53)

1.100 A car of mass 1 t has a track width of 1.5 m. The centre of gravity is 600 mm above road level. The car travels round a curve of 60 m radius at 72 km/h. If the track is banked at 30°, find the total normal reaction on the outer wheels. (6.25 kN)

1.101 A railway carriage built on the pendulum-car principle has a maximum angle of tilt of 9°. What is the maximum allowable speed on a 600 m radius unbanked curve and what is the corresponding side thrust on the track if the carriage has a mass of 50 t? (110 km/h; 77.6 kN)

Overturning of vehicles

The tendency of a vehicle to slide outwards when rounding a curve has been shown to result in a limiting speed at which sliding just occurs. In addition there is also a limiting speed at which the vehicle will overturn. This is an example of dynamic instability. To maintain a vehicle in a circular path requires a centripetal force at the centre of mass, but this force can only be supplied by friction at the road surface or the side thrust of a rail track. This lateral force is equivalent to the same force at the centre of mass together with a couple tending to rotate the vehicle about the centre of mass (Fig. 1.48). The two forces forming this couple are the lateral force at the track surface and the inertia force at the centre of mass. Alternatively, the inertia force acting radially outwards may be thought of as tending to tip the vehicle about its offside wheels. The weight together with the upwards directed ground reaction at the outer wheels provides the balancing couple tending to maintain stable equilibrium and prevent tipping.

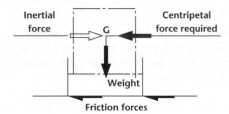

Fig. 1.48

Example 1.37

A vehicle has a track width of 1.4 m and its centre of gravity is 650 mm above the road surface in the centre plane. If the limiting coefficient of friction between tyres and road is 0.6, determine whether the vehicle will first overturn or sideslip when rounding a curve of 120 m radius at speed on a level track. State the maximum permissible speed on the curve.

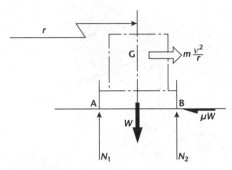

Fig. 1.49

Solution

Figure 1.49 shows the free-body diagram for the vehicle. Let v be speed of vehicle in metres per second and r = radius of curve (120 m). For sideslip to occur, the inertia force must be just equal to or greater than the total limiting inward friction force, i.e.

$$\frac{mv^2}{r} = \mu W = \mu mg$$

or
$$\frac{v^2}{120} = 0.6 \times 9.8$$

ie. $\quad\quad v = 6.6$ m/s or 95.6 km/h

For overturning to occur, the ground reaction N_1 at the *inner* wheels must be zero, i.e. the tilting moment due to the inertia force about the outer wheels must be greater than the stabilizing moment due to the dead weight. Taking moments about the outer wheel track B, thereby eliminating N_2 and μW, and assuming the car just about to overturn:

$$\frac{mv^2}{r} \times 0.65 = W \times 0.7$$

i.e. $\quad\quad \dfrac{mv^2 \times 0.65}{120} = m \times 9.8 \times 0.7$

i.e. $\quad\quad\quad\quad v = 35.6$ m/s or 128 km/h

Sideslip takes place first at the lower speed of **95.6 km/h** and this, therefore, is the maximum speed permissible on the curve.

Example 1.38 Calculate the maximum speed at which a car may traverse a banked track of 30 m radius without overturning if the centre of gravity of the car is 0.9 m above ground level and the track width of the wheels is 1.5 m. The track is banked at 30° to the horizontal.

Solution

When overturning starts, the inner wheels at A (Fig. 1.50) just lift and the car starts to rotate about the outer wheels at B. Hence the total reaction R of

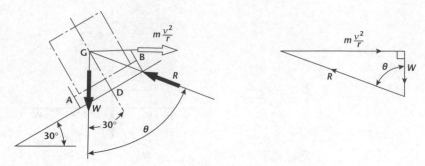

Fig. 1.50

the track on the car must pass through B. The condition for (unstable) equilibrium is that R, the weight W and the inertia force mv^2/r shall all pass through one point. Since both the weight and the inertia force act through the centre of gravity G then the reaction R must act along BG at an angle θ to the vertical. From the geometry of the car

$$\theta = 30° + \angle\,DGB$$

and, since

$$\tan\angle\,DGB = \frac{DB}{GD} = \frac{0.75}{0.9} = 0.833$$

then $\angle\,DGB = 39°48'$

hence $\theta = 30° + 39°48'$

$$= 69°48'$$

From the triangle of forces:

$$\tan\theta = \frac{mv^2}{r} \div W$$

or $\tan 69°48' = \dfrac{v^2}{9.8 \times 30}$ since $W = mg$

thus $v^2 = 9.8 \times 30 \times \tan 69°48'$

and $v = 28.2$ m/s   or   **101.5 km/h**

The student should rework this example, resolving forces parallel and perpendicular to the slope, and taking moments about B.

Problems

1.102 Calculate the maximum speed at which a car can traverse an unbanked curve of 24 m radius if its wheels are 1.8 m apart and its centre of gravity is 1.2 m above the road. Assume that slipping does not occur.   (13.3 m/s or 47.8 km/h)

1.103 Calculate the smallest radius unbanked curve which a racing car can traverse at 200 km/h without overturning if its wheels are 1.5 m apart and its centre of gravity is 650 mm above the road.

(273 m)

1.104 A sports car is to be built capable of rounding a 100 m curve at 120 km/h and its wheels are to be 1.5 m apart. Calculate the maximum allowable height of its centre of gravity above ground level.

(0.66 m)

1.105 Calculate the maximum speed at which a car can traverse a 30 m radius track banked at 20° to the horizontal. Its centre of gravity is 0.9 m above the ground and its wheels are 1350 mm apart.

(76.3 km/h)

1.106 A double-deck bus whose wheels are 2.4 m apart and whose centre of gravity is 1.5 m above the ground is to round a road banked at 10° to the horizontal at 50 km/h. Calculate the minimum radius of the curve if overturning is not to occur. (17.4 m)

1.107 A four-wheeled vehicle turns a corner of radius 10 m on a level track. Its centre of gravity is 0.9 m above road level and its wheels are 1.5 m apart. Calculate (a) the fastest speed at which it may traverse the bend without the inner wheels leaving the ground; (b) the fastest speed at which it may travel round on two outer wheels without tipping more than 30°. (9.03 m/s; 4.13 m/s)

1.108 Determine the speed at which overturning will occur for a vehicle whose wheels are 1.5 m apart and whose centre of gravity is 0.9 m above the ground, when travelling round a banked track of 60 m radius: the banking is 10° away from the inside of the curve. Calculate the angle of banking which would tip the vehicle when at rest. (26.3 m/s; 39°48′)

1.109 A car of mass 1120 kg is travelling along a curved unbanked road of radius 60 m. Its wheel track is 1.35 m and its centre of gravity is 0.9 m above the ground, and midway between front and rear axles. The coefficient of friction is 0.5. Find (a) the vertical ground reaction at each wheel when the car is travelling at 15 m/s; (b) the maximum speed without overturning; (c) the skidding speed.

(1340 N; 4140 N; 21.1 m/s; 17.15 m/s)

Network theorems

Many practical circuits can be understood in terms of series and parallel circuits. However, some electrical engineering applications, especially in electronic engineering, involve networks with large numbers of components. In this section we shall develop a variety of techniques such as Nodal analysis, the Superposition theorem, Thévenin's theorem and Norton's theorem, which will speed up the analysis of the more complicated networks. It is always a good idea to make life as easy as possible!

Not all loads are connected in series or in parallel. There are two other arrangements known as star and delta. They are not so common but, because they are interchangeable, we can readily find a solution to any network in which they appear – so long as we can transform the one into the other.

We have seen that the function of a circuit is to deliver energy or power to a load. It may have crossed your mind – what is the condition for the greatest power to be developed? Well, we shall answer that later in this section. It is a question which is important to the electronic engineer.

New circuit analysis techniques

A direct application of Kirchhoff's current and voltage laws can solve many circuit problems. However, there are a variety of techniques, all based on these two laws, that can simplify circuit analysis. The main techniques, to be introduced in this section are:

- Mesh analysis.
- Nodal analysis.
- Thévenin's theorem.
- Norton's theorem.

Each of these techniques has particular strengths aimed at solving particular types of circuit problem. In this way, what would be laborious using one method can be straightforward using another. Familiarization with all the different methods will enable you to choose the method which best suits a particular problem. This simplifies circuit solution and makes less work overall!

Kirchhoff's laws and network solution

Kirchhoff's laws can be applied to network solution in any of the following ways:
1. By direct application to the network in conjunction with Ohm's law.
2. By indirect application to the network in conjunction with the manipulation of the component resistances.
3. By direct application to the network resulting in solution by simultaneous equations.

These statements appear to be most complicated, but the following series of examples will illustrate the forms of application of the laws to network solution. The form that ought to be most obvious is the first form, in which the laws are directly applied; curiously this form of solution tends to be so obvious that it is all too often neglected, as will be illustrated.

Example 1.39

For the network shown in Fig. 1.51, determine the supply current and the source e.m.f.

Since R_3 and R_4 are in parallel

$$V_3 = I_4 R_4 = 3 \times 8 = 24 \text{ V} = I_3 R_3 = I_3 \times 16$$

$$I_3 = \frac{24}{16} = 1.5 \text{ A}$$

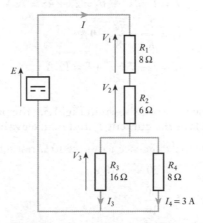

Fig. 1.51   Circuit diagram for Example 1.39

By Kirchhoff's first law

$$I = I_3 + I_4 = 1.5 + 3 = \textbf{4.5 A}$$

Also $V_1 = IR_1 = 4.5 \times 8 = \textbf{36 V}$

$$V_2 = IR_2 = 4.5 \times 6 = \textbf{27 V}$$

By Kirchhoff's second law

$$E = V_1 + V_2 + V_3 = 36 + 27 + 24 = \textbf{87 V}$$

This is not the only form of solution to the given problem. For instance, the supply current could have been derived directly from I_3 by applying the current-sharing rule, or the source e.m.f. could have been derived from the product of the supply current and the total effective resistance which could have been determined – but the direct solution is readily available without the need to resort to such devices. The following two examples illustrate again the availability of a direct approach to network problems.

Example 1.40   Given the network shown in Fig. 1.52, determine I_1, E, I_3 and I.

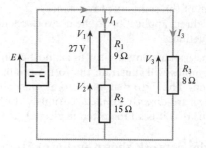

Fig. 1.52   Circuit diagram for Example 1.40

$$I_1 = \frac{V_1}{R_1} = \frac{27}{9} = \textbf{3 A}$$

$$V_2 = I_1 R_2 = 3 \times 15 = \textbf{45 V}$$

$$E = V = V_1 + V_2 = 27 + 45 = \textbf{72 V}$$

$$I_3 = \frac{V}{R_3} = \frac{72}{8} = \textbf{9 A}$$

$$I = I_1 + I_3 = 3 + 9 = \textbf{12 A}$$

Example 1.41   For the network shown in Fig. 1.53, the power dissipated in R_3 is 20 W. Calculate the current I_3 and hence evaluate R_1, R_3, I_1, I_2 and V.

Potential difference across the 10 Ω resistor is $1 \times 10 = 10$ V. For resistor R_3,

$$P = 20 \text{ W} = 10 \times I_3$$

Hence $I_3 = \dfrac{20}{10} = \textbf{2 A}$

$$P = I_3^2 R_3 = 20$$

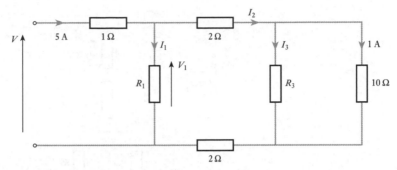

Fig. 1.53 Circuit diagram for Example 1.41

hence $\quad 20 = 2^2 \times R_3$

$\qquad R_3 = 5 \ \Omega$

$\qquad I_2 = 2 + 1 = 3 \ \text{A}$

Potential difference across each of the two 2 Ω resistors is $3 \times 2 = 6$ V. Thus

$\qquad V_1 = 6 + 10 + 6 = 22 \ \text{V}$

$\qquad I_1 = 5 - 3 = 2 \ \text{A}$

$\qquad R_1 = \dfrac{V_1}{I_1} = \dfrac{22}{2} = 11 \ \Omega$

Potential difference across the 1 Ω resistor is $5 \times 1 = 5$ V, hence

$\qquad V = 5 + 22 = \textbf{27 V}$

This last example in particular illustrates that a quite complicated network can readily be analysed by this direct approach. However, it is not always possible to proceed in this way, either because most of the information given relates to the resistances or because there is insufficient information concerning any one component of the network.

An instance of the information being presented mainly in terms of resistance is given in Example 1.42 and it also brings us to the second form of application of Kirchhoff's laws.

Example 1.42

For the network shown in Fig. 1.54, determine the supply current and current I_4.

In essence this network consists of three parts in series, but one of them comprises R_3 and R_4 in parallel. These can be replaced by an equivalent resistance, thus

$$R_e = \frac{R_3 R_4}{R_3 + R_4} = \frac{16 \times 8}{16 + 8} = 5.33 \ \Omega$$

Replacing R_3 and R_4 by R_e, the network becomes that shown in Fig. 1.55.

Now that the network has been reduced to a simple series circuit the total effective resistance is

$$R = R_1 + R_2 + R_e = 8 + 6 + 5.33 = 19.33 \ \Omega$$

$$I = \frac{V}{R} = \frac{87}{19.33} = \textbf{4.5 A}$$

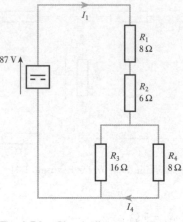

Fig. 1.54   Circuit diagram for Example 1.42

Reverting now to the original network,

$$I_4 = \frac{R_3}{R_3 + R_4} \cdot I = \frac{16}{16 + 8} \times 4.5 = 3\,\text{A}$$

This example compares with Example 1.39 and the figures are in fact the same. However, in this second instance the given voltage and current information stemmed from the source and not from the load, hence the emphasis of the calculation lay in dealing with the resistances of the network. The calculation was based on network reduction, i.e. by replacing two or more resistors by one equivalent resistor. A further example of this approach is given below, in which two instances of network reduction transform the problem into a form that can be readily analysed.

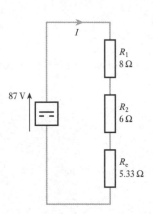

Fig. 1.55   Circuit diagram for Example 1.42

Example 1.43

Determine V_{AB} in the network shown in Fig. 1.56.

This is quite a complex network. However, there are two instances of parallel resistors that may be replaced by equivalent resistors. For the 10 Ω and 15 Ω resistors

$$R = \frac{10 \times 15}{10 + 15} = 6\,\Omega$$

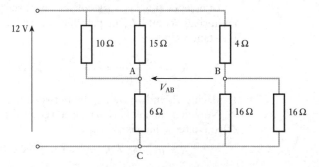

Fig. 1.56   Circuit diagram for Example 1.43

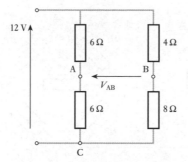

Fig. 1.57   Circuit diagram for Example 1.43

For the two 16 Ω resistors in parallel

$$R = \frac{16 \times 16}{16 + 16} = 8\,\Omega$$

If these equivalent values are inserted into the network, the network transforms into that shown in Fig. 1.57. Thus

$$V_{AC} = \frac{6}{6 + 6} \times 12 = 6\text{ V}$$

and

$$V_{BC} = \frac{8}{4 + 8} \times 12 = 8\text{ V}$$

$$V_{AB} = V_{AC} - V_{BC} = 6 - 8 = -2\text{ V}$$

Having now observed the two methods of analysis being demonstrated, you may well wonder how to tell when each should be used. As a general rule, if the information given concerns the voltage or the current associated with one or more components of the network, then you would apply the first form of approach. However, if the information given concerns the supply voltage or current, then you would try to apply the second form of approach by network reduction. This is not always possible because resistors may be connected in a manner that is neither series nor parallel – such an arrangement is shown in Fig. 1.58.

Example 1.44   **For the network shown in Fig. 1.58, calculate the currents in each of the resistors.**

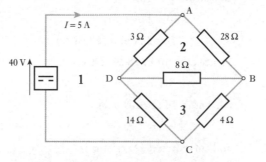

Fig. 1.58   Circuit diagram for Example 1.44

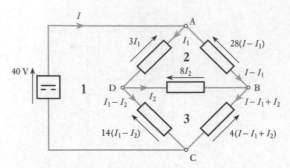

Fig. 1.59   Circuit diagram for Example 1.44

In this network the resistors are neither in series nor in parallel and therefore a more difficult method of analysis must be employed. Let the current in the 3 Ω resistor be I_1 and therefore by Kirchhoff's first law, the current in the 28 Ω resistor is $I - I_1$. Further, let the current in the 8 Ω resistor flowing from D to B be I_2. It follows that the current in the 14 Ω resistor is $I_1 - I_2$ while that in the 4 Ω resistor is $I - I_1 + I_2$. The resulting volt drops are shown in Fig. 1.59.

Applying Kirchhoff's second law to loop 1 (comprising source to ADC):

$$40 = 3I_1 + 14(I_1 - I_2)$$

$$40 = 17I_1 - 14I_2 \tag{a}$$

Applying Kirchhoff's second law to loop 2 (ABD):

$$0 = 28(I - I_1) - 8I_2 - 3I_1$$

$$= 28I - 31I_1 - 8I_2$$

But $I = 5$ A

Therefore

$$140 = 31I_1 + 8I_2 \tag{b}$$

(a) × 4 $160 = 68I_1 - 56I_2$ (c)

(b) × 7 $980 = 217I_1 + 56I_2$ (d)

(c) + (d) $1140 = 285I_1$

$$I_1 = 4 \text{ A in 3 } \Omega \text{ resistor}$$

Substituting in (b),

$$140 = 124 + 8I_2$$

$$I_2 = 2 \text{ A in 8 } \Omega \text{ resistor}$$

Hence current in 28 Ω resistor is

$$5 - 4 = 1 \text{ A}$$

current in 14 Ω resistor is

$$4 - 2 = 2 \text{ A}$$

and current in 4 Ω resistor is

$$5 - 4 + 2 = 3 \text{ A}$$

This form of solution requires that you proceed with great caution, otherwise it is a simple matter to make mistakes during the mathematical processes. However, in the instance given, it is necessary to involve such an analysis; had a different current been given in this example, such a solution would not have been required since it would then have been possible to achieve a solution by applying the first approach, i.e. directly applying Kirchhoff's laws.

If two parallel e.m.f.s appear in a network as exemplified by Fig. 1.60, it might again be necessary to employ the approach using simultaneous equations resulting from the application of Kirchhoff's laws.

Example 1.45 **Calculate the currents in the network shown in Fig. 1.60.**

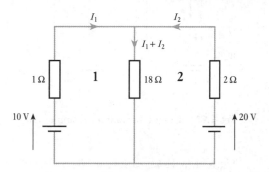

Fig. 1.60 Circuit diagram for Example 1.45

Applying Kirchhoff's second law to loop 1:

$$10 = 1I_1 + 18(I_1 + I_2)$$

$$10 = 19I_1 + 18I_2 \qquad\qquad\qquad (a)$$

Applying Kirchhoff's second law to loop 2:

$$20 = 2I_2 + 18(I_1 + I_2)$$

$$20 = 18I_1 + 20I_2 \qquad\qquad\qquad (b)$$

(a) × 10 $100 = 190I_1 + 180I_2$ $\qquad\qquad (c)$

(b) × 9 $180 = 162I_1 + 180I_2$ $\qquad\qquad (d)$

(d) − (c) $80 = -28I_1$

$$I_1 = -2.85 \text{ A}$$

Substituting in (a)

$$10 = -54.34 + 18I_2$$

$$I_2 = 3.57 \text{ A}$$

Current in 18 Ω resistor is

$$3.57 - 2.85 = \mathbf{0.72 \text{ A}}$$

This form of solution is fraught with the danger of mathematical mistakes and therefore should only be employed when all else fails. This section commenced by stating that the obvious solution is all too easily ignored. Thus if the 2 Ω resistor were removed from the network shown in Fig. 1.60, it might be overlooked that the 20 V battery is now directly applied to the 18 Ω resistor and so, knowing the voltage drop across one of the components, it is possible to revert to the first form of analysis as shown in Example 1.46.

Example 1.46   **Calculate the currents in the network shown in Fig. 1.61.**

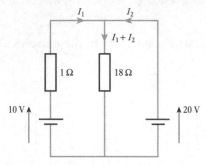

Fig. 1.61   Circuit diagram for Example 1.46

Current in 18 Ω resistor is

$$\frac{20}{18} = 1.1\,\text{A}$$

Applying Kirchhoff's second law to the outside loop:

$$20 - 10 = -I_1 \times 1$$

$$I_1 = -10\,\text{A}$$

$$I_2 = -(-10) + 1.1 = 11.1\,\text{A}$$

Mesh analysis   This method is given a number of different names – all of which are an indication of the analysis technique employed. It is variously known as Maxwell's circulating current method, loop analysis or Mesh current analysis. The terminology is chosen to distinguish it from the familiar 'branch current' technique, in which currents are assigned to individual branches of a circuit. Mesh analysis, of course, relies on Kirchhoff's laws just the same. The technique proceeds as follows:

- Circulating currents are allocated to closed loops or meshes in the circuit rather than to branches.
- An equation for each loop of the circuit is then obtained by equating the algebraic sum of the e.m.f.s round that loop to the algebraic sum of the potential differences (in the direction of the loop, mesh or circulating current), as required by Kirchhoff's voltage (second) law.
- Branch currents are found thereafter by taking the algebraic sum of the loop currents common to individual branches.

Example 1.47   Calculate the current in each branch of the network shown in Fig. 1.62.

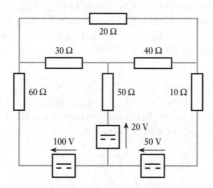

Fig. 1.62   Circuit diagram for Example 1.47

Let the circulating loop currents be as shown in Fig. 1.63.

In loop ①:

$$100 - 20 = I_1(60 + 30 + 50) - I_2 50 - I_3 30$$

$$\therefore \qquad 80 = 140I_1 - 50I_2 - 30I_3 \qquad\qquad (a)$$

In loop ②:

$$50 + 20 = I_2(50 + 40 + 10) - I_1 50 - I_3 40$$

$$\therefore \qquad 70 = -50I_1 + 100I_2 - 40I_3 \qquad\qquad (b)$$

In loop ③:

$$0 = I_3(30 + 20 + 40) - I_1 30 - I_2 40$$

$$\therefore \qquad 0 = -30I_1 - 40I_2 + 90I_3 \qquad\qquad (c)$$

Solving for these equations gives

$$I_1 = 1.65 \text{ A} \qquad I_2 = 2.16 \text{ A} \qquad I_3 = 1.50 \text{ A}$$

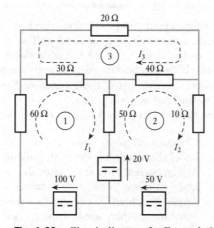

Fig. 1.63   Circuit diagram for Example 1.47

Current in 60 $\Omega = I_1 = \mathbf{1.65}$ **A** in direction of I_1
Current in 30 $\Omega = I_1 - I_3 = \mathbf{0.15}$ **A** in direction of I_1
Current in 50 $\Omega = I_2 - I_1 = \mathbf{0.51}$ **A** in direction of I_2
Current in 40 $\Omega = I_2 - I_3 = \mathbf{0.66}$ **A** in direction of I_2
Current in 10 $\Omega = I_2 = \mathbf{2.16}$ **A** in direction of I_2
Current in 20 $\Omega = I_3 = \mathbf{1.50}$ **A** in direction of I_3.

In Example 1.47 all the circulating loop currents have been taken in the same direction (i.e. clockwise). This is not essential when using this method, but if the same direction is adopted for the loop currents then the equations will always be of the form:

$$E_1 = R_{11}I_1 - R_{12}I_2 - R_{13}I_3 \ldots - R_{1n}I_n$$

$$E_2 = -R_{21}I_1 + R_{22}I_2 - R_{23}I_3 \ldots - R_{2n}I_n$$

$$E_3 = -R_{31}I_1 - R_{32}I_2 + R_{33}I_3 \ldots - R_{3n}I_n$$

$$E_n = -R_{n1}I_1 - R_{n12}I_2 - R_{n3}I_3 \ldots + R_{nn}I_n$$

where E_1 = the algebraic sum of the e.m.f.s in loop ① in the direction of I_1;
      E_2 = the algebraic sum of the e.m.f.s in loop ② in the direction of I_2, etc.;
      R_{11} = sum of resistances in loop ①;
      R_{22} = sum of resistances in loop ②, etc.;
      R_{12} = total resistance common to loops ① and ②;
      R_{23} = total resistance common to loops ② and ③, etc.

By their definitions $R_{12} = R_{21}$, $R_{23} = R_{32}$, etc. Note that in the equation derived from each loop it is only the term in the loop's own circulating current that is positive.

By observing these rules the equations necessary for the solution of the circuit problem can be written down by inspection of the circuit. This can be confirmed by examination of equations (a), (b) and (c) in Example 1.47.

Nodal analysis

This technique of circuit solution, also known as the Node Voltage method, is based on the application of Kirchhoff's first (current) law at each junction (node) of the circuit, to find the node voltages. It should be noted that, in contrast, both the branch current and Mesh current techniques of circuit analysis are based on the applications of Kirchhoff's second (voltage) law, often to find unknown currents.

The Node Voltage method generally proceeds as follows:

Step 1: Choose a reference node to which all node voltages can be referred. Label all the other nodes with (unknown) values of voltage, V_1, V_2, etc.
Step 2: Assign currents in each connection to each node, except the reference node, in terms of the node voltages, V_1, V_2, etc.
Step 3: Apply Kirchhoff's current law at each node, obtaining as many equations as there are unknown node voltages.
Step 4: Solve the resulting equations to find the node voltages.

Example 1.48   Using Nodal analysis, calculate the voltages V_1 and V_2 in the circuit of Fig. 1.64.

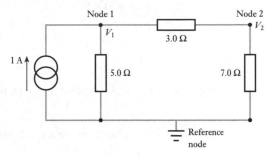

Fig. 1.64   Network for Example 1.48

Refer to the four steps previously indicated:

Step 1: Reference node chosen. Voltages V_1 and V_2 assigned to the other two nodes.

Step 2: Assign currents in each connection to each node (Fig. 1.65).

Step 3: Apply Kirchhoff's current law to sum the currents at each node.

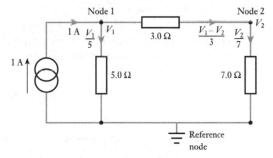

Fig. 1.65   Part of Example 1.48

At node 1:

$$\frac{V_1}{5} + \left(\frac{V_1 - V_2}{3}\right) = 1$$

which can be simplified to

$$V_1\left(\frac{1}{5} + \frac{1}{3}\right) - \frac{V_2}{3} = 1 \tag{a}$$

At node 2:

$$\frac{V_1 - V_2}{3} = \frac{V_2}{7}$$

which simplifies to

$$\frac{V_1}{3} - V_2\left(\frac{1}{3} + \frac{1}{7}\right) = 0 \tag{b}$$

Step 4: Solve node voltage equations (a) and (b).

From equation (b), by multiplying each term by 21,

$$7V_1 - V_2(7 + 3) = 0$$

$$\therefore \quad 7V_1 = 10V_2$$

so $$V_2 = \frac{7}{10}V_1 \qquad\qquad (c)$$

From equation (a), by multiplying each term by 15,

$$8V_1 - 5V_2 = 15 \qquad\qquad (d)$$

Substitute for V_2, from equation (c), in equation (d):

$$8V_1 - \frac{35V_1}{10} = 15$$

so $$4.5V_1 = 15$$

$$V_1 = \frac{10}{3}\,\text{V}$$

From (c)

$$V_2 = \frac{7}{3}\,\text{V}$$

To check the accuracy of the calculation, see for yourself if Kirchhoff's current law is obeyed for each node. It will be seen that the currents are as in the circuit of Fig. 1.66.

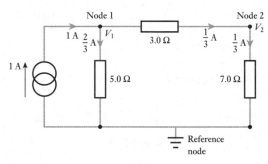

Fig. 1.66   Part of Example 1.48

Example 1.49   Using the Node Voltage method calculate the voltages V_1 and V_2 in Fig. 1.67 and hence calculate the currents in the 8 Ω resistor.

Step 1: Reference node shown. Voltages V_1 and V_2 assigned.
Step 2: Assign currents in each connection to each node (Fig. 1.68).
Step 3: Apply Kirchhoff's current law at each node.

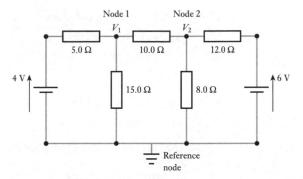

Fig. 1.67   Network for Example 1.49

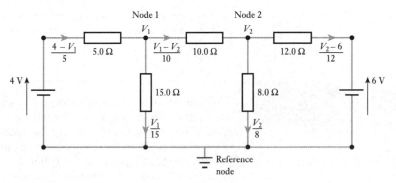

Fig. 1.68   Part of Example 1.49

At node 1:

$$\frac{4 - V_1}{5} = \frac{V_1 - V_2}{10} + \frac{V_1}{15}$$

Multiply each term by 30:

$$24 - 6V_1 = 3V_1 - 3V_2 + 2V_1$$

$$11V_1 - 3V_2 = 24 \qquad\qquad\qquad (a)$$

At node 2:

$$\frac{V_1 - V_2}{10} = \frac{V_2 - 6}{12} + \frac{V_2}{8}$$

Multiply each term by 120:

$$12V_1 - 12V_2 = 10V_2 - 60 + 15V_2$$

$$12V_1 - 37V_2 = -60 \qquad\qquad\qquad (b)$$

Step 4: Solve for V_1 and V_2.

Equation (a) $\times \dfrac{12}{11}$ gives:

$$12V_1 - \frac{36V_2}{11} = \frac{24 \times 12}{11} \qquad\qquad\qquad (c)$$

Equation (c) − equation (b) gives

$$33.37V_2 = 86.18$$

$$V_2 = 2.55 \text{ V}$$

From (a)

$$11V_1 = 24 + 3 + 2.55 = 31.65$$

$$V_1 = 2.88 \text{ V}$$

Hence the current in the 8 Ω resistor is

$$\frac{V_2}{8} = 0.32 \text{ A}$$

A second method of solving this problem by Nodal analysis, using source conversion techniques, is shown in the section 'The constant-current generator' on p. 100.

Superposition theorem

The Superposition theorem states that in any network containing more than one source, the current in, or the p.d. across, any branch can be found by considering each source separately and adding their effects: omitted sources of e.m.f. are replaced by resistances equal to their internal resistances.

This sounds very complicated, but is really quite simple when demonstrated by example. Example 1.50 illustrates the manner in which Example 1.45 would be solved by means of the Superposition theorem.

Example 1.50

By means of the Superposition theorem, calculate the currents in the network shown in Fig. 1.69(a).

Because there are two sources of e.m.f. in the network, then two separate networks need to be considered, each having one source of e.m.f. Figure 1.69(b) shows the network with the 20 V source replaced by a short-circuit, there being zero internal resistance indicated. Also Fig. 1.69(c) shows the network with the 10 V source similarly replaced.

For the (b) arrangement, the total resistance is

$$1 + \frac{2 \times 18}{2 + 18} = 2.8 \ \Omega$$

thus $\quad I_{1b} = \dfrac{10}{2.8} = 3.57 \text{ A}$

and $\quad I_{2b} = -\dfrac{18}{2 + 18} \times 3.57 = -3.21 \text{ A}$

also $\quad I_{1b} + I_{2b} = 3.57 - 3.21 = 0.36 \text{ A}$

Note: the current I_{2b} is negative due to the direction in which it has been shown.

For the (c) arrangement, the total resistance is

$$2 + \frac{1 \times 18}{1 + 18} = 2.95 \ \Omega$$

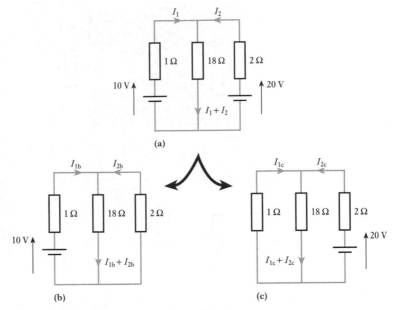

Fig. 1.69 Circuit diagrams for Example 1.50

thus $\qquad I_{2c} = \dfrac{20}{2.95} = 6.78 \text{ A}$

and $\qquad I_{1c} = -\dfrac{18}{1 + 18} \times 6.78 = -6.42 \text{ A}$

$I_{2c} + I_{1c} = 6.78 - 6.42 = 0.36 \text{ A}$

Thus $\qquad I_1 = I_{1b} + I_{1c} = 3.57 - 6.42 = -2.85 \text{ A}$

and $\qquad I_2 = I_{2b} + I_{2c} = -3.21 + 6.78 = 3.57 \text{ A}$

also $\qquad I_1 + I_2 = -2.85 + 3.57 = 0.72 \text{ A}$

Thévenin's theorem

The current through a resistor R connected across any two points A *and* B *of an active network* [i.e. a network containing one or more sources of e.m.f.] *is obtained by dividing the p.d. between* A *and* B*, with R disconnected, by (R + r), where r is the resistance of the network measured between points* A *and* B *with R disconnected and the sources of e.m.f. replaced by their internal resistances.*

An alternative way of stating Thévenin's theorem is as follows: *An active network having two terminals* A *and* B *can be replaced by a constant-voltage source having an e.m.f.* E *and an internal resistance r. The value of E is equal to the open-circuit p.d. between* A *and* B*, and r is the resistance of the network measured between* A *and* B *with the load disconnected and the sources of e.m.f. replaced by their internal resistances.*

Suppose A and B in Fig. 1.70(a) to be the two terminals of a network consisting of resistors having resistances R_2 and R_3 and a battery having an

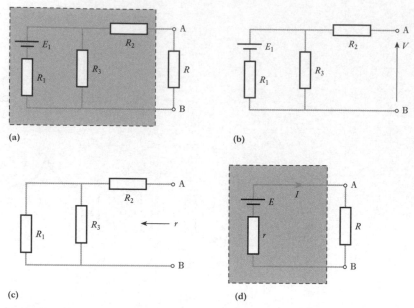

Fig. 1.70 Networks to illustrate Thévenin's theorem

e.m.f. E_1 and an internal resistance R_1. It is required to determine the current through a load of resistance R connected across AB. With the load disconnected as in Fig. 1.70(b),

$$\text{Current through } R_3 = \frac{E_1}{R_1 + R_3}$$

and

$$\text{PD across } R_3 = \frac{E_1 R_3}{R_1 + R_3}$$

Since there is no current through R_2, p.d. across AB is

$$V = \frac{E_1 R_3}{R_1 + R_3}$$

Figure 1.70(c) shows the network with the load disconnected and the battery replaced by its internal resistance R_1. Resistance of network between A and B is

$$r = R_2 + \frac{R_1 R_3}{R_1 + R_3}$$

Thévenin's theorem merely states that the active network enclosed by the dotted line in Fig. 1.70(a) can be replaced by the very simple circuit enclosed by the dotted line in Fig. 1.70(d) and consisting of a source having an e.m.f. E equal to the open-circuit potential difference V between A and B, and an internal resistance r, where V and r have the values determined above. Hence

$$\text{Current through } R = I = \frac{E}{r + R}$$

Thévenin's theorem – sometimes referred to as Helmholtz's theorem – is an application of the Superposition theorem. Thus, if a source having an e.m.f. E equal to the open-circuit p.d. between A and B in Fig. 1.70(b) were inserted in the circuit between R and terminal A in Fig. 1.70(a), the positive terminal of the source being connected to A, no current would flow through R. Hence, this source could be regarded as circulating through R a current superimposed upon but opposite in direction to the current through R due to E_1 *alone*. Since the resultant current is zero, it follows that a source of e.m.f. E connected in series with R and the equivalent resistance r of the network, as in Fig. 1.70(d), would circulate a current I having the same value as that through R in Fig. 1.70(a), but in order that the direction of the current through R may be from A towards B, the polarity of the source must be as shown in Fig. 1.70(d).

Example 1.51

In Fig. 1.71(a) C and D represent the two terminals of an active network. Calculate the current through R_3.

With R_3 disconnected, as in Fig. 1.71(b),

$$I_1 = \frac{6 - 4}{2 + 3} = 0.4 \, \text{A}$$

and p.d. across CD is $E_1 - I_1 R_1$,

i.e. $E = 6 - (0.4 \times 2) = 5.2 \, \text{V}$

When the e.m.f.s are removed, as in Fig. 1.71(c), total resistance between C and D is

$$\frac{2 \times 3}{2 + 3}, \quad \text{i.e.} \quad r = 1.2 \, \Omega$$

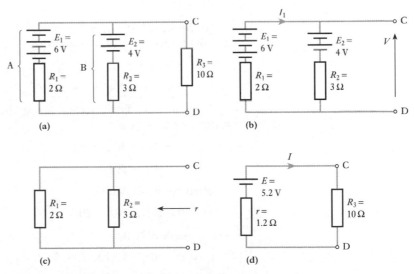

Fig. 1.71   Circuit diagrams for Example 1.49

Hence the network AB in Fig. 1.71(a) can be replaced by a single source having an e.m.f. of 5.2 V and an internal resistance of 1.2 Ω, as in Fig. 1.71(d); consequently

$$I = \frac{5.2}{1.2 + 10} = 0.46 \text{ A}$$

Example 1.52

The resistances of the various arms of a bridge are given in Fig. 1.72. The battery has an e.m.f. of 2.0 V and a negligible internal resistance. Determine the value and direction of the current in BD, using:

(a) Kirchhoff's laws;
(b) Thévenin's theorem.

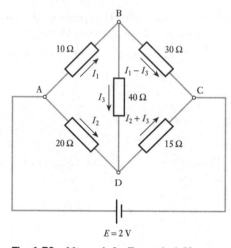

Fig. 1.72   Network for Example 1.52

(a) *By Kirchhoff's laws.* Let I_1, I_2 and I_3 be the currents in arms AB, AD and BD respectively, as shown in Fig. 1.72. Then by Kirchhoff's first law,

Current in BC $= I_1 - I_3$

and   Current in DC $= I_2 + I_3$

Applying Kirchhoff's second law to the mesh formed by ABC and the battery, we have

$$2 = 10I_1 + 30(I_1 - I_3)$$

$$= 40I_1 - 30I_3 \tag{a}$$

Similarly for mesh ABDA,

$$0 = 10I_1 + 40I_3 - 20I_2 \tag{b}$$

and for mesh BDCB,

$$0 = 40I_3 + 15(I_2 + I_3) - 30(I_1 - I_3)$$

$$= -30I_1 + 15I_2 + 85I_3 \tag{c}$$

Multiplying (b) by 3 and (c) by 4, and adding the two expressions thus obtained, we have

$$0 = -90I_1 + 460I_3$$

∴ $\quad I_1 = 5.111I_3$

Substituting for I_1 in (a), we have

$$I_3 = 0.0115 \text{ A} = \textbf{11.5 mA}$$

Since the value of I_3 is positive, the direction of I_3 is that assumed in Fig. 1.72, namely from B and D.

(b) *By Thévenin's theorem.* Since we require to find the current in the 40 Ω resistor between B and D, the first step is to remove this resistor, as in Fig. 1.73(a). Then p.d. between A and B is

$$2 \times \frac{10}{10 + 30} = 0.5 \text{ V}$$

and p.d. between A and D is

$$2 \times \frac{20}{20 + 15} = 1.143 \text{ V}$$

therefore p.d. between B and D is

$$1.143 - 0.5 = 0.643 \text{ V}$$

B being positive relative to D. Consequently, current in the 40 Ω resistor, when connected between B and D, will flow from B to D.

The next step is to replace the battery by a resistance equal to its internal resistance. Since the latter is negligible in this problem, junctions A and C can be short-circuited as in Fig. 1.73(b). Equivalent resistance of BA and BC is

$$\frac{10 \times 30}{10 + 30} = 7.5 \text{ Ω}$$

and equivalent resistance of AD and CD is

$$\frac{20 \times 15}{20 + 15} - 8.57 \text{ Ω}$$

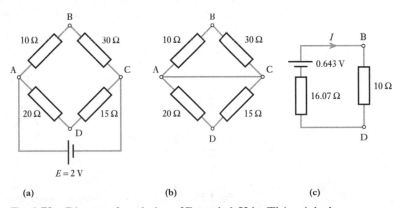

Fig. 1.73   Diagrams for solution of Example 1.52 by Thévenin's theorem

therefore total resistance of network between B and D = 16.07 Ω. Hence the network of Fig. 1.73(a) is equivalent to a source having an e.m.f. of 0.643 V and an internal resistance of 16.07 Ω as in Fig. 1.73(c).

$$\therefore \qquad \text{Current through BD} = \frac{0.643}{16.07 + 40} = 0.0115\,\text{A}$$

$$= 11.5\,\text{mA from B to D}$$

The constant-current generator

It was shown in 'Thévenin's theorem' (p. 95) that a source of electrical energy could be represented by a source of e.m.f. in series with a resistance. This is not, however, the only form of representation. Consider such a source feeding a load resistor R_L as shown in Fig. 1.74.

From this circuit:

$$I_L = \frac{E}{R_s + R_L} = \frac{\frac{E}{R_s}}{\frac{R_s + R_L}{R_s}}$$

$$\therefore \qquad \boxed{I_L = \frac{R_s}{R_s + R_L} \times I_s} \qquad\qquad [1.6]$$

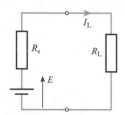

Fig. 1.74 Energy source feeding load

where $I_s = E/R_s$ is the current which would flow in a short-circuit across the output terminals of the source.

It can be seen from relation [1.6] that, when viewed from the load, the source appears as a source of current (I_s) which is dividing between the internal resistance (R_s) and the load resistor (R_L) connected in parallel. For the solution of problems, either form of representation can be used. In many practical cases an easier solution is obtained using the current form. Figure 1.75 illustrates the equivalence of the two forms.

The resistance of the constant-current generator must be taken as infinite, since the resistance of the complete source must be R_s as is obtained with the constant-voltage form.

The ideal constant-voltage generator would be one with zero internal resistance so that it would supply the same voltage to all loads. Conversely, the ideal constant-current generator would be one with infinite internal resistance so that it supplied the same current to all loads. These ideal conditions can be approached quite closely in practice.

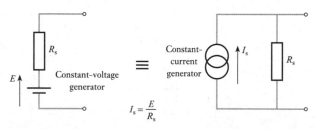

Fig. 1.75 Equivalence of constant-voltage generator and constant-current generator forms of representation

Example 1.53   Represent the network shown in Fig. 1.76 by one source of e.m.f. in series with a resistance.

Potential difference across output terminals is

$$V_o = 1 \times 15 = 15 \text{ V}$$

Resistance looking into output terminals is

$$5 + 15 = 20 \text{ }\Omega$$

therefore the circuit can be represented as shown in Fig. 1.77.

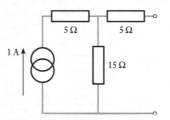
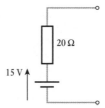

Fig. 1.76   Network for Example 1.52

Fig. 1.77   Part of Example 1.51

Example 1.54   The Node Voltage technique (Nodal analysis) lends itself to circuit models having current instead of voltage sources. To illustrate the technique, we will convert all the voltage sources of Fig. 1.67 to current sources and replace them in the circuit of Fig. 1.78. This produces Fig. 1.79 to which we apply the rules of Nodal analysis.

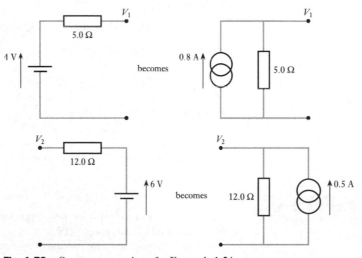

Fig. 1.78   Source conversions for Example 1.54

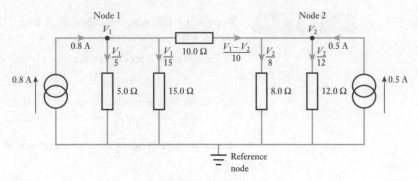

Fig. 1.79   New circuit for Example 1.54

At node 1:

$$0.8 = \frac{V_1}{5} + \frac{V_1}{15} + \frac{V_1 - V_2}{10}$$

$$0.8 = V_1\left(\frac{1}{5} + \frac{1}{15} + \frac{1}{10}\right) - \frac{V_2}{10}$$

Multiply by 30:

$$24 = V_1(6 + 2 + 3) - 3V_2$$

$$24 = 11V_1 - 3V_2 \tag{a}$$

At node 2:

$$0.5 = \frac{V_2}{8} + \frac{V_2}{12} - \left(\frac{V_1 - V_2}{10}\right)$$

$$0.5 = \frac{-V_1}{10} + V_2\left(\frac{1}{8} + \frac{1}{10} + \frac{1}{12}\right)$$

Multiply by 120:

$$60 = -12V_1 + V_2(15 + 12 + 10)$$

$$60 = -12V_1 + 37V_2 \tag{b}$$

(a) $\times \dfrac{12}{11}$ $26.8 = 12V_1 - 3.273V_2$ $\tag{c}$

(c) + (b) $86.8 = 33.727V_2$

$$V_2 = 2.55 \text{ V}$$

Hence the current in the 8 Ω resistor ($V_2/8$) = **0.32 A** as before.

Norton's theorem

When a branch in a circuit is open–circuited the remainder of the circuit can be represented by one source of e.m.f. in series with a resistor; it follows from what has been said in 'The constant-current generator' (p. 100) that it could equally well be represented by a source of current in parallel with the same resistor. Norton's theorem is therefore a restatement of Thévenin's theorem using an equivalent current-generator source instead of the equivalent voltage-generator source. It can therefore be stated that:

> The current which flows in any branch of a network is the same as that which would flow in the branch if it were connected across a source of electrical energy, the short-circuit current of which is equal to the current that would flow in a short-circuit across the branch, and the internal resistance of which is equal to the resistance which appears across the open-circuited branch terminals.

Norton's theorem is illustrated in Fig. 1.80.

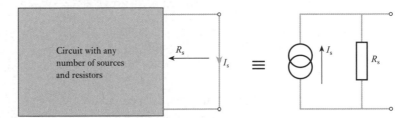

Fig. 1.80 Norton's theorem

Example 1.55 **Calculate the potential difference across the 2.0 Ω resistor in the network shown in Fig. 1.81.**

Short-circuiting the branch containing the 2.0 Ω resistor gives the network shown in Fig. 1.82.

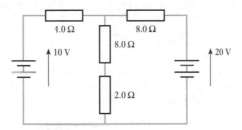

Fig. 1.81 Network for Example 1.55

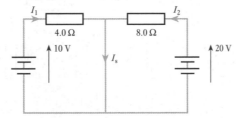

Fig. 1.82 Part of Example 1.55

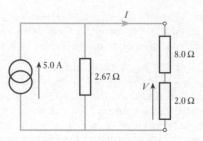

Fig. 1.83   Part of Example 1.55

$$10 = 4.0I_1 \quad \therefore \quad I_1 = \frac{10}{4.0} = 2.5 \text{ A}$$

$$20 = 8.0I_2 \quad \therefore \quad I_2 = \frac{20}{8.0} = 2.5 \text{ A}$$

$$\therefore \qquad I_s = I_1 + I_2 = 5.0 \text{ A}$$

Resistance across open-circuited branch is

$$\frac{4.0 \times 8.0}{4.0 + 8.0} = 2.67 \,\Omega$$

therefore the circuit reduces to that shown in Fig. 1.83.

$$I = \frac{2.67}{2.67 + 10.0} \times 5.0 = 1.06 \text{ A}$$

$$\therefore \qquad V = 1.06 \times 2.0 = \textbf{2.1 V}$$

Example 1.56   **Calculate the current in the 5.0 Ω resistor in the network shown in Fig. 1.84.**

Short-circuiting the branch containing the 5.0 Ω resistor gives the circuit shown in Fig. 1.85. Since the branch containing the 4 Ω and 6 Ω is short-circuited, we can ignore it, thus the source current is divided between the 8 Ω branch and the short-circuit branch which still has the 2 Ω resistance in series with the short circuit.

$$I_s = \frac{8.0}{8.0 + 2.0} \times 10 = 8.0 \text{ A}$$

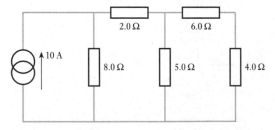

Fig. 1.84   Network for Example 1.56

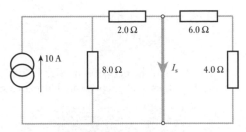

Fig. 1.85 Part of Example 1.56

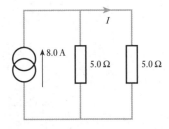

Fig. 1.86 Part of Example 1.56

When obtaining the equivalent source resistance seen from the terminal of the open-circuit (i.e. when the 5.0 Ω has been removed) the current generator is replaced by an open-circuit, hence the resistance looking into the output terminals is

$$\frac{(2.0 + 8.0)(6.0 + 4.0)}{(2.0 + 8.0) + (6.0 + 4.0)} = \frac{10 \times 10}{20} = 5.0\,\Omega$$

therefore the circuit reduces to that shown in Fig. 1.86.

$$I = \frac{5.0}{5.0 + 5.0} \times 8.0 = 4.0\,\text{A}$$

Delta–star transformation

Figure 1.87(a) shows three resistors R_1, R_2 and R_3 connected in a closed mesh or *delta* to three terminals A, B and C, *their numerical subscripts 1, 2 and 3 being opposite to the terminals A, B and C respectively*. It is possible to replace these delta-connected resistors by three resistors R_a, R_b and R_c connected respectively between the same terminals A, B and C and a common point S, as in Fig. 1.87(b). Such an arrangement is said to be *star-connected*. It will be noted that the letter subscripts are now those of the terminals to which the respective resistors are connected. If the star-connected network is to be equivalent to the delta-connected network, the resistance between any two terminals in Fig. 1.87(b) must be the same as that between the same two terminals in Fig. 1.87(a). Thus, if we consider terminals A and B in Fig. 1.87(a), we have a circuit having a resistance R_3 in parallel with a circuit having resistances R_1 and R_2 in series; hence

$$R_{AB} = \frac{R_3(R_1 + R_2)}{R_1 + R_2 + R_3}$$ [1.7]

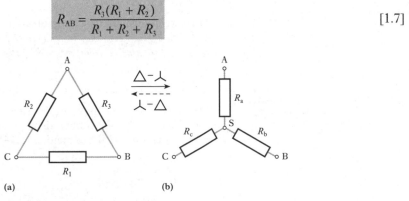

(a)   (b)

Fig. 1.87 Delta–star transformation

For Fig. 1.87(b), we have

$$R_{AB} = R_a + R_b \qquad [1.8]$$

In order that the networks of Fig. 1.87(a) and (b) may be equivalent to each other, the values of R_{AB} represented by expressions [1.7] and [1.8] must be equal.

$$\therefore \qquad R_a + R_b = \frac{R_1R_3 + R_2R_3}{R_1 + R_2 + R_3} \qquad [1.9]$$

Similarly

$$R_b + R_c = \frac{R_1R_2 + R_1R_3}{R_1 + R_2 + R_3} \qquad [1.10]$$

and

$$R_a + R_c = \frac{R_1R_2 + R_2R_3}{R_1 + R_2 + R_3} \qquad [1.11]$$

Subtracting equation [1.10] from [1.11], we have

$$R_a - R_c = \frac{R_2R_3 - R_1R_2}{R_1 + R_2 + R_3} \qquad [1.12]$$

Adding equations [1.11] and [1.12] and dividing by 2, we have

$$R_a = \frac{R_2R_3}{R_1 + R_2 + R_3} \qquad [1.13]$$

Similarly

$$R_b = \frac{R_3R_1}{R_1 + R_2 + R_3} \qquad [1.14]$$

and

$$R_c = \frac{R_1R_2}{R_1 + R_2 + R_3} \qquad [1.15]$$

These relationships may be expressed thus: *the equivalent star resistance connected to a given terminal is equal to the product of the two delta resistances connected to the same terminal divided by the sum of the delta resistances.*

Star–delta transformation

Let us next consider how to replace the star-connected network of Fig. 1.87(b) by the equivalent delta-connected network of Fig. 1.87(a). Dividing equation [1.13] by equation [1.14], we have

$$\frac{R_a}{R_b} = \frac{R_2}{R_1}$$

$$\therefore \qquad R_2 = \frac{R_1R_a}{R_b}$$

Similarly, dividing equation [1.13] by equation [1.15], we have

$$\frac{R_a}{R_c} = \frac{R_3}{R_1}$$

$$\therefore \qquad R_3 = \frac{R_1 R_a}{R_c}$$

Substituting for R_2 and R_3 in equation [1.13], we have

$$R_1 = R_b + R_c + \frac{R_b R_c}{R_a} \qquad\qquad [1.16]$$

Similarly

$$R_2 = R_c + R_a + \frac{R_c R_a}{R_b} \qquad\qquad [1.17]$$

and

$$R_3 = R_a + R_b + \frac{R_a R_b}{R_c} \qquad\qquad [1.18]$$

These relationships may be expressed thus: *the equivalent delta resistance between two terminals is the sum of the two star resistances connected to those terminals plus the product of the same two star resistances divided by the third star resistance.*

Maximum power transfer

Let us consider a source, such as a battery or a d.c. generator, having an e.m.f. E and an internal resistance r, as shown enclosed by the dotted rectangle in Fig. 1.88. A variable resistor is connected across terminals A and B of the source. If the value of the load resistance is R, then

$$I = \frac{E}{r + R}$$

and power transferred to load is

$$I^2 R = \frac{E^2 R}{(r + R)^2} = \frac{E^2 R}{r^2 + 2rR + R^2}$$

$$I^2 R = \frac{E^2}{(r^2/R) + 2r + R} \qquad\qquad [1.19]$$

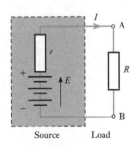

Source   Load

Fig. 1.88 Resistance matching

This power is a maximum when the denominator of [1.19] is a minimum, i.e. when

$$\frac{d}{dR}\left(\frac{r^2}{R} + 2r + R\right) = 0$$

$$\therefore \qquad -\frac{r^2}{R^2} + 1 = 0$$

or $\qquad R = r \qquad\qquad [1.20]$

To check that this condition gives the minimum and not the maximum value of the denominator in expression [1.19], expression $\{-(r^2/R^2) + 1\}$ should be differentiated with respect to R, thus

$$\frac{\mathrm{d}}{\mathrm{d}R}\left\{1 - \frac{r^2}{R^2}\right\} = 2r^2/R^3$$

Since this quantity is positive, expression [1.20] is the condition for the denominator of equation [1.19] to be a minimum and therefore the output power to be a maximum. Hence the power transferred from the source to the load is a maximum when the resistance of the load is equal to the internal resistance of the source. This condition is referred to as *resistance matching*.

Resistance matching is of importance in communications and electronic circuits where the source usually has a relatively high resistance and where it is desired to transfer the largest possible amount of power from the source to the load. In the case of power sources such as generators and batteries, the internal resistance is so low that it is impossible to satisfy the above condition without overloading the source.

Direct-current machines

General arrangement of a d.c. machine

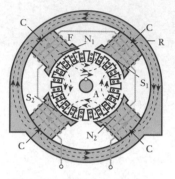

Fig. 1.89 General arrangement of a four-pole d.c. machine

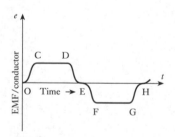

Fig. 1.90 Waveform of e.m.f. generated in a conductor

Figure 1.89 shows the general arrangement of a four-pole d.c. motor or generator. The fixed part consists of four steel cores C, referred to as *pole cores*, attached to a steel ring R, called the *yoke*. The pole cores are usually made of steel plates riveted together and bolted to the yoke, which may be of cast steel or fabricated rolled steel. Each pole core has pole tips, partly to support the field winding and partly to increase the cross-sectional area and thus reduce the reluctance of the airgap. Each pole core carries a winding F so connected as to excite the poles alternately N and S.

The armature core A consists of steel laminations, about 0.4–0.6 mm thick, insulated from one another and assembled on the shaft in the case of small machines and on a cast-steel spider in the case of large machines. The purpose of laminating the core is to reduce the eddy-current loss. Slots are stamped on the periphery of the laminations, partly to accommodate and provide mechanical security to the armature winding and partly to give a shorter airgap for the magnetic flux to cross between the pole face and the armature 'teeth'. In Fig. 1.89, each slot has two circular conductors, insulated from each other.

The term *conductor*, when applied to armature windings, refers to the active portion of the winding, namely that part which cuts the flux, thereby generating an e.m.f.; for example, if an armature has 40 slots and if each slot contains 8 wires, the armature is said to have 8 conductors per slot and a total of 320 conductors.

The dotted lines in Fig. 1.89 represent the distribution of the *useful* magnetic flux, namely that flux which passes into the armature core and is therefore cut by the armature conductors when the armature revolves. It will be seen from Fig. 1.89 that the magnetic flux which emerges from N_1 divides, half going towards S_1 and half towards S_2. Similarly, the flux emerging from N_2 divides equally between S_1 and S_2.

Suppose the armature to revolve clockwise, as shown by the curved arrow in Fig. 1.89. Applying Fleming's right-hand rule, we find that the e.m.f. generated in the conductors is towards the paper in those moving under the N poles and outwards from the paper in those moving under the S poles. If the airgap is of uniform length, the e.m.f. generated in a conductor remains constant while it is moving under a pole face, and then decreases rapidly to zero when the conductor is midway between the pole tips of adjacent poles.

Figure 1.90 shows the variation of the e.m.f. generated in a conductor while the latter is moving through two pole pitches, a *pole pitch* being the distance between the centres of adjacent poles. Thus, at instant O, the conductor is midway between the pole tips of, say, S_2 and N_1, and CD represents the e.m.f. generated while the conductor is moving under the pole face of N_1, the e.m.f. being assumed positive when its direction is towards the paper in Fig. 1.89. At instant E, the conductor is midway between the pole tips of N_1 and S_1, and portion EFGH represents the variation of the e.m.f. while the conductor is moving through the next pole pitch. The variation of e.m.f. during interval OH in Fig. 1.90 is repeated indefinitely, so long as the speed is maintained constant.

A d.c. machine, however, has to give a voltage that remains constant in direction and in magnitude, and it is therefore necessary to use a *commutator* to enable a steady or direct voltage to be obtained from the alternating e.m.f. generated in the rotating conductors.

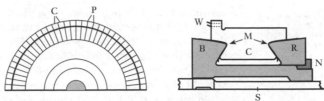

Fig. 1.91 Commutator of a d.c. machine

Figure 1.91 shows a longitudinal or axial section and an end elevation of half of a relatively small commutator. It consists of a large number of wedge-shaped copper segments or bars C, assembled side by side to form a ring, the segments being insulated from one another by thin mica sheets P. The segments are shaped as shown so that they can be clamped securely between a V-ring B, which is part of a cast-iron bush or sleeve, and another V-ring R which is tightened and kept in place by a nut N. The bush is keyed to shaft S.

The copper segments are insulated from the V-rings by collars of mica-based insulation M, a composite of mica flakes bonded with epoxy resin, fabricated to the exact shape of the rings. These collars project well beyond the segments so as to reduce surface leakage of current from the commutator to the shaft. At the end adjacent to the winding, each segment has a milled slot to accommodate two armature wires W which are soldered to the segment.

Double-layer drum windings

The term *armature* is generally associated with the rotating part of the d.c. machine. It essentially refers only to the rotating winding into which an e.m.f. is induced, thus we have the armature winding mounted on the armature core. By usage, the term armature, however, is frequently used to describe the entire rotating arrangement, i.e. the rotor. This can be misleading because, in a.c. machines, the e.m.f.s are induced into the fixed windings on the stator, i.e. the yoke, in which case the armature windings are the static windings. 'Armature' therefore tends to have a rather specialized interpretation when used in respect of a d.c. machine.

Let us consider a four-pole armature with, say, 11 slots, as in Fig. 1.92. In order that all the coils may be similar in shape and therefore may be wound to the correct shape before being assembled on the core, they have to be made such that if side 1 of a coil occupies the outer half of one slot, the other side 1′ occupies the inner half of another slot. This necessitates a kink in the end connections in order that the coils may overlap one another as they are being assembled. Figure 1.93 shows the shape of the end connections of a single coil consisting of a number of turns, and Fig. 1.93(b) shows how three coils, 1–1′, 2–2′ and 3–3′, are arranged in the slots so that their end connections overlap one another, the end elevation of the end connections of coils 1–1′ and 3–3′ being as shown in Fig. 1.94(a). The end connection of coil 2–2′ has been omitted from Fig. 1.94(a) to enable the shape of the other end connections to be shown more clearly. In Fig. 1.93, the two ends of the coil are brought out to P and Q, and as far as the connections to the commutator segments are concerned, the number of turns on each coil is of no consequence.

From Fig. 1.92 it is evident that if the e.m.f.s generated in conductors 1 and 1′ are to assist each other, 1′ must be moving under a S pole when 1 is

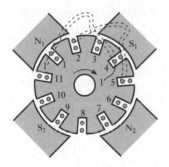

Fig. 1.92 Arrangement of a double-layer winding

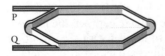

Fig. 1.93 An armature coil

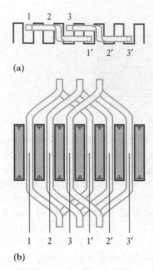

Fig. 1.94 Arrangement of overlap of end connections

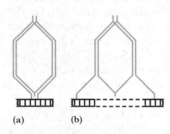

Fig. 1.95 (a) Coil of a lap winding; (b) coil of a wave winding

moving under an N pole; thus, by applying the right-hand rule (section 6.9) to Fig. 1.92 and assuming the armature to be rotated clockwise, we find that the direction of the e.m.f. generated in conductor 1 is towards the paper, whereas that generated in conductor 1′ is outwards from the paper. Hence, the distance between coil sides 1 and 1′ must be approximately a pole pitch. With 11 slots it is impossible to make the distance between 1 and 1′ exactly a pole pitch, and in Fig. 1.92 one side of coil 1–1′ is shown in slot 1 and the other side is in slot 4. The coil is then said to have a *coil span* of 4–1, namely 3. In practice, the coil span must be a whole number and is approximately equal to

$$\frac{\text{Total number of slots}}{\text{Total number of poles}}$$

In the example shown in Fig. 1.92 a very small number of slots has for simplicity been chosen. In actual machines the number of slots per pole usually lies between 10 and 15 and the coil span is slightly less than the value given by the above expression.

Let us now return to the consideration of the 11-slot armature. The 11 coils are assembled in the slots with a coil span of 3, and we are now faced with the problem of connecting to the commutator segments the 22 ends that are projecting from the winding.

Apart from a few special windings, armature windings can be divided into two groups, depending upon the manner in which the wires are joined to the commutator, namely:

1. Lap windings.
2. Wave windings.

In lap windings the two ends of any one coil are taken to adjacent segments as in Fig. 1.95(a), where a coil of two turns is shown, whereas in wave windings the two ends of each coil are bent in opposite directions and taken to segments some distance apart, as in Fig. 1.95(b).

A lap winding has as many paths in parallel between the negative and positive brushes as there are of poles; for instance, with an eight-pole lap winding, the armature conductors form eight parallel paths between the negative and positive brushes. A wave winding, on the other hand, has only two paths in parallel, irrespective of the number of poles. Hence, if a machine has p pairs of poles

No. of parallel paths with a lap winding $= 2p$

and   No. of parallel paths with a wave winding $= 2$

For a given cross-sectional area of armature conductor and a given current density in the conductor, it follows that the total current from a lap winding is p times that from a wave winding. On the other hand, for a given number of armature conductors, the number of conductors in series per path in a wave winding is p times that in a lap winding. Consequently, for a given generated e.m.f. per conductor, the voltage between the negative and positive brushes with a wave winding is p times that with a lap winding. Hence it may be said that, in general, lap windings are used for low-voltage, heavy-current machines.

Example 1.57   An eight-pole armature is wound with 480 conductors. The magnetic flux and the speed are such that the average e.m.f. generated in each conductor is 2.2 V, and each conductor is capable of carrying a full-load current of 100 A. Calculate the terminal voltage on no load, the output current on full load and the total power generated on full load when the armature is

(a) lap-connected;
(b) wave-connected.

(a) With the armature lap-connected, number of parallel paths in the armature winding = number of poles = 8.

$$\therefore \qquad \text{No. of conductors per path} = \frac{480}{8} = 60$$

Terminal voltage on no load = e.m.f. per conductor × number of conductors per path which is

$$2.2 \times 60 = \textbf{132 V}$$

Output current on full load is

Full-load current per conductor

× no. of parallel paths

$$= 100 \times 8 = \textbf{800 A}$$

Total power generated on full load is

Output current

× generated e.m.f.

$$= 800 \times 132 = 105\ 600\ \text{W}$$

$$= \textbf{105.6 kW}$$

(b) With the armature wave-connected,

No. of parallel paths = 2

$$\therefore \qquad \text{No. of conductors per path} = \frac{480}{2} = 240$$

Terminal voltage on no load = $2.2 \times 240 = \textbf{528 V}$

Output current on full load = $100 \times 2 = \textbf{200 A}$

Total power generated on full load is

$$200 \times 528 = 105\ 600\ \text{W}$$

$$= \textbf{105.6 kW}$$

It will be seen from Example 1.57 that the total power generated by a given machine is the same whether the armature winding is lap- or wave-connected.

Calculation of e.m.f. generated in an armature winding

When an armature is rotated through one revolution, each conductor cuts the magnetic flux emanating from all the N poles and also that entering all the S poles. Consequently, if Φ is the useful flux per pole, in webers, entering or leaving the armature, p the number of *pairs* of poles and N_r the speed in revolutions per minute,

$$\text{Time of one revolution} = \frac{60}{N_r} \text{ seconds}$$

and time taken by a conductor to move one pole pitch is

$$\frac{60}{N_r} \cdot \frac{1}{2p} \text{ seconds}$$

Therefore average rate at which conductor cuts the flux is

$$\Phi \div \left(\frac{60}{N_r} \cdot \frac{1}{2p} \right) = \frac{2\Phi N_r p}{60} \text{ webers per second}$$

and average e.m.f. generated in each conductor is

$$\frac{2\Phi N_r p}{60} \text{ volts}$$

If Z is the total number of armature conductors, and c the number of parallel paths through winding between positive and negative brushes (2 for a wave winding, and $2p$ for a lap winding)

$$\therefore \qquad \frac{Z}{c} = \text{number of conductors in series in each path}$$

The brushes are assumed to be in contact with segments connected to conductors in which no e.m.f. is being generated, and the e.m.f. generated in each conductor, while it is moving between positions of zero e.m.f., varies as shown by curve OCDE in Fig. 1.90. The number of conductors in series in each of the parallel paths between the brushes remains practically constant; hence total e.m.f. between brushes is

Average e.m.f. per conductor

$\times$ no. of conductors in series per path

$$= \frac{2\Phi N_r p}{60} \times \frac{Z}{c}$$

i.e.
$$E = 2 \frac{Z}{c} \times \frac{N_r p}{60} \times \Phi \text{ volts} \qquad \qquad [1.21]$$

Example 1.58

A four-pole wave-connected armature has 51 slots with 12 conductors per slot and is driven at 900 r/min. If the useful flux per pole is 25 mWb, calculate the value of the generated e.m.f.

Total number of conductors $= Z = 51 \times 12 = 612$; $c = 2$; $p = 2$; $N = 900$ r/min; $\Phi = 0.025$ Wb.

Using expression [1.21], we have

$$E = 2 \times \frac{612}{2} \times \frac{900 \times 2}{60} \times 0.025$$

$$= \mathbf{459\ V}$$

Example 1.59

An eight-pole lap-connected armature, driven at 350 r/min, is required to generate 260 V. The useful flux per pole is about 0.05 Wb. If the armature has 120 slots, calculate a suitable number of conductors per slot.

For an eight-pole lap winding, $c = 8$. Hence

$$260 = 2 \times \frac{Z}{8} \times \frac{350 \times 4}{60} \times 0.05$$

$$\therefore \qquad Z = 890 \text{ (approximately)}$$

and number of conductors per slot = 890/120 = 7.4 (approx.).

This value must be an even number; hence **eight conductors per slot** would be suitable.

Since this arrangement involves a total of 8 × 120 = 960 conductors, and since a flux of 0.05 Wb per pole with 890 conductors gave 260 V, then with 960 conductors, the same e.m.f. is generated with a flux of 0.05 × (890/960) − 0.0464 Wb per pole.

Armature reaction

Armature reaction is the effect of armature ampere-turns upon the value and the distribution of the magnetic flux entering and leaving the armature core.

Let us, for simplicity, consider a two-pole machine having an armature with eight slots and two conductors per slot, as shown in Fig. 1.96. The curved lines between the conductors and the commutator segments represent the front end connections of the armature winding and those on the outside of the armature represent the back end connections. The armature winding – like all modern d.c. windings – is of the double-layer type, the end connections of the outer layer being represented by full lines and those of the inner layer by dotted lines.

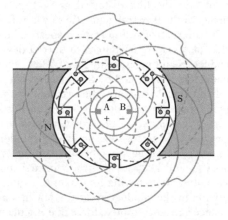

Fig. 1.96   A two-pole armature winding

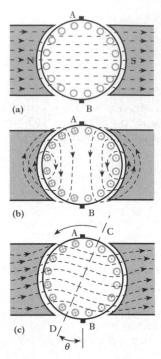

Fig. 1.97 Flux distribution due to (a) field current alone, (b) armature current alone, (c) field and armature currents of a d.c. motor

Brushes A and B are placed so that they are making contact with conductors which are moving midway between the poles and have therefore no e.m.f. induced in them. If the armature moves anticlockwise, the direction of the e.m.f.s generated in the various conductors is opposite to that of the currents, which are indicated in Fig. 1.97(b) by the dots and crosses.

In diagrams where the end connections are omitted, it is usual to show the brushes midway between the poles, as in Fig. 1.97.

In general, an armature has 10 to 15 slots per pole, so that the conductors are more uniformly distributed around the armature core than is suggested by Fig. 1.96, and for simplicity we may omit the slots and consider the conductors uniformly distributed as in Fig. 1.97(a). The latter shows the distribution of flux when there is no armature current, the flux in the gap being practically radial and uniformly distributed.

Figure 1.97(b) shows the distribution of the flux set up by current flowing through the armature winding in the direction that it will actually flow when the machine is loaded as a motor. It will be seen that at the centre of the armature core and in the pole shoes the direction of this flux is at right angles to that due to the field winding; hence the reason why the flux due to the armature current is termed *cross flux*.

The pole tip which is first met during revolution by a point on the armature or stator surface is known as the *leading tip* and the other as the *trailing pole tip*.

Figure 1.97(c) shows the resultant distribution of the flux due to the combination of the fluxes in Fig. 1.97(a) and (b); thus over the trailing halves of the pole faces the cross flux is in opposition to the main flux, thereby reducing the flux density, whereas over the leading halves the two fluxes are in the same direction, so that the flux density is strengthened. Apart from the effect of magnetic saturation, the increase of flux over one half of the pole face is the same as the decrease over the other half, and the total flux per pole remains practically unaltered. Hence, in a motor, the effect of armature reaction is to twist or distort the flux against the direction of rotation.

One important consequence of this distortion of the flux is that the magnetic neutral axis is shifted through an angle θ from AB to CD; in other words, with the machine on no load and the flux distribution of Fig. 1.97(a), conductors are moving parallel to the magnetic flux and therefore generating no e.m.f. when they are passing axis AB. When the machine is loaded as a motor and the flux distorted as in Fig. 1.97(c), conductors are moving parallel to the flux and generating no e.m.f. when they are passing axis CD.

An alternative and in some respects a better method of representing the effect of armature current is to draw a developed diagram of the armature conductors and poles, as in Fig. 1.98(a). The direction of the current in the conductors is indicated by the dots and crosses.

In an actual armature, the two conductors forming one turn are situated approximately a pole pitch apart, as in Fig. 1.96, but *as far as the magnetic effect of the currents in the armature conductors is concerned*, the end connections could be arranged as shown by the dotted lines in Fig. 1.98(a). From the latter, it will be seen that the conductors situated between the vertical axes CC_1 and DD_1 act as if they formed concentric coils producing a magnetomotive force having its maximum value along axis AA_1. Similarly, the currents in the conductors to the left of axis CC_1 and to the right of DD_1 produce a magnetomotive force that is a maximum along axis BB_1. Since the conductors are assumed to be distributed uniformly around the armature periphery, the distribution of the m.m.f. is represented by the chain-dotted

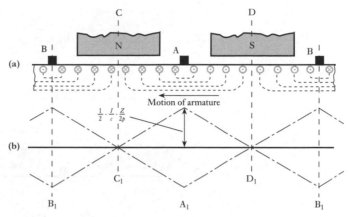

Fig. 1.98 Distribution of armature m.m.f.

line in Fig. 1.98(b). These lines pass through zero at points C_1 and D_1 midway between the brushes.

If I is the *total* armature current, in amperes, Z the number of armature conductors, c the number of parallel paths and p the number of pairs of poles

$$\text{Current per conductor} = \frac{I}{c}$$

and $$\text{Conductors per pole} = \frac{Z}{2p}$$

∴ $$\text{Ampere-conductors per pole} = \frac{I}{c} \cdot \frac{Z}{2p}$$

Since two armature conductors constitute one turn,

$$\text{Ampere-turns per pole} = \frac{1}{2} \cdot \frac{I}{c} \cdot \frac{Z}{2p} \qquad [1.22]$$

This expression represents the armature m.m.f. at each brush axis.

The effect of the armature ampere-turns upon the distribution of the magnetic flux is represented in Fig. 1.99. The dotted lines in Fig. 1.99(a) represent the distribution of the magnetic flux in the airgap on *no load*. The corresponding variation of the flux density over the periphery of the armature is represented by the ordinates of Fig. 1.99(b). Figure 1.99(c) and (d) represent the cross flux due to the armature ampere-turns alone, the armature current being assumed in the direction in which it flows when the machine is loaded as a generator. It will be seen that the flux density in the gap increases from zero at the centre of the pole face to a maximum at the pole tips and then decreases rapidly owing to the increasing length of the path of the fringing flux, until it is a minimum midway between the poles.

Figure 1.99(e) represents the machine operating as a motor, and the distribution of the flux density around the armature core is approximately the resultant of the graphs of Fig. 1.99(b) and (d), and is represented in Fig. 1.99(f). The effect of magnetic saturation would be to reduce the flux density at the leading pole tips, as indicated by the shaded areas P, and thereby to reduce the total flux per pole.

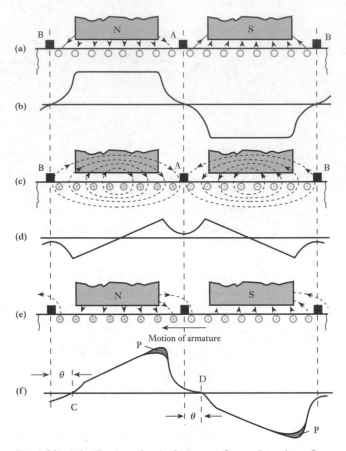

Fig. 1.99 Distribution of main flux, cross flux and resultant flux

It will also be seen from Fig. 1.99(f) that the points of zero flux density, and therefore of zero generated e.m.f. in the armature conductors, have been shifted through an angle θ against the direction of rotation to points C and D.

If the machine had been operated as a generator instead of as a motor, the field patterns illustrated in Fig. 1.99 would still apply provided that the direction of the armature were reversed. The result of this observation is that the effect of magnetic saturation would be to reduce the flux density at the trailing pole tips, as indicated by the shaded areas P, and again thereby to reduce the total flux per pole.

It would also be seen from Fig. 1.99(f) that, with the armature rotating in the opposite (clockwise) direction, the points of zero flux density, and therefore of zero generated e.m.f. in the armature conductors, have been shifted through an angle θ in the direction of rotation to points C and D.

Armature reaction in a d.c. motor

The direction of the armature current in a d.c. motor is *opposite* to that of the generated e.m.f., whereas in a generator the current is in the *same* direction as the generated e.m.f. It follows that in a d.c. motor the flux is distorted backwards; and the brushes have to be shifted backwards if they are to be on the magnetic neutral axis when the machine is loaded. A backward shift in a motor gives rise to demagnetizing ampere-turns, and the reduction of flux tends to cause an increase of speed; in fact, this method – commutation permitting – may be used to compensate for the effect of the IR drop in the armature, thereby maintaining the speed of a shunt motor practically constant at all loads.

Commutation

The e.m.f. generated in a conductor of a d.c. armature is an alternating e.m.f. and the current in a conductor is in one direction when the conductor is moving under a N pole and in the reverse direction when it is moving under a S pole. This reversal of current in a coil has to take place while the two commutator segments to which the coil is connected are being short-circuited by a brush, and the process is termed *commutation*. The duration of this short-circuit is usually about 0.002 s. The reversal of, say, 100 A in an inductive circuit in such a short time is likely to present difficulty and might cause considerable sparking at the brushes.

For simplicity, in considering the variation of current in the short-circuited coil, we can represent the coils and the commutator segments as in Fig. 1.100 where the two ends of any one coil are connected to adjacent segments, as in a lap winding.

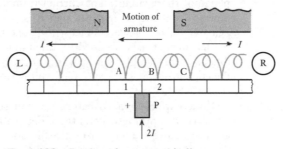

Fig. 1.100   Portion of armature winding

If the current per conductor is I and if the armature is moving from right to left, then – assuming the brush to be positive – coil C is carrying current from right to left (R to L), whereas coil A is carrying current from L or R. We shall therefore examine the variation of current in coil B which is connected to segments 1 and 2.

The current in coil B remains at its full value from R to L until segment 2 begins to make contact with brush P, as in Fig. 1.101(a). As the area of contact with segment 2 increases, current i_1 flowing to the brush via segment 2 increases and current $(I - i_1)$ through coil B decreases. If the current distribution between segments 1 and 2 were determined by the areas of contact only, the current through coil B would decrease linearly, as shown by line M in Fig. 1.102. It follows that when the brush is making equal areas of contact with segments 1 and 2, current through B would be zero, and further movement of the armature would cause the current through B to grow in the reverse direction.

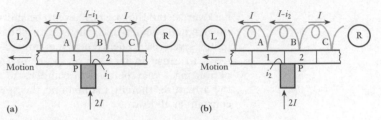

(a)   (b)

Fig. 1.101   Coil B near the beginning and the end of commutation

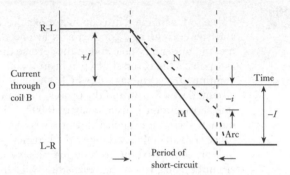

Fig. 1.102   Variation of current in the short–circuited coil

Figure 1.101(b) represents the position of the coils near the end of the period of short-circuit. The current from segment 1 to P is then i_2 and that flowing from left to right through B is $(I - i_2)$. The short-circuit is ended when segment 1 breaks contact with P, and the current through coil B should by that instant have attained its full value from L to R. Under these conditions there should be no sparking at the brush, and this linear variation of the current in the short-circuited coil is referred to as *straight line* or *linear commutation*.

It was explained in 'Armature reaction' (p. 115) that the armature current gives rise to a magnetic field; thus, Fig. 1.97(b) shows the flux set up by the armature current alone. From the direction of this cross flux and assuming anticlockwise rotation, we can deduce that an e.m.f. is generated towards the paper in a conductor moving in the vicinity of brush A, namely in the direction in which current was flowing in the conductor before the latter was shortcircuited by the brush. The same conclusion may be derived from a con-sideration of the resultant distribution of flux given in Fig. 1.99(e), where a conductor moving in the region of brush A is generating an e.m.f. in the same direction as that generated when the conductor was moving under the preceding main pole. This generated e.m.f. – often referred to as the *reactance voltage* – is responsible for delaying the reversal of the current in the short-circuited coils as shown by curve N in Fig. 1.102. The result is that when segment 1 is due to break contact with the brush, as in Fig. 1.103, the current through coil B has grown to some value i (Fig. 1.102); and the remainder, namely $(I - i)$, has to pass between segment 1 and the brush in the form of an arc. This arc is rapidly drawn out and the current through B grows quickly from i to I, as shown in Fig. 1.102.

It is this reactance voltage that is mainly responsible for sparking at the brushes of d.c. machines, and most methods of reducing sparking are directed towards the reduction or neutralization of the reactance voltage.

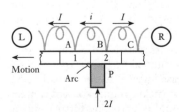

Fig. 1.103   Arcing when segment leaves brush

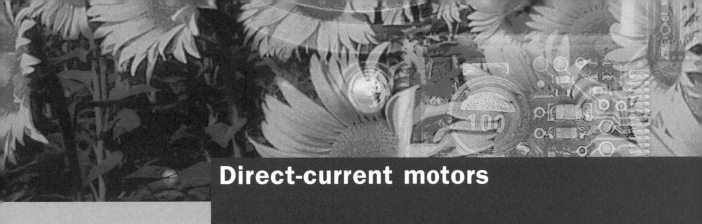

Direct-current motors

There is no difference of construction between a d.c. motor and a d.c. generator. In fact, the only difference is that in a motor the generated e.m.f. is less than the terminal voltage, whereas in a generator the generated e.m.f. is greater than the terminal voltage.

For instance, suppose a shunt generator D shown in Fig. 1.104 to be driven by an engine and connected through a centre-zero ammeter A to a battery B. If the field regulator R is adjusted until the reading on A is zero, the e.m.f., E_D, generated in D is then exactly equal to the e.m.f., E_B, of the battery. If R is now reduced, the e.m.f. generated in D exceeds that of B, and the excess e.m.f. is available to circulate a current I_D through the resistance of the armature circuit, the battery and the connecting conductors. Since I_D is in the same direction as E_D, machine D is a generator of electrical energy.

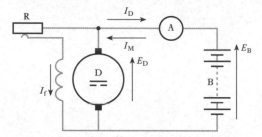

Fig. 1.104   Shunt-wound machine as generator or motor

Next, suppose the supply of steam or oil to the engine driving D to be cut off. The speed of the set falls, and as E_D decreases, I_D becomes less, until, when $E_D = E_B$, there is no circulating current. But E_D continues to decrease and becomes less than E_B, so that a current I_M flows in the reverse direction. Hence B is now supplying electrical energy to drive D as an electric motor.

The speed of D continues to fall until the difference between E_D and E_B is sufficient to circulate the current necessary to maintain the rotation of D. It will be noticed that the direction of the field current I_f is the same whether D is running as a generator or a motor.

The relationship between the current, the e.m.f., etc. for machine D may be expressed thus. If E is the e.m.f. generated in armature, V the terminal voltage, R_a the resistance of armature circuit and I_a the armature current, then, when D is operating as a generator,

$$E = V + I_a R_a \qquad [1.22]$$

When the machine is operating as a motor, the e.m.f., E, is less than the applied voltage V, and the direction of the current I_a is the reverse of that when the machine is acting as a generator; hence

$$E = V - I_a R_a$$

or $$V = E + I_a R_a \qquad [1.23]$$

Since the e.m.f. generated in the armature of a motor is in opposition to the applied voltage, it is sometimes referred to as a *back e.m.f.*

Example 1.60   The armature of a d.c. machine has a resistance of 0.1 Ω and is connected to a 250 V supply. Calculate the generated e.m.f. when it is running

(a) as a generator giving 80 A;
(b) as a motor taking 60 A.

(a) Voltage drop due to armature resistance $= 80 \times 0.1 = 8$ V. From equation [1.22]

Generated e.m.f. $= 250 + 8 = \mathbf{258\ V}$

(b) Voltage drop due to armature resistance $= 20 \times 0.1 = 6$ V. From equation [1.23]

Generated e.m.f. $= 250 - 6 = \mathbf{244\ V}$

Speed of a motor

Equation [1.21] showed that the relationship between the generated e.m.f., speed, flux, etc. is represented by

$$E = 2\frac{Z}{c} \cdot \frac{N_r p}{60} \cdot \Phi$$

For a given machine, Z, c and p are fixed; in such a case we can write

$$E = kN_r\Phi$$

where $k = 2\dfrac{Z}{c} \cdot \dfrac{p}{60}$

Substituting for E in expression [1.23] we have

$$V = kN_r\Phi + I_a R_a$$

$\therefore$ $$N_r = \frac{V - I_a R_a}{k\,\Phi} \qquad [1.24]$$

The value of $I_a R_a$ is usually less than 5 per cent of the terminal voltage V, so that

$$N_r \propto \frac{V}{\Phi} \qquad [1.25]$$

In words, this expression means that the speed of an electric motor is approximately proportional to the voltage applied to the armature and inversely proportional to the flux; all methods of controlling the speed involve the use of either or both of these relationships.

Example 1.61   A four-pole motor is fed at 440 V and takes an armature current of 50 A. The resistance of the armature circuit is 0.28 Ω. The armature winding is wave-connected with 888 conductors and the useful flux per pole is 0.023 Wb. Calculate the speed.

From expression [1.23] we have

$$440 = \text{generated e.m.f.} + 50 \times 0.28$$

$\therefore$ Generated e.m.f. $= 440 - 14 = 426$ V

Substituting in the e.m.f. equation [1.21], we have

$$426 = 2 \times \frac{888}{2} \times \frac{N_r \times 2}{60} \times 0.023$$

$$N_r = \textbf{626 r/min}$$

Example 1.62

A motor runs at 900 r/min off a 460 V supply. Calculate the approximate speed when the machine is connected across a 200 V supply. Assume the new flux to be 0.7 of the original flux.

If Φ is the original flux, then from expression [1.25]:

$$900 = \frac{460}{k\Phi}$$

$$\therefore \qquad k\Phi = 0.511$$

and   New speed $= \dfrac{\text{new voltage}}{k \times \text{original flux} \times 0.7}$ (approximately)

$$N_r = \frac{200}{0.511 \times 0.7} = \textbf{559 r/min}$$

Torque of an electric motor

If we start with equation [1.23] and multiply each term by I_a, namely the total armature current, we have

$$VI_a = EI_a + I_a^2 R_a$$

But VI_a represents the total electrical power supplied to the armature, and $I_a^2 R_a$ represents the loss due to the resistance of the armature circuit. The difference between these two quantities, namely EI_a, therefore represents the mechanical power developed by the armature. All of this mechanical power is not available externally, since some of it is absorbed as friction loss at the bearings and at the brushes and some is wasted as hysteresis loss and in circulating eddy currents in the ferromagnetic core.

If M is the torque, in newton metres, exerted on the armature to develop the mechanical power just referred to, and if N_r is the speed in revolutions per minute, then,

$$\text{Mechanical power developed} = \frac{2\pi M N_r}{60} \text{ watts}$$

Hence $\dfrac{2\pi M N_r}{60} = EI_a$ [1.26]

$$= 2\frac{Z}{c} \cdot \frac{N_r p}{60} \cdot \Phi \cdot I_a$$

$\therefore$ $M = 0.318 \dfrac{I_a}{c} \cdot Zp\Phi$ newton metres   [1.27]

For a given machine, Z, c and p are fixed, in which case

$$M \propto I_a \times \Phi \qquad \qquad [1.28]$$

Or, in words, the torque of a given d.c. motor is proportional to the product of the armature current and the flux per pole.

Example 1.63 A d.c. motor takes an armature current of 110 A at 480 V. The resistance of the armature circuit is 0.2 Ω. The machine has six poles and the armature is lap-connected with 864 conductors. The flux per pole is 0.05 Wb. Calculate

(a) the speed;
(b) the gross torque developed by the armature.

(a)   Generated e.m.f. $= 480 - (110 \times 0.2)$

$$= 458 \text{ V}$$

Since the armature winding is lap-connected, $c = 6$.
Substituting in expression [1.21], we have

$$458 = 2 \times \frac{864}{6} \times \frac{N_r \times 3}{60} \times 0.05$$

$$N_r = \textbf{636 r/min}$$

(b) Mechanical power developed by armature is

$$110 \times 458 = 50\ 380 \text{ W}$$

Substituting in expression [1.26] we have

$$2\pi M \times \frac{636}{60} = 50\ 380$$

$$= \textbf{756 N m}$$

Alternatively, using expression [1.27] we have

$$M = 0.318 \times \frac{110}{6} \times 864 \times 3 \times 0.05$$

$$= \textbf{756 N m}$$

Example 1.64 The torque required to drive a d.c. generator at 15 r/s is 2 kN m. The core, friction and windage losses in the machine are 8.0 kW. Calculate the power generated in the armature winding.

Driving torque $= 2$ kN m $= 2000$ N m

Power required to drive the generator is

$$2\pi \times 2000\ [\text{N m}] \times 15\ [\text{r/s}]$$

$$= 188\ 400 \text{ W} = 188.4 \text{ kW}$$

Since core, friction and windage losses are 8.0 kW,

$\therefore$ Power generated in armature winding $= 188.4 - 8.0$

$= 180.4 \text{ kW}$

Speed characteristics of electric motors

With very few exceptions, d.c. motors are shunt-, series- or compound-wound. The connections of a shunt motor are given in Fig. 1.105, and Figs 1.106 and 1.107 show the connections for series and compound motors respectively, the starter in each case being shown in the ON position. It is good practice to include starters in diagrams of motor connections. In compound motors, the series and shunt windings almost invariably assist each other, as indicated in Fig. 1.107.

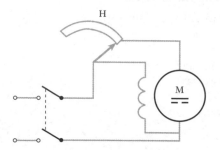

Fig. 1.105   Shunt-wound motor

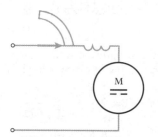

Fig. 1.106   Series-wound motor

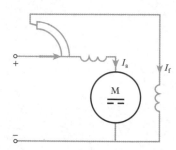

Fig. 1.107   Compound-wound motor

The speed characteristic of a motor usually represents the variation of speed with input current or input power, and its shape can be easily derived from expression [1.24], namely

$$N_r = \frac{V - I_a R_a}{k\Phi}$$

In shunt motors, the flux Φ is only slightly affected by the armature current and the value of $I_a R_a$ at full load rarely exceeds 5 per cent of V, so that the variation of speed with input current may be represented by curve A in Fig. 1.108. Hence shunt motors are suitable where the speed has to remain approximately constant over a wide range of load.

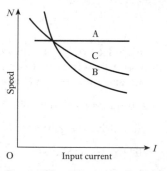

Fig. 1.108   Speed characteristics of shunt, series and compound motors

In series motors, the flux increases at first in proportion to the current and then less rapidly owing to magnetic saturation (Fig. 1.103). Also R_a in the above expression now includes the resistance of the field winding. Hence the speed is roughly inversely proportional to the current, as indicated by curve B in Fig. 1.108. It will be seen that if the load falls to a very small value, the speed may become dangerously high. A series motor should therefore not be employed when there is any such risk; for instance, it should never be belt-coupled to its load except in very small machines such as vacuum cleaners.

Since the compound motor has a combination of shunt and series excitations, its characteristic (curve C in Fig. 1.108) is intermediate between those of the shunt and series motors, the exact shape depending upon the values of the shunt and series ampere-turns.

Torque characteristics of electric motors

In 'Torque of an electric motor', p. 124 it was shown that for a given motor:

Torque $\propto$ armature current $\times$ flux per pole

$$M \propto I_a \Phi$$

Since the flux in a shunt motor is practically independent of the armature current

$\therefore$ Torque of a shunt motor $\propto$ armature current

$$M \propto I_a$$

and is represented by the straight line A in Fig. 1.109.

In a series motor the flux is approximately proportional to the current up to full load, so that

Torque of a series motor $\propto$ (armature current)^2, approx.

$$M \propto I_a^2$$

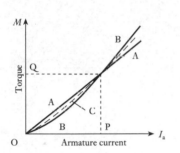

Fig. 1.109 Torque characteristics of shunt, series and compound motors

Above full load, magnetic saturation becomes more marked and the torque does not increase so rapidly.

Curves A, B and C in Fig. 1.109 show the relative shapes of torque curves for shunt, series and compound motors having the same full-load torque OQ with the same full-load armature current OP, the exact shape of curve C depending upon the relative value of the shunt and series ampere-turns at full load.

From Fig. 1.109 it is evident that for a given current below the full-load value the shunt motor exerts the largest torque, but for a given current above that value the series motor exerts the largest torque.

The maximum permissible current at starting is usually about 1.5 times the full-load current. Consequently where a large starting torque is required, such as for hoists, cranes, electric trains, etc., the series motor is the most suitable machine.

Single-phase series circuits

Basic a.c. circuits

In order to make our approach as simple as possible, we will limit the content of this section to circuits which contain a single generator producing a pure sinusoidal voltage. This is a reasonably good approximation to the electricity supply we meet at home. Such circuits are termed single-phase circuits.

Alternating current in a resistive circuit

Consider a circuit having a resistance R ohms connected across the terminals of an a.c. generator G, as in Fig. 1.10, and suppose the alternating voltage to be represented by the sine wave of Fig. 1.111. If the value of the voltage at any instant B is v volts, the value of the current at that instant is given by

$$i = \frac{v}{R} \text{ amperes}$$

When the voltage is zero, the current is also zero; and since the current is proportional to the voltage, the waveform of the current is exactly the same as that of the voltage. Also the two quantities are *in phase* with each other; that is, they pass through their zero values at the same instant and attain their maximum values in a given direction at the same instant. Hence the current wave is as shown in Fig. 1.111.

If V_m and I_m are the maximum values of the voltage and current respectively, it follows that

$$I_m = \frac{V_m}{R} \qquad\qquad [1.29]$$

But the r.m.s. value of a sine wave is 0.707 times the maximum value, so that

RMS value of voltage $= V = 0.707 V_m$

and   RMS value of current $= I = 0.707 I_m$

Substituting for I_m and V_m in equation [1.29] we have

$$\frac{I}{0.707} = \frac{V}{0.707R}$$

$$I = \frac{V}{R} \qquad\qquad [1.30]$$

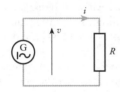

Fig. 1.110 Circuit with resistance only

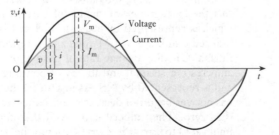

Fig. 1.111   Voltage and current waveforms for a resistive circuit

Hence Ohm's law can be applied without any modification to an a.c. circuit possessing resistance only.

If the instantaneous value of the applied voltage is represented by

$$v = V_m \sin \omega t$$

then instantaneous value of current in a resistive circuit is

$$i = \frac{V_m}{R} \sin \omega t \qquad [1.31]$$

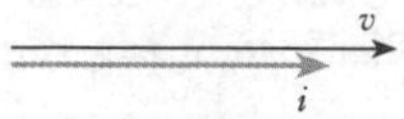

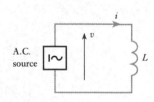

Fig. 1.112 Phasor diagram for a resistive circuit

The phasors representing the voltage and current in a resistive circuit are shown in Fig. 1.112. The two phasors are actually coincident, but are drawn slightly apart so that the identity of each may be clearly recognized. It is usual to draw the phasors in the position corresponding to $\omega t = 0$. Hence the phasors representing the voltage and current of expression [1.31] are drawn along the x-axis.

Finally let us briefly return to Fig. 1.110. The symbol used to represent the source generator was circular. Such a symbol indicates that the generator was a rotating machine but this only arises in power situations. In electronics situations, the a.c. source is static and therefore it is better to use the general symbol shown in Fig. 1.113, i.e. a square, which represents any form of source. The sinusoid indicates that it is an a.c. source and the 1 is optional. Normally it would be included in power situations and left out in electronics and communications applications.

Alternating current in an inductive circuit

Let us consider the effect of a sinusoidal current flowing through a coil having an inductance of L henrys and a negligible resistance, as in Fig. 1.113. For instance, let us consider what is happening during the first quarter-cycle of Fig. 1.114. This quarter-cycle has been divided into three equal intervals, OA, AC and CF seconds. During interval OA, the current increases from zero to AB; hence the average rate of change of current is AB/OA amperes per second, and is represented by ordinate JK drawn midway between O and A. The e.m.f., in volts, induced in a coil is

$L \times$ rate of change of current in amperes per second

Fig. 1.113 Circuit with inductance only

consequently, the average value of the induced e.m.f. during interval OA is $L \times$ AB/OA, namely $L \times$ JK volts, and is represented by ordinate JQ in Fig. 1.114.

Similarly, during interval AC, the current increases from AB to CE, so that the average rate of change of current is DE/AC amperes per second, which is represented by ordinate LM in Fig. 1.114; and the corresponding induced e.m.f. is $L \times$ LM volts and is represented by LR. During the third interval CF, the average rate of change of current is GH/CF, namely NP amperes per second; and the corresponding induced e.m.f. is $L \times$ NP volts and is represented by NS. At instant F, the current has ceased growing but has not yet begun to decrease; consequently the rate of change of current is then zero. The induced e.m.f. will therefore have decreased from a maximum at O to zero at F. Curves can now be drawn through the derived points, as shown in Fig. 1.114.

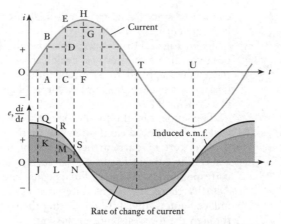

Fig. 1.114   Waveforms of current, rate of change of current and induced e.m.f.

During the second quarter-cycle, the current decreases, so that the rate of change of current is negative and the induced e.m.f. becomes positive, tending to prevent the current decreasing. Since the sine wave of current is symmetrical about ordinate FH, the curves representing the rate of change of current and the e.m.f. induced in the coil will be symmetrical with those derived for the first quarter-cycle. Since the rate of change of current at any instant is proportional to the slope of the current wave at that instant, it is evident that the value of the induced e.m.f. increases from zero at F to a maximum at T and then decreases to zero at U in Fig. 1.114.

By using shorter intervals, for example by taking ordinates at intervals of 10° and noting the corresponding values of the ordinates with the aid of a calculator with trigonometric functions, it is possible to derive fairly accurately the shapes of the curves representing the rate of change of current and the induced e.m.f.

From Fig. 1.114 it will be seen that the induced e.m.f. attains its maximum positive value a quarter of a cycle before the current has done the same thing – in fact, it goes through all its variations a quarter of a cycle before the current has gone through similar variations. Hence the induced e.m.f. is said to lead the current by a quarter of a cycle or the current is said to lag the induced e.m.f. by a quarter of a cycle.

Since the resistance of the coil is assumed negligible, we can regard the whole of the applied voltage as being the induced e.m.f. Hence the curve of applied voltage in Fig. 1.115 can be drawn the same as that of the induced

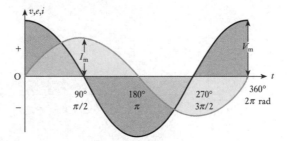

Fig. 1.115   Voltage and current waveforms for a purely inductive circuit

e.m.f.; and since the latter is sinusoidal, the wave of applied voltage must also be a sine curve.

From Fig. 1.115 it is seen that the applied voltage attains its maximum positive value a quarter of a cycle earlier than the current; in other words, the voltage applied to a purely inductive circuit leads the current by a quarter of a cycle or 90°, or the current lags the applied voltage by a quarter of a cycle or 90°.

The student might quite reasonably ask: If the applied voltage is neutralized by the induced e.m.f., how can there be any current? The answer is that if there were no current there would be no flux, and therefore no induced e.m.f. The current has to vary at such a rate that the e.m.f. induced by the corresponding variation of flux is equal and opposite to the applied voltage. Actually there is a slight difference between the applied voltage and the induced e.m.f., this difference being the voltage required to send the current through the low resistance of the coil.

Current and voltage in an inductive circuit

Suppose the instantaneous value of the current through a coil having inductance L henrys and negligible resistance to be represented by

$$i = I_m \sin \omega t = I_m \sin 2\pi f t \qquad [1.32]$$

where t is the time, in seconds, after the current has passed through zero from negative to positive values, as shown in Fig. 1.116.

Suppose the current to increase by di amperes in dt seconds, then instantaneous value of induced e.m.f. is

$$e = L \cdot \frac{di}{dt}$$

$$= LI_m \frac{d}{dt}(\sin 2\pi f t)$$

$$= 2\pi f L I_m \cos 2\pi f t$$

$$e = 2\pi f L I_m \sin\left(2\pi f t + \frac{\pi}{2}\right) \qquad [1.33]$$

Since f represents the number of cycles per second, the duration of 1 cycle $= 1/f$ seconds. Consequently when

$$t = 0, \quad \cos 2\pi f t = 1$$

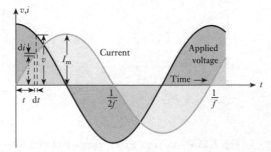

Fig. 1.116   Voltage and current waveforms for a purely inductive circuit

and   Induced e.m.f. $= 2\pi f L I_{\mathrm{m}}$

When $t = 1/(2f)$, $\cos 2\pi f t = \cos \pi = -1$

and   Induced e.m.f. $= -2\pi f L I_{\mathrm{m}}$

Hence the induced e.m.f. is represented by the curve in Fig. 1.116, leading the current by a quarter of a cycle.

Since the resistance of the circuit is assumed negligible, the whole of the applied voltage is equal to the induced e.m.f., therefore instantaneous value of applied voltage is

$$v = e$$

$$= 2\pi f L I_{\mathrm{m}} \cos 2\pi f t$$

$$v = 2\pi f L I_{\mathrm{m}} \sin(2\pi f t + \pi/2) \qquad [1.34]$$

Comparison of expressions [1.32] and [1.34] shows that the applied voltage leads the current by a quarter of a cycle. Also, from expression [1.34], it follows that the maximum value V_{m} of the applied voltage is $2\pi f L I_{\mathrm{m}}$, i.e.

$$V_{\mathrm{m}} = 2\pi f L I_{\mathrm{m}} \quad \text{so that} \quad \frac{V_{\mathrm{m}}}{I_{\mathrm{m}}} = 2\pi f L$$

If I and V are the r.m.s. values, then

$$\frac{V}{I} = \frac{0.707 V_{\mathrm{m}}}{0.707 I_{\mathrm{m}}} = 2\pi f L$$

$$= \textit{inductive reactance}$$

Inductive reactance   Symbol: X_L Unit: **ohm (Ω)**

The inductive reactance is expressed in ohms and is represented by the symbol X_L. Hence

$$I = \frac{V}{2\pi f L} = \frac{V}{X_L} \qquad [1.35]$$

where $X_L = 2\pi f L$

The inductive reactance is proportional to the frequency and the current produced by a given voltage is inversely proportional to the frequency, as shown in Fig. 1.117.

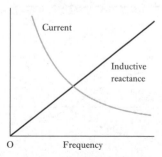

Fig. 1.117 Variation of reactance and current with frequency for a purely inductive circuit

The phasor diagram for a purely inductive circuit is given in Fig. 1.118, where E represents the r.m.s. value of the e.m.f. induced in the circuit, and V, equal to E, represents the r.m.s. value of the applied voltage.

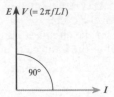

Fig. 1.118   Phasor diagram for a purely inductive circuit

Mechanical analogy of an inductive circuit

One of the most puzzling things to a student commencing the study of alternating currents is the behaviour of a current in an inductive circuit. For instance, why should the current in Fig. 1.115 be at its maximum value when there is no applied voltage? Why should there be no current when the applied voltage is at its maximum? Why should it be possible to have a voltage applied in one direction and a current flowing in the reverse direction, as is the case during the second and fourth quarter-cycles in Fig. 1.115?

It might therefore be found helpful to consider a simple mechanical analogy – the simpler the better. In mechanics, the *inertia* of a body opposes any change in the *speed* of that body. The effect of inertia is therefore analogous to that of *inductance* in opposing any change in the *current*.

Suppose we take a heavy metal cylinder C (Fig. 1.119), and roll it backwards and forwards on a horizontal surface between two extreme positions A and B. Let us consider the forces and the speed while C is being rolled from A to B. At first the speed is zero, but the force applied to the body is at its maximum, causing C to accelerate towards the right. This applied force is reduced – as indicated by the length of the arrows in Fig. 1.119 – until it is zero when C is midway between A and B; C ceases to accelerate and will therefore have attained its maximum speed from left to right.

Immediately after C has passed the mid-point, the direction of the applied force is reversed and increased until the body is brought to rest at B and then begins its return movement.

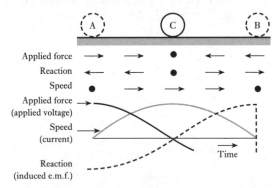

Fig. 1.119   Mechanical analogy of a purely inductive circuit

The reaction of C, on the other hand, is equal and opposite to the applied force and corresponds to the e.m.f. induced in the inductive circuit.

From an inspection of the arrows in Fig. 1.119 it is seen that the speed in a given direction is a maximum of a quarter of a complete oscillation after the applied force has been a maximum in the same direction, but a quarter of an oscillation before the reaction reaches its maximum in that direction. This is analogous to the current in a purely inductive circuit lagging the applied voltage by a quarter of a cycle. Also it is evident that when the speed is a maximum the applied force is zero, and that when the applied force is a maximum the speed is zero; and that during the second half of the movement indicated in Fig. 1.119, the direction of motion is opposite to that of the applied force. These relationships correspond exactly to those found for a purely inductive circuit.

Resistance and inductance in series

Having considered the effects of resistance and inductance separately in a circuit, it is now necessary to consider their combined effects. This can be most simply achieved by connecting the resistance and inductance in series, as shown in Fig. 1.120(a).

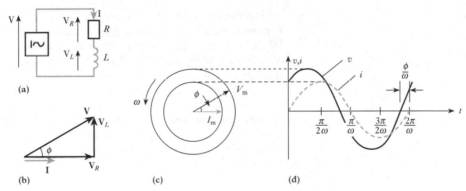

Fig. 1.120 Resistance and inductance in series. (a) Circuit diagram; (b) phasor diagram; (c) instantaneous phasor diagram; (d) wave diagram

The phasor diagram results from an application of Kirchhoff's second law. For convenience, the current is taken as reference since it is common to all the elements of a series circuit. The circuit voltage may then be derived from the following relations:

$$\mathbf{V}_R = \mathbf{I}R, \text{ where } \mathbf{V}_R \text{ is in phase with } \mathbf{I}$$

$$\mathbf{V}_L = \mathbf{I}X_L, \text{ where } \mathbf{V}_L \text{ leads } \mathbf{I} \text{ by } 90°$$

$$\mathbf{V} = \mathbf{V}_R + \mathbf{V}_L \quad \text{(phasor sum)} \qquad [1.36]$$

It will be remembered that bold symbols represent phasor quantities.

In the phasor diagram, shown in Fig. 1.120(b), the total voltage is thus obtained from relation [1.36], which is a complexor summation. The arithmetical sum of V_R and V_L is incorrect, giving too large a value for the total voltage V.

The angle of phase difference between **V** and **I** is termed the phase angle and is represented by ϕ. Also

$$V = (V_R^2 + V_L^2)^{\frac{1}{2}}$$
$$= (I^2 R^2 + I^2 X_L^2)^{\frac{1}{2}}$$
$$= I(R^2 + X_L^2)^{\frac{1}{2}}$$

Hence $V = IZ$ volts   [1.37]

where $Z = (R^2 + X_L^2)^{\frac{1}{2}}$

or $Z = (R^2 + \omega^2 L^2)^{\frac{1}{2}}$ ohms   [1.38]

Here Z is termed the impedance of the circuit. Relation [1.37] will be seen to be a development of the relation $V = IR$ used in d.c. circuit analysis. However, for any given frequency, the impedance is constant and hence Ohm's law also applies to a.c. circuit analysis.

Impedance   Symbol: Z Unit: **ohm (Ω)**

The instantaneous phasor diagram, and the resulting wave diagram, show that the current lags the voltage by a phase angle greater than 0° but less than 90°. The phase angle between voltage and current is determined by the ratio of resistance to inductive reactance in the circuit. The greater the value of this ratio, the less will be the angle ϕ.

This statement can be developed by again considering the phasor diagram. Each side of the summation triangle has the same factor I. Consequently the triangle can be drawn to some other scale using only the values of resistance, reactance and impedance, as shown in Fig. 1.121. Such a triangle is termed an impedance triangle.

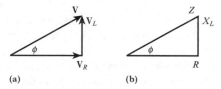

(a)   (b)

Fig. 1.121   Voltage and impedance triangles. (a) Voltage diagram; (b) impedance diagram

Just as in Fig. 1.120(b), the triangle is again right-angled. This compares with relation [1.38]. By the geometry of the diagram:

$$\phi = \tan^{-1}\frac{V_L}{V_R} = \tan^{-1}\frac{IX_L}{IR}$$

$$\phi = \tan^{-1}\frac{X_L}{R}$$ [1.39]

To emphasize that the current lags the voltage, it is usual to give either the resulting angle as a negative value or else to use the word 'lag' after the angle. This is illustrated in Example 1.65.

The phase angle may also be derived as follows:

$$\phi = \cos^{-1}\frac{V_R}{V} = \cos^{-1}\frac{R}{Z} \qquad [1.40]$$

hence $\qquad \phi = \cos^{-1}\dfrac{R}{(R^2 + \omega^2 L^2)^{\frac{1}{2}}}$

Example 1.65

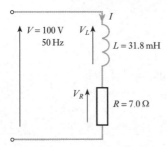

Fig. 1.122 Circuit diagram for Example 1.65

A resistance of 7.0 Ω is connected in series with a pure inductance of 31.8 mH and the circuit is connected to a 100 V, 50 Hz, sinusoidal supply (Fig. 1.122). Calculate:

(a) the circuit current;
(b) the phase angle.

$$X_L = 2\pi f L = 2\pi 50 \times 31.8 \times 10^{-3} = 10.0 \ \Omega$$
$$Z = (R^2 + X_L^2)^{\frac{1}{2}} = (7.0^2 + 10.0^2)^{\frac{1}{2}} = 12.2 \ \Omega$$
$$I = \frac{V}{Z} = \frac{100}{12.2} = 8.2 \ \text{A}$$
$$\phi = \tan^{-1}\frac{X_L}{R} = \tan^{-1}\frac{10.0}{7.0} = 55.1° \ \text{lag or} -55.1°$$

Example 1.66

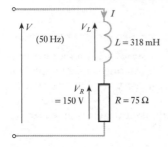

Fig. 1.123 Circuit diagram for Example 1.66

A pure inductance of 318 mH is connected in series with a pure resistance of 75 Ω. The circuit is supplied from a 50 Hz sinusoidal source and the voltage across the 75 Ω resistor is found to be 150 V (Fig. 1.123). Calculate the supply voltage.

$$V_R = 150 \ \text{V}$$
$$I = \frac{V}{R} = \frac{150}{75} = 2 \ \text{A}$$
$$X_L = 2\pi f L = 2\pi 50 \times 318 \times 10^{-3} = 100 \ \Omega$$
$$V_L = I X_L = 2 \times 100 = 200 \ \text{V}$$
$$V = (V_R^2 + V_L^2)^{\frac{1}{2}} = (150^2 + 200^2)^{\frac{1}{2}} = 250 \ \text{V}$$

Alternatively

$$Z = (R^2 + X_L^2)^{\frac{1}{2}} = (75^2 + 100^2)^{\frac{1}{2}} = 125 \ \Omega$$
$$V = IZ = 2 \times 125 = 250 \ \text{V}$$

Example 1.67

A coil, having both resistance and inductance, has a total effective impedance of 50 Ω and the phase angle of the current through it with respect to the voltage across it is 45° lag. The coil is connected in

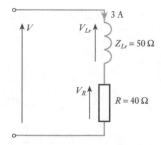

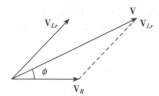

Fig. 1.124 Circuit diagram for Example 1.67

Fig. 1.125 Phasor diagram for Example 1.67

series with a 40 Ω resistor across a sinusoidal supply (Fig. 1.124). The circuit current is 3.0 A; by constructing a phasor diagram, estimate the supply voltage and the circuit phase angle.

$$V_R = IR = 3 \times 40 = 120 \text{ V}$$

$$V_{Lr} = IZ_{Lr} = 3 \times 50 = 150 \text{ V}$$

The use of subscript notation should be noted in the previous line. It would have been incorrect to write that $V_{Lr} = IZ$, since Z is used to represent the total circuit impedance. In more complex problems, numbers can be used, i.e. Z_1, Z_2, Z_3, etc. In this example, such a procedure would be tedious.

The phasor diagram (Fig. 1.125) is constructed by drawing the phasor $\mathbf{V}_R$ to some appropriate scale. The direction of this phasor will coincide with that of the current I. Since the voltage across the coil will lead the current by 45°, phasor $\mathbf{V}_{Lr}$ can also be drawn. Complexor summation of the two voltages gives an estimate of the total voltage.

From the diagram

$$V = \mathbf{250 \text{ V}}$$

$$\phi = \mathbf{25° \text{ lag}}$$

We could have calculated the solution as follows:

$$V^2 = V_R^2 + V_{Lr}^2 + 2V_R V_{Lr} \cos \phi_{Lr}$$

$$= 120^2 + 150^2 + 2 \cdot 120 \cdot 150 \cdot 0.707$$

$$= 62\,500$$

$$\therefore \quad V = \mathbf{250 \text{ V}}$$

$$\cos \phi = \frac{V_R + V_{Lr} \cos \phi_{Lr}}{V} = \frac{120 + (150 \times 0.707)}{250}$$

$$= 0.904$$

$$\therefore \quad \phi = \mathbf{25° \text{ lag}}$$

Alternating current in a capacitive circuit

Figure 1.126 shows a capacitor C connected in series with an ammeter A across the terminals of an a.c. source; and the alternating voltage applied to C is represented in Fig. 1.127. Suppose this voltage to be positive when it makes plate D positive relative to plate E.

If the capacitance is C farads, then the charging current i is given by

$$i = C \times \text{rate of change of p.d.}$$

In Fig. 1.127, the p.d. is increasing positively at the maximum rate at instant zero; consequently the charging current is also at its maximum positive value at that instant. A quarter of a cycle later, the applied voltage has reached its maximum value V_m, and for a very brief interval of time the p.d. is neither increasing nor decreasing, so that there is no current. During the next quarter of a cycle, the applied voltage is decreasing. Consequently the capacitor discharges, the discharge current being in the negative direction.

When the voltage is passing through zero, the slope of the voltage curve is at its maximum, i.e. the p.d. is varying at the maximum rate; consequently the current is also a maximum at that instant.

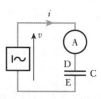

Fig. 1.126 Circuit with capacitance only

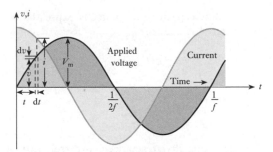

Fig. 1.127   Voltage and current waveforms for a purely capacitive circuit

Current and voltage in a capacitive circuit

In this case we start with the voltage wave, whereas with inductance we started with the current wave. The reason for this is that in the case of inductance, we derive the induced e.m.f. by differentiating the current expression; whereas with capacitance, we derive the current by differentiating the voltage expression.

Suppose that the instantaneous value of the voltage applied to a capacitor having capacitance C farads is represented by

$$v = V_{\mathrm{m}} \sin \omega t = V_{\mathrm{m}} \sin 2\pi ft \qquad [1.41]$$

If the applied voltage increases by $\mathrm{d}v$ volts in $\mathrm{d}t$ seconds (Fig. 1.127) then, instantaneous value of current is

$$i = C \frac{\mathrm{d}v}{\mathrm{d}t}$$

$$= C \frac{\mathrm{d}}{\mathrm{d}t}(V_{\mathrm{m}} \sin 2\pi ft)$$

$$= 2\pi fC V_{\mathrm{m}} \cos 2\pi ft$$

$$i = 2\pi fC V_{\mathrm{m}} \sin\left(2\pi ft + \frac{\pi}{2}\right) \qquad [1.42]$$

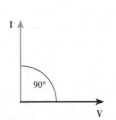

Fig. 1.128   Phasor diagram for a purely capacitive circuit

Comparison of expressions [1.41] and [1.42] shows that the current leads the applied voltage by a quarter of a cycle, and the current and voltage can be represented by phasors as in Fig. 1.128.

From expression [1.42] it follows that the maximum value I_{m} of the current is $2\pi fC V_{\mathrm{m}}$,

$$\frac{V_{\mathrm{m}}}{I_{\mathrm{m}}} = \frac{1}{2\pi fC}$$

Hence, if I and V are the r.m.s. values

$$\frac{V}{I} = \frac{1}{2\pi fC} = capacitive\ reactance \qquad [1.43]$$

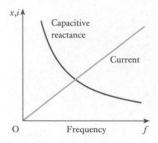

Fig. 1.129 Variation of reactance and current with frequency for a purely capacitive circuit

The capacitive reactance is expressed in ohms and is represented by the symbol X_C. Hence

$$I = 2\pi f C V = \frac{V}{X_C}$$

$$\therefore \qquad X_C = \frac{1}{2\pi f C} \qquad\qquad\qquad [1.44]$$

The capacitive reactance is inversely proportional to the frequency, and the current produced by a given voltage is proportional to the frequency, as shown in Fig. 1.129.

Capacitive reactance   Symbol: X_C Unit: **ohm (Ω)**

Example 1.68

A **30 μF capacitor is connected across a 400 V, 50 Hz supply. Calculate:**

(a) **the reactance of the capacitor;**
(b) **the current.**

(a) From expression [1.44]:

$$\text{reactance } X_C = \frac{1}{2 \times 3.14 \times 50 \times 30 \times 10^{-6}} = 106.2\ \Omega$$

(b) From expression [1.43]:

$$\text{Current} = \frac{400}{106.2} = 3.77\ \text{A}$$

Analogies of a capacitance in an a.c. circuit

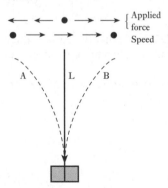

Fig. 1.130 Mechanical analogy of a capacitive circuit

If a piston P is moved backwards and forwards, the to-and-fro movement of the water causes the diaphragm to be distended in alternate directions. This hydraulic analogy, when applied to capacitance in an a.c. circuit, becomes rather complicated owing to the inertia of the water and of the piston, and as we do not want to take the effect of inertia into account at this stage, it is more convenient to consider a very light flexible strip L (Fig. 1.130), such as a metre rule, having one end rigidly clamped. Let us apply an alternating force comparatively slowly by hand so as to oscillate L between positions A and B.

When L is in position A, the applied force is at its maximum towards the *left*. As the force is reduced, L moves towards the *right*. Immediately L has passed the centre position, the applied force has to be increased towards the right, while the speed in this direction is decreasing. These variations are indicated by the lengths of the arrows in Fig. 1.130. From the latter it is seen that the speed towards the right is a maximum a quarter of a cycle before the applied force is a maximum in the same direction. The speed is therefore the analogue of the alternating current, and the applied force is that of the applied voltage. Hence capacitance in an electrical circuit is analogous to elasticity in mechanics, whereas inductance is analogous to inertia (see 'Mechanical analogy of an inductive circuit', p. 134).

**Resistance and
capacitance in series**

The effect of connecting resistance and capacitance in series is illustrated in Fig. 1.131. The current is again taken as reference.

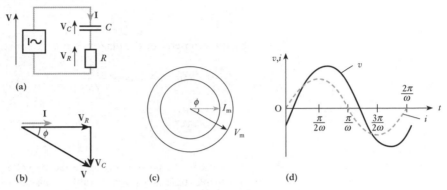

(a)

(b)

(c)

(d)

Fig. 1.131 Resistance and capacitance in series. (a) Circuit diagram; (b) phasor diagram; (c) instantaneous phasor diagram; (d) wave diagram

The circuit voltage is derived from the following relations:

$\mathbf{V}_R = \mathbf{I}R$, where $\mathbf{V}_R$ is in phase with $\mathbf{I}$

$\mathbf{V}_C = \mathbf{I}X_C$, where $\mathbf{V}_C$ lags $\mathbf{I}$ by $90°$

$\mathbf{V} = \mathbf{V}_R + \mathbf{V}_C$ (phasor sum)

Also

$$V = (V_R^2 + V_C^2)^{\frac{1}{2}}$$

$$= (I^2 R^2 + I^2 X_C^2)^{\frac{1}{2}}$$

$$= I(R^2 + X_C^2)^{\frac{1}{2}}$$

Hence $V = IZ$

where $Z = (R^2 + X_C^2)^{\frac{1}{2}}$ [1.45]

and $Z = \left(R^2 + \dfrac{1}{\omega^2 C^2} \right)^{\frac{1}{2}}$

Again Z is the impedance of the circuit. For any given frequency, the impedance remains constant and is thus the constant used in Ohm's law, i.e. the impedance is the ratio of the voltage across the circuit to the current flowing through it, other conditions remaining unchanged.

The instantaneous phasor diagram, and the resulting wave diagram, show that the current leads the applied voltage by a phase angle greater than $0°$ but less than $90°$. The phase angle between voltage and current is determined by the ratio of resistance to capacitive reactance in the circuit. The greater the value of this ratio, the less will be the angle ϕ. This can be illustrated by drawing the impedance triangle for the circuit, as shown in Fig. 1.132.

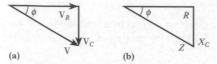

Fig. 1.132 Voltage and impedance diagrams. (a) Voltage diagram; (b) impedance diagram

By the geometry of the diagram:

$$\phi = \tan^{-1}\frac{V_C}{V_R} = \tan^{-1}\frac{IX_C}{IR}$$

$$\phi = \tan^{-1}\frac{X_C}{R} \qquad\qquad [1.46]$$

To emphasize that the current leads the voltage, it is usual either to give the resulting angle as a positive value or else to use the word 'lead' after the angle. This is illustrated in Example 1.69.

The phase angle can also be derived as follows:

$$\phi = \cos^{-1}\frac{V_R}{V} = \cos^{-1}\frac{R}{Z}$$

$$\phi = \cos^{-1}\frac{R}{\left(R^2 + \dfrac{1}{\omega^2 C^2}\right)^{\frac{1}{2}}} \qquad\qquad [1.47]$$

Example 1.69

A capacitor of 8.0 μF takes a current of 1.0 A when the alternating voltage applied across it is 230 V. Calculate:

(a) the frequency of the applied voltage;
(b) the resistance to be connected in series with the capacitor to reduce the current in the circuit to 0.5 A at the same frequency;
(c) the phase angle of the resulting circuit.

(a) $X_C = \dfrac{V}{I} = \dfrac{230}{1.0} = 230\ \Omega$

$$= \frac{1}{2\pi fC}$$

∴ $f = \dfrac{1}{2\pi CX_C} = \dfrac{1}{2\pi \times 8 \times 10^{-6} \times 230} = 86.5\ \text{Hz}$

(b) When a resistance is connected in series with the capacitor, the circuit is now as given in Fig. 1.133.

$$Z = \frac{V}{I} = \frac{230}{0.5} = 460\ \Omega$$

$$= (R^2 + X_C^2)^{\frac{1}{2}}$$

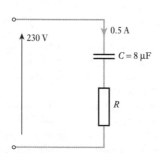

Fig. 1.133 Circuit diagram for Example 1.69

but $X_C = 230 \ \Omega$

hence $R = 398 \ \Omega$

(c) $\phi = \cos^{-1} \dfrac{R}{Z} = \cos^{-1} \dfrac{398}{460} = +30° \text{ or } 30° \text{ lead}$

Alternating current in an *RLC* circuit

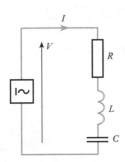

Fig. 1.134 Circuit with R, L and C in series

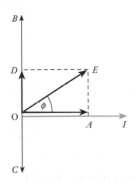

Fig. 1.135 Phasor diagram for Fig. 1.134

We have already considered resistive, inductive and capacitive circuits separately. However, we know that a practical inductor possesses inductance and resistance effectively in series. It follows that our analysis of R and L in series is equivalent to the analysis of a circuit including a practical inductor.

We can now consider the general case of R, L and C in series. This combines the instances of R and L in series with that of R and C in series. However, by producing the general case, we can adapt the results to the other two cases by merely omitting the capacitive or the inductive reactance from the expressions derived for the general case.

Before we start the general analysis, let us remind ourselves about the drawing of the phasor diagrams. Sometimes it is hard to know where to start, but the rule is simple: start with the quantity that is common to the components of the circuit. We are dealing with a series circuit, therefore the current is the common quantity so that in Fig. 1.135 the current phasor is the first to be drawn. Later we will come to parallel circuits in which case the voltage is the common quantity, hence the voltage phasor is the first to be drawn.

Figure 1.134 shows a circuit having resistance R ohms, inductance L henrys and capacitance C farads in series, connected across an a.c. supply of V volts (r.m.s.) at a frequency of f hertz. Let I be the r.m.s. value of the current in amperes.

From 'Alternating current in a resistive circuit', p. 129, the p.d. across R is RI volts in phase with the current and is represented by phasor OA in phase with OI in Fig. 1.135. From 'Current and voltage in an inductive circuit', p. 132, the p.d. across L is $2\pi f L I$, and is represented by phasor OB, leading the current by 90°; and from section 'Alternating current in a capacitive circuit', p. 138, the p.d. across C is $I/(2\pi f C)$ and is represented by phasor OC lagging the current by 90°.

Since OB and OC are in direct opposition, their resultant is OD = OB − OC, OB being assumed greater than OC in Fig. 1.135; and the supply voltage is the phasor sum of OA and OD, namely OE. From Fig. 1.135,

$$\text{OE}^2 = \text{OA}^2 + \text{OD}^2 = \text{OA}^2 + (\text{OB} - \text{OC})^2$$

$$\therefore \qquad V^2 = (RI)^2 + \left(2\pi f L I - \frac{I}{2\pi f C} \right)^2$$

so that

$$I = \frac{V}{\sqrt{\left\{ R^2 + \left(2\pi f L - \dfrac{1}{2\pi f C} \right)^2 \right\}}} = \frac{V}{Z} \qquad [1.48]$$

where $Z = $ *impedance* of circuit in ohms

$$Z = \frac{V}{I} = \sqrt{\left\{ R^2 + \left(2\pi fL - \frac{1}{2\pi fC} \right)^2 \right\}}$$ [1.49]

From this expression it is seen that

$$\text{Resultant reactance} = 2\pi fL - \frac{1}{2\pi fC}$$

$$= \text{inductive reactance} - \text{capacitive reactance}$$

If ϕ is the phase difference between the current and the supply voltage

$$\tan \phi = \frac{AE}{OA} = \frac{OD}{OA} = \frac{OB - OC}{OA} = \frac{2\pi fLI - I/(2\pi fC)}{RI}$$

$$= \frac{\text{inductive reactance} - \text{capacitive reactance}}{\text{resistance}}$$

$\therefore$ $$\tan \phi = \frac{X_L - X_C}{R}$$ [1.50]

$$\cos \phi = \frac{OA}{OE} = \frac{RI}{ZI} = \frac{\text{resistance}}{\text{impedance}}$$

$\therefore$ $$\cos \phi = \frac{R}{Z}$$ [1.51]

and

$$\sin \phi = \frac{AE}{OE} = \frac{\text{resultant reactance}}{\text{impedance}}$$

$\therefore$ $$\sin \phi = \frac{X}{Z}$$ [1.52]

If the inductive reactance is greater than the capacitive reactance, $\tan \phi$ is positive and the current lags the supply voltage by an angle ϕ; if less, $\tan \phi$ is negative, signifying that the current leads the supply voltage by an angle ϕ. Note the case where $X_L = X_C$, and $I = V/R$. The current is in phase with the voltage. This condition is termed series resonance and is discussed later in the chapter (see 'Resonance in AC circuits', p. 175).

Example 1.70   A coil having a resistance of 12 Ω and an inductance of 0.1 H is connected across a 100 V, 50 Hz supply. Calculate:

(a) the reactance and the impedance of the coil;
(b) the current;
(c) the phase difference between the current and the applied voltage.

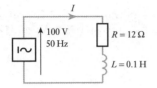

Fig. 1.136 Circuit diagram for Example 1.70

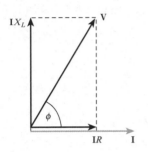

Fig. 1.137 Phasor diagram for Example 1.70

When solving problems of this kind, students should first of all draw a circuit diagram (Fig. 1.136) and insert all the known quantities. They should then proceed with the phasor diagram (Fig. 1.137). It is not essential to draw the phasor diagram to exact scale, but it is helpful to draw it approximately correctly since it is then easy to make a rough check of the calculated values.

(a)   Reactance $= X_L = 2\pi fL$

$$= 2\pi \times 50 \times 0.1 = 31.4 \ \Omega$$

Impedance $= Z = \sqrt{(R^2 + X_L^2)}$

$$= \sqrt{(12^2 + 31.4^2)} = 33.6 \ \Omega$$

(b)   Current $= I = \dfrac{V}{Z} = \dfrac{100}{33.6} = 2.97$ A

(c) $\tan \phi = \dfrac{X}{R} = \dfrac{31.4}{12} = 2.617$

∴ $\phi = 69°$

Example 1.71   A metal-filament lamp, rated at 750 W, 100 V, is to be connected in series with a capacitor across a 230 V, 60 Hz supply. Calculate:

(a) the capacitance required;
(b) the phase angle between the current and the supply voltage.

(a) The circuit is given in Fig. 1.138, where R represents the lamp. In the phasor diagram of Fig. 1.139, the voltage $\mathbf{V}_R$ across R is in phase with the current $\mathbf{I}$, while the voltage $\mathbf{V}_C$ across C lags $\mathbf{I}$ by 90°. The resultant voltage $\mathbf{V}$ is the phasor sum of $\mathbf{V}_R$ and $\mathbf{V}_C$, and from the diagram:

$$V^2 = V_R^2 + V_C^2$$

∴ $(230)^2 = (100)^2 + V_C^2$

∴ $V_C = 270$ V

$$\text{Rated current of lamp} = \frac{750 \text{ W}}{100 \text{ V}} = 7.5 \text{ A}$$

From equation [1.43],

$$7.5 = 2 \times 3.14 \times 60 \times C \times 207$$

$$C = 96 \times 10^{-6} \text{ F} = 96 \ \mu\text{F}$$

(b) If ϕ is the phase angle between the current and the supply voltage

$$\cos \phi = \frac{V_R}{V} \quad \text{(from Fig. 1.139)}$$

$$= \frac{100}{230} = 0.435$$

$$\phi = 64°12'$$

Fig. 1.138 Circuit diagram for Example 1.71

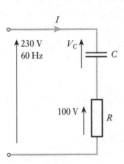

Fig. 1.139 Phasor diagram for Example 1.71

Example 1.72   A circuit having a resistance of 12 Ω, an inductance of 0.15 H and a capacitance of 100 μF in series, is connected across a 100 V, 50 Hz supply. Calculate:

(a) the impedance;
(b) the current;
(c) the voltages across R, L and C;
(d) the phase difference between the current and the supply voltage.

The circuit diagram is the same as that of Fig. 1.134.

(a) From equation [1.49],

$$Z = \sqrt{\left\{(12)^2 + \left(2 \times 3.14 \times 50 \times 0.15 - \frac{10^6}{2 \times 3.14 \times 50 \times 100}\right)^2\right\}}$$

$$= \sqrt{\{144 + (47.1 - 31.85)^2\}} = \mathbf{19.4\ \Omega}$$

(b) Current $= \dfrac{V}{Z} = \dfrac{100}{19.4} = \mathbf{5.15\ A}$

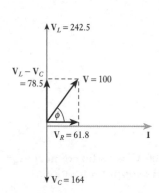

(c)   Voltage across $R = V_R = 12 \times 5.15 = 61.8$ V

Voltage across $L = V_L = 47.1 \times 5.15 = 242.5$ V

and   Voltage across $C = V_C = 31.85 \times 5.15 = 164.0$ V

Fig. 1.140   Phasor diagram for Example 1.72

These voltages and current are represented by the respective phasors in Fig. 1.140.

(d) Phase difference between current and supply voltage is

$$\phi = \cos^{-1} \frac{V_R}{V} = \cos^{-1} \frac{61.8}{100} = \mathbf{51°50'}$$

Or, alternatively, from equation [1.50],

$$\phi = \tan^{-1} \frac{47.1 - 31.85}{12} = \tan^{-1} 1.271 = \mathbf{51°48'}$$

Note: the determined values for ϕ are slightly different and this is because we have inferred too great an accuracy to the angles. Given that the input information is only accurate to two decimal places, it follows that the angles can only be given to about one decimal point of a degree, i.e. the answer might better be given as 51.8°.

Single-phase parallel networks

Basic a.c. parallel circuits

It is most common to think of circuits and networks being supplied from a voltage source. A circuit comprises a single load being supplied from the voltage source. However, there is no reason not to supply a second load from the same supply, in which case the loads are in parallel.

However, while it is relatively simple to consider parallel circuits supplied from a d.c. source, we have to allow for the phase difference between the currents in the parallel branches. It is therefore necessary to develop our analysis of a.c. parallel circuits.

Simple parallel circuits

There are two arrangements of simple parallel circuits which require analysis; these are resistance in parallel with inductance and resistance in parallel with capacitance.

When analysing a parallel circuit, it should be remembered that it consists of two or more series circuits connected in parallel. Therefore each branch of the circuit can be analysed separately as a series circuit and then the effect of the separate branches can be combined by applying Kirchhoff's first law, i.e. the currents of the branches can be added complexorially: that is, by phasor diagram.

The circuit for resistance and inductance in parallel is shown in Fig. 1.141(a). In the resistive branch, the current is given by

$$I_R = \frac{V}{R}, \text{ where } I_R \text{ and } V \text{ are in phase}$$

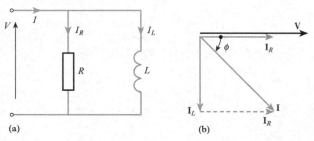

Fig. 1.141 Resistance and inductance in parallel. (a) Circuit diagram; (b) phasor diagram

In the inductive branch, the current is given by

$$I_L = \frac{V}{X_L}, \text{ where } \mathbf{I}_L \text{ lags } \mathbf{V} \text{ by } 90°$$

The resulting phasor diagram is shown in Fig. 1.141(b). The voltage which is common to both branches is taken as reference. Since parallel circuits are more common, this is one reason that it is usual to take the voltage as reference in circuit analysis. The total supply current I is obtained by adding the branch currents complexorially, i.e.

$$\mathbf{I} = \mathbf{I}_R + \mathbf{I}_L \quad \text{(phasor sum)} \qquad [1.53]$$

From the complexor diagram:

$$I = (I_R^2 + I_L^2)^{\frac{1}{2}}$$

$$= \left\{ \left(\frac{V}{R} \right)^2 + \left(\frac{V}{X_L} \right)^2 \right\}^{\frac{1}{2}}$$

$$= V \left(\frac{1}{R^2} + \frac{1}{X_L^2} \right)^{\frac{1}{2}}$$

$$\frac{V}{I} = Z = \cfrac{1}{\left(\cfrac{1}{R^2} + \cfrac{1}{X_L^2} \right)^{\frac{1}{2}}} \qquad [1.54]$$

It can be seen from the phasor diagram that the phase angle ϕ is a lagging angle.

$$\phi = \tan^{-1} \frac{I_L}{I_R} = \tan^{-1} \frac{R}{X_L} = \tan^{-1} \frac{R}{\omega L} \qquad [1.55]$$

Also $\qquad \phi = \cos^{-1} \dfrac{I_R}{I}$

$\therefore \qquad \phi = \cos^{-1} \dfrac{Z}{R} \qquad [1.56]$

In the case of resistance and capacitance connected in parallel, as shown in Fig. 1.142(a), the current in the resistive branch is again given by

$$I_R = \frac{V}{R}, \text{ where } \mathbf{I}_R \text{ and } \mathbf{V} \text{ are in phase}$$

In the capacitive branch, the current is given by

$$I_C = \frac{V}{X_C}, \text{ where } \mathbf{I}_C \text{ leads } \mathbf{V} \text{ by } 90°$$

The phasor diagram is constructed in the usual manner based on the relation

$$\mathbf{I} = \mathbf{I}_R + \mathbf{I}_C \quad \text{(phasor sum)} \qquad [1.57]$$

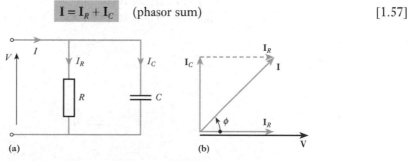

(a) (b)

Fig. 1.142 Resistance and capacitance in parallel. (a) Circuit diagram; (b) phasor diagram

From the phasor diagram:

$$I = (I_R^2 + I_C^2)^{\frac{1}{2}}$$

$$= \left\{ \left(\frac{V}{R}\right)^2 + \left(\frac{V}{X_C}\right)^2 \right\}^{\frac{1}{2}}$$

$$= V \left(\frac{1}{R^2} + \frac{1}{X_C^2}\right)^{\frac{1}{2}}$$

$$\frac{V}{I} = Z = \frac{1}{\left(\dfrac{1}{R^2} + \dfrac{1}{X_C^2}\right)^{\frac{1}{2}}} \qquad [1.58]$$

It can be seen from the phasor diagram that the phase angle ϕ is a leading angle. It follows that parallel circuits behave in a similar fashion to series circuits in that the combination of resistance with inductance produces a lagging circuit while the combination of resistance with capacitance gives rise to a leading circuit.

$$\phi = \tan^{-1}\frac{I_C}{I_R} = \tan^{-1}\frac{R}{X_C} = \tan^{-1} R\omega C \qquad [1.59]$$

Also $\qquad \phi = \cos^{-1}\dfrac{I_R}{I}$

$\therefore \qquad \phi = \cos^{-1}\dfrac{Z}{R} \qquad [1.60]$

Example 1.73

A circuit consists of a 115 Ω resistor in parallel with a 41.5 μF capacitor and is connected to a 230 V, 50 Hz supply (Fig. 11.3). Calculate:

(a) the branch currents and the supply current;
(b) the circuit phase angle;
(c) the circuit impedance.

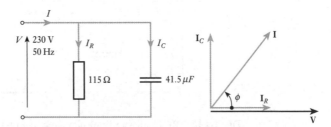

Fig. 1.143 Circuit and phasor diagrams for Example 1.73

$$I_R = \frac{V}{R} = \frac{230}{115} = 2.0 \text{ A}$$

$$X_C = \frac{1}{2\pi fC} = \frac{1}{2\pi 50 \times 41.5 \times 10^{-6}} = 76.7 \ \Omega$$

$$I_C = \frac{V}{X_C} = \frac{230}{76.7} = 3.0 \text{ A}$$

$$I = (I_R^2 + I_C^2)^{\frac{1}{2}} = (2.0^2 + 3.0^2)^{\frac{1}{2}} = 3.6 \text{ A}$$

$$\phi = \cos^{-1}\frac{I_R}{I} = \cos^{-1}\frac{2.0}{3.6} = 56.3° \text{ lead}$$

$$Z = \frac{V}{I} = \frac{230}{3.6} = 63.9 \ \Omega$$

Example 1.74   Three branches, possessing a resistance of 50 Ω, an inductance of 0.15 H and a capacitance of 100 μF respectively, are connected in parallel across a 100 V, 50 Hz supply. Calculate:

(a) the current in each branch;
(b) the supply current;
(c) the phase angle between the supply current and the supply voltage.

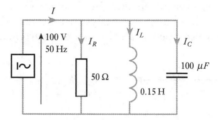

Fig. 1.144   Circuit diagram for Example 1.74

(a) The circuit diagram is given in Fig. 1.144, where I_R, I_L and I_C represent the currents through the resistance, inductance and capacitance respectively.

$$I_R = \frac{100}{50} = 2.0 \text{ A}$$

$$I_L = \frac{100}{2 \times 3.14 \times 50 \times 0.15} = 2.12 \text{ A}$$

and $I_C = 2 \times 3.14 \times 50 \times 100 \times 10^{-6} \times 100 = 3.14 \text{ A}$

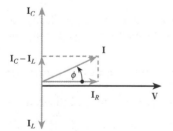

Fig. 1.145   Phasor diagram for Example 1.74

In the case of parallel branches, the first phasor (Fig. 1.145) to be drawn is that representing the quantity that is common to those circuits, namely the voltage. Then $\mathbf{I}_R$ is drawn in phase with $\mathbf{V}$, $\mathbf{I}_L$ lagging 90° and $\mathbf{I}_C$ leading 90°.

(b) The capacitor and inductor branch currents are in antiphase, hence the resultant of I_C and I_L is

$$I_C - I_L = 3.14 - 2.12$$
$$= 1.02 \text{ A, leading by } 90°$$

The current I taken from the supply is the resultant of I_R and $(I_C - I_L)$, and from Fig. 1.145:

$$I^2 = I_R^2 + (I_C - I_L)^2 = 2^2 + (1.015)^2 = 5.03$$
$$\therefore \qquad I = 2.24 \text{ A}$$

(c) From Fig. 1.145:

$$\cos \phi = \frac{I_R}{I} = \frac{2}{2.24} = 0.893$$
$$\phi = 26°45'$$

Since I_C is greater than I_L, the supply current leads the supply voltage by **26°45'**.

Parallel impedance circuits

The analysis of impedances in parallel is similar to that of the section 'Simple parallel circuits', p. 148 in that the voltage is taken as reference and the branch currents are calculated with respect to the voltage. However, the summation of the branch currents is now made more difficult since they do not necessarily remain either in phase or quadrature with one another. Thus before it is possible to analyse parallel impedance networks, it is necessary to introduce a new analytical device – current components.

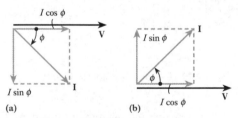

Fig. 1.146   Components of a current. (a) Lagging power factor; (b) leading power factor

Consider Fig. 1.146 in which the current **I** is shown to lag (or lead) the voltage **V** by a phase angle ϕ. This current may be made up by two components at right angles to one another:

1. $I \cos \phi$, which is in phase with the voltage and is termed the *active* or *power* component.
2. $I \sin \phi$, which is in quadrature with the voltage and is termed the *quadrature* or *reactive* component.

By the geometry of the diagram:

$$I^2 = (I \cos \phi)^2 + (I \sin \phi)^2$$

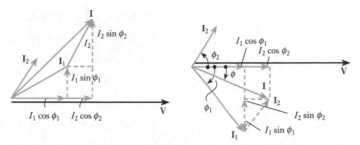

Fig. 1.147 Addition of current phasors

The reactive component will either lag (or lead) the voltage by 90° depending on whether the current **I** lags (or leads) the voltage **V**.

Consider the addition of the currents I_1 and I_2 as shown in Fig. 1.147, i.e.

$$\mathbf{I} = \mathbf{I}_1 + \mathbf{I}_2 \quad \text{(phasor sum)}$$

The value of **I** can be achieved by drawing a phasor diagram to scale, but this is not generally practicable. It can, however, be calculated if the currents are resolved into components, then

$$I \cos \phi = I_1 \cos \phi_1 + I_2 \cos \phi_2$$

$$I \sin \phi = I_1 \sin \phi_1 + I_2 \sin \phi_2$$

But $\quad I^2 = (I \cos \phi)^2 + (I \sin \phi)^2$

Hence $\quad I^2 = (I_1 \cos \phi_1 + I_2 \cos \phi_2)^2 + (I_1 \sin \phi_1 + I_2 \sin \phi_2)^2 \quad$ [1.61]

Also $\quad \phi = \tan^{-1} \dfrac{I_1 \sin \phi_1 + I_2 \sin \phi_2}{I_1 \cos \phi_1 + I_2 \cos \phi_2}$

$$\phi = \cos^{-1} \dfrac{I_1 \cos \phi_1 + I_2 \cos \phi_2}{I} \quad [1.62]$$

Example 1.75

A parallel network consists of branches A, B and C. If $\mathbf{I}_A = 10\angle{-60°}$ A, $\mathbf{I}_B = 5\angle{-30°}$ A and $\mathbf{I}_C = 10\angle{90°}$ A, all phase angles, being relative to the supply voltage, determine the total supply current.

With reference to the circuit and phasor diagrams in Fig. 1.148,

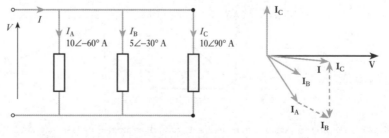

Fig. 1.148 Circuit and phasor diagrams for Example 1.75

$$\mathbf{I} = \mathbf{I}_A + \mathbf{I}_B + \mathbf{I}_C \quad \text{(phasor sum)}$$

$$I \cos \phi = I_A \cos \phi_A + I_B \cos \phi_B + I_C \cos \phi_C$$

$$= 10 \cos\angle-60° + 5 \cos\angle-30° + 10 \cos\angle90°$$

$$= 9.33 \text{ A}$$

$$I \sin \phi = I_A \sin \phi_A + I_B \sin \phi_B + I_C \sin \phi_C$$

$$= 10 \sin\angle-60° + 5 \sin\angle-30° + 10 \sin\angle90°$$

$$= -1.16 \text{ A}$$

The negative sign indicates that the reactive current component is lagging, so the overall power factor will also be lagging.

$$I = ((I \cos \phi)^2 + (I \sin \phi)^2)^{\frac{1}{2}}$$

$$= (9.33^2 + 1.16^2)^{\frac{1}{2}} = 9.4 \text{ A}$$

$$\phi = \tan^{-1} \frac{I \sin \phi}{I \cos \phi} = \tan^{-1} \frac{1.16}{9.33} = 7.1° \text{ lag}$$

$$\mathbf{I} = 9.4\angle-7.1° \text{ A}$$

Consider the circuit shown in Fig. 1.149 in which two series circuits are connected in parallel. To analyse the arrangement, the phasor diagrams for each branch have been drawn as shown in Figs 1.149(b) and 1.149(c). In each branch the current has been taken as reference; however, when the branches are in parallel, it is easier to take the supply voltage as reference, hence Figs 1.149(b) and 1.149(c) have been separately rotated and then superimposed on one another to give Fig. 1.149(d). The current phasors may then be added to give the total current in correct phase relation to the voltage. The analysis of the diagram is carried out in the manner noted above.

The phase angle for the network shown in Fig. 1.149(a) is a lagging angle if $I_1 \sin \phi_1 > I_2 \sin \phi_2$ and is a leading angle if $I_1 \sin \phi_1 < I_2 \sin \phi_2$. It should be noted, however, that this was only an example of the method of analysis. Both circuit branches could have been inductive or capacitive. Alternatively, there could have been more than two branches. The main concern of this study has been to illustrate the underlying principles of the method of analysis.

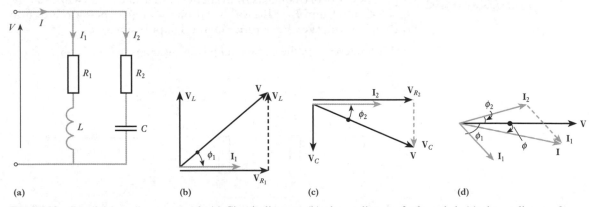

Fig. 1.149 Parallel–impedance network. (a) Circuit diagram; (b) phasor diagram for branch 1; (c) phasor diagram for branch 2; (d) phasor diagram for complete circuit

Example 1.76   A coil of resistance 50 Ω and inductance 0.318 H is connected in parallel with a circuit comprising a 75 Ω resistor in series with a 159 μF capacitor. The resulting circuit is connected to a 230 V, 50 Hz a.c. supply (Fig. 1.150). Calculate:

(a) the supply current;
(b) the circuit impedance, resistance and reactance.

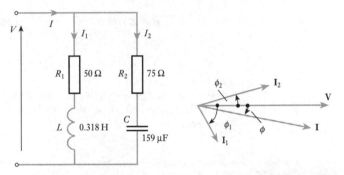

Fig. 1.150   Circuit and phasor diagrams for Example 1.76

(a) $X_L = 2\pi f L = 2\pi 50 \times 0.318 = 100 \ \Omega$

$Z_1 = (R_1^2 + X_L^2)^{\frac{1}{2}} = (50^2 + 100^2)^{\frac{1}{2}} = 112 \ \Omega$

$I_1 = \dfrac{V}{Z_1} = \dfrac{230}{112} = 2.05 \ \text{A}$

$\phi_1 = \cos^{-1}\dfrac{R_1}{Z_1} = \cos^{-1}\dfrac{50}{112} = \cos^{-1} 0.447 = 63.5° \ \text{lag}$

$\mathbf{I_1} = 2.05\angle{-63.5°} \ \text{A}$

$X_C = \dfrac{1}{2\pi f C} = \dfrac{1}{2\pi 50 \times 159 \times 10^{-6}} = 20 \ \Omega$

$Z_2 = (R_2^2 + X_C^2)^{\frac{1}{2}} = (75^2 + 20^2)^{\frac{1}{2}} = 77.7 \ \Omega$

$I_2 = \dfrac{V}{Z_2} = \dfrac{230}{77.7} = 2.96 \ \text{A}$

$\phi_2 = \tan^{-1}\dfrac{X_C}{R_2} = \tan^{-1}\dfrac{20}{77.7} = \tan^{-1} 0.267 = 15° \ \text{lead}$

In this last equation the solution incorporating the use of the tangent is used because ϕ_2 is relatively small.

$\mathbf{I_2} = 2.96\angle 15° \ \text{A}$

$\mathbf{I} = \mathbf{I_1} + \mathbf{I_2} \quad \text{(phasor sum)}$

$I \cos\phi = I_1 \cos\phi_1 + I_2 \cos\phi_2$

$= 2.05 \cos\angle{-63.5°} + 2.96 \cos\angle 15° = 3.77 \ \text{A}$

$$I \sin \phi = I_1 \sin \phi_1 + I_2 \sin \phi_2$$

$$= 2.05 \sin\angle{-63.5°} + 2.96 \sin\angle 15° = -1.07 \text{ A}$$

$$I = ((I \cos \phi)^2 + (I \sin \phi)^2)^{\frac{1}{2}} = (3.77^2 + 1.07^2)^{\frac{1}{2}}$$

$$= 3.9 \text{ A}$$

(b)
$$Z = \frac{V}{I} = \frac{230}{3.92} = 58.7 \ \Omega$$

$$R = Z \cos \phi = Z \cdot \frac{I \cos \phi}{I} = 58.7 \times \frac{3.77}{3.92} = 56 \ \Omega$$

$$X = Z \sin \phi = Z \cdot \frac{I \sin \phi}{I} = 58.7 \times \frac{1.07}{3.92} = 16 \ \Omega$$

Since $I \sin \phi$ is negative, the reactance must be inductive. Thus the circuit is equivalent to a 56 Ω resistor in series with a 16 Ω inductive reactance.

Polar impedances

In Example 1.76, the impedance was derived from the current and voltage. However, it may be questioned why could not the parallel impedances have been handled in a similar manner to parallel resistors? Consider then three impedances connected in parallel as shown in Fig. 1.151.

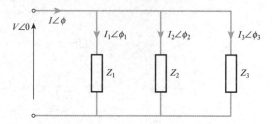

Fig. 1.151 Polar impedances in parallel

In the first branch

$$\mathbf{V} = \mathbf{I}_1 \mathbf{Z}_1$$

However, if consideration is given to the phase angles of **V** and **I** then to maintain balance, an impedance must also act like a complexor and have a phase angle, i.e.

$$V\angle 0 = I_1 \angle \phi_1 \cdot Z_1 \angle{-\phi_1}$$

The impedance phase angle is the conjugate of the circuit phase angle. This compares with the impedance triangles previously shown (apart from the reversal of the 'polarity').

In complexor notation:

$$\mathbf{I} = \mathbf{I}_1 + \mathbf{I}_2 + \mathbf{I}_3 \quad \text{(phasor sum)}$$

In polar notation:

$$I\angle\phi = I_1 \angle\phi_1 + I_2 \angle\phi_2 + I_3 \angle\phi_3$$

$$\therefore \qquad \frac{V\angle 0}{Z\angle -\phi} = \frac{V\angle 0}{Z_1\angle -\phi_1} + \frac{V\angle 0}{Z_2\angle -\phi_2} + \frac{V\angle 0}{Z_3\angle -\phi_3}$$

$$\therefore \qquad \boxed{\frac{1}{Z\angle -\phi} = \frac{1}{Z_1\angle -\phi_1} + \frac{1}{Z_2\angle -\phi_2} + \frac{1}{Z_3\angle -\phi_3}} \qquad [1.63]$$

This relation compares with that for parallel resistors, but it has the complication of having to consider the phase angles. Because of this, it is not considered, at this introductory stage, prudent to use the polar approach to the analysis of parallel impedances; the method used in Example 1.76 is more suitable and less prone to error.

It is most important that the impedance phase angles are not ignored. If we were to use the magnitudes only of the impedances, we would have the following statement **which is completely wrong!**

$$\frac{1}{Z} = \frac{1}{Z_1} + \frac{1}{Z_2} + \frac{1}{Z_3}$$

Always remember to use the phase angles!

A similar situation occurs when impedances are connected in series. Consider the case shown in Fig. 1.152.

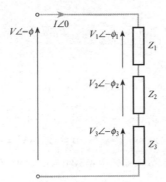

Fig. 1.152   Polar impedances in series

In complexor notation:

$$\mathbf{V} = \mathbf{V}_1 + \mathbf{V}_2 + \mathbf{V}_3 \quad \text{(phasor sum)}$$

In polar notation:

$$V\angle -\phi = V_1\angle -\phi_1 + V_2\angle -\phi_2 + V_3\angle -\phi_3$$

$$I\angle 0 \cdot Z\angle -\phi = I\angle 0 \cdot Z_1\angle -\phi_1 + I\angle 0 \cdot Z_2\angle -\phi_2 + I\angle 0 \cdot Z_3\angle -\phi_3$$

$$\boxed{Z\angle -\phi = Z_1\angle -\phi_1 + Z_2\angle -\phi_2 + Z_3\angle -\phi_3} \qquad [1.64]$$

However, it has been shown (see 'Alternating current in an *RLC* circuit', p. 143) that in a series circuit

$$Z\cos\phi = Z_1\cos\phi_1 + Z_2\cos\phi_2 + Z_3\cos\phi_3$$

hence $\qquad \boxed{R = R_1 + R_2 + R_3} \qquad [1.65]$

Similarly

$$X = X_1 + X_2 + X_3 \qquad [1.66]$$

As previously, it would have been incorrect to state that

$$Z = Z_1 + Z_2 + Z_3$$

It may therefore be concluded that, while it is practical to deal with impedances in series using polar notation, it is not practical to deal with impedances in parallel in this manner. Parallel network calculations are better approached on the basis of analysing the branch currents.

Example 1.77   Two impedances of $20\angle-45°$ Ω and $30\angle30°$ Ω are connected in series across a certain supply and the resulting current is found to be 10 A (Fig. 1.153). If the supply voltage remains unchanged, calculate the supply current when the impedances are connected in parallel.

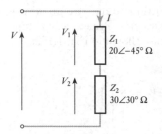

Fig. 1.153   Circuit diagram for Example 1.77. Impedances connected in series

$$R_1 = Z_1 \cos\angle-\phi_1 = 20 \cos\angle-45° = 14.1 \ \Omega$$

$$X_1 = Z_1 \sin\angle-\phi_1 = 20 \sin\angle-45° = -14.1 \ \Omega, \text{ i.e. capacitive}$$

$$R_2 = Z_2 \cos\angle-\phi_2 = 30 \cos\angle30° = 26.0 \ \Omega$$

$$X_2 = Z_2 \sin\angle-\phi_2 = 30 \sin\angle30° = 15.0 \ \Omega, \text{ i.e. inductive}$$

$$Z = \{(R_1 + R_2)^2 + (X_1 + X_2)^2\}^{\frac{1}{2}}$$

$$= \{(14.1 + 26.0)^2 + (-14.1 + 15.0)^2\}^{\frac{1}{2}}$$

$$= 40.1 \ \Omega$$

$$V = IZ = 10 \times 40.1 = 401 \ \text{V}$$

We now connect the impedances in parallel as shown in Fig. 1.154 and calculate the current in each branch.

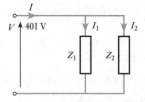

Fig. 1.154   Circuit diagram for Example 1.77. Impedance connected in parallel

$$I_1 = \frac{V}{Z_1} = \frac{401}{20} = 20.1 \text{ A}$$

$$\phi_1 = 45°$$

$$I_1 \cos \phi_1 = 20.1 \times 0.707 = 14.2 \text{ A}$$

$$I_1 \sin \phi_1 = 20.1 \times 0.707 = 14.2 \text{ A}$$

$$I_2 = \frac{V}{Z_2} = \frac{401}{30} = 13.4 \text{ A}$$

$$\phi_2 = -30°$$

$$I_2 \cos \phi_2 = 13.4 \times 0.866 = 11.6 \text{ A}$$

$$I_2 \sin \phi_2 = 13.4 \times (-0.50) = -6.7 \text{ A}$$

For total current

$$I \cos \phi = I_1 \cos \phi_1 + I_2 \cos \phi_2$$

$$= 14.2 + 11.6$$

$$= 25.8 \text{ A}$$

$$I \sin \phi = I_1 \sin \phi_1 + I_2 \sin \phi_2$$

$$= 14.2 - 6.7 = 7.5 \text{ A}$$

$$I = ((I \cos \phi)^2 + (I \sin \phi)^2)^{\frac{1}{2}}$$

$$= (25.8^2 + 7.5^2)^{\frac{1}{2}}$$

$$= \textbf{26.9 A}$$

Polar admittances

An alternative approach to parallel a.c. circuits using polar notation can be made through admittance instead of impedance. The admittance is the inverse of the impedance in the same way that the conductance is the inverse of the resistance. The admittance Y is measured in siemens (abbreviated to S).

Thus in any branch of a parallel network

$$\frac{V}{Z} = I = VY \qquad\qquad [1.67]$$

Admittance　　Symbol: Y　　Unit: **siemens (S)**

When the phase angles are included in this relation, it becomes

$$I\angle\phi = V\angle 0 \cdot Y\angle\phi = \frac{V\angle 0}{Z\angle -\phi}$$

$$Y\angle\phi = \frac{1}{Z\angle -\phi}$$

The resulting change in sign of the phase angle should be noted when the inversion takes place. Hence from relation [1.63]:

$$Y\angle\phi = Y_1\angle\phi_1 + Y_2\angle\phi_2 + Y_3\angle\phi_3 \qquad [1.68]$$

Hence $Y\cos\phi = Y_1\cos\phi_1 + Y_2\cos\phi_2 + Y_3\cos\phi_3$

$$G = G_1 + G_2 + G_3$$

Here G is the conductance of the circuit as in the d.c. circuit analysis. This must be the case since the current and voltage are in phase; this corresponds to the resistance of a circuit. Also

$$Y\sin\phi = Y_1\sin\phi_1 + Y_2\sin\phi_2 + Y_3\sin\phi_3$$

$$B = B_1 + B_2 + B_3$$

where B is termed the susceptance of the circuit and is the reactive component of the admittance.

Susceptance   Symbol: B Unit: **siemens (S)**

Figure 1.155(a) and (b) respectively show the impedance and admittance triangles.

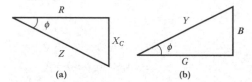

Fig. 1.155   (a) Impedance triangle and (b) admittance triangle for capacitive circuit

For the conductance

$$G = Y\cos\phi = Y\cdot\frac{R}{Z} = \frac{1}{Z}\cdot\frac{R}{Z}$$

$$\therefore \qquad G = \frac{R}{Z^2} \qquad [1.69]$$

For the susceptance

$$B = Y\sin\phi = Y\cdot-\frac{X}{Z} = \frac{1}{Z}\cdot-\frac{X}{Z}$$

$$\therefore \qquad B = -\frac{X}{Z^2} \qquad [1.70]$$

The negative sign in this expression is due to the change of sign of the phase angle noted above. Except in a purely resistive circuit, it must be remembered that $G \neq 1/R$.

Example 1.78   Three impedances $10\angle-30°\ \Omega$, $20\angle60°\ \Omega$ and $40\angle0°\ \Omega$ are connected in parallel (Fig. 1.156). Calculate their equivalent impedance.

$$Y_1\angle\phi_1 = \frac{1}{Z_1\angle-\phi_1} = \frac{1}{10\angle-30°} = 0.1\angle30°\ S$$

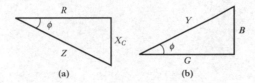

Fig. 1.156 Circuit diagram for Example 1.78

Similarly

$$Y_2\angle\phi_2 = 0.05\angle-60° \text{ S}$$

$$Y_3\angle\phi_3 = 0.025\angle0° \text{ S}$$

$$G = G_1 + G_2 + G_3$$

$$= 0.1 \cos\angle30° + 0.05 \cos\angle-60° + 0.025 \cos\angle0°$$

$$= 0.087 + 0.025 + 0.025 = 0.137 \text{ S}$$

$$B = B_1 + B_2 + B_3$$

$$= 0.1 \sin\angle30° + 0.05 \sin\angle-60° + 0.025 \sin\angle0°$$

$$= 0.05 - 0.043 + 0.0 = 0.007 \text{ S}$$

$$Y = (G^2 + B^2)^{\frac{1}{2}} = (0.137^2 + 0.007^2)^{\frac{1}{2}}$$

$$= 0.137 \text{ S}$$

$$\phi = \tan^{-1}\frac{B}{G} = \tan^{-1}\frac{0.007}{0.137} = 3°$$

$$Z\angle-\phi = \frac{1}{Y\angle\phi} = \frac{1}{0.137\angle3°} = 7.32\angle-3° \text{ }\Omega$$

Summary of important formulae	For R and L in parallel	
	$\mathbf{I} = \mathbf{I}_R + \mathbf{I}_L$ (phasor sum)	[1.53]
	For R and C in parallel	
	$\mathbf{I} = \mathbf{I}_R + \mathbf{I}_C$ (phasor sum)	[1.57]

Power in AC circuits

The impossible power

When alternating current systems were first introduced, learned scientists claimed that it was impossible to deliver energy by such a means. Their argument was that power transfer would take place during the first half of the cycle – and then it would transfer back during the second half.

Curiously there was some truth in what they claimed, but they had overlooked the basic relationship $p = i^2R$. The square of the current means that the power is positive no matter whether the current has a positive or a negative value. But it is only the resistive element that dissipates energy from the circuit. Inductors and capacitors do not dissipate energy which supports the theory of the impossible power.

Let us therefore examine in more detail the energy transfer process which takes place first in resistive circuits and then in reactive circuits.

Power in a resistive circuit

When an alternating current flows through a resistor of R ohms, the average heating effect over a complete cycle is I^2R watts, where I is the r.m.s. value of the current in amperes.

If V volts is the r.m.s. value of the applied voltage, then for a non-reactive circuit having constant resistance R ohms, $V = IR$.

The waveform diagrams for resistance are shown in Fig. 1.157. To the current and voltage waves, there have been added the waves of the product vi. Since the instantaneous values of vi represent the instantaneous power p, it follows that these waves are the power waves. Because the power is continually fluctuating, the power in an a.c. circuit is taken to be the average value of the wave.

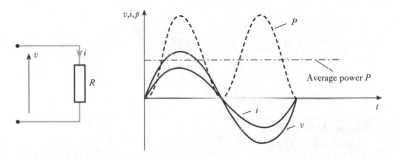

Fig. 1.157   Waveform diagrams for a resistive circuit

In the case of the pure resistance, the average power can be most easily obtained from the definition of the r.m.s. current in the circuit, i.e.

$$P = I^2R \tag{1.71}$$

This relation can also be expressed as

$$P = VI \tag{1.72}$$

Hence the power in a non-reactive circuit is given by the product of the ammeter and voltmeter readings, exactly as in a d.c. circuit.

The power associated with energy transfer from the electrical system to another system such as heat, light or mechanical drives is termed active power, thus the average given by I^2R is the active power of the arrangement.

Alternatively, the average power can be derived from a formal analysis of the power waveform.

$$P = \frac{\omega}{2\pi} \int_0^{\frac{2\pi}{\omega}} (V_m \sin \omega t \cdot I_m \sin \omega t)\, dt$$

$$= V_m I_m \frac{\omega}{2\pi} \int_0^{\frac{2\pi}{\omega}} (\sin^2 \omega t)\, dt$$

$$= V_m I_m \frac{\omega}{2\pi} \int_0^{\frac{2\pi}{\omega}} \left(\frac{1 - \cos 2\omega t}{2} \right) dt$$

From this relation it can be seen that the wave has a frequency double that of the component voltage and current waves. This can be seen in Fig. 1.157; however, it also confirms that the wave is sinusoidal although it has been displaced from the horizontal axis.

$$P = V_m I_m \frac{\omega}{2\pi} \left[\frac{t}{2} - \frac{\sin 2\omega t}{4\omega} \right]_0^{\frac{2\pi}{\omega}}$$

$$= V_m I_m \frac{\omega}{2\pi} \cdot \frac{2\pi}{2\omega}$$

$$P = \frac{V_m I_m}{2} \qquad\qquad\qquad [1.73]$$

$$P = VI$$

Power in a purely inductive circuit

Consider a coil wound with such thick wire that the resistance is negligible in comparison with the inductive reactance X_L ohms. If such a coil is connected across a supply voltage V, the current is given by $I = V/X_L$ amperes. Since the resistance is very small, the heating effect and therefore the active power are also very small, even though the voltage and the current are large. Such a curious conclusion – so different from anything we have experienced in d.c. circuits – requires fuller explanation if its significance is to be properly understood. Let us therefore consider Fig. 1.158, which shows the applied voltage and the current for a purely inductive circuit, the current lagging the voltage by a quarter of a cycle.

The power at any instant is given by the product of the voltage and the current at that instant; thus at instant L, the applied voltage is LN volts and the current is LM amperes, so that the power at that instant is LN × LM watts and is represented to scale by LP.

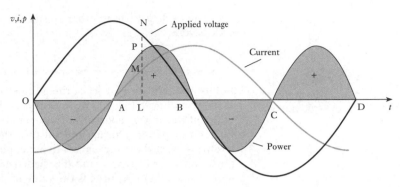

Fig. 1.158   Power curve for a purely inductive circuit

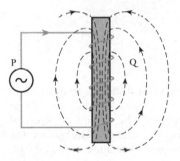

Fig. 1.159   Magnetic field of an
inductive circuit

By repeating this calculation at various instants we can deduce the curve representing the variation of power over one cycle. It is seen that during interval OA the applied voltage is positive, but the current is negative, so that the power is negative; and that during interval AB, both the current and the voltage are positive, so that the power is positive.

The power curve is found to be symmetrical about the horizontal axis OD. Consequently the shaded areas marked '−' are exactly equal to those marked '+', so that the mean value of the power over the complete cycle OD is zero.

It is necessary, however, to consider the significance of the positive and negative areas if we are to understand what is really taking place. So let us consider an a.c. generator P (Fig. 1.159) connected to a coil Q whose resistance is negligible, and let us assume that the voltage and current are represented by the graphs in Fig. 1.158. At instant A, there is no current and therefore no magnetic field through and around Q. During interval AB, the growth of the current is accompanied by a growth of flux as shown by the dotted lines in Fig. 1.159. But the existence of a magnetic field involves some kind of a strain in the space occupied by the field and the storing up of energy in that field, as already dealt with in section 8.10. The current, and therefore the magnetic energy associated with it, reach their maximum values at instant B; and, since the loss in the coil is assumed negligible, it follows that at that instant the whole of the energy supplied to the coil during interval AB, and represented by the shaded area marked '+', is stored up in the magnetic field.

During the interval BC the current and its magnetic field are decreasing; and the e.m.f. induced by the collapse of the magnetic flux is in the same direction as the current. But any circuit in which the current and the induced or generated e.m.f. are in the same direction acts as a source of electrical energy. Consequently the coil is now acting as a generator transforming the energy of its magnetic field into electrical energy, the latter being sent to generator P to drive it as a motor. The energy thus returned is represented by the shaded area marked '−' in Fig. 1.158; and since the positive and negative areas are equal, it follows that during alternate quarter-cycles electrical energy is being sent from the generator to the coil, and during the other quarter-cycles the same amount of energy is sent back from the coil to the generator. Consequently the net energy absorbed by the coil during a complete cycle is zero; in other words, the average power over a complete cycle is zero.

Power in a purely capacitive circuit

In this case, the current leads the applied voltage by a quarter of a cycle, as shown in Fig. 1.160; and by multiplying the corresponding instantaneous values of the voltage and current, we can derive the curve representing the variation of power. During interval OA, the voltage and current are both positive so that the power is positive, i.e. power is being supplied from the generator to the capacitor, and the shaded area enclosed by the power curve during interval OA represents the value of the electrostatic energy stored in the capacitor at instant A.

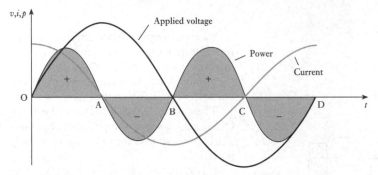

Fig. 1.160   Power curve for a purely capacitive circuit

During interval AB, the p.d. across the capacitor decreases from its maximum value to zero and the whole of the energy stored in the capacitor at instant A is returned to the generator; consequently the net energy absorbed during the half-cycle OB is zero. Similarly, the energy absorbed by the capacitor during interval BC is returned to the generator during interval CD. Hence the average power over a complete cycle is zero.

That the inductive and capacitive circuits do not dissipate power can be proved by an analysis of the power wave. Consider the case of the capacitor.

$$P = \frac{\omega}{2\pi} \int_0^{\frac{2\pi}{\omega}} (V_m \sin \omega t \cdot I_m \cos \omega t)\, dt$$

$$= V_m I_m \frac{\omega}{2\pi} \int_0^{\frac{2\pi}{\omega}} (\sin \omega t \cdot \cos \omega t)\, dt$$

$$= V_m I_m \frac{\omega}{2\pi} \int_0^{\frac{2\pi}{\omega}} \frac{\sin 2\omega t}{2} \cdot dt$$

$$= V_m I_m \frac{\omega}{2\pi} \left[-\frac{\cos 2\omega t}{4\omega} \right]_0^{\frac{2\pi}{\omega}}$$

$$P = 0 \qquad\qquad\qquad\qquad [1.74]$$

Power in a circuit with resistance and reactance

Let us consider the general case of the current differing in phase from the applied voltage; thus in Fig. 1.161(a), the current is shown lagging the voltage by an angle ϕ.

Let instantaneous value of voltage be

$$v = V_\mathrm{m} \sin \omega t$$

then instantaneous value of current is

$$i = I_\mathrm{m} \sin(\omega t - \phi)$$

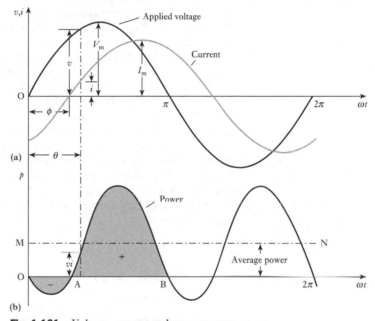

Fig. 1.161 Voltage, current and power curves

At any instant, the value of the power is given by the product of the voltage and the current at that instant, i.e. instantaneous value of power = vi watts.

By multiplying the corresponding instantaneous values of voltage and current, the curve representing the variation of power in Fig. 1.161(b) can be derived, i.e. instantaneous power is

$$vi = V_\mathrm{m} \sin \omega t \cdot I_\mathrm{m} \sin(\omega t - \phi)$$
$$= \tfrac{1}{2} V_\mathrm{m} I_\mathrm{m} \{\cos \phi - \cos(2\omega t - \phi)\}$$
$$= \tfrac{1}{2} V_\mathrm{m} I_\mathrm{m} \cos \phi - \tfrac{1}{2} V_\mathrm{m} I_\mathrm{m} \cos(2\omega t - \phi)$$

From this expression, it is seen that the instantaneous value of the power consists of two components:

1. $\tfrac{1}{2} V_\mathrm{m} I_\mathrm{m} \cos \phi$, which contains no reference to ωt and therefore remains constant in value.
2. $\tfrac{1}{2} V_\mathrm{m} I_\mathrm{m} \cos(2\omega t - \phi)$, the term $2\omega t$ indicating that it varies at twice the supply frequency; thus in Fig. 1.161(b) it is seen that the power undergoes two cycles of variation for one cycle of the voltage wave. Furthermore, since the average value of a cosine curve over a *complete* cycle is zero, it

follows that this component does not contribute anything towards the *average* value of the power taken from the generator.

Hence, average power over one cycle is

$$\tfrac{1}{2}V_\mathrm{m}I_\mathrm{m}\cos\phi = \frac{V_\mathrm{m}}{\sqrt{2}}\cdot\frac{I_\mathrm{m}}{\sqrt{2}}\cdot\cos\phi$$

$$\therefore \qquad \boxed{P = VI\cos\phi} \qquad\qquad\qquad [1.75]$$

where V and I are the r.m.s. values of the voltage and current respectively. In Fig. 1.161(b), the average power is represented by the height above the horizontal axis of the dotted line MN drawn midway between the positive and negative peaks of the power curve.

It will be noticed that during interval OA in Fig. 1.161(b), the power is negative, and the shaded negative area represents energy returned from the circuit to the generator. The shaded positive area during interval AB represents energy supplied from the generator to the circuit, and the difference between the two areas represents the net energy absorbed by the circuit during interval OB. The larger the phase difference between the voltage and current, the smaller is the difference between the positive and negative areas and the smaller, therefore, is the average power over the complete cycle.

The average power over the complete cycle is the active power, which is measured in watts.

The product of the voltage and the current in an a.c. circuit is termed the apparent power.

Apparent power   Symbol: S Unit: **voltampere (V A)**

$$\boxed{S = VI} \qquad\qquad\qquad [1.76]$$

$$\therefore \qquad P = VI\cos\phi$$

and $\qquad \boxed{P = S\cos\phi} \qquad\qquad\qquad [1.77]$

Example 1.79

A coil having a resistance of 6 Ω and an inductance of 0.03 H is connected across a 50 V, 60 Hz supply. Calculate:

(a) the current;
(b) the phase angle between the current and the applied voltage;
(c) the apparent power;
(d) the active power.

(a) The phasor diagram for such a circuit is given in Fig. 1.162.

$$\text{Reactance of circuit} = 2\pi fL = 2\times 3.14\times 60\times 0.03$$
$$= 11.31\ \Omega$$

From equation [1.38]

$$\text{Impedance} = \sqrt{\{6^2 + (11.31)^2\}} = 12.8\ \Omega$$

and $\qquad \text{Current} = \dfrac{50}{12.8} = 3.9\ \text{A}$

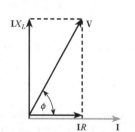

Fig. 1.162 Phasor diagram for Example 1.79

(b)   From equation [1.39]

$$\tan \phi = \frac{X}{R} = \frac{11.31}{6} = 1.885$$

$$\phi = 62°3'$$

(c)   Apparent power $S = 50 \times 3.91 = \mathbf{196\ V\ A}$

(d)   Active power = apparent power $\times \cos \phi$

$$= 195.5 \times 0.469 = \mathbf{92\ W}$$

Alternatively:

$$\text{Active power} = I^2 R = (3.91)^2 \times 6 = \mathbf{92\ W}$$

Example 1.80

An inductor coil is connected in series with a pure resistor of 30 Ω across a 230 V, 50 Hz supply. The voltage measured across the coil is 180 V and the voltage measured across the resistor is 130 V (Fig. 1.163). Calculate the power dissipated in the coil.

The complexor diagram is constructed by first drawing the complexor I (Fig. 1.164). The resistor voltage complexor V_R is then drawn in phase with I. Since neither the coil phase angle nor the circuit phase angle are known, it is necessary to derive the remainder of the diagram by construction to scale. Circles of radius V and V_{Lr} are drawn radiating from the appropriate ends of V_R. The point of intersection of the circles satisfies the relation

$$\mathbf{V} = \mathbf{V}_R + \mathbf{V}_{Lr} \quad \text{(phasor sum)}$$

By the geometry of the diagram:

$$V^2 = V_R^2 + V_{Lr}^2 + 2 V_R V_{Lr} \cos \phi_{Lr}$$

$$230^2 = 130^2 + 180^2 + 2 \times 130 \times 180 \times \cos \phi_{Lr}$$

$$\cos \phi_{Lr} = 0.077 \text{ lag}$$

$$I = \frac{V_R}{R} = \frac{130}{30} = 4.33 \text{ A}$$

$$P_r = V_{Lr} I \cos \phi_{Lr} = 180 \times 4.33 \times 0.077 = \mathbf{60\ W}$$

Alternatively:

$$Z_{Lr} = \frac{V_{Lr}}{I} = \frac{180}{4.33} = 41.5 \text{ Ω}$$

$$r = Z_{Lr} \cos \phi_{Lr} = 41.5 \times 0.077 = 3.20 \text{ Ω}$$

$$P_r = I^2 r = 4.33^2 \times 3.20 = \mathbf{60\ W}$$

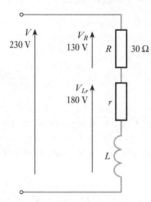

Fig. 1.163   Circuit diagram for Example 1.80

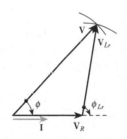

Fig. 1.164   Phasor diagram for Example 1.80

Power factor

In a.c. work, the product of the r.m.s. values of the applied voltage and current is VI. It has already been shown that the active power $P = VI \cos \phi$ and the value of $\cos \phi$ has to lie between 0 and 1. It follows that the active power P can be either equal to or less than the product VI, which is termed the apparent power and is measured in voltamperes (V A).

The ratio of the active power P to the apparent power S is termed the power factor, i.e.

$$\frac{\text{Active power } P \text{ in watts}}{\text{Apparent power } S \text{ in voltamperes}} = \text{power factor}$$

$\therefore$

$$\cos \phi = \frac{P}{S} = \frac{P}{VI}$$

[1.78]

or $\boxed{\text{Active power } P = \text{apparent power } S \times \text{power factor}}$ [1.79]

Comparison of expressions [1.75] and [1.78] shows that for *sinusoidal* voltage and current:

Power factor $= \cos \phi$

From the general phasor diagram of Fig. 1.135 for a *series* circuit, it follows that

$$\cos \phi = \frac{IR}{V} = \frac{IR}{IZ} = \frac{\text{resistance}}{\text{impedance}}$$

$\therefore$

$$\cos \phi = \frac{R}{Z}$$

[1.80]

It has become the practice to say that the power factor is *lagging* when the *current lags the supply voltage*, and *leading* when the *current leads the supply voltage*. This means that the supply voltage is regarded as the reference quantity.

Example 1.81

An inductor coil is connected to a supply of 230 V at 50 Hz and takes a current of 5.0 A. The coil dissipates 750 W (Fig. 1.165). Calculate:

(a) the resistance and the inductance of the coil;
(b) the power factor of the coil.

In this example, the symbol r will be used to denote the resistance of the coil instead of R. This is done to draw attention to the fact that the resistance is not a separate component of the circuit but is an integral part of the inductor coil. This device was also used in Example 1.80.

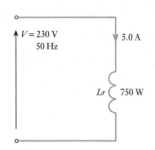

Fig. 1.165   Circuit diagram for Example 1.81

(a) $$Z = \frac{V}{I} = \frac{230}{5} = 46 \ \Omega$$

$$r = \frac{P}{I^2} = \frac{750}{5^2} = 30 \ \Omega$$

$$X_L = (Z^2 - r^2)^{\frac{1}{2}} = (46^2 - 30^2)^{\frac{1}{2}} = 34.87 \ \Omega$$

$$L = \frac{X_L}{2\pi f} = \frac{34.87}{2\pi 50} = \frac{34.87}{314} = 0.111 \ \text{H} = \textbf{111 mH}$$

(b)   Power factor $= \cos \phi = \dfrac{P}{S} = \dfrac{R}{VI} = \dfrac{750}{230 \times 5} = \textbf{0.65 lag}$

Active and reactive currents

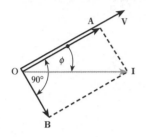

Fig. 1.166 Active and reactive components of current

If a current I lags the applied voltage V by an angle ϕ, as in Fig. 1.166, it can be resolved into two components, OA in phase with the voltage and OB lagging by 90°.

If the phasor diagram in Fig. 1.166 refers to a circuit possessing resistance and inductance in series, OA and OB must not be labelled I_R and I_L respectively. Such terms should only be applied to branch currents as would be the case if R and L were in parallel. This error of applying parallel terms to series circuits is easily made by beginners – **you have been warned!**

Since

$$\text{Power} = IV \cos \phi = V \times \text{OI} \cos \phi = V \times \text{OA watts}$$

therefore OA is termed the *active* component of the current, i.e.

$$\boxed{\text{Active component of current} = I \cos \phi} \qquad [1.81]$$

Power due to component OB is

$$V \times \text{OB} \cos 90° = 0$$

so that OB is termed the *reactive* component of the current, i.e.

$$\boxed{\text{Reactive component of current} = I \sin \phi} \qquad [1.82]$$

and   Reactive power Q in vars $= VI \sin \phi$

The term 'var' is short for voltampere reactive.

$\therefore \qquad \boxed{Q = VI \sin \phi} \qquad [1.83]$

also $\qquad P^2 + Q^2 = (VI \cos \phi)^2 + (VI \sin \phi)^2$

$$= (VI)^2(\cos^2\phi + \sin^2\phi) = (VI)^2 = S^2$$

$$\boxed{S^2 = P^2 + Q^2} \qquad [1.84]$$

Example 1.82

A single-phase motor operating off a 400 V, 50 Hz supply is developing 10 kW with an efficiency of 84 per cent and a power factor (p.f.) of 0.7 lagging. Calculate:

(a) the input apparent power;
(b) the active and reactive components of the current;
(c) the reactive power (in kilovars).

(a)   Efficiency $= \dfrac{\text{output power in watts}}{\text{input power in watts}}$

$$= \dfrac{\text{output power in watts}}{IV \times \text{p.f.}}$$

$\therefore \qquad\qquad 0.84 = \dfrac{10 \times 1000}{IV \times 0.7}$

so that $\qquad IV = 17\,000$ V A

$\therefore \qquad$ Input $= \textbf{17.0 kV A}$

(b)   Current taken by motor $= \dfrac{\text{input volt amperes}}{\text{voltage}}$

$$= \dfrac{17\ 000}{400} = 42.5\ \text{A}$$

therefore active component of current is

$$42.5 \times 0.7 = 29.75\ \text{A}$$

Since

$$\sin \phi = \sqrt{(1 - \cos^2\phi)} = \sqrt{\{1 - (0.7)^2\}}$$

$$= 0.714$$

therefore reactive component of current is

$$42.5 \times 0.714 = \mathbf{30.4\ A}$$

(c)   Reactive power $= 400 \times \dfrac{30.35}{1000}$

$$= \mathbf{12.1\ kvar}$$

Example 1.83

Calculate the capacitance required in parallel with the motor of Example 1.82 to raise the supply power factor to 0.9 lagging.

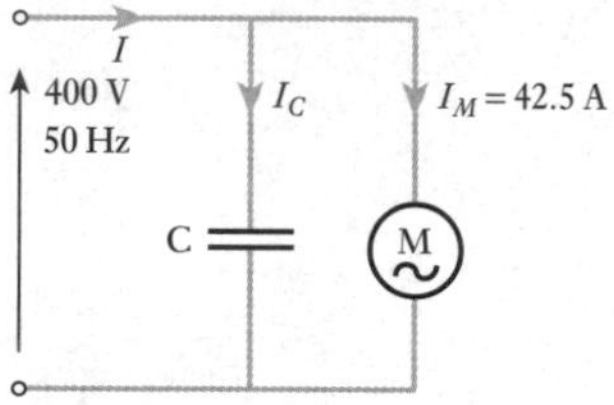

The circuit and phasor diagrams are given in Figs 1.167 and 1.168 respectively, M being the motor taking a current I_M of 42.5 A.

Current I_C taken by the capacitor must be such that when combined with I_M, the resultant current I lags the voltage by an angle ϕ, where $\cos \phi = 0.9$. From Fig. 1.168,

Active component of $I_M = I_M \cos \phi_M$

$$= 42.5 \times 0.7$$

$$= 29.75\ \text{A}$$

and active component of I is

$$I \cos \phi = I \times 0.9$$

These components are represented by OA in Fig. 1.168.

$$\therefore \qquad I = \dfrac{29.75}{0.9} = 33.06\ \text{A}$$

Reactive component of $I_M = I_M \sin \phi_M$

$$= 30.35\ \text{A (from Example 1.82)}$$

and reactive component of I is

$$I \sin \phi = 33.06\sqrt{\{1 - (0.9)^2\}}$$

$$= 33.06 \times 0.436$$

$$= 14.4\ \text{A}$$

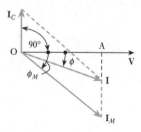

Fig. 1.167 Circuit diagram for Example 1.83

Fig. 1.168 Phasor diagram for Fig. 1.167

From Fig. 1.168 it will be seen that

$$I_C = \text{reactive component of } I_M - \text{reactive component of } I$$
$$= 30.35 - 14.4$$
$$= 15.95 \text{ A}$$

But $\qquad I_C = 2\pi f C V$

$\therefore \qquad 15.95 = 2 \times 3.14 \times 50 \times C \times 400$

and $\qquad C = 127 \times 10^{-6} \text{ F} = \mathbf{127 \, \mu F}$

From Example 1.83 it will be seen that the effect of connecting a **127** μF capacitor in parallel with the motor is to reduce the current taken from the supply from 42.5 to 33.1 A, without altering either the current or the power taken by the motor. This enables an economy to be effected in the size of the generating plant and in the cross-sectional area of conductor in the supply cable.

Example 1.84 An a.c. generator is supplying a load of 300 kW at a power factor of 0.6 lagging. If the power factor is raised to unity, how much more power (in kilowatts) can the generator supply for the same kilovolt-ampere loading?

Since the power in kW is number of kilovoltamperes × power factor, therefore number of kilovoltamperes is

$$\frac{300}{0.6} = 500 \text{ kV A}$$

When the power factor is raised to unity:

Number of kilowatts = number of kilovoltamperes = 500 kW

Hence increased power supplied by generator is

500 − 300 = **200 kW**

The practical importance of power factor

If an a.c. generator is rated to give, say, 2000 A at a voltage of 400 V, it means that these are the highest current and voltage values the machine can give without the temperature exceeding a safe value. Consequently the rating of the generator is given as 400 × 2000/1000 = 800 kV A. The phase difference between the voltage and the current depends upon the nature of the load and not upon the generator. Thus if the power factor of the load is unity, the 800 kV A are also 800 kW, and the engine driving the generator has to be capable of developing this power together with the losses in the generator. But if the power factor of the load is, say, 0.5, the power is only 400 kW, so that the engine is developing only about one-half of the power of which it is capable, though the generator is supplying its rated output of 800 kV A.

Similarly, the conductors connecting the generator to the load have to be capable of carrying 2000 A without excessive temperature rise. Consequently they can transmit 800 kW if the power factor is unity, but only 400 kW at 0.5 power factor for the same rise of temperature.

It is therefore evident that the higher the power factor of the load, the greater is the *active power* that can be generated by a given generator and transmitted by a given conductor.

The matter may be put another way by saying that, for a *given power*, the lower the power factor, the larger must be the size of the source to generate that power and the greater must be the cross-sectional area of the conductor to transmit it; in other words, the greater is the cost of generation and transmission of the electrical energy. This is the reason why supply authorities do all they can to improve the power factor of their loads, either by the installation of capacitors or special machines or by the use of tariffs which encourage consumers to do so.

Electronics engineers generally have little interest in power factor except when paying for their power supplies. Electronic circuits for the most part deal with such small levels of power that the additional heating effects due to the current not being in phase with the voltage are negligible.

Measurement of power in a single-phase circuit

Since the product of the voltage and current in an a.c. circuit must be multiplied by the power factor to give the active power in watts, the most convenient method of measuring the power is to use a wattmeter.

Summary of important formulae

For a general circuit

Active power $P = VI \cos \phi$ (watts)   [1.75]

Reactive power $Q = VI \sin \phi$ (vars)   [1.83]

Apparent power $S = VI$ (voltamperes)

Power factor (p.f.) $\cos \phi = P/S$ [1.78]

$$S^2 = P^2 + Q^2$$ [1.84]

Resonance in AC circuits

Introduction

When introducing a.c. circuits, a supply was defined by its voltage and frequency. For many applications, they are constant; for example, the source of supply to our homes. It is also true for many data and control circuit applications. However, many communications systems involve circuits in which either the supply voltage (in such applications it is usually called a signal) operates with a varying frequency, or a number of signals operate together, each with its own frequency. An understanding of communications systems including radio, television and telephones, as well as machine control systems, requires a knowledge of how circuits are affected by a variation of the frequency. In particular, the condition known as resonance will be investigated, which will be introduced by analysing the effect of frequency variation on the capacitive and inductive reactances of a series RLC circuit.

Frequency variation in a series *RLC* circuit

Let us consider the series RLC circuit in Fig. 1.169.

We have seen ('Alternating current in an RLC circuit, p. 143) that the impedance Z of this circuit is given by

$$Z = \sqrt{\left\{R^2 + \left(\omega L - \frac{1}{\omega C}\right)^2\right\}} \qquad [1.85]$$

The value of the reactance X of the circuit $\omega L - 1/(\omega C)$ (i.e. inductive reactance – capacitive reactance) will depend on frequency.

For the inductive reactance:

$$|X_L| = \omega L = 2\pi f L$$

which will increase with frequency.

For the capacitive reactance:

$$|X_C| = \frac{1}{\omega C} = \frac{1}{2\pi f C}$$

which is largest at low frequencies.

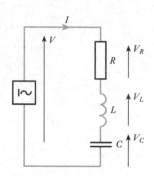

Fig. 1.169   Circuit with R, L and C in series

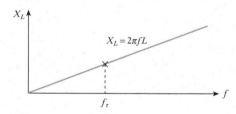

Fig. 1.170   Inductive reactance increases linearly with frequency

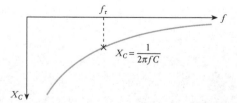

Fig. 1.171   Capacitive reactance decreases with frequency

By comparing Figs 1.170 and 1.171, it can be seen that:

- at frequency f_r, $|X_L| = |X_C|$ so the impedance Z, from equation [1.85], is purely resistive;
- below f_r, $|X_L| < |X_C|$ so the circuit is capacitive;
- above f_r, $|X_L| > |X_C|$ so the circuit is inductive.

The overall variation of the impedance $|Z|$ can be seen in Fig. 1.172. This figure shows that, for frequency f_r, the inductive reactance AB and the capacitive reactance AC are equal in magnitude so that the resultant reactance is zero. Consequently, the impedance is then only the resistance AD of the circuit. Furthermore, as the frequency is reduced below f_r or increased above f_r, the impedance increases and therefore the current decreases. The actual shapes and relative magnitudes of these curves depend on the actual values of R, L and C in the series resonant circuit.

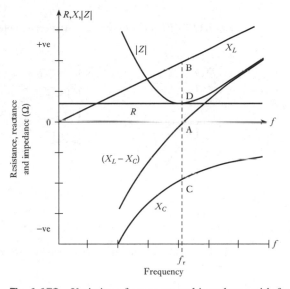

Fig. 1.172   Variation of reactance and impedance with frequency

Also, it will be seen from Fig. 1.173 that, when the frequency is f_r, the voltages across L and C are equal (but opposite in phase so they cancel) and each is much greater than the supply voltage. Such a condition is referred to as *resonance*, an effect that is extremely important in communications, e.g. radio, partly because it provides a simple method of increasing the sensitivity of a receiver and partly because it provides *selectivity*, i.e. it enables a signal of given frequency to be considerably magnified so that it can be separated from signals of other frequencies.

The phase of the circuit impedance (from equation [1.50]) is given by

$$\phi = \tan^{-1}\frac{(X_L - X_C)}{R} \qquad [1.86]$$

and will also depend on frequency as the values of X_L and X_C change. Figure 1.174 shows phasor diagrams of impedance below f_r, at f_r and above f_r.

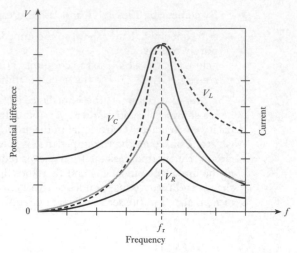

Fig. 1.173   Effect of frequency variation on voltages across R, L and C

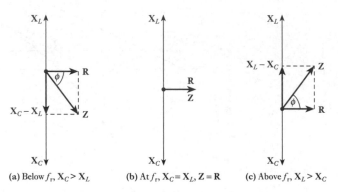

(a) Below f_r, $\mathbf{X}_C > \mathbf{X}_L$ **(b)** At f_r, $\mathbf{X}_C = \mathbf{X}_L$, $\mathbf{Z} = \mathbf{R}$ **(c)** Above f_r, $\mathbf{X}_L > \mathbf{X}_C$

Fig. 1.174   Impedance diagrams (a) below, (b) at and (c) above the resonant frequency

Hence it can be seen that:

- below resonance $X_L < X_C$, ϕ is negative, the circuit is capacitive;
- at resonance (f_r) $X_L = X_C$, ϕ is zero, the circuit is purely resistive;
- above resonance $X_L > X_C$, ϕ is positive, the circuit is inductive.

Figure 1.175 shows the overall variation of phase as the frequency is increased.

The resonant frequency of a series _RLC_ circuit

At the frequency f_r, $|X_L| = |X_C|$:

$$2\pi f_r L = \frac{1}{2\pi f_r C}$$

so $$\boxed{f_r = \frac{1}{2\pi \sqrt{(LC)}}}$$ [1.87]

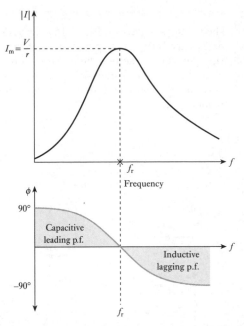

Fig. 1.175 Variation of magnitude $|I|$ and phase ϕ of current with frequency in a series RLC circuit

At this frequency f_r, known as the resonant frequency, $Z = R$ and $I = V/R$. The angular frequency ω_r, at resonance, is

$$\omega_r = \frac{1}{\sqrt{(LC)}}$$

The current in a series _RLC_ circuit

Since

$$I = \frac{V}{Z\angle\phi} = \frac{V\angle-\phi}{Z}$$

from equations [1.85] and [1.86]:

$$I = \frac{V}{\sqrt{\left\{R^2 + \left(\omega L - \dfrac{1}{\omega C}\right)^2\right\}}}\angle-\tan^{-1}\frac{(\omega L - 1/(\omega C))}{R} \qquad [1.88]$$

The variation of the magnitude and phase of the current with frequency is shown in Fig. 1.175. I is a maximum when $\omega L = 1/(\omega C)$, when the circuit is resistive ($\phi = 0$). Hence

$$I_m = \frac{V}{R}$$

**Voltages in a series
RLC circuit**

The voltages, shown in Fig. 1.169, across the inductor (V_L) and the capacitor (V_C) are 180° out of phase with each other. They are both 90° out of phase with the voltage across the resistor. The current I and V_R are always in phase. Figure 1.176 shows the phasor diagram of the voltages in the series *RLC* circuit below and above the resonant frequency and at the resonant frequency f_r.

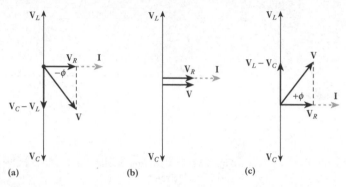

(a)　　　　　　　　　　(b)　　　　　　　　　　(c)

Fig. 1.176　Phasor diagram of series *RLC* circuit. (a) Capacitive, **I** leads **V**. Below resonant frequency f_r. (b) Resistive **V** and **I** in phase. At resonant frequency f_r. (c) Inductive, **I** lags **V**. Above resonant frequency f_r

Quality factor *Q*

At resonance, the voltages across L and C can be very much greater than the applied voltage:

$$V_C = IX_C \angle -90°$$

Substituting for I (refer to equation [1.88], and neglecting phase),

$$|V_C| = \frac{V \cdot X_C}{\sqrt{\{R^2 + (X_L - X_C)^2\}}} \qquad [1.89]$$

At resonance $X_L = X_C$, $\omega = \omega_r$ and $X_C = 1/(\omega_r C)$. So

$$V_C = \frac{V}{R}X_C$$

$$V_C = \frac{V}{\omega_r CR} = QV \qquad [1.90]$$

where　$Q = \dfrac{1}{\omega_r CR}$

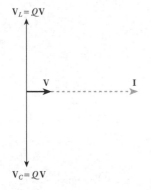

Fig. 1.177   Voltage magnification Q in series resonant circuit

Q is termed the Q factor or voltage magnification, because V_C equals Q multiplied by the source voltage V:

$$Q = \frac{1}{\omega_r CR} = \frac{\omega_r L}{R} \qquad [1.91]$$

Also, since $\omega_r = 1/\sqrt{(LC)}$

$$Q = \frac{1}{R}\sqrt{\frac{L}{C}} \qquad [1.92]$$

In a series RLC circuit, values of V_L and V_C can actually be very large at resonance and can lead to component damage if not recognized and subject to careful design. Figure 1.177 illustrates the voltage magnification in a series resonant circuit.

Example 1.85

A circuit, having a resistance of 4.0 Ω and inductance of 0.50 H and a variable capacitance in series, is connected across a 100 V, 50 Hz supply. Calculate:

(a) the capacitance to give resonance;
(b) the voltages across the inductance and the capacitance;
(c) the Q factor of the circuit.

(a) For resonance:

$$2\pi f_r L = 1/(2\pi f_r C)$$

∴
$$C = \frac{1}{(2 \times 3.14 \times 50)^2 \times 0.5}$$

$$= 20.3 \times 10^{-6} \text{ F} = \textbf{20.3 } \mu\textbf{F}$$

(b) At resonance:

$$I = \frac{V}{R} = \frac{100}{4} = 25 \text{ A}$$

∴   PD across inductance $= V_L \times 2 \times \pi \times 50 \times 0.5 \times 25$

$$= \textbf{3930 V}$$

and   PD across capacitor $= V_C - \textbf{3930 V}$

Or alternatively:

$$V_C = IX_C$$

∴
$$V_C = \frac{25 \times 10^6}{2 \times 3.14 \times 50 \times 20.3} = \textbf{3930 V}$$

(c) From equation [14.7]

$$Q \text{ factor} = \frac{2 \times 3.14 \times 50 \times 0.5}{4} = \textbf{39.3}$$

The voltages and current are represented by the respective phasors, but not to scale, in Fig. 1.176. Figure 1.178 shows how the current taken by this

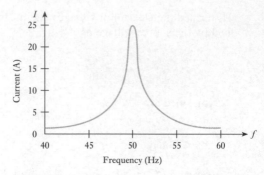

Fig. 1.178   Variation of current with frequency for circuit of Example 1.85

circuit varies with frequency, the applied voltage being assumed constant at 100 V.

Example 1.86

A coil of resistance 5.0 Ω and inductance 1.0 mH is connected in series with a 0.20 *μ*F capacitor. The circuit is connected to a 2.0 V, variable frequency supply (Fig. 1.179). Calculate the frequency at which resonance occurs, the voltages across the coil and the capacitor at this frequency and the *Q* factor of the circuit.

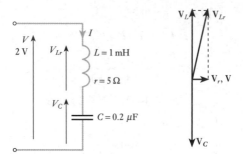

Fig. 1.179   Circuit and phasor diagrams for Example 1.86

Now

$$f_r = \frac{1}{2\pi\sqrt{(LC)}}$$

$$= \frac{1}{2\pi\sqrt{(1\times10^{-3}\times0.2\times10^{-6})}}$$

$$= 11.25 \text{ kHz}$$

and

$$I_r = \frac{V}{R} = \frac{2}{5} = 0.4 \text{ A}$$

$$X_L = X_C = 2\pi f_r L = 2\pi \times 11\,250 \times 1 \times 10^{-3} = 70.7 \ \Omega$$

$$Z_{Lr} = (r^2 + X_L^2)^{\frac{1}{2}} = (5^2 + 70.7^2)^{\frac{1}{2}} = 71.0 \ \Omega$$

so

$$V_{Lr} = I_r Z_{Lr} = 0.4 \times 71.0 = \mathbf{28.4\ V}$$

$$V_C = I_r X_C = 0.4 \times 70.7 = \mathbf{28.3\ V}$$

and

$$Q \text{ factor} = \frac{\omega_r L}{r} = \frac{70.7}{5} = \mathbf{14.1}$$

In Example 1.85 the voltages across the inductance and the capacitance at resonance are each nearly 40 times the supply voltage while the voltage magnification in Example 1.86 is about 14.

Oscillation of energy at resonance

The capacitive and inductive reactances store energy that oscillates between them, the energy being at one moment stored as electrostatic energy in the capacitor, and a quarter of a cycle later as magnetic energy in the inductor. At the resonant frequency, when the capacitive and inductive reactances are equal, they transfer equal energy, and the circuit appears resistive. The maximum magnetic energy stored in L at any instant is $\frac{1}{2}LI_m^2$ joules, where I_m is the maximum value of current in the inductor, and the maximum electrostatic energy in C at instant B is $\frac{1}{2}CV_m^2$ joules, where V_m represents the maximum value of the voltage across the capacitor. However, energy is dissipated as I^2R losses in the resistance of the circuit as the energy is passed backwards and forwards between L and C.

This leads to a more general definition of Q factor. It is defined as the ratio of the reactive power, of either the capacitor or the inductor to the average power of the resistor at resonance:

$$Q = \frac{\text{reactive power}}{\text{average power}} \qquad [1.93]$$

The lower the value of R, the lower is the power dissipated in the resistor. The value of Q is in turn higher and the more defined is the resonance peak.

For inductive reactance X_L at resonance:

$$Q = \frac{\text{reactive power}}{\text{average power}} = \frac{I^2 X_L}{I^2 R} = \frac{X_L}{R} = \frac{\omega_r L}{R}$$

as derived in equation [14.7].

For capacitive reactance X_C at resonance:

$$Q = \frac{\text{reactive power}}{\text{average power}} = \frac{I^2 X_C}{I^2 R} = \frac{X_C}{R} = \frac{1}{\omega_r CR}$$

as derived in equation [1.91].

Mechanical analogy of a resonant circuit

It was pointed out in 'Mechanical analogy of an inductive circuit' (p. 134) that inertia in mechanics is analogous to inMechanical analogy of an inductive ductance in the electrical circuit, and in 'Analogies of capacitance in an a.c. circuit' (p. 140) that elasticity is analogous to capacitance. A very simple mechanical analogy of an electrical circuit possessing inductance, capacitance

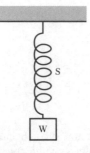

Fig. 1.180 Mechanical analogy of a resonant circuit

and a very small resistance can therefore be obtained by attaching a mass W (Fig. 1.180) to the lower end of a helical spring S, the upper end of which is rigidly supported. If W is pulled down a short distance and then released, it will oscillate up and down with gradually decreasing amplitude. By varying the mass of W and the length of S it can be shown that the greater the mass and the more flexible the spring, the lower is the natural frequency of oscillation of the system.

If W is set into a slight oscillation and then given a small downward tap each time it is moving downwards, the oscillations may be made to grow to a large amplitude. In other words, when the frequency of the applied force is the same as the natural frequency of oscillation, a small force can build up large oscillations, the work done by the applied force being that required to supply the losses involved in the transference of energy backwards and forwards between the kinetic and potential forms of energy.

Examples of mechanical resonance are very common; for instance, the rattling of a loose member of a vehicle at a particular speed or of a loudspeaker diaphragm when reproducing a sound of a certain pitch, and the oscillations of the pendulum of a clock and of the balance wheel of a watch due to the small impulse given regularly through the escapement mechanism from the mainspring.

Series resonance using complex notation

Consider the circuit diagram of Fig. 1.181 in which the inductive and capacitive reactances are presented in their complex form.

From Kirchhoff's voltage law:

$$V = V_R + V_L + V_C \quad \text{(phasor sum)}$$

$$= IR + Ij\omega L + \frac{I}{j\omega C}$$

$$= I\left\{ R + j\left(\omega L - \frac{1}{\omega C} \right) \right\}$$

$$\therefore \quad I = \frac{V}{R + j\left(\omega L - \dfrac{1}{\omega C} \right)} = \frac{V}{Z} \qquad [1.94]$$

At resonance, we have already seen that $\omega L = 1/(\omega C)$ and $Z = R$.

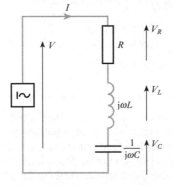

Fig. 1.181 Series resonant RLC circuit using j operator

Bandwidth

The bandwidth of a circuit is defined as the frequency range between the half-power points when $I = I_{max}/\sqrt{2}$. This is illustrated in Fig. 1.182.

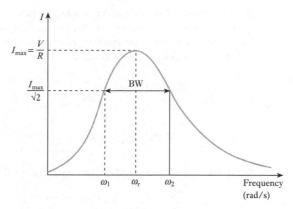

Fig. 1.182   The resonance peak, bandwidth and half-power frequencies

The bandwidth, BW, equals $\omega_2 - \omega_1$, where the frequencies ω_2 and ω_1 are referred to as half-power points or frequencies. They are also referred to as cut-off frequencies. The term half-power frequency can be justified by consideration of the conditions for maximum and half-power for the series RLC circuit.

At maximum power, when $\omega = \omega_r$,

$$I_{max} = \frac{V}{R}$$

$$\therefore \qquad P_{max} = I_{max}^2 R = \frac{V^2}{R}$$

At the half-power points

$$P_1 = P_2 = \frac{I_{max}^2 \cdot R}{2} = \left(\frac{I_{max}}{\sqrt{2}}\right)^2 \cdot R$$

Thus, the condition for half-power is given when

$$|I| = \frac{I_{max}}{\sqrt{2}} = \frac{V}{R\sqrt{2}}$$

The vertical lines either side of $|I|$ indicate that only the magnitude of the current is under consideration – but the phase angle will not be neglected. To obtain the condition for half-power in the circuit, when $|Z| = R\sqrt{2}$, refer to the impedance diagrams of Fig. 1.174. It can be deduced that this occurs both above and below the resonant frequency when, including the phase angle,

$$Z = R\sqrt{2}\angle\pm45°$$

or, to use the complex form,

$$Z = R(1 \pm j1)$$

Thus for half-power:

$$I = \frac{V}{R(1 \pm j1)} \quad \text{and} \quad Z = R(1 \pm j1) \tag{1.95}$$

Note that, at the half-power points, the phase angle of the current is 45°. Below the resonant frequency, at ω_1, the circuit is capacitive and $Z = R(1 - j1)$. Above the resonant frequency, at ω_2, the circuit is inductive and $Z = R(1 + j1)$. If we consider, from equation [1.94],

$$Z = R + j\left(\omega L - \frac{1}{\omega C}\right)$$

$$= R\left\{1 + j\left(\frac{\omega L}{R} - \frac{1}{\omega C R}\right)\right\}$$

at the half-power points, from equation [1.95],

$$\frac{\omega L}{R} - \frac{1}{\omega C R} = \pm 1$$

Since, from equation [1.91],

$$Q = \frac{1}{\omega_r C R} = \frac{\omega_r L}{R}$$

then, at the half-power points,

$$Q\left(\frac{\omega}{\omega_r} - \frac{\omega_r}{\omega}\right) = \pm 1$$

For ω_2:

$$Q\left(\frac{\omega_2}{\omega_r} - \frac{\omega_r}{\omega_2}\right) = 1 \tag{1.96}$$

For ω_1:

$$Q\left(\frac{\omega_1}{\omega_r} - \frac{\omega_r}{\omega_1}\right) = -1 \tag{1.97}$$

It can be deduced directly from equations [1.96] and [1.97] that

$$\omega_2 = \frac{\omega_r}{2Q} + \omega_r\sqrt{1 + \frac{1}{4Q^2}}$$

and

$$\omega_1 = \frac{-\omega_r}{2Q} + \omega_r\sqrt{1 + \frac{1}{4Q^2}}$$

Hence the bandwidth

$$\text{BW} = \omega_2 - \omega_1 = \frac{\omega_r}{Q}$$

i.e.

$$\text{Bandwidth} = \frac{\text{resonant frequency}}{Q \text{ factor}} \tag{1.98}$$

Note also that $\omega_1 \omega_2 = \omega_r^2$.

Selectivity

It can be deduced from equation [1.98] that the shape of the resonance curve depends on the Q factor. The bandwidth, the range of frequencies for which the power is greater than half-power, is narrower, the higher Q is.

A circuit is said to be selective if the response has a sharp peak and narrow bandwidth and is achieved with a high Q factor. Q is therefore a measure of selectivity. It should be noted that in practice the curve of $|I|$ against ω is not symmetrical about the resonant frequency. This can be observed in Fig. 1.183. In fact, the curve is the inverse of the impedance Z (see Fig. 1.172), but the larger the value of Q, the more symmetrical the curve appears about the resonant frequency. It can be assumed here that the resonant frequency lies at the midpoint of the bandwidth.

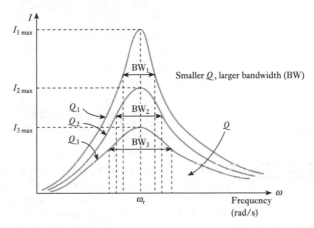

Fig. 1.183   The effect of Q on I_{max} and on the bandwidth (BW)

In order to obtain higher selectivity, Q must be large. Since

$$Q = \frac{\omega_r L}{R} = \frac{1}{\omega_r CR}$$

thus, for high selectivity, R must be small. This means that the total series resistance of the circuit including the source resistance must be small. Therefore a series tuned circuit must be driven by a voltage source having a low internal resistance if it is to exhibit a resonance peak and be selective. Examples 1.87 and 1.88 illustrate the design of series resonant circuits to be selective of a small range of frequencies, the bandwidth. Such circuits are the basis of circuits known as *bandpass* or *passband filters*.

Example 1.87

The bandwidth of a series resonant circuit is 500 Hz. If the resonant frequency is 6000 Hz, what is the value of Q? If $R = 10\ \Omega$, what is the value of the inductive reactance at resonance? Calculate the inductance and capacitance of the circuit.

From equation [1.98]:

$$\text{Bandwidth (BW)} = \frac{\text{resonant frequency}}{Q \text{ factor}}$$

Hence

$$Q = \frac{f_r}{BW} = \frac{6000}{500} = 12$$

From equation [1.91]:

$$Q = \frac{X_L}{R}$$

$$\therefore \quad X_L = QR = 12 \times 10 = 120 \ \Omega$$

$$X_L = 2\pi f_r L$$

$$\therefore \quad L = \frac{X_L}{2\pi f_r} = \frac{120}{2\pi 6000} = 3.18 \ \text{mH}$$

$$|X_L| = |X_C| = 120 \ \Omega$$

$$\therefore \quad X_C = \frac{1}{2\pi f_r C} = 120 \ \Omega$$

$$C = \frac{1}{2\pi \times 6000 \times 120} = 0.22 \ \mu\text{F}$$

Example 1.88

For the series resonant circuit in Fig. 1.184, calculate I at resonance. What are the voltages across the three series components, R, L and C? Calculate Q. If the resonant frequency is 6000 Hz find the bandwidth. What are the half-power frequencies and what is the power dissipated in the circuit at the two frequencies?

At the resonant frequency, $Z = R$.

$$\therefore \quad I_{max} = \frac{20\angle 0°}{4} = 5\angle 0°$$

$$V_R = I_{max} R = 5\angle 0° \times 4 \ \Omega$$

$$V_R = 20\angle 0° \ \text{V}$$

$$V_L = I_{max} X_L = 5\angle 0.20° \angle 90°$$

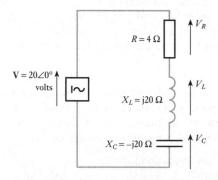

Fig. 1.184   Circuit for Example 1.88

$$V_L = 100\angle 90° \text{ V}$$

$$V_C = I_{max} X_C = 5\angle 0.20° \angle -90°$$

$$V_C = 100\angle -90° \text{ V}$$

$$Q = \frac{X_L}{R} = \frac{20}{4} = 5$$

From equation [1.98]:

$$\text{Bandwidth} = \frac{\text{resonant frequency}}{Q \text{ factor}}$$

$$\therefore \qquad \text{BW} = \frac{6000}{5} = \textbf{1200 Hz}$$

The half-power frequencies are at frequencies 600 Hz above and below the resonant frequency of 6000 Hz:

$$\therefore \qquad f_2 = 6000 + 600 = \textbf{6600 Hz}$$

$$f_1 = 6000 - 600 = \textbf{5400 Hz}$$

$$P_{max} = I_{max}^2 R$$

$$= 5^2 \times 4 \ \Omega$$

$$= 100 \text{ W}$$

At the half-power frequencies f_1 and f_2:

$$P_{\text{half-power}} = \frac{1}{2} P_{max} = \textbf{50 W}$$

Parallel resonance

Consider first the three-branch parallel resonant circuit in Fig. 1.185. In practice, the inductor L would have some resistance, so it is more practical to consider a circuit in which this is included, as will be discussed in 'The two-branch parallel resonant circuit' (p. 193). However, the mathematics involved in the analysis of Fig. 1.185 is simpler and important similarities with the series resonant circuit can be discussed.

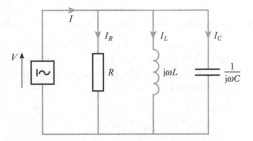

Fig. 1.185 The three-branch parallel resonant circuit

In Fig. 1.185, $V = IZ$, where Z is the net impedance of the three parallel branches. In parallel circuits of this nature, it is simpler to consider the total admittance Y of the three branches. Thus

$$V = IZ = \frac{I}{Y}$$

where $\quad Y = G + \dfrac{1}{j\omega L} + j\omega C$

$$= G - \frac{j}{\omega L} + j\omega C$$

$\therefore \qquad Y = G + j\left(\omega C - \dfrac{1}{\omega L}\right)$

so $\qquad V = \dfrac{I}{G + j\left(\omega C - \dfrac{1}{\omega L}\right)}$ [1.99]

Hence by comparison with the series resonant circuit equation [1.94], we have dual equations:

Series	Parallel

$$I = \frac{V}{R + j\left(\omega L - \dfrac{1}{\omega C}\right)} = \frac{V}{Z} \qquad V = \frac{I}{G + j\left(\omega C - \dfrac{1}{\omega L}\right)} = \frac{I}{Y}$$

Therefore, the same results apply, except that V is used instead of I, Y instead of Z and G instead of R. Thus for both a parallel and a series resonant circuit, resonance occurs when

$$\omega C = \frac{1}{\omega L}$$

Therefore: $\quad \omega_r = \dfrac{1}{\sqrt{(LC)}}$

At the resonant frequency, $Y = G$, the conductance of the parallel resistance, and $I = VG$.

Current magnification

At resonance, $|X_L| = |X_C|$. Note that the vertical lines either side of these symbols indicate that the magnitudes of the inductive and capacitive reactances are equal. (The phases are opposite.) From Fig. 1.185, at the resonant frequency ω_r,

$$I_L = \frac{V}{j\omega_r L}$$

Since, at resonance, $V = I/G$

$$I_L = \frac{I}{j\omega_r LG}$$

$$\therefore \qquad |I_L| = \frac{I}{\omega_r LG} = QI$$

where Q is the current magnification

$$\therefore \qquad Q = \frac{1}{\omega_r LG} = \frac{\omega_r C}{G} = \frac{B}{G} = \frac{R}{X} \qquad\qquad [1.100]$$

where B is the inductive or capacitive susceptance and X is the inductive or capacitive reactance.

By substituting $\omega_r = 1/\sqrt{(LC)}$ into equation [1.100],

$$Q = \frac{1}{G}\sqrt{\frac{C}{L}} = R\sqrt{\frac{C}{L}}$$

From equation [1.93], at resonance,

$$Q = \frac{\text{reactive power}}{\text{average power}}$$

For the parallel circuit:

$$Q = \frac{V^2/X}{V^2/R} = \frac{R}{X} = \frac{1}{\omega_r LG}$$

This is as expected from equation [1.100], which confirms that Q has the same inherent definition for both parallel and series circuits. It may appear, at first glance, that the expressions for Q for a series and a parallel resonant circuit are quite different. It will be shown, in 'The two-branch parallel resonant circuit' (p. 193), that they are the same. Meanwhile, it should be remembered that R and X in equation [1.100] are parallel circuit components – unlike R and X in the series circuit.

Parallel and series equivalents

It has already been mentioned that, in practice, the inductor L would have some resistance. It is more practical therefore to consider a circuit in which this is included, such as, for example, that of Fig. 1.186.

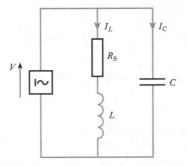

Fig. 1.186   The two-branch parallel resonant circuit

However, if the inductive branch of the circuit of Fig. 1.186, containing series inductance and resistance, can be represented mathematically as two parallel components of inductance and resistance, the analysis of the two-branch circuit will revert to that carried out in 'Parallel resonance' (p. 189) for a three-branch circuit. Consider, therefore, the circuits of Fig. 1.187.

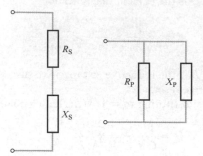

Fig. 1.187 Series and parallel equivalent circuits

For equivalence:

$$R_S + jX_S = \frac{R_P \cdot jX_P}{R_P + jX_P}$$

$$= \frac{(R_P - jX_P)R_P \cdot jX_P}{R_P^2 + X_P^2}$$

$$= \frac{R_P \cdot X_P^2}{R_P^2 + X_P^2} + j\frac{R_P^2 \cdot X_P}{R_P^2 + X_P^2}$$

$$= \frac{R_P}{1 + \dfrac{R_P^2}{X_P^2}} + j\frac{X_P}{1 + \dfrac{X_P^2}{R_P^2}}$$

Since, from equation [1.100], in a parallel circuit $Q = R_P/X_P$

$$R_S + jX_S = \frac{R_P}{1 + Q^2} + \frac{jX_P}{1 + \dfrac{1}{Q^2}}$$

Equating real and imaginary terms,

$$R_S = \frac{R_P}{1 + Q^2} \simeq \frac{R_P}{Q^2} \quad \text{when } Q \gg 1$$

$$X_S = \frac{X_P}{1 + Q^2} \simeq X_P \quad \text{when } Q \gg 1$$

Similarly

$$R_P = (1 + Q^2)R_S \simeq Q^2 R_S \quad \text{when } Q \gg 1$$

and

$$X_P = (1 + Q^2)X_S \simeq X_S \quad \text{when } Q \gg 1$$

It can be assumed that, in resonant circuits typically designed to have high Q factors, such an approximation is justified practically. These equivalents can now be used to analyse the two-branch parallel resonant circuit.

The two-branch parallel resonant circuit

As has already been mentioned, it is more practical to consider parallel resonance in the two-branch parallel circuit of Fig. 1.186. However, using the method described in 'Parallel and series equivalents' (p. 191), the series L and R of the coil can be converted into their parallel equivalent circuit after which the three-branch circuit analysis of 'Parallel resonance' (p. 189) applies. For series and parallel equivalence in Fig. 1.188, using the equivalents derived in 'Parallel and series equivalents' for high values of Q (>10):

$$R_P = Q^2 R_S \quad \text{and} \quad L_P = L_S$$

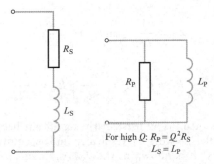

For high Q: $R_P = Q^2 R_S$
$L_S = L_P$

Fig. 1.188   Series and parallel equivalent circuits

Figure 1.186 can be redrawn as shown in Fig. 1.189.

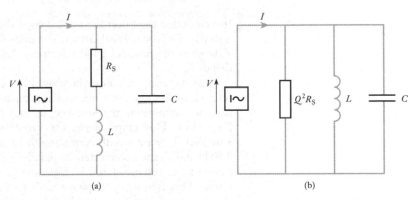

Fig. 1.189   (a) Two–branch and (b) equivalent three–branch parallel resonant circuits

The expressions developed in 'Parallel and series equivalents' now apply, i.e. equation [1.99] and $\omega_r = 1/\sqrt{(LC)}$. It should be noted again that, as explained in 'Current magnification' (p. 190), Q is the same for both parallel and series resonant circuits:

Series resonant circuit	Parallel resonant circuit

$$Q_S = \frac{\omega_r L}{R_S} \qquad\qquad Q_P = \frac{R_P}{\omega_r L}$$

$$\omega_r L = Q_S R_S \qquad\qquad \omega_r L = \frac{R_P}{Q_P}$$

Since $\quad Q_S = Q_P$

$$\omega_r L = Q_S R_S = \frac{R_P}{Q_P}$$

and $R_P = Q^2 R_S$ as expected.

Since

$$\omega_1^2 = \frac{1}{LC} \quad \text{and} \quad Q = \frac{\omega_r L}{R}$$

$$R_P = Q^2 R_S = \left(\frac{\omega_r L}{R_S}\right)^2 R_S = \frac{L}{CR_S}$$

This quantity is particularly significant because it is the impedance of the parallel network at resonance and is equivalent to a resistor of $L/(CR_S)$ ohms. It is known as the *dynamic resistance* and also, though it is wholly resistive, as the *dynamic impedance*:

$$Z_r = \frac{L}{CR_S} \tag{1.101}$$

It is clear that the lower the resistance of the coil, the higher is the dynamic impedance of the parallel circuit. For high-Q coils, R_S is small, which makes Z_r large as required for good selectivity. Example 1.89 illustrates a calculation of Z_r.

This type of circuit, when used in communication applications, is referred to as a *rejector*, since its impedance is a maximum and the resultant current a minimum at resonance, as may be observed from the graph of Fig. 1.190. This graph shows the variation of current with frequency in a parallel resonant circuit consisting of an inductor of 4.0 Ω resistance and 0.50 H inductance connected in parallel with a 20.3 μF capacitor across a constant a.c. voltage of 100 V. Equation [1.99] might be used to verify this result. This frequency response is that of a stopband filter, which allows all frequencies to pass except those lying within a small range of frequencies – the stopband. In this case the reject or stopband lies around the resonant frequency of the parallel resonant circuit, where the current is small.

In conclusion, it should be noted that a more exact expression for the resonant frequency in a two-branch parallel resonant circuit is given by:

$$f_r = \frac{1}{2\pi} \sqrt{\left(\frac{1}{LC} - \frac{R_S^2}{L^2}\right)}$$

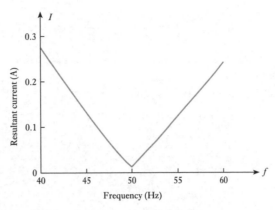

Fig. 1.190 Resonance curve for a rejector

If R_S is very small compared with $\omega_r L$, as in communications circuits,

$$f_r = \frac{1}{2\pi\sqrt{(LC)}}$$

which is the same as the resonant frequency of a series circuit. This is an acceptable approximation for the resonant frequency of the two-branch circuit for the purpose of understanding the principles of parallel resonance.

Example 1.89

A coil of 1 kΩ resistance and 0.15 H inductance is connected in parallel with a variable capacitor across a 2.0 V, 10 kHz a.c. supply as shown in Fig. 1.191. Calculate:

(a) the capacitance of the capacitor when the supply current is a minimum;
(b) the effective impedance Z_r of the network at resonance;
(c) the supply current.

The network supply current is a minimum when the network is in resonance.

(a) $$f_r = \frac{1}{2\pi\sqrt{(LC)}}$$

$$f_r^2 = \frac{1}{4\pi^2 LC}$$

$\therefore$ $$C = \frac{1}{4\pi^2 L f_r^2}$$

$$= \frac{1}{4\pi^2 \times 0.15^2 \times 10^8}$$

$$= 0.169 \times 10^{-8} = \mathbf{1.69\ nF}$$

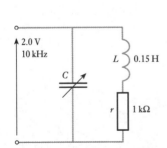

Fig. 1.191 Circuit diagram for Example 1.89

(b) $$Z_r = \frac{L}{CR_S} = \frac{0.15}{1.69 \times 10^{-9} \times 1000} = \mathbf{89\ k\Omega}$$

(c) $I_S = \dfrac{V}{Z_r} = \dfrac{2}{89 \times 10^3} = 22.5 \times 10^{-6}$ A

Summary of important formulae

For an *RLC* series circuit:

At the resonant frequency f_r

$$|X_L| = |X_C| \quad \text{so} \quad \omega_r L = \frac{1}{\omega_r C}$$

$$f_r = \frac{1}{2\pi \sqrt{(LC)}}$$

Q factor: $Q = \dfrac{1}{\omega_r CR} = \dfrac{\omega_r L}{R}$ [1.91]

$$Q = \frac{\text{reactive power}}{\text{average power}} \quad [1.93]$$

$$\text{Bandwidth (BW)} = \frac{\text{resonant frequency}}{Q \text{ factor}} \quad [1.98]$$

For a parallel *RLC* network:

Q factor: $Q = \dfrac{1}{\omega_r LG} = \dfrac{\omega_r C}{G} = \dfrac{B}{G} = \dfrac{R}{X}$ [1.100]

Resonant frequency: $f_r = \dfrac{1}{2\pi} \sqrt{\left(\dfrac{1}{LC} - \dfrac{R_S^2}{L^2} \right)}$

If R_S is very small compared with $\omega_r L$, as in communications circuits,

$$f_r = \frac{1}{2\pi \sqrt{(LC)}}$$

which is the same as the resonant frequency of a series circuit.

Dynamic impedance: $Z_r = \dfrac{L}{CR_S}$ [1.101]

Transformers

Introduction

One of the main advantages of a.c. transmission and distribution is the ease with which an alternating voltage can be increased or reduced. For instance the general practice is to generate at voltages about 22 kV, then step up by means of transformers to higher voltages for the transmission lines. At suitable points, other transformers are introduced to step the voltage down to values suitable for motors, lamps, heaters, etc. A medium-sized transformer has a full-load efficiency of about 97–98 per cent, so that the loss at each point of transformation is small (although 2 per cent of 100 MW is not insignificant!). Since there are no moving parts in a transformer, the amount of supervision is practically negligible.

Although transformers are generally associated with power system applications, they also occur in many low-power applications including electronic circuits. However, it is best to first consider the common power-system transformer.

The common form of transformer involves a ferromagnetic core in order to ensure high values of magnetic flux linkage. There are factors about the ferromagnetic core which affect the construction of transformers and rotating machines; these factors are responsible for part of the loss associated with power transfer and require a brief explanation before considering the principle of action of a transformer.

Core factors

The flux linking coils can be greatly improved by the introduction of a ferromagnetic core. Although this improved action has been explained by reference to the *B/H* characteristic, the explanation did not continue to consider the effect of varying the magnetizing force. When the core is energized from an a.c. source, the magnetizing force rises and falls in accordance with the magnetizing current which is basically sinusoidal. This variation does not cause *B* and *H* to vary according to the magnetic characteristic, but rather as shown in Fig. 1.192. This loop is called the *hysteresis loop*.

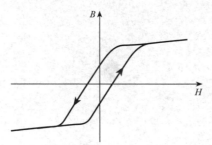

Fig. 1.192　Hysteresis loop

When drawn to scale, the larger the loop the greater the energy required to create the magnetic field – and this energy has to be supplied during each cycle of magnetization. This requirement of supplying energy to magnetize the core is known as the *hysteresis loss*. We need not explore it further at this stage, and it is sufficient to think of it as the cost we pay to get better magnetic linkage.

There is an unfortunate loss which is associated with the hysteresis loss. The varying flux in the core induces e.m.f.s and hence currents in the core material. These give rise to I^2R losses. These losses are called *eddy-current losses*.

The sum of the hysteresis loss and the eddy-current losses is known as the *core loss*. As with the I^2R losses in conductors, they are the imperfections which we have to accept, but it is better to consider them in detail after we understand the principle of machine action.

Principle of action of a transformer	Figure 1.193 shows the general arrangement of a transformer. A steel core C consists of laminated sheets, about 0.35–0.7 mm thick, insulated from one another. The purpose of laminating the core is to reduce the eddy-current loss. The vertical portions of the core are referred to as *limbs* and the top and bottom portions are the *yokes*. Coils P and S are wound on the limbs. Coil P is connected to the supply and is therefore termed the *primary*; coil S is connected to the load and is termed the *secondary*.

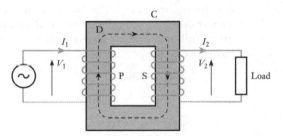

Fig. 1.193   A transformer

An alternating voltage applied to P circulates an alternating current through P and this current produces an alternating flux in the steel core, the mean path of this flux being represented by the dotted line D. If the whole of the flux produced by P passes through S, the e.m.f. induced in each turn is the same for P and S. Hence, if N_1 and N_2 are the number of turns on P and S respectively,

$$\frac{\text{Total e.m.f. induced in S}}{\text{Total e.m.f. induced in P}} = \frac{N_2 \times \text{e.m.f. per turn}}{N_1 \times \text{e.m.f. per turn}} = \frac{N_2}{N_1}$$

When the secondary is on open circuit, its terminal voltage is the same as the induced e.m.f. The primary current is then very small, so that the applied voltage V_1 is practically equal and opposite to the e.m.f. induced in P. Hence:

$$\frac{V_2}{V_1} \simeq \frac{N_2}{N_1} \tag{1.102}$$

Since the full-load efficiency of a transformer is nearly 100 per cent,

$$I_1 V_1 \times \text{primary power factor} \simeq I_2 V_2 \times \text{secondary power factor}$$

But the primary and secondary power factors at full load are nearly equal,

$\therefore$

$$\frac{I_1}{I_2} \simeq \frac{V_2}{V_1} \qquad [1.103]$$

An alternative and more illuminating method of deriving the relationship between the primary and secondary currents is based upon a comparison of the primary and secondary ampere-turns. When the secondary is on open circuit, the primary current is such that the primary ampere-turns are just sufficient to produce the flux necessary to induce an e.m.f. that is practically equal and opposite to the applied voltage. This magnetizing current is usually about 3–5 per cent of the full-load primary current.

When a load is connected across the secondary terminals, the secondary current – by Lenz's law – produces a demagnetizing effect. Consequently the flux and the e.m.f. induced in the primary are reduced slightly. But this small change can increase the difference between the applied voltage and the e.m.f. induced in the primary from, say, 0.05 per cent to, say, 1 per cent, in which case the new primary current would be 20 times the no-load current. The demagnetizing ampere-turns of the secondary are thus nearly neutralized by the increase in the primary ampere-turns; and since the primary ampere-turns on no load are very small compared with the full-load ampere-turns, full-load primary ampere-turns are approximately equal to full-load secondary ampere-turns, i.e.

$$I_1 N_1 \simeq I_2 N_2$$

so that

$$\frac{I_1}{I_2} \simeq \frac{N_2}{N_1} \simeq \frac{V_2}{V_1} \qquad [1.104]$$

It will be seen that the magnetic flux forms the connecting link between the primary and secondary circuits and that any variation of the secondary current is accompanied by a small variation of the flux and therefore of the e.m.f. induced in the primary, thereby enabling the primary current to vary approximately proportionally to the secondary current.

This balance of primary and secondary ampere-turns is an important relationship wherever transformer action occurs.

EMF equation of a transformer

Suppose the maximum value of the flux to be Φ_m webers and the frequency to be f hertz. From Fig. 34.3 it is seen that the flux has to change from $+\Phi_m$ to $-\Phi_m$ in half a cycle, namely in $\frac{1}{2f}$ seconds.

$\therefore$ Average rate of change of flux $= 2\Phi_m \div \dfrac{1}{2f}$

$$= 4f\Phi_m \text{ webers per second}$$

and average e.m.f. induced per turn is

$$4f\Phi_m \text{ volts}$$

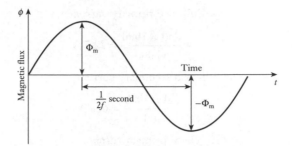

Fig. 1.194 Waveform of flux variation

But for a sinusoidal wave the r.m.s. or effective value is 1.11 times the average value,

$\therefore$ RMS value of e.m.f. induced per turn $= 1.11 \times 4f\,\Phi_m$

Hence, r.m.s. value of e.m.f. induced in primary is

$$E_1 = 4.44 N_1 f \Phi_m \quad \text{volts} \qquad\qquad [1.105]$$

and r.m.s. value of e.m.f. induced in secondary is

$$E_2 = 4.44 N_2 f \Phi_m \quad \text{volts} \qquad\qquad 1.106]$$

An alternative method of deriving these formulae is as follows.

If $\phi =$ instantaneous value of flux in webers

       $= \Phi_m \sin 2\pi f t$

therefore instantaneous value of induced e.m.f. per turn is $d\phi/dt$ volts

$d\phi/dt = 2\pi f \Phi_m \times \cos 2\pi f t$ volts

$$d\phi/dt = 2\pi f \Phi_m \times \sin(2\pi f t + \pi/2) \qquad\qquad [1.107]$$

therefore maximum value of induced e.m.f. per turn $= 2\pi f\,\Phi_m$ volts and r.m.s. value of induced e.m.f. per turn is

$0.707 \times 2\pi f \Phi_m = 4.44 f \Phi_m$ volts

Hence r.m.s. value of primary e.m.f. is

$E_1 = 4.44 N_1 f \Phi_m$ volts

and r.m.s. value of secondary e.m.f. is

$E_2 = 4.44 N_2 f \Phi_m$ volts

Example 1.90   A 250 kVA, 11 000 V/400 V, 50 Hz single-phase transformer has 80 turns on the secondary. Calculate:

     (a) the approximate values of the primary and secondary currents;
     (b) the approximate number of primary turns;
     (c) the maximum value of the flux.

(a) Full-load primary current

$$\simeq \frac{250 \times 1000}{11\,000} = 22.7 \text{ A}$$

and full-load secondary current

$$= \frac{250 \times 1000}{400} = 625 \text{ A}$$

(b) No. of primary turns

$$\simeq \frac{80 \times 11\,000}{400} = 2200$$

(c) From expression [35.5]

$$400 = 4.44 \times 80 \times 50 \times \Phi_{\mathrm{m}}$$

$$\Phi_{\mathrm{m}} = 22.5 \text{ mWb}$$

Phasor diagram for a transformer on no load

It is most convenient to commence the phasor diagram with the phasor representing the quantity that is common to the two windings, namely the flux Φ. This phasor can be made any convenient length and may be regarded merely as a reference phasor, relative to which other phasors have to be drawn.

In the preceding section, expression [1.107] shows that the e.m.f. induced by a sinusoidal flux leads the flux by a quarter of a cycle. Consequently the e.m.f. E_1 induced in the primary winding is represented by a phasor drawn 90° ahead of Φ, as in Fig. 1.195. Note that expression [1.107] is comparable to expression [1.33]; in the latter, we can replace LI by $N\phi$ and hence obtain [1.107].

The e.m.f. E_2 also leads the flux by 90°, but the effect which this produces at the terminals of the transformer depends on the manner in which the secondary winding is constructed and, more importantly, the manner in which the ends of the winding are connected to the transformer terminals. In practice, the normal procedure ensures that V_2 is in phase with V_1 and only a very few transformers depart from this arrangement.

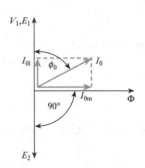

Fig. 1.195 Phasor diagram for transformer on no load

However, if V_2 and V_1 were drawn in phase with one another on Fig. 1.195, the diagram would become cluttered and therefore, for convenience, it is usual to show E_1 and E_2 in phase opposition with one another, thus ensuring that V_2 appears in the opposite quadrant of the phasor diagram from V_1. This gives the appearance that the voltages are in antiphase and it should be remembered that the manner of drawing is for convenience only and that the voltages are in fact in phase.

The values of E_2 and E_1 are proportional to the number of turns on the secondary and primary windings, since practically the whole of the flux set up by the primary winding is linked with the secondary winding when the latter is on open circuit. Another matter of convenience in drawing these transformer phasor diagrams is that it has been assumed that N_2 and N_1 are equal so that $E_2 = E_1$, as shown in Fig. 1.195.

Since the difference between the value of the applied voltage V_1 and that of the induced e.m.f. E_1 is only about 0.05 per cent when the transformer is on no load, the phasor representing V_1 can be drawn equal to that representing E_1. Since we have accepted that back e.m.f.s are treated as volt drops, V_1 and E_1 are drawn in phase with one another.

The no-load current, I_0, taken by the primary consists of two components:

1. A reactive or magnetizing component, I_{0m}, producing the flux and therefore in phase with the latter.*
2. An active or power component, I_{0l}, supplying the hysteresis and eddy-current losses in the core and the negligible I^2R loss in the primary winding. Component I_{0l} is in phase with the applied voltage, i.e. $I_{0l}V_1$ = core loss. This component is usually very small compared with I_{0m}, so that the no-load power factor is very low.

From Fig. 1.195 it will be seen that no-load current is

$$I_0 = \sqrt{(I_{0l}^2 + I_{0m}^2)} \qquad\qquad [1.108]$$

and power factor on no load is

$$\cos \phi_0 = I_{0l}/I_0 \qquad\qquad [1.109]$$

Example 1.91   A single-phase transformer has 480 turns on the primary and 90 turns on the secondary. The mean length of the flux path in the core is 1.8 m and the joints are equivalent to an airgap of 0.1 mm. The value of the magnetic field strength for 1.1 T in the core is 400 A/m, the corresponding core loss is 1.7 W/kg at 50 Hz and the density of the core is 7800 kg/m³.

If the maximum value of the flux density is to be 1.1 T when a p.d. of 2200 V at 50 Hz is applied to the primary, calculate:

(a) the cross-sectional area of the core;
(b) the secondary voltage on no load;
(c) the primary current and power factor on no load.

(a) From [1.105],

$$2200 = 4.44 \times 480 \times 50 \times \Phi_m$$

$$\Phi_m = 0.0206 \text{ Wb}$$

and cross-sectional area of core is

$$\frac{0.0206}{1.1} = 0.0187 \text{ m}^2$$

This is the net area of the core; the gross area of the core is about 10 per cent greater than this value to allow for the insulation between the laminations.

(b) Secondary voltage on no load is

$$2200 \times \frac{90}{480} = 413 \text{ V}$$

---

* The waveform of this component is discussed on p. 220.

(c) Total magnetomotive force for the core is

$$400 \times 1.8 = 720 \text{ A}$$

and magnetomotive force for the equivalent airgap is

$$\frac{1.1}{4\pi \times 10^{-7}} \times 0.0001 = 87.5 \text{ A}$$

Therefore total m.m.f. to produce the maximum flux density is

$$720 + 87.5 = 807.5 \text{ A}$$

therefore maximum value of magnetizing current is

$$\frac{807.5}{480} = 1.682 \text{ A}$$

Assuming the current to be sinusoidal, r.m.s. value of magnetizing current is

$$I_{0m} = 0.707 \times 1.682 = 1.19 \text{ A}$$

$$\text{Volume of core} = 1.8 \times 0.0187$$

$$= 0.0337 \text{ m}^3$$

$$\therefore \qquad \text{Mass of core} = 0.0337 \times 7800$$

$$= 263 \text{ kg}$$

and $$\text{Core loss} = 263 \times 1.7 = 447 \text{ W}$$

Therefore core-loss component of current is

$$I_{01} = \frac{447}{2200} = 0.203 \text{ A}$$

From equation [1.108],

$$\text{No-load current} = I_0$$

$$= \sqrt{\{(1.19)^2 + (0.203)^2\}}$$

$$= \mathbf{1.21 \text{ A}}$$

and from equation [1.109], power factor on no load is

$$\frac{0.203}{1.21} = \mathbf{0.168 \text{ lagging}}$$

Phasor diagram for an ideal loaded transformer

With this assumption, it follows that the secondary terminal voltage V_2 is the same as the e.m.f. E_2 induced in the secondary, and the primary applied voltage V_1 is equal to the e.m.f. E_1 induced in the primary winding. Also, if we again assume equal number of turns on the primary and secondary windings, then $E_1 = E_2$.

Let us consider the general case of a load having a lagging power factor $\cos \phi_2$; hence the phasor representing the secondary current I_2 lags V_2 by an angle ϕ_2, as shown in Fig. 1.196. Phasor $I_{2'}$ represents the component of the primary current to neutralize the demagnetizing effect of the secondary current and is drawn equal and opposite to I_2. Here $I_{2'}$ is described as 'I_2 referred'; I_0 is the no-load current of the transformer, already discussed in 'Phasor

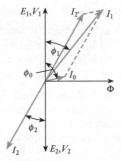

Fig. 1.196 Phasor diagram for a loaded transformer having negligible voltage drop in windings

diagram for a transformer on no load' (p. 202). The phasor sum of $I_{2'}$ and I_0 gives the total current I_1 taken from the supply, and the power factor on the primary side is cos ϕ_1, where ϕ_1 is the phase difference between V_1 and I_1.

In Fig. 1.196 the phasor representing I_0 has, for clarity, been shown far larger relative to the other current phasors than it is in an actual transformer.

Example 1.92 **A single-phase transformer has 1000 turns on the primary and 200 turns on the secondary. The no-load current is 3 A at a power factor 0.2 lagging when the secondary current is 280 A at a power factor of 0.8 lagging. Calculate the primary current and power factor. Assume the voltage drop in the windings to be negligible.**

If $I_{2'}$ represents the component of the primary current to neutralize the demagnetizing effect of the secondary current, the ampere-turns due to $I_{2'}$ must be equal and opposite to those due to I_2, i.e.

$$I_{2'} \times 1000 = 280 \times 200$$

$\therefore \qquad I_{2'} = 56 \text{ A}$

$$\cos \phi_2 = 0.8 \quad \therefore \sin \phi_2 = 0.6$$

and $\qquad \cos \phi_0 = 0.2 \quad \therefore \sin \phi_0 = 0.98$

From Fig. 1.196 it will be seen that

$$I_1 \cos \phi_1 = I_{2'} \cos \phi_2 + I_0 \cos \phi_0$$

$$= (56 \times 0.8) + (3 \times 0.2) = 45.4 \text{ A}$$

and $\qquad I_1 \sin \phi_1 = I_{2'} \sin \phi_2 + I_0 \sin \phi_0$

$$= (56 \times 0.6) + (3 \times 0.98) = 36.54 \text{ A}$$

Hence, $\qquad I_1^2 = (45.4)^2 + (36.45)^2 = 3398$

so that $\qquad I_1 = 58.3 \text{ A}$

Also, $\qquad \tan \phi_1 = \dfrac{36.54}{45.4} = 0.805$

so that $\qquad \phi_1 = 38°50'$

Hence primary power factor is

$$\cos \phi_1 = \cos 38°50' \equiv \mathbf{0.78 \text{ lagging}}$$

**Useful and
leakage fluxes
in a transformer**

When the secondary winding of a transformer is on open circuit, the current taken by the primary winding is responsible for setting up the magnetic flux and providing a very small power component to supply the loss in the core. To simplify matters in the present discussion, let us assume:

1. The core loss and the I^2R loss in the primary winding to be negligible.
2. The permeability of the core to remain constant, so that the magnetizing current is proportional to the flux.
3. The primary and secondary windings to have the same number of turns, i.e. $N_1 = N_2$.

Figure 1.197 shows all the flux set up by the primary winding passing through the secondary winding. There is a very small amount of flux returning through the air space around the primary winding, but since the relative

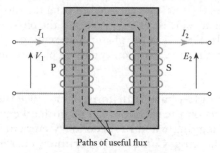

Paths of useful flux

Fig. 1.197   Transformer on no load

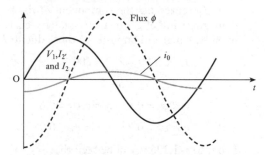

Fig. 1.198   Waveforms of voltages, current and flux of a transformer on no load

permeability of transformer core is of the order of 1000 or more, the reluctance of the air path is 1000 times that of the parallel path through the limb carrying the secondary winding. Consequently the flux passing through the air space is negligible compared with that through the secondary. It follows that the e.m.f.s induced in the primary and secondary windings are equal and that the primary applied voltage, V_1, is equal to the e.m.f., E_1, induced in the primary, as shown in Figs 1.198 and 1.199.

Next, let us assume a load having a power factor such that the secondary current is in phase with E_2. As already explained on p. 202 the primary current, I_1, must now have two components:

1. I_{0m} to maintain the useful flux, the maximum value of which remains constant within about 2 per cent between no load and full load.
2. A component, $I_{2'}$, to neutralize the demagnetizing effect of the secondary current, as shown in Figs 1.200(a) and 1.201.

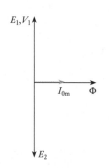

Fig. 1.199   Phasor diagram for
Fig. 1.198

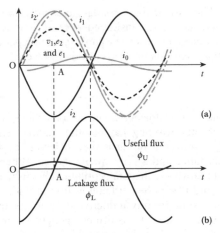

Fig. 1.200 Waveforms of induced e.m.f.s, currents and fluxes in a transformer on load

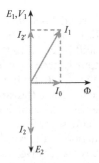

Fig. 1.201 Phasor diagram for Fig. 1.200

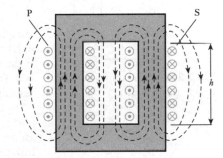

Fig. 1.202 Paths of leakage flux

At instant A in Fig. 1.200(a), the magnetizing current is *zero*, but I_2 and $I_{2'}$ are at their *maximum* values; and if the direction of the current in primary winding P is such as to produce flux upwards in the left-hand limb of Fig. 1.202, the secondary current must be in such a direction as to produce flux upwards in the right-hand limb, and the flux of each limb has to return through air. Since the flux of each limb is linked only with the winding by which it is produced, it is referred to as *leakage* flux and is responsible for inducing an e.m.f. of self-inductance in the winding with which it is linked. The reluctance of the paths of the leakage flux, Φ_L, is almost entirely due to the long air paths and is therefore practically constant. Consequently the value of the leakage flux is proportional to the load current, whereas the value of the useful flux remains almost independent of the load. The reluctance of the paths of the leakage flux is very high, so that the value of this flux is relatively small even on full load when the values of $I_{2'}$ and I_2 are about 20–30 times the magnetizing current I_{0m}.

From the above discussion it follows that the actual flux in a transformer can be regarded as being due to the two components shown in Fig. 1.200(b), namely:

1. The useful flux, Φ_U, linked with both windings and remaining practically constant in value at all loads.
2. The leakage flux, Φ_L, half of which is linked with the primary winding and half with the secondary, and its value is proportional to the load.

The case of the secondary current in phase with the secondary induced e.m.f. has been considered because it is easier to see that the useful and the leakage fluxes can be considered independently of each other for this condition than it is for loads of other power factors.

Leakage flux responsible for the inductive reactance of a transformer

When a transformer is on no load there is no secondary current, and the secondary winding has not the slightest effect upon the primary current. The primary winding is then behaving as an inductor, having a very high inductance and a very low resistance. When the transformer is supplying a load, however, this conception of the inductance of the windings is of little use and it is rather difficult at first to understand why the useful flux is not responsible for any inductive drop in the transformer. So let us first of all assume an ideal transformer, namely a transformer the windings of which have negligible resistance and in which there is no core loss and no magnetic leakage. Also, for convenience, let us assume unity transformation ratio, i.e. $N_1 = N_2$.

If such a transformer were enclosed in a box and the ends of the windings brought to terminals A, B, C and D on the lid, as shown in Fig. 1.203 the p.d. between C and D would be equal to that between A and B; and, as far as the effect upon the output voltage is concerned, the transformer behaves as if A were connected to C and B to D. In other words, the useful flux is not responsible for any voltage drop in a transformer.

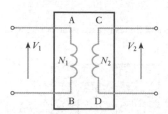

Fig. 1.203 Ideal transformer enclosed in a box

In the preceding section it was explained that the leakage flux is proportional to the primary and secondary currents and that its effect is to induce e.m.f.s of self-induction in the windings. Consequently the effect of leakage flux can be considered as equivalent to inductive reactors X_1 and X_2 connected in series with a transformer having no leakage flux, as shown in Fig. 1.204; these reactors being such that the flux-linkages produced by the primary current through X_1 are equal to those due to the leakage flux linked with the primary winding, and the flux-linkages produced by the secondary current through X_2 are equal to those due to the leakage flux linked with the secondary winding of the actual transformer. The straight line drawn between the primary and secondary windings in Fig. 1.204 is the symbol used to indicate that the transformer has a ferromagnetic core.

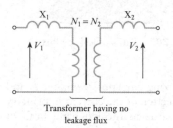

Transformer having no leakage flux

Fig. 1.204 Transformer with leakage reactances

Methods of reducing leakage flux

The leakage flux can be practically eliminated by winding the primary and secondary, one over the other, uniformly around a laminated ferromagnetic ring of uniform cross-section. But such an arrangement is not commercially practicable except in very small sizes, owing to the cost of threading a large number of turns through the ring.

The principal methods used in practice are:

1. Making the transformer 'window' long and narrow.
2. Arranging the primary and secondary windings concentrically (see Fig. 1.205).
3. Sandwiching the primary and secondary windings (see Fig. 1.206).
4. Using shell-type construction (see Fig. 1.207).

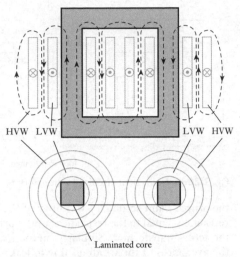

Fig. 1.205 Concentric windings. HVW = high-voltage winding; LVW = low-voltage winding

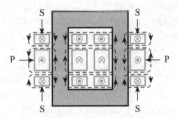

Fig. 1.206 Sandwiched windings

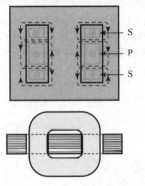

Fig. 1.207 Shell-type construction

Equivalent circuit of a transformer

The behaviour of a transformer may be conveniently considered by assuming it to be equivalent to an ideal transformer, i.e. a transformer having no losses and no magnetic leakage and a ferromagnetic core of infinite permeability requiring no magnetizing current, and then allowing for the imperfections of the actual transformer by means of additional circuits or impedances inserted between the supply and the primary winding and between the secondary and the load. Thus, in Fig. 1.208 P and S represent

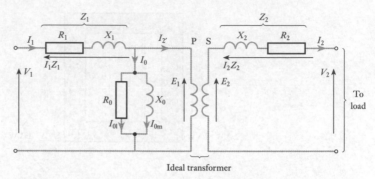

Fig. 1.208   Equivalent circuit of a transformer

the primary and secondary windings of the ideal transformer, R_1 and R_2 are resistances equal to the resistances of the primary and secondary windings of the actual transformer. Similarly, inductive reactances X_1 and X_2 represent the reactances of the windings due to leakage flux in the actual transformer, as already explained in 'Leakage flux responsible for the inductive reactance of a transformer' (p. 208).

The inductive reactor X_0 is such that it takes a reactive current equal to the magnetizing current I_{0m} of the actual transformer. The core losses due to hysteresis and eddy currents are allowed for by a resistor R_0 of such value that it takes a current I_{0l} equal to the core-loss component of the primary current, i.e. $I_{0l}^2 R_0$ is equal to the core loss of the actual transformer. The resultant of I_{0m} and I_{0l} is I_0, namely the current which the transformer takes on no load. The phasor diagram for the equivalent circuit on no load is exactly the same as that given in Fig. 1.195.

Phasor diagram for a transformer on load

For convenience let us assume an equal number of turns on the primary and secondary windings, so that $E_1 = E_2$. As shown in Fig. 1.209 E_1 leads the flux by 90°, and represents the voltage across the primary of the ideal transformer.

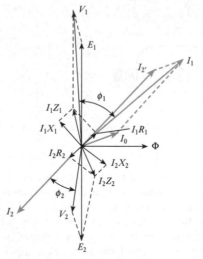

Fig. 1.209   Phasor diagram for a transformer on load

Let us also assume the general case of a load having a lagging power factor; consequently, in Fig. 1.209 I_2 has been drawn lagging E_2 by about 45°. Then

$$I_2 R_2 = \text{voltage drop due to secondary resistance}$$

$$I_2 X_2 = \text{voltage drop due to secondary leakage reactance}$$

and $\quad I_2 Z_2 = \text{voltage drop due to secondary impedance}$

The secondary terminal voltage V_2 is the phasor difference of E_2 and $I_2 Z_2$; in other words, V_2 must be such that the phasor sum of V_2 and $I_2 Z_2$ is E_2, and the derivation of the phasor representing V_2 is evident from Fig. 1.209. The power factor of the load is $\cos \phi_2$, where ϕ_2 is the phase difference between V_2 and I_2, $I_{2'}$ represents the component of the primary current to neutralize the demagnetizing effect of the secondary current and is drawn equal and opposite to I_2. Here I_0 is the no-load current of the transformer ('Phasor diagram for a transformer on no load', p. 202). The phasor sum of $I_{2'}$ and I_0 gives the total current I_1 taken from the supply.

$$I_1 R_1 = \text{voltage drop due to primary resistance}$$

$$I_1 X_1 = \text{voltage drop due to primary leakage reactance}$$

$$I_1 Z_1 = \text{voltage drop due to primary impedance}$$

and $\quad \mathbf{V_1 = E_1 + I_1 Z_1} = \text{supply voltage}$

If ϕ_1 is the phase difference between V_1 and I_1, then $\cos \phi_1$ is the power factor on the primary side of the transformer. In Fig. 1.209 the phasors representing the no-load current and the primary and secondary voltage drops are, for clearness, shown far larger relative to the other phasors than they are in an actual transformer.

Approximate equivalent circuit of a transformer

Since the no-load current of a transformer is only about 3–5 per cent of the full-load primary current, we can omit the parallel circuits R_0 and X_0 in Fig. 1.208 without introducing an appreciable error when we are considering the behaviour of the transformer on full load. Thus we have the simpler equivalent circuit of Fig. 1.210.

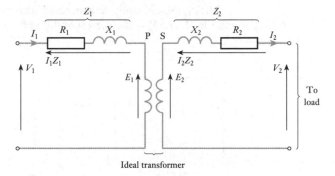

Fig. 1.210 Approximate equivalent circuit of a transformer

Simplification of the approximate equivalent circuit of a transformer

We can replace the resistance R_2 of the secondary of Fig. 1.210 by inserting additional resistance $R_{2'}$ in the primary circuit such that the power absorbed in $R_{2'}$ when carrying the primary current is equal to that in R_2 due to the secondary current, i.e.

$$I_1^2 R_{2'} = I_2^2 R_2$$

$$R_{2'} = R_2 \left(\frac{I_2}{I_1}\right)^2 \simeq R_2 \left(\frac{V_1}{V_2}\right)^2$$

Hence if R_e is a single resistance in the primary circuit equivalent to the primary and secondary resistances of the actual transformer then

$$R_e = R_1 + R_{2'} = R_1 + R_2 \left(\frac{V_1}{V_2}\right)^2 \qquad [1.110]$$

Similarly, since the inductance of a coil is proportional to the square of the number of turns, the secondary leakage reactance X_2 can be replaced by an equivalent reactance $X_{2'}$ in the primary circuit, such that

$$X_{2'} = X_2 \left(\frac{N_1}{N_2}\right)^2 \simeq X_2 \left(\frac{V_1}{V_2}\right)^2$$

If X_e is the single reactance in the primary circuit equivalent to X_1 and X_2 of the actual transformer

$$X_e = X_1 + X_{2'} = X_1 + X_2 \left(\frac{V_1}{V_2}\right)^2 \qquad [1.111]$$

If Z_e is the equivalent impedance of the primary and secondary windings referred to the primary circuit

$$Z_e = \sqrt{(R_e^2 + X_e^2)} \qquad [1.112]$$

If ϕ_e is the phase difference between I_1 and $I_1 Z_e$, then

$$R_e = Z_e \cos \phi_e \quad \text{and} \quad X_e = Z_e \sin \phi_e$$

The simplified equivalent circuit of the transformer is given in Fig. 1.211, and Fig. 1.212(a) is the corresponding phasor diagram.

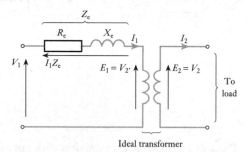

Fig. 1.211 Simplified equivalent circuit of a transformer

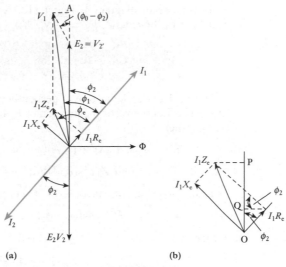

Fig. 1.212 Phasor diagram for Fig. 1.211

<table>
<tr><td>**Voltage regulation of a transformer**</td><td>The voltage regulation of a transformer is defined as the variation of the secondary voltage between no load and full load, expressed as either a per-unit or a percentage of the *no-load* voltage, the primary voltage being assumed constant, i.e.</td></tr>
</table>

$$\text{Voltage regulation} = \frac{\text{no-load voltage} - \text{full-load voltage}}{\text{no-load voltage}} \qquad [1.113]$$

If V_1 is primary applied voltage

$$\text{Secondary voltage on no load} = V_1 \times \frac{N_2}{N_1}$$

since the voltage drop in the primary winding due to the no-load current is negligible.

If V_2 is secondary terminal voltage on full load,

$$\text{Voltage regulation} = \frac{V_1\dfrac{N_2}{N_1} - V_2}{V_1\dfrac{N_2}{N_1}}$$

$$= \frac{V_1 - V_2\dfrac{N_1}{N_2}}{V_1} \text{ per unit}$$

$$= \frac{V_1 - V_2\dfrac{N_1}{N_2}}{V_1} \times 100 \text{ per cent}$$

In the phasor diagram of Fig. 1.212, N_1 and N_2 were assumed equal, so that $V_{2'} = V_2$. In general, $V_{2'} = V_2(N_1/N_2)$,

$\therefore$ Per-unit voltage regulation $= \dfrac{V_1 - V_{2'}}{V_1}$ [1.114]

In Fig. 1.212(a), let us draw a perpendicular from V_1 to meet the extension of $V_{2'}$ at A. Let the vertical extension of $V_{2'}$ be $V_{2'}A$ and the perpendicular line be V_1A; then

$$V_1^2 = (V_{2'} + V_{2'}A)^2 + (V_1A)^2$$
$$= \{V_{2'} + I_1 Z_e \cos(\phi_e - \phi_2)\}^2 + \{I_1 Z_e \sin(\phi_e - \phi_2)\}^2$$

In actual practice, $I_1 Z_e \sin(\phi_e - \phi_2)$ is very small compared with $V_{2'}$, so that

$$V_1 \simeq V_{2'} + I_1 Z_e \cos(\phi_e - \phi_2)$$

Hence

$$\text{Per-unit voltage regulation} = \frac{V_1 - V_{2'}}{V_1}$$

Per-unit voltage regulation $= \dfrac{I_1 Z_e \cos(\phi_e - \phi_2)}{V_1}$ [1.115]

Since

$$Z_e \cos(\phi_e - \phi_2) = Z_e(\cos \phi_e \cdot \cos \phi_2 + \sin \phi_e \cdot \sin \phi_2)$$
$$= R_e \cos \phi_2 + X_e \sin \phi_2$$

therefore

Per-unit voltage regulation $= \dfrac{I_1(R_e \cos \phi_2 + X_e \sin \phi_2)}{V_1}$ [1.116]

This expression can also be derived by projecting $I_1 R_e$ and $I_1 Z_e$ on to OA, as shown enlarged in Fig. 1.212(b), from which it follows that

$$V_{2'}A \text{ in Fig. 1.212(a)} = \text{OP in Fig. 1.212(b)}$$
$$= \text{OQ} + \text{QP}$$
$$= I_1 R_e \cos \phi_2 + I_1 X_e \sin \phi_2$$

therefore per-unit voltage regulation is

$$\frac{V_1 - V_{2'}}{V_1} \simeq \frac{V_{2'}A}{V_1} = \frac{\text{OP}}{V_1}$$
$$= \frac{I_1(R_e \cos \phi_2 + X_e \sin \phi_2)}{V_1}$$

The above expressions have been derived on the assumption that the power factor is lagging. Should the power factor be leading, the angle in expression [1.115] would be $(\phi_e + \phi_2)$ and the term in brackets in expression [1.116] would be $(R_e \cos \phi_2 - X_e \sin \phi_2)$.

Example 1.93   A 100 kVA transformer has 400 turns on the primary and 80 turns on the secondary. The primary and secondary resistances are 0.3 Ω and 0.01 Ω respectively, and the corresponding leakage reactances are 1.1 Ω and 0.035 Ω respectively. The supply voltage is 2200 V. Calculate:

(a) the equivalent impedance referred to the primary circuit;
(b) the voltage regulation and the secondary terminal voltage for full load having a power factor of (i) 0.8 lagging and (ii) 0.8 leading.

(a) From equation [1.110], equivalent resistance referred to primary is

$$R_e = 0.3 + 0.01 \left(\frac{400}{80}\right)^2 = 0.55 \ \Omega$$

From equation [1.111], equivalent leakage reactance referred to primary is

$$X_e = 1.1 + 0.035 \left(\frac{400}{80}\right)^2 = 1.975 \ \Omega$$

From equation [1.112], equivalent impedance referred to primary is

$$Z_e = \sqrt{\{(0.55)^2 + (1.975)^2\}} = \textbf{2.05 } \Omega$$

(b) (i) Since $\cos \phi_2 = 0.8$, therefore $\sin \phi_2 = 0.6$.

$$\text{Full-load primary current} \simeq \frac{100 \times 1000}{2200} = 45.45 \text{ A}$$

Substituting in equation [1.116], we have voltage regulation for power factor 0.8 lagging is

$$\frac{45.45(0.55 \times 0.8 + 1.975 \times 0.6)}{2200} = \textbf{0.0336 per unit}$$

$$= \textbf{3.36 per cent}$$

Secondary terminal voltage on no load is

$$2200 \times \frac{80}{400} = 440 \text{ V}$$

Therefore decrease of secondary terminal voltage between no load and full load is

$$440 \times 0.0336 = 14.8 \text{ V}$$

Therefore secondary terminal voltage on full load is

$$440 - 14.8 = \textbf{425 V}$$

(ii) Voltage regulation for power factor 0.8 leading is

$$\frac{45.45(0.55 \times 0.8 - 1.975 \times 0.6)}{2200} = \textbf{-0.0154 per unit}$$

$$= \textbf{-1.54 per cent}$$

Increase of secondary terminal voltage between no load and full load is

$$440 \times 0.0154 = 6.78 \text{ V}$$

Therefore secondary terminal voltage on full load is

$$440 + 6.78 = \mathbf{447} \text{ V}$$

Example 1.94   Calculate the per-unit and the percentage resistance and leakage reactance drops of the transformer referred to in Example 1.93.

Per-unit resistance drop of a transformer

$$= \frac{\left(\begin{array}{c} \text{full-load primary} \\ \text{current} \end{array} \right) \times \left(\begin{array}{c} \text{equivalent resistance} \\ \text{referred to primary circuit} \end{array} \right)}{\text{primary voltage}}$$

$$= \frac{\left(\begin{array}{c} \text{full-load secondary} \\ \text{current} \end{array} \right) \times \left(\begin{array}{c} \text{equivalent resistance} \\ \text{referred to secondary circuit} \end{array} \right)}{\text{secondary voltage on no load}}$$

Thus, for Example 1.93, full-load primary current $\simeq 45.45$ A, and equivalent resistance referred to primary circuit $= 0.55 \ \Omega$,

$$\text{Resistance drop} = \frac{45.45 \times 0.55}{2200} = \mathbf{0.0114 \text{ per unit}}$$

$$= \mathbf{1.14 \text{ per cent}}$$

Alternatively, full-load secondary current

$$\simeq 45.45 \times 400/80$$

$$= 227.2 \text{ A}$$

and equivalent resistance referred to secondary circuit is

$$0.01 + 0.3 \left(\frac{80}{400} \right)^2 = 0.022 \ \Omega$$

Secondary voltage on no load $= 440$ V

$$\therefore \qquad \text{Resistance drop} = \frac{227.2 \times 0.022}{440} = \mathbf{0.0114 \text{ per unit}}$$

$$= \mathbf{1.14 \text{ per cent}}$$

Similarly, leakage reactance drop of a transformer

$$= \frac{\left(\begin{array}{c} \text{full-load primary} \\ \text{current} \end{array} \right) \times \left(\begin{array}{c} \text{equivalent leakage resistance} \\ \text{referred to primary circuit} \end{array} \right)}{\text{primary voltage}}$$

$$= \frac{45.45 \times 1.975}{2200} = \mathbf{0.0408 \text{ per unit} = 4.08 \text{ per cent}}$$

It is usual to refer to the per-unit or the percentage resistance and leakage reactance drops on full load as merely the per-unit or the percentage resistance and leakage reactance of the transformer; thus, the above transformer has a per-unit resistance and leakage reactance of 0.0114 and 0.0408 respectively or a percentage resistance and leakage reactance of 1.14 and 4.08 respectively.

Efficiency of a transformer

The losses which occur in a transformer on load can be divided into two groups:

1. I^2R losses in primary and secondary windings, namely $I_1^2R_1 + I_2^2R_2$.
2. Core losses due to hysteresis and eddy currents. The factors determining these losses have already been discussed in the first two parts of this section.

Since the maximum value of the flux in a normal transformer does not vary by more than about 2 per cent between no load and full load, it is usual to assume the core loss constant at all loads.

Hence, if P_c = total core loss, total losses in transformer are

$$P_c + I_1^2R_1 + I_2^2R_2$$

and $\quad$ Efficiency $= \dfrac{\text{output power}}{\text{input power}} = \dfrac{\text{output power}}{\text{output power} + \text{losses}}$

$$\text{Efficiency} = \frac{I_2V_2 \times \text{p.f.}}{I_2V_2 \times \text{p.f.} + P_c + I_1^2R_1 + I_2^2R_2} \qquad [1.117]$$

Greater accuracy is possible by expressing the efficiency thus:

$$\text{Efficiency} = \frac{\text{output power}}{\text{input power}} = \frac{\text{input power} - \text{losses}}{\text{input power}}$$

$$\eta = 1 - \frac{\text{losses}}{\text{input power}} \qquad [1.118]$$

Example 1.95

The primary and secondary windings of a 500 kVA transformer have resistances of 0.42 Ω and 0.0019 Ω respectively. The primary and secondary voltages are 11 000 V and 400 V respectively and the core loss is 2.9 kW, assuming the power factor of the load to be 0.8. Calculate the efficiency on

(a) full load;
(b) half load.

(a) Full-load secondary current is

$$\frac{500 \times 1000}{400} = 1250 \text{ A}$$

and $\quad$ Full-load primary current $\simeq \dfrac{500 \times 1000}{11\,000} = 45.5 \text{ A}$

Therefore secondary I^2R loss on full load is

$$(1250)^2 \times 0.0019 = 2969 \text{ W}$$

and primary I^2R loss on full load is

$$(45.5)^2 \times 0.42 = 870 \text{ W}$$

$\therefore$ Total I^2R loss on full load $= 3839 \text{ W} = 3.84 \text{ kW}$

and   Total loss on full load $= 3.84 + 2.9 = 6.74 \text{ kW}$

Output power on full load $= 500 \times 0.8 = 400 \text{ kW}$

$\therefore$ Input power on full load $= 400 + 6.74 = 406.74 \text{ kW}$

From equation [1.118], efficiency on full load is

$$\left(1 - \frac{6.74}{406.74}\right) = 0.983 \text{ per unit}$$

$$= \textbf{98.3 per cent}$$

(b) Since the I^2R loss varies as the square of the current,

$\therefore$ Total I^2R loss on half load $= 3.84 \times (0.5)^2 = 0.96 \text{ kW}$

and   Total loss on half load $= 0.96 + 2.9 = 3.86 \text{ kW}$

$\therefore$ Efficiency on half load $= \left(1 - \dfrac{3.86}{203.86}\right) = 0.981 \text{ per unit}$

$$= \textbf{98.1 per cent}$$

<table>
<tr><td>**Condition for maximum efficiency of a transformer**</td><td>If R_{2e} is the equivalent resistance of the primary and secondary windings referred to the *secondary* circuit,</td></tr>
</table>

$$R_{2e} = R_1 \left(\frac{N_2}{N_1}\right)^2 + R_2$$

$\qquad$ = a constant for a given transformer

Hence for any load current I_2

$\qquad$ Total I^2R loss $= I_2^2 R_{2e}$

and   Efficiency $= \dfrac{I_2 V_2 \times \text{p.f.}}{I_2 V_2 \times \text{p.f.} + P_c + I_2^2 R_{2e}}$

$$\text{Efficiency} = \frac{V_2 \cos \phi}{V_2 \cos \phi + (P_c / I_2) + I_2 R_{2e}} \qquad [1.119]$$

For a normal transformer, V_2 is approximately constant, hence for a load of given power factor the efficiency is a maximum when the denominator of equation [1.119] is a minimum, i.e. when

$$\frac{\mathrm{d}}{\mathrm{d}I_2}\left(V_2 \times \text{p.f.} + \frac{P_c}{I_2} + I_2R_{2e}\right) = 0$$

$$\therefore \qquad -\frac{P_c}{I_2^2} + R_{2e} = 0$$

or $\qquad \boxed{I_2^2R_{2e} = P_c} \qquad\qquad\qquad\qquad\qquad$ [1.120]

To check that this condition gives the minimum and not the maximum value of the denominator in expression [1.119], $(-P_c/I_2^2 + R_{2e})$ should be differentiated with respect to I_2, thus:

$$\frac{\mathrm{d}}{\mathrm{d}I_2}\left(-\frac{P_c}{I_2^2} + R_{2e}\right) = \frac{2P_c}{I_2^3}$$

Since this quantity is positive, expression [1.120] is the condition for the minimum value of the denominator of equation [1.119] and therefore the maximum value of the efficiency. Hence the efficiency is a maximum when the variable I^2R loss is equal to the constant core loss.

Example 1.96   Assuming the power factor of the load to be 0.8, find the output at which the efficiency of the transformer of Example 1.95 is a maximum and calculate its value.

With the full-load output of 500 kVA, the total I^2R loss is 3.86 kW.

Let n = fraction of full-load apparent power (in kVA) at which the efficiency is a maximum.

Corresponding total I^2R loss $= n^2 \times 3.86$ kW

Hence, from equation [1.120],

$$\therefore \qquad\qquad n^2 \times 3.86 = 2.9$$

$$n = 0.867$$

and $\qquad$ Output at maximum efficiency $= 0.867 \times 500$

$$= 433 \text{ kVA}$$

It will be noted that the value of the apparent power at which the efficiency is a maximum is independent of the power factor of the load.

Since the I^2R and core losses are equal when the efficiency is a maximum,

$$\therefore \qquad\qquad \text{Total loss} = 2 \times 2.9 = 5.8 \text{ kW}$$

$$\text{Output power} = 433 \times 0.8 = 346.4 \text{ kW}$$

$$\therefore \qquad \text{Maximum efficiency} = \left(1 - \frac{5.8}{346.4 + 5.8}\right) = \textbf{0.984 per unit}$$

$$= \textbf{98.4 per cent}$$

Current transformers

It is difficult to construct ammeters and the current coils of wattmeters, energy (kW h) meters and relays to carry alternating currents greater than about 100 A. Furthermore, if the voltage of the system exceeds 500 V, it is dangerous to connect such instruments directly to the high voltage. These difficulties are overcome by using current transformers. Figure 1.213(a) shows an ammeter A supplied through a current transformer. The ammeter is usually arranged to give full-scale deflection with 5 A, and the ratio of the primary to secondary turns must be such that full-scale ammeter reading is obtained with full-load current in the primary. Thus, if the primary has four turns and the full-load primary current is 50 A, the full-load primary ampere-turns are 200; consequently, to circulate 5 A in the secondary, the number of secondary turns must be 200/5, namely 40.

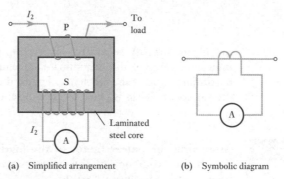

(a) Simplified arrangement   (b) Symbolic diagram

Fig. 1.213 A current transformer

If the number of primary turns were reduced to *one* and the secondary winding had 40 turns, the primary current to give full-scale reading of 5 A on the ammeter would be 200 A. Current transformers having a single-turn primary are usually constructed as shown in Fig. 1.214, where P represents the primary conductor passing through the centre of a laminated steel ring C. The secondary winding S is wound uniformly around the ring.

The secondary circuit of a current transformer must on no account be opened while the primary winding is carrying a current, since all the primary ampere-turns would then be available to produce flux. The core loss due to the high flux density would cause excessive heating of the core and windings, and a dangerously high e.m.f. might be induced in the secondary winding. Hence if it is desired to remove the ammeter from the secondary circuit, the secondary winding must first be short-circuited. This will not be accompanied by an excessive secondary current, since the latter is proportional to the primary current; and since the primary winding is in *series* with the load, the primary current is determined by the value of the load and not by that of the secondary current.

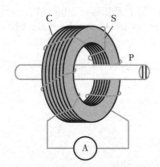

Fig. 1.214 A bar-primary current transformer

Waveform of the magnetizing current of a transformer

In Fig. 1.195 the phasor for the no-load current of a transformer is shown leading the magnetic flux. A student may ask: is the flux not a maximum when this current is a maximum? The answer is that they are at their maximum values at the same instant (assuming the eddy-current loss to be negligible); but if the applied voltage is sinusoidal, then the magnetizing current

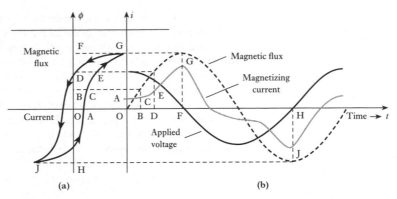

Fig. 1.215   Waveform of magnetizing current

of a ferromagnetic-core transformer is not sinusoidal, and a non-sinusoidal quantity cannot be represented by a phasor.

Suppose the relationship between the flux and the magnetizing current for the ferromagnetic core to be represented by the hysteresis loop in Fig. 1.215(a). Also, let us assume that the waveform of the flux is sinusoidal as shown by the dotted curve in Fig. 1.215(b). It was shown in 'EMF equation of a transformer' (p. 200) that when the flux is sinusoidal, the e.m.f. induced in the primary is also sinusoidal and lags the flux by a quarter of a cycle. Hence the voltage applied to the primary must be sinusoidal and leads the flux by a quarter of a cycle as shown in Fig. 1.215(b).

At instant O in Fig. 1.215(b), the flux is zero and the magnetizing current is OA. At instant B, the flux is OB in Fig. 1.215(a), and the current is BC. When the flux is at its maximum value OF, the current is also at its maximum value FG. Thus, by projecting from Fig. 1.215(a) to the flux curve in Fig. 1.215(b) and erecting ordinates representing the corresponding values of the current, the waveform of the magnetizing current can be derived. It can be shown that this waveform contains a sinusoidal component having the same frequency as the supply voltage and referred to as the *fundamental* component, together with other sinusoidal components having frequencies that are odd multiples of the supply frequency. The fundamental current component lags the applied voltage by an angle ϕ that is a little less than $90°$, and

$$\text{Hysteresis loss} = \text{r.m.s. fundamental current component}$$

$$\times \text{ r.m.s. voltage} \times \cos \phi$$

Most power transformers are operated near to full load, in which case the magnetizing current has negligible effect. Thus, although the magnetizing current is not sinusoidal, the total input current including the magnetizing current is almost sinusoidal. Therefore the effect of the non-sinusoidal component of the current can generally be ignored in most power applications.

However, if a transformer is designed for small loads, the effect of the magnetizing current on the total input current becomes more pronounced. This is particularly important when the transformer is incorporated into electronic circuits or even the power supply to electronic equipment. In these applications, we are normally involved with analogue signals in which it is essential not to introduce distortion – distortion would of course result from the magnetizing current component.

There are two methods responding to the needs of electronic circuits. The first is to use a better material for the core so that the magnetizing current is almost sinusoidal – this involves much more expensive material which is acceptable in small transformers. This method is not perfect, but bearing in mind that the transistors also do not have absolutely linear characteristics, we can look on the effect of the transformer as being just another small source of distortion. The transformer, however, has the advantage that it can be relatively compact and has little leakage of its magnetic field.

The alternative method is to do away with the ferromagnetic core; this arrangement is the air-cored transformer.

CHAPTER 2

Electrical and Electronic Principles

Unit 5: Electrical and Electronic Principles

Unit code: R/601/1453

QCF level: 5

Credit value: 15

Aim

This unit provides an understanding of electrical and electronic principles used in a range of engineering careers and provides the basis for further study of more specialist areas of electrical/electronic engineering.

Unit abstract

Circuits and their characteristics are fundamental to any study of electrical and electronic engineering and therefore a good understanding is important to any engineer.

The engineer must be able to take complex electrical circuit problems, break them down into acceptable elements and apply techniques to solve or analyse the characteristics. Additionally, fine tuning of the circuits can be performed to obtain required output dynamics.

This unit draws together a logical appreciation of the topic and offers a structured approach to the development of the broad learning required at this level. Learners will begin by investigating circuit theory and the related theorems to develop solutions to electrical networks.

In learning outcome 2 the concept of an attenuator is introduced by considering a symmetrical two-port network and its characteristics. The design and testing of both T and π networks is also covered.

Learning outcome 3 considers the properties of complex waveforms and Fourier analysis is used to evaluate the Fourier coefficients of a complex periodic waveform.

Finally, learning outcome 4 introduces the use of Laplace transforms as a means of solving first order differential equations used to model RL and RC networks, together with the evaluation of circuit responses to a step input in practical situations.

Learning outcomes

On successful completion of this unit a learner will:

1 Be able to apply electrical and electronic circuit theory
2 Be able to apply two-port network models
3 Understand the use of complex waves
4 Be able to apply transients in R–L–C circuits

Unit content

1 Be able to apply electrical and electronic circuit theory

Transformation theorems: energy sources as constant-voltage and constant-current generators; Thévenin's and Norton's theorems; delta-star and star-delta transformation

Circuit theory: maximum power transfer conditions for resistive and complex circuits; mesh and nodal analysis; the principle of superposition

Magnetically coupled circuits: mutual inductance; the use of dot notation; equivalent circuits for transformers including the effects of resistive and reactive features

R-L-C tuned circuits: series and parallel resonant circuits; impedance; phase angle; dynamic resistance; Q-factor; bandwidth; selectivity and resonant frequency; the effects of loading on tuned circuit performance

2 Be able to apply two-port network models

Network models: symmetrical two-port network model; characteristic impedance, Z_o; propagation coefficient (expressed in terms of attenuation, α, and phase change ß); input impedance for various load conditions including $Z_L = Z_o$; relationship between the neper and the dB; insertion loss

Symmetrical attenuators: T and π attenuators; the expressions for R_o and α in terms of component values

3 Understand the use of complex waves

Properties: power factor; rms value of complex periodic waveforms

Analyse: Fourier coefficients of a complex periodic voltage waveform eg Fourier series for rectangular, triangular or half-wave rectified waveform, use of a tabular method for determining the Fourier series for a complex periodic waveform; use of a waveform analyser; use of an appropriate software package

4 Be able to apply transients in R-L-C circuits

Laplace transforms: definition of the Laplace transform of a function; use of a table of Laplace transforms

Transient analysis: expressions for component and circuit impedance in the s-plane; first order systems must be solved by Laplace (ie RL and RC networks); second order systems could be solved by Laplace or computer-based packages

Circuit responses: over, under, zero and critically damped response following a step input; zero initial conditions being assumed

Learning outcomes and assessment criteria

Learning outcomes On successful completion of this unit a learner will:	Assessment criteria for pass The learner can:
LO1 Be able to apply electrical and electronic circuit theory	1.1 calculate the parameters of AC equivalent circuits using transformation theorems 1.2 apply circuit theory techniques to the solution of AC circuit problems 1.3 analyse the operation of magnetically coupled circuits 1.4 use circuit theory to solve problems relating to series and parallel R-L-C tuned circuits
LO2 Be able to apply two-port network models	2.1 apply two-port network model to the solution of practical problems 2.2 design and test symmetrical attenuators against computer models
LO3 Understand the use of complex waves	3.1 calculate the properties of complex periodic waves 3.2 analyse complex periodic waves
LO4 Be able to apply transients in R-L-C circuits	4.1 use Laplace transforms for the transient analysis of networks 4.2 calculate circuit responses to a step input in practical situations

Guidance

Links

This unit relies heavily on the use of mathematical analysis to support the underlying theory and practical work. Consequently it is assumed that *Unit 1: Analytical Methods for Engineers* has been taught previously or is being delivered in parallel. It may also be linked with *Unit 2: Engineering Science*.

Essential requirements

Learners will require access to a range of electronic test equipment, eg oscilloscopes, signal generators, etc.

Employer engagement and vocational contexts

Delivery of this unit will benefit from centres establishing strong links with employers willing to contribute to the delivery of teaching, work–based placements and/or detailed case study materials.

Network theorems applied to AC networks

One stage further

In Chapter 1, we were introduced to a number of techniques by which we could analyse d.c. circuit and network performance. Since then we have been introduced to a.c. circuits and networks. Each introduction involved a degree of complexity so far as handling the mathematical terms. Could it be that things become too difficult to handle when we apply a.c. signals to complicated networks?

Fortunately we have been introduced to complex notation. Provided we apply it to the a.c. quantities, we can readily apply the network theorems in almost the same ways which we used in the d.c. circuits and networks. As with the theorems for d.c. circuits and networks, the easiest way to demonstrate the analysis of a.c. circuits and networks is to look at a number of examples.

Kirchhoff's laws and network solution

Let us look at a simple application of Kirchhoff's laws to an a.c. network.

Example 2.1

For the network shown in Fig. 2.1, determine the supply current and the source e.m.f.

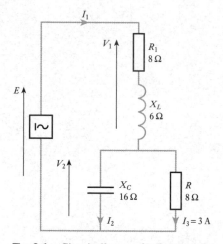

Fig. 2.1 Circuit diagram for Example 2.1

Let $\quad \mathbf{I}_3 = (3 + \mathrm{j}0)$ A

$\therefore \quad \mathbf{V}_2 = \mathbf{I}_3 R = (3 + \mathrm{j}0)(8 + \mathrm{j}0) = (24 + \mathrm{j}0)$ V

$$\mathbf{I}_2 = \frac{V_2}{X_\mathrm{C}} = \frac{(24 + \mathrm{j}0)}{(0 - \mathrm{j}16)} = (0 + \mathrm{j}1.5)\ \text{A}$$

$$\mathbf{I}_1 = \mathbf{I}_2 + \mathbf{I}_3 = (0 + \mathrm{j}1.5) + (3 + \mathrm{j}0) = (3 + \mathrm{j}1.5)\ \text{A}$$

$\therefore \quad I_1 = (3^2 + 1.5^2)^{\frac{1}{2}} = \mathbf{3.35\,A}$

$\quad \mathbf{V}_1 = \mathbf{I}_1(R + \mathrm{j}X_\mathrm{L}) = (3 + \mathrm{j}1.5)(8 + \mathrm{j}6) = (15 + \mathrm{j}30)$ V

$\quad \mathbf{E} = \mathbf{V}_1 + \mathbf{V}_2 = (15 + \mathrm{j}30) + (24 + \mathrm{j}0) = (39 + \mathrm{j}30)$ V

$\therefore \quad E = (39^2 + 30^2)^{\frac{1}{2}} = \mathbf{49.2\,V}$

This is not the only form of solution which could have been given. For instance, we could have applied the current-sharing rule to the current in the 8 Ω resistor to obtain the supply current directly. Or we could have determined the effective impedance of the network and hence obtained the source e.m.f. by obtaining the product of supply current and effective impedance. It is always preferable to seek the simplest solution but any solution which appeals is valid.

Let us look at other examples illustrating the direct and most simple approach.

Example 2.2   **Given the network shown in Fig. 2.2, determine I_1, E, I_2 and I.**

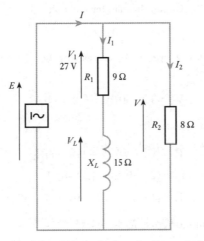

Fig. 2.2   Circuit diagram for Example 2.2

$$I_1 = \frac{\mathbf{V}_1}{R_1} = \frac{(27 + j0)}{9 + j0} = (3 + j0)\,\text{A}$$

$$\therefore \qquad I_1 = (3^2 + 0^2)^{\frac{1}{2}} = 3\,\text{A}$$

$$\mathbf{V}_L = \mathbf{I}X_L = (3 + j0)(0 + j15) = (0 + j45)\,\text{V}$$

$$\mathbf{E} = \mathbf{V}_1 + \mathbf{V}_L = (27 + j0) + (0 + j45)$$

$$= (27 + j45)\,\text{V}$$

$$\therefore \qquad E = (27^2 + 45^2)^{\frac{1}{2}} = \mathbf{52.5\,V}$$

$$\mathbf{I}_2 = \frac{\mathbf{E}}{R_2} = \frac{(27 + j45)}{8 + j0} = (3.38 + j5.63)\,\text{A}$$

$$\therefore \qquad I_2 = (3.38^2 + 5.63^2)^{\frac{1}{2}} = 6.56\,\text{A}$$

$$\mathbf{I} = \mathbf{I}_1 + \mathbf{I}_2 = (3 + j0) + (3.38 + j5.64)$$

$$= (6.38 + j5.63)\,\text{A}$$

$$\therefore \qquad I = (6.38^2 + 5.63^2)^{\frac{1}{2}} = \mathbf{8.5\,A}$$

Example 2.3   For the network shown in Fig. 2.3, the power dissipated in R is 20 W. Determine I and V.

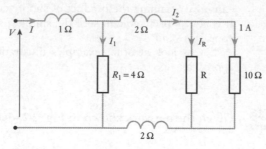

Fig. 2.3 Circuit diagram for Example 2.3

Let current in 10 Ω resistor be $(1 + j0)$ A. Therefore voltage across resistor is

$$\mathbf{V}_{10} = (1 + j0)10 = (10 + j0) \text{ V}$$

For resistor R:

$$\mathbf{P} = (20 + j0) \text{ W} = (10 + j0)\mathbf{I}_R$$

$$\therefore \qquad \mathbf{I}_R = (2 - j0) \text{ A} = (2 + j0) \text{ A}$$

$$\mathbf{I}_2 = (1 + j0) + (2 + j0) = (3 + j0) \text{ A}$$

Voltage across R_1 is given by

$$\mathbf{V}_1 = (3 + j0)(0 + j2) + (10 + j0) + (3 + j0)(0 + j2)$$

$$= (10 + j12) \text{ V}$$

$$\mathbf{I}_1 = \frac{(10 + j12)}{(4 + j0)} = (2.5 + j3) \text{ A}$$

$$\mathbf{I} = \mathbf{I}_1 + \mathbf{I}_2 = (2.5 + j3) + (3 + j0) = (5.5 + j3) \text{ A}$$

$$\therefore \qquad I = (5.5^2 + 3^2)^{\frac{1}{2}} = \mathbf{6.3\,A}$$

Voltage across 1 Ω resistor is given by

$$(5.5 + j3)(1 + j0) = (5.5 + j3) \text{ V}$$

$$\therefore \qquad \mathbf{V} = (5.5 + j3) + (10 + j12) = (15.5 + j15) \text{ V}$$

$$\therefore \qquad V = (15.5^2 + 15^2)^{\frac{1}{2}} = \mathbf{21.6\,V}$$

Example 2.3 shows that quite a complicated network can be analysed by a direct approach using a simple application of Kirchhoff's laws. It is not always possible to proceed in this way. For instance, let us look again at the network used in Example 2.1, but pose a slightly different situation.

Example 2.4

For the network shown in Fig. 2.4, determine the supply current I_1 and the branch current I_3.

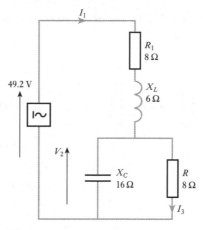

Fig. 2.4 Circuit diagram for Example 2.4

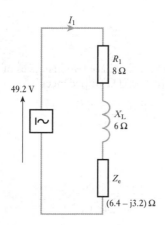

Fig. 2.5 Circuit diagram for Example 2.4

Essentially this network consists of three parts in series, but one of them comprises X_C and R in parallel. These can be replaced by an equivalent impedance thus

$$\mathbf{Z}_e = \frac{(R)(-jX_C)}{R - jX_C} = \frac{-j128}{8 - j16} = \frac{(-j128)(8 + j16)}{(8^2 + 16^2)}$$

$$= (6.4 - j3.2)\ \Omega$$

Replace R and X_C by Z_e as shown in Fig. 2.5.

Now the network has been reduced to a simple series circuit, the total effective impedance is

$$\mathbf{Z}_1 = 8 + j6 + (6.4 - j3.2) = (14.4 + j2.8)\ \Omega$$

$$\therefore \qquad Z_1 = (14.4^2 + 2.8^2)^{\frac{1}{2}} = 14.7\ \Omega$$

$$\therefore \qquad I_1 = \frac{49.2}{14.7} = 3.35\ \mathrm{A}$$

$$I_3 = \left| \frac{-jX_C}{R - jX_C} \right| \cdot I_1 = \left| \frac{-j16}{8 - j16} \right| \cdot 3.35 = \frac{16}{(8^2 + 16^2)^{\frac{1}{2}}} \cdot 3.35$$

$$= 3\ \mathrm{A}$$

In this example, the voltage and current information come from the source and not from the load. It is for this reason that the calculation has to be based on an analysis of the impedances. The calculation was therefore based on network reduction, i.e. by replacing two components by one equivalent impedance.

It is worth noting how we slipped out of using complex notation whenever it was not needed. Had we determined first I_1 and then I_3 in complex form, we would have obtained the same outcomes, but we would have undertaken unnecessary calculations.

Let us now look at a network in which network reduction transforms a complicated problem into a reasonably simple one.

Example 2.5 Determine V_{AB} in the network shown in Fig. 2.6.

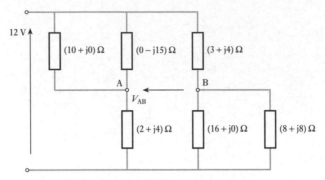

Fig. 2.6 Circuit diagram for Example 2.5

This is quite a complicated network. However, there are two instances of parallel impedances. For the $(10 + j0)\ \Omega$ and $(0 - j15)\ \Omega$ impedances

$$Z = \frac{(10 + j0) \cdot (0 - j15)}{10 + j0 + 0 - j15} = \frac{-j150}{10 - j15} = \frac{-j150(10 + j15)}{10^2 + 15^2}$$

$$= (6.92 - j4.62)\ \Omega$$

For the $(16 + j0)\ \Omega$ and $(8 + j8)\ \Omega$ in parallel

$$Z = \frac{(16 + j0) \cdot (8 + j8)}{16 + j0 + 8 + j8} = \frac{128 + j128}{24 + j8} = \frac{(128 + j128)(24 - j8)}{24^2 + 8^2}$$

$$= (6.4 + j3.2)\ \Omega$$

We can now redraw the network as shown in Fig. 2.7.

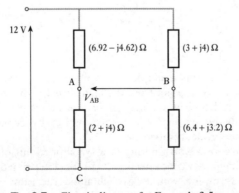

Fig. 2.7 Circuit diagram for Example 2.5

$$\mathbf{V}_{AC} = \frac{2 + j4}{(6.92 - j4.62) + (2 + j4)} \cdot (12 + j0) = \frac{24 + j48}{8.92 - j0.62}$$

$$= (2.62 + j5.54) \text{ V}$$

$$\mathbf{V}_{BC} = \frac{6.4 + j3.2}{(3 + j4) + (6.4 + j3.2)} \cdot (12 + j0) = \frac{76.8 - j38.4}{9.4 + j7.2}$$

$$= (2.4 + j0) \text{ V}$$

$$\mathbf{V}_{AB} = \mathbf{V}_{AC} - \mathbf{V}_{BC} = (2.62 + j5.54) - (7.12 - j1.37) = (-4.5 + j6.91) \text{ V}$$

$$\therefore \qquad V_{AB} = (4.5^2 + 6.91^2)^{\frac{1}{2}} = \mathbf{8.25 \text{ V}}$$

Once again we have observed two methods of circuit analysis. We have already been confronted with this difficult choice; we met it in Chapter 1 (see 'Kirchhoff's laws in network solution', p. 81). The decision as to which choice we should take remains the same – if the information provided relates to the component voltages or currents then take the first method of approach, i.e. applying the simplest forms of Kirchhoff's laws to the components. However, if the information depends on the supply voltage or current then we should try network reduction techniques.

We were shown in Chapter 1 that resistors were not always either in series or in parallel. Impedances are no different and Example 2.6 demonstrates a common situation – an a.c. bridge.

Example 2.6 For the network shown in Fig. 2.8, calculate the current in the $(3 + j4) \ \Omega$ impedance.

The solution will be obtained by Mesh analysis to illustrate that technique applied to a circuit with complex impedances. The circulating or mesh currents are added on loops 1, 2 and 3 as shown in Fig 2.9.

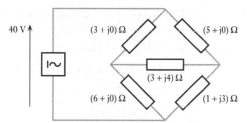

Fig. 2.8 Circuit diagram for Example 2.6

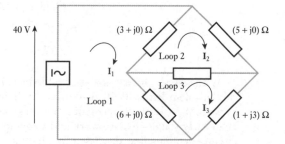

Fig. 2.9 Circuit diagram for Example 2.6

In loop 1: $\quad 40 = 9\mathbf{I}_1 - 3\mathbf{I}_2 - 6\mathbf{I}_3$ $\hfill$ (1)

In loop 2: $\quad 0 = -3\mathbf{I}_1 + (11 + j4)\mathbf{I}_2 - (3 + j4)\mathbf{I}_3$ $\hfill$ (2)

In loop 3: $\quad 0 = -6\mathbf{I}_1 - (3 + j4)\mathbf{I}_2 + (10 + j7)\mathbf{I}_3$ $\hfill$ (3)

Multiply equation (2) by 3:

$$0 = -9\mathbf{I}_1 + (33 + j12)\mathbf{I}_2 - (9 + j12)\mathbf{I}_3$$

Add to equation (1):

$$40 = (30 + j12)\mathbf{I}_2 - (15 + j12)\mathbf{I}_3 \qquad (4)$$

Multiply equation (2) by 2:

$$0 = -6\mathbf{I}_1 + (22 + j8)\mathbf{I}_2 - (6 + j8)\mathbf{I}_3$$

Subtract from equation (3):

$$0 = -(25 + j12)\mathbf{I}_2 + (16 + j15)\mathbf{I}_3$$

Hence: $\quad \mathbf{I}_2 = \dfrac{16 + j15}{25 + j12}\, \mathbf{I}_3$

$$= \frac{21.93\angle 43.2}{27.72\angle 25.6}\, \mathbf{I}_3$$

$$= 0.791\angle 17.56\mathbf{I}_3$$

$$= 0.754 + j0.239\mathbf{I}_3 \qquad (5)$$

Substituting for $\mathbf{I}_2$ in equation (4) gives:

$$40 = (30 + j12)(0.754 + j0.239)\mathbf{I}_3 - (15 + j12)\mathbf{I}_3$$

$$= (4.75 + j4.2)\mathbf{I}_3$$

$$\mathbf{I}_3 = \frac{40}{6.34\angle 41.5} = 6.31\angle{-41.5} = 4.73 - j4.18 \text{ A}$$

Substituting in equation (5) gives:

$$\mathbf{I}_2 = (0.791\angle 17.56)(6.31\angle{-41.5})$$

$$= 4.99\angle{-23.94}$$

$$= 4.56 - j2.02 \text{ A}$$

Current in $(3 + j4)$ impedance $= \mathbf{I}_3 - \mathbf{I}_2$

$$= (4.73 - j4.18) - (4.56 - j2.02)$$

$$= 0.17 - j2.16$$

$$= \mathbf{2.17\angle{-85.5} \text{ A}}$$

While Mesh current analysis yielded a solution without undue difficulty, this problem lends itself to solution by Thévenin's theorem. Indeed, it is important to learn to recognize the most appropriate method of solution at an early stage – to save work and to avoid error. Consequently, the other circuit theorems first discussed in Chapter 1 will now be introduced in the context of a.c. circuits.

Nodal analysis (Node Voltage method)

We have already discussed the method in Chapter 1 in relation to d.c. circuit analysis. Now, Nodal analysis is applied to an a.c. circuit in which we consider impedances instead of resistances.

Example 2.7

Calculate the output voltage V_o in the circuit of Fig. 2.10 using nodal analysis.

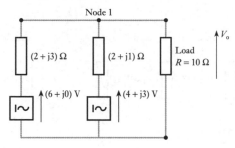

Fig. 2.10 Circuit diagram for Example 2.7

Apply Kirchhoff's current law ($\Sigma I = 0$) at node 1:

$$\frac{V_o - (6 + j0)}{2 + j3} + \frac{V_o - (4 + j3)}{2 + j1} + \frac{V_o}{10} = 0$$

Multiply by $(2 + j1)(2 + j3)$:

$$(2 + j1)(V_o - 6) + (2 + j3)V_o - (2 + j3)(4 + j3) + \frac{(2 + j1)(2 + j3)V_o}{10} = 0$$

$$V_o[2 + j1] + V_o[2 + j3] + \frac{V_o}{10}[4 - 3 + j8] - 12 - j6 - [-1 + j18] = 0$$

$$4.1V_o + j4.8V_o = 12 + j6 - 1 + j18$$

$$V_o = \frac{11 + j24}{4.1 + j4.8} = \frac{26.4\angle 65.4°}{6.31\angle 49.5°}$$

$$V_o = 4.18\angle 15.9°$$

Superposition theorem

We already know the concept of this theorem from Chapter 1 (see 'Superposition theorem', p. 94) so let us apply it to an example.

Example 2.8

By means of the Superposition theorem, determine the currents in the network shown in Fig. 2.11(a).

Because there are two sources of e.m.f. in the network, two separate networks need to be considered, each having one source of e.m.f. Figure 2.11(b) shows the network with the $(6 + j8)$ V source replaced by a short-circuit, there being no internal impedance indicated. Also, Fig. 2.11(c) shows the network with the $(10 + j0)$ V source similarly replaced.

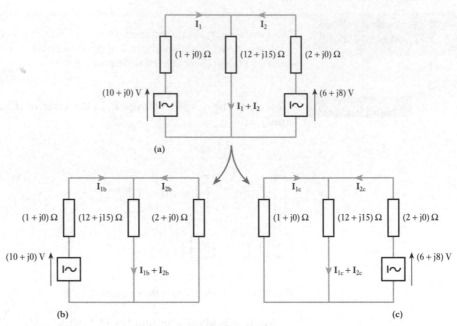

Fig. 2.11   Circuit diagrams for Example 2.8

For the Fig. 2.11(b) arrangement, the total impedance is

$$\mathbf{Z} = 1 + j0 + \frac{(12 + j15)(2 + j0)}{12 + j15 + 2 + j0} = 1 + \frac{24 + j30}{14 + j15}$$

$$= (2.87 + j0.14)\ \Omega$$

$$\therefore \qquad \mathbf{I}_{1b} = \frac{(10 + j0)}{2.87 + j0.14} = \frac{10(2.87 - j0.14)}{2.87^2 + 0.14^2} = (3.48 - j0.17)\ \text{A}$$

$$\mathbf{I}_{2b} = -(3.48 - j0.17)\frac{(12 + j15)}{(12 + j15) + (2 + j0)} = -(3.24 + j0.09)\ \text{A}$$

$$\therefore \qquad \mathbf{I}_{1b} + \mathbf{I}_{2b} = (3.48 - j0.17) - (3.24 + j0.09) = (0.24 - j0.26)\ \text{A}$$

For the Fig. 2.11(c) arrangement, the total impedance is

$$\mathbf{Z} = (2 + j0) + \frac{(12 + j15)(1 + j0)}{(12 + j15 + 1 + j0)} = 2 + \frac{12 + j15}{13 + j15}$$

$$= (2.97 + j0.04)\ \Omega$$

$$\mathbf{I}_{2c} = \frac{(6 + j8)}{(2.97 + j0.04)} = \frac{(6 + j8)(2.97 - j0.04)}{(8.823)}$$

$$= (2.06 + j2.67)\ \text{A}$$

$$\mathbf{I}_{1c} = -(2.06 + j2.67)\frac{(12 + j15)}{(12 + j15) + (1 + j0)}$$

$$= -(1.83 + j2.59)\ \text{A}$$

$$\therefore \qquad \mathbf{I}_{1c} + \mathbf{I}_{2c} = (0.23 + j0.08)\ \text{A}$$

Putting the two arrangements back together, we obtain:

$$\mathbf{I_1} = \mathbf{I_{1b}} + \mathbf{I_{1c}} = (3.48 - j0.17) - (1.83 + j2.59)$$

$$= (1.65 - j2.76) \text{ A}$$

$$\therefore \qquad I_1 = \mathbf{3.22 \text{ A}}$$

$$\mathbf{I_2} = \mathbf{I_{2b}} + \mathbf{I_{2c}} = (-3.24 - j0.09) + (2.06 + j2.67)$$

$$= (-1.18 + j2.58) \text{ A}$$

$$\therefore \qquad I_2 = \mathbf{2.84 \text{ A}}$$

$$\mathbf{I_1} + \mathbf{I_2} = (1.65 - j2.76) + (-1.18 + j2.58) = (0.47 - j0.18) \text{ A} = \mathbf{I_3}$$

$$\therefore \qquad I_3 = \mathbf{0.50 \text{ A}}$$

In this problem, it will be noted that the currents flowing in the sources are relatively large, especially when it is noted that both source e.m.f.s are 10 V. The reason is that the two voltages, although equal in magnitude, are not in phase opposition.

When applying the Superposition theorem, as in Example 2.8, it is assumed that the operational frequency of both sources is the same. If the frequencies were different, we could still determine the component currents, but they could not be added together. However, sources with different frequencies take us into more advanced techniques which we need only to consider in circuits such as communications circuits.

Thévenin's theorem

As with the concept of the Superposition theorem, the principles of application are the same except that we consider impedances instead of resistances. Thus the theorem can be stated as follows:

> Any two-terminal a.c. network can be replaced by an equivalent circuit consisting of a voltage source equal to the open circuit voltage at the terminals and a series impedance equal to the internal impedance as seen from the terminals.

Many networks from those involved with the highest to the lowest power levels can be represented in this way. The principle of operation needs to be demonstrated by a number of situations.

Example 2.9

Determine the Thévenin equivalent circuit for the network supplying the load shown in Fig. 2.12.

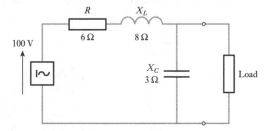

Fig. 2.12 Circuit diagram for Example 2.9

Let

$$\mathbf{V} = (100 + j0) \text{ V}$$

To determine the open-circuit voltage, let us consider the network shown in Fig. 2.13.

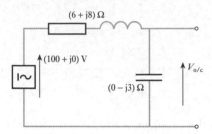

Fig. 2.13   Circuit diagram for Example 2.9

$$\frac{\mathbf{V}_{o/c}}{\mathbf{V}} = \frac{0 - j3}{(6 + j8) + (0 - j3)} = \frac{(-j3)(6 - j5)}{61} = (-0.246 - j0.295)$$

$$\therefore \qquad \mathbf{V}_{o/c} = (-24.6 - j29.5) \text{ V}$$

To determine the internal impedance, short-circuit the source and consider the circuit shown in Fig. 2.14.

$$\mathbf{Z}_{in} = \frac{(0 - j3) \cdot (6 + j8)}{(0 - j3) + (6 + j8)} = \frac{24 - j18}{6 + j5} = \frac{(24 - j18) \cdot (6 - j5)}{6^2 + 5^2}$$

$$= (0.89 - j3.74) \ \Omega$$

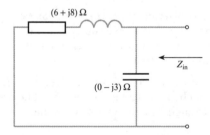

Fig. 2.14   Circuit diagram for Example 2.9

The equivalent circuit is therefore that shown in Fig. 2.15.

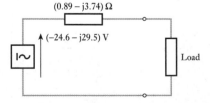

Fig. 2.15   Circuit diagram for Example 2.9

Example 2.10

For the circuit shown in Fig. 2.16, A and B represent the two terminals of a network. Calculate the load current. Note that this problem was solved earlier using Nodal analysis. In Example 2.7, V_{AB} was calculated.

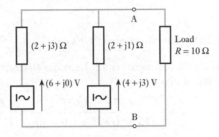

Fig. 2.16   Circuit diagram for Example 2.10

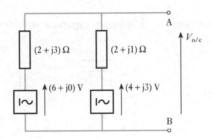

Fig. 2.17   Circuit diagram for Example 2.10

The open-circuit voltage can be obtained from the circuit shown in Fig. 2.17. The circuit will have a circulating current as follows:

$$I = \frac{(6 + j0) - (4 + j3)}{(2 + j3) + (2 + j1)} = \frac{2 - j3}{4 + j4}$$

$$= \frac{(2 - j3)(4 - j4)}{32} = \frac{-4 - j20}{32}$$

$$= -0.125 - j0.625$$

$$\therefore \quad V_{o/c} = [6 + j0] + (0.125 + j0.625)(2 + j3)$$

$$= 6 - 1.875 + 0.25 + j1.25 + j0.375$$

$$= 4.375 + j1.625 \text{ V}$$

or $V_{o/c} = 4.66\angle 20.4°$

To obtain the internal impedance, the sources are short-circuited and the circuit shown in Fig. 2.18 is used to determine the value.

Fig. 2.18   Circuit diagram for Example 2.10

$$Z_{in} = \frac{(2 + j3) \cdot (2 + j1)}{(2 + j3) + (2 + j1)} = \frac{1 + j8}{4 + j4} = (1.125 + j0.875) \ \Omega$$

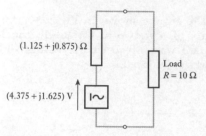

Fig. 2.19   Circuit diagram for Example 2.10

The total equivalent circuit becomes that shown in Fig. 2.19. Hence the load current is given by

$$\mathbf{I} = \frac{4.375 + j1.625}{1.125 + j0.875 + (10 + j0)} = \frac{4.66\angle 20.4°}{11.16\angle 4.5°}$$

$$\mathbf{I} = \mathbf{0.418\angle 15.9°}$$

Compare this method of solution with that of Example 2.7.

Example 2.11   **Determine the Thévenin equivalent circuit for the network shown in Fig. 2.20.**

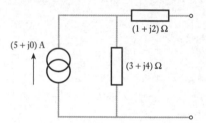

Fig. 2.20   Circuit diagram for Example 2.11

The open–circuit voltage is given by

$$\mathbf{V}_{o/c} = (5 + j0) \cdot (3 + j4) = \mathbf{(15 + j20)\ V}$$

The internal impedance is given by

$$\mathbf{Z}_{in} = (1 + j2) + (3 + j4) = \mathbf{(4 + j6)\ \Omega}$$

The equivalent circuit is therefore that shown in Fig. 2.21.

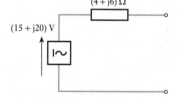

Fig. 2.21   Circuit diagram for Example 2.11

Example 2.12   **For the bridge network shown in Fig. 2.22, determine the current in the 10 Ω resistor.**

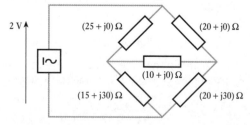

Fig. 2.22   Circuit diagram for Example 2.12

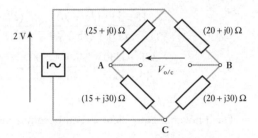

Fig. 2.23 Circuit diagram for Example 2.12

To determine the equivalent circuit as seen from the 10 Ω resistor consider first the open-circuit as illustrated in Fig. 2.23. Let

$$\mathbf{V} = (2 + j0) \text{ V}$$

$$\mathbf{V}_{AB} = \mathbf{V}_{AC} - \mathbf{V}_{BC}$$

$$= \left[\frac{15 + j30}{(15 + j30) + (25 + j0)} \cdot (2 + j0) \right] - \left[\frac{20 + j30}{(20 + j30) + (20 + j0)} \cdot (2 + j0) \right]$$

$$= \frac{30 + j60}{40 + j30} - \frac{40 + j60}{40 + j30} = \frac{-10 + j0}{40 + j30} = (-0.16 + j0.12) \text{ V}$$

Obtaining the internal impedance requires the source to be short-circuited as shown in Fig. 2.24.

Sometimes it is difficult to see the way in which to reduce the network in Fig. 2.24. It may help to redraw it as shown in Fig. 2.25. Careful comparison of Figs 2.24 and 2.25 will show that they are effectively the same.

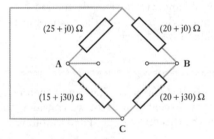

Fig. 2.24 Circuit diagram for Example 2.12

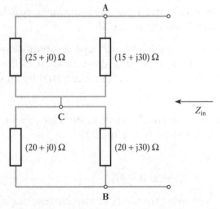

Fig. 2.25 Alternative circuit diagram to Fig. 2.24

$$Z_{in} = \frac{(15 + j30)(25 + j0)}{(15 + j30) + (25 + j0)} + \frac{(20 + j30)(20 + j0)}{(20 + j30) + (20 + j0)}$$

$$= \frac{375 + j750}{40 + j30} + \frac{400 + j600}{40 + j30} = \frac{775 + j1350}{40 + j30}$$

$$= (28.6 + j12.3) \ \Omega$$

The Thévenin equivalent circuit becomes that shown in Fig. 2.26.

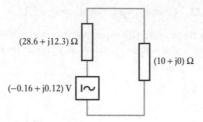

Fig. 2.26   Circuit diagram for Example 2.12

Current in 10 Ω resistor is given by

$$I = \frac{-0.16 + j0.12}{(28.6 + j12.3) + (10 + j0)} = \frac{-0.16 + j0.12}{38.6 + j12.3}$$

$$\therefore \qquad I = 6.17 \ \text{mA}$$

It is interesting to compare this solution with that of Example 2.6 since the problems were essentially the same. The length of the second solution was much the same, but the chances of making an analytical mistake were considerably reduced.

Norton's theorem

As with the concept of Thévenin's theorem, the principles of application are the same except that again we consider impedances instead of resistances. Thus the theorem can be stated as follows:

> Any two-terminal a.c. network can be replaced by an equivalent circuit consisting of a current source equal to the short-circuit current at the terminals and a parallel impedance equal to the internal impedance as seen from the terminals.

Norton's equivalent network is commonly associated with light current applications, especially those of semiconductor devices. Again the application of the theorem is best illustrated by an example.

Example 2.13

Determine the Norton equivalent circuit for the network supplying the load shown in Fig. 2.27.

Let

$$V = (100 + j0) \ V$$

To determine the short-circuit current, let us consider the network shown in Fig. 2.28.

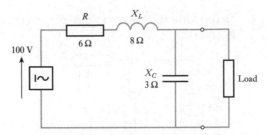

Fig. 2.27   Circuit diagram for Example 2.13

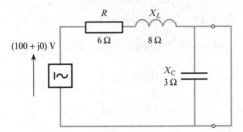

Fig. 2.28   Circuit diagram for Example 2.13

$$\mathbf{I}_{s/c} = \frac{100 + j0}{6 + j8} = \frac{100(6 - j8)}{100} = (6 - j8) \, \text{A}$$

To determine the internal impedance, short-circuit the source and consider the network shown in Fig. 2.29.

$$\mathbf{Z}_{in} = \frac{(0 - j3) \cdot (6 + j8)}{(0 - j3) + (6 + j8)} = \frac{24 - j18}{6 + j5} = \frac{(24 - j18) \cdot (6 - j5)}{6^2 + 5^2}$$

$$= (0.89 - j3.74) \, \Omega$$

The equivalent network is therefore that shown in Fig. 2.30.

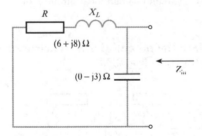

Fig. 2.29   Circuit diagram for Example 2.13

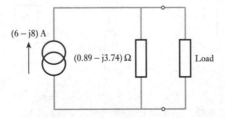

Fig. 2.30   Circuit diagram for Example 2.13

Example 2.14   Determine the Norton equivalent circuit for the network shown in Fig. 2.31.

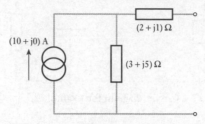

Fig. 2.31   Circuit diagram for Example 2.14

The short-circuit current is given by

$$\mathbf{I}_{s/c} = (10 + j0) \cdot \frac{3 + j5}{(3 + j5) + (2 + j1)} = \frac{30 + j50}{5 + j6}$$

$$= \frac{(30 + j50)(5 - j6)}{61} = (7.38 - j0.82) \, \mathbf{A}$$

The internal impedance is given by

$$\mathbf{Z}_{in} = (3 + j5) + (2 + j1) = (5 + j6) \, \Omega$$

The equivalent circuit therefore is that shown in Fig. 2.32.

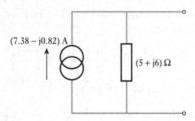

Fig. 2.32   Circuit diagram for Example 2.14

Example 2.15   Calculate the potential difference across the 2 Ω resistor in the network shown in Fig. 2.33.

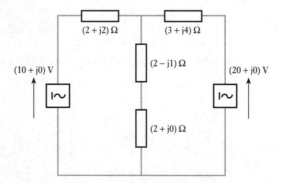

Fig. 2.33   Circuit diagram for Example 2.15

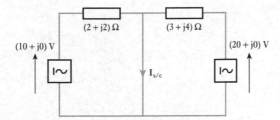

Fig. 2.34 Circuit diagram for Example 2.15

Short-circuit the branch containing the 2 Ω resistor as shown in Fig. 2.34.

$$\mathbf{I}_{s/c} = \frac{10 + j0}{2 + j2} + \frac{20 + j0}{3 + j4} = \frac{20 - j20}{2^2 + 2^2} + \frac{60 - j80}{3^2 + 4^2}$$

$$= 2.5 - j2.5 + 2.4 - j3.2 = (4.9 - j5.7) \text{ A}$$

To obtain the internal impedance, replace the sources with short-circuits and look into the network from the ends of the branch.

$$\mathbf{Z}_{in} = \frac{(2 + j2) \cdot (3 + j4)}{(2 + j2) + (3 + j4)} = \frac{-2 + j14}{5 + j6} = \frac{(-2 + j14)(5 - j6)}{61}$$

$$= (1.21 + j1.34) \text{ Ω}$$

The circuit therefore reduces to that given in Fig. 2.35.

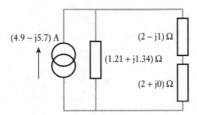

Fig. 2.35 Circuit diagram for Example 2.15

For the 2 Ω resistor:

$$\mathbf{I} = (4.9 - j5.7) \frac{(1.21 + j1.34)}{(1.21 + j1.34) + [(2 + j0) + (2 - j1)]}$$

$$= (4.9 - j5.7) \frac{(1.21 + j1.34)}{(5.21 + j0.34)} = 7.52\angle -49.3° \cdot \frac{1.81\angle 47.9°}{5.22\angle 3.7°}$$

$$= 2.61\angle -5.1° \text{ A}$$

Therefore for the 2 Ω resistor:

$$V = 2.61\angle -5.1° \times 2 = 5.22\angle -5.1° \text{ V} \quad \text{or} \quad (5.20 - j0.46) \text{ V}$$

Hence

$$V = \mathbf{5.22 \text{ V}}$$

Inductance in a DC circuit

Mutual inductance

If two coils A and C are placed relative to each other as in Fig. 2.36, then, when S is closed, some of the flux produced by the current in A becomes linked with C, and the e.m.f. induced in C circulates a momentary current through galvanometer G. Similarly when S is opened the collapse of the flux induces an e.m.f. in the reverse direction in C. Since a change of current in one coil is accompanied by a change of flux linked with the other coil and therefore by an e.m.f. induced in the latter, the two coils are said to have *mutual inductance*.

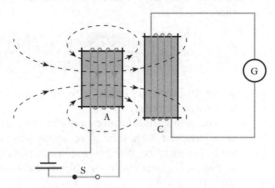

Fig. 2.36   Mutual inductance

The unit of mutual inductance is the same as for self-inductance, namely the *henry*; and *two coils have a mutual inductance of 1 henry if an e.m.f. of 1 volt is induced in one coil when the current in the other coil varies uniformly at the rate of 1 ampere per second.*

Mutual inductance   Symbol: M Unit: **henry (H)**

If two circuits possess a mutual inductance of M henrys and if the current in one circuit – termed the *primary* circuit – increases by di amperes in dt seconds, e.m.f. induced in *secondary* circuit is

$$M \cdot \frac{di}{dt} \text{ volts} \qquad [2.1]$$

The induced e.m.f. tends to circulate a current in the secondary circuit in such a direction as to oppose the increase of flux due to the increase of current in the primary circuit.

If $d\phi$ webers is the increase of flux linked with the secondary circuit due to the increase of di amperes in the primary, e.m.f. induced in secondary circuit is

$$N_2 \cdot \frac{d\phi}{dt} \text{ volts} \qquad [2.2]$$

where N_2 is the number of secondary turns. From expressions [2.1] and [2.2]

$$M \cdot \frac{\mathrm{d}i}{\mathrm{d}t} = N_2 \cdot \frac{\mathrm{d}\phi}{\mathrm{d}t}$$

$$\therefore \qquad M = N_2 \cdot \frac{\mathrm{d}\phi}{\mathrm{d}i} \qquad\qquad [2.3]$$

$$= \frac{\text{change of flux-linkages with secondary}}{\text{change of current in primary}}$$

If the relative permeability of the magnetic circuit remains constant, the ratio $\mathrm{d}\phi/\mathrm{d}i$ must also remain constant and is equal to the flux per ampere, so that

$$M = \frac{\text{flux-linkages with secondary}}{\text{current in primary}} = \frac{N_2 \Phi_2}{I_1} \qquad [2.4]$$

where Φ_2 is the flux linked with the secondary circuit due to a current I_1 in the primary circuit.

The mutual inductance between two circuits, A and B, is precisely the same, whether we assume A to be the primary and B the secondary or vice versa; for instance, if the two coils are wound on a non-metallic cylinder, as in Fig. 2.37, then energy in the magnetic field due to current I_A in coil A alone is

$$\tfrac{1}{2}L_A I_A^2 \text{ joules}$$

and energy in the magnetic field due to current I_B in coil B alone is

$$\tfrac{1}{2}L_B I_B^2 \text{ joules}$$

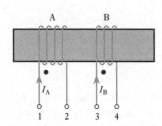

Fig. 2.37 Mutual inductance

Suppose the current in B to be maintained steady at I_B amperes in the direction shown in Fig. 2.37, and the current in A to be increased by $\mathrm{d}i$ amperes in $\mathrm{d}t$ seconds, then

$$\text{EMF induced in B} = M_{12} \cdot \frac{\mathrm{d}i}{\mathrm{d}t} \text{ volts}$$

where M_{12} is the mutual inductance when A is primary.

If the direction of I_A is that indicated by the arrowhead in Fig. 2.37, then, by Lenz's law, the direction of the e.m.f. induced in B is anticlockwise when the coil is viewed from the right-hand end, i.e. the induced e.m.f. is in opposition to I_B and the p.d. across terminals 3 and 4 has to be increased by $M_{12} \cdot \mathrm{d}i/\mathrm{d}t$ volts to maintain I_B constant. Hence the *additional* electrical energy absorbed by coil B in time $\mathrm{d}t$ is

$$I_B M_{12}\left(\frac{\mathrm{d}i}{\mathrm{d}t}\right) \times \mathrm{d}t = I_B M_{12} \cdot \mathrm{d}i \text{ joules}$$

Since I_B remains constant, the I^2R loss in B is unaffected, and there is no e.m.f. induced in coil A apart from that due to the increase of I_A; therefore this additional energy supplied to coil B is absorbed by the magnetic field. Hence, when the current in A has increased to I_A, total energy in magnetic field is

$$\tfrac{1}{2}L_A I_A^2 + \tfrac{1}{2}L_B I_B^2 + \int_0^{I_A} I_B M_{12} \cdot di$$

$$= \tfrac{1}{2}L_A I_A^2 + \tfrac{1}{2}L_B I_B^2 + M_{12} I_A I_B \text{ joules}$$

If the direction of either I_A or I_B was reversed, the direction of the e.m.f. induced in B, while the current in A was increasing, would be the same as that of I_B, and coil B would then be acting as a source. By the time the current in A would have reached its steady value I_A, the energy withdrawn from the magnetic field and generated in coil B would be $M_{12}I_A I_B$ joules, and final energy in magnetic field would be

$$\tfrac{1}{2}L_A I_A^2 + \tfrac{1}{2}L_B I_B^2 - M_{12} I_A I_B \text{ joules}$$

Hence, in general, total energy in magnetic field is

$$\tfrac{1}{2}L_A I_A^2 + \tfrac{1}{2}L_B I_B^2 \pm M_{12} I_A I_B \quad \text{joules} \qquad [2.5]$$

the sign being positive when the ampere-turns due to I_A and I_B are additive, and negative when they are in opposition.

If M_{21} were the mutual inductance with coil B as primary, it could be shown by a similar procedure that the total energy in the magnetic field is

$$\tfrac{1}{2}L_A I_A^2 + \tfrac{1}{2}L_B I_B^2 \pm M_{21} I_A I_B \text{ joules}$$

Since the final conditions are identical in the two cases, the energies must be the same,

$$\therefore \qquad M_{12} I_A I_B = M_{21} I_A I_B$$

or $$M_{12} = M_{21} = (\text{say}) \ M$$

i.e. the mutual inductance between two circuits is the same whichever circuit is taken as the primary.

When the two coils are shown on a common core, as in Fig. 2.37, it is obvious that the magnetomotive forces due to I_A and I_B are additive when the directions of the currents are as indicated by the arrowheads. If, however, the coils are drawn as in Fig. 2.38, it is impossible to state whether the magnetomotive forces due to currents I_A and I_B are additive or in opposition; and it is to remove this ambiguity that the dot notation has been adopted. Thus, in Figs 2.37 and 2.38, dots are inserted at ends 1 and 3 of the coils to indicate that when currents *enter both* coils (or *leave both* coils) at these ends, as in Fig. 2.38(a), the magnetomotive forces of the coils are additive,

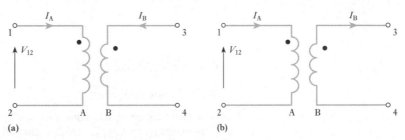

(a)   (b)

Fig. 2.38   Application of the dot notation

and the mutual inductance is then said to be *positive*. But if I_A *enters* coil A at the dotted end and I_B *leaves* coil B at the dotted end, as in Fig. 2.38(b), the m.m.f.s of the coils are in opposition and the mutual inductance is then said to be *negative*.

Coupling coefficient

Suppose a ring of non-magnetic material to be wound *uniformly* with two coils, A and B, the turns of one coil being as close as possible to those of the other coil, so that the whole of the flux produced by current in one coil is linked with all the turns of the other coil.

The reluctance S for a magnetic circuit is given by

$$S = \frac{F}{\Phi} = \frac{NI}{\Phi}$$

If coil A has N_1 turns and B has N_2 turns, and if the reluctance of the magnetic circuit is S amperes per weber, then the self-inductances of A and B are

$$L_1 = \frac{N_1\Phi_1}{I_1} = \frac{N_1^2\Phi_1}{I_1N_1} = \frac{N_1^2}{S} \qquad [2.6]$$

and

$$L_2 = \frac{N_2\Phi_2}{I_2} = \frac{N_2^2}{S} \qquad [2.7]$$

where Φ_1 and Φ_2 are the magnetic fluxes due to I_1 in coil A and I_2 in coil B respectively, and

$$S = \frac{I_1N_1}{\Phi_1} = \frac{I_2N_2}{\Phi_2}$$

Since the whole of flux Φ_1 due to I_1 is linked with coil B, it follows from expression [2.4] that

$$M = \frac{N_2\Phi_1}{I_1} = \frac{N_1N_2\Phi_1}{I_1N_1}$$

$$M = \frac{N_1N_2}{S} \qquad [2.8]$$

Hence, from equations [2.6], [2.7] and [2.8],

$$L_1L_2 = \frac{N_1^2N_2^2}{S^2} = M^2$$

so that

$$M = \sqrt{(L_1L_2)} \qquad [2.9]$$

We have assumed that

1. The reluctance remains constant.
2. The magnetic leakage is zero, i.e. that all the flux produced by one coil is linked with the other coil.

The first assumption means that expression [2.9] is strictly correct only when the magnetic circuit is of non-magnetic material. It is, however, approximately correct for a ferromagnetic core if the latter has one or more gaps of air or non-magnetic material, since the reluctance of such a magnetic circuit is approximately constant.

When there is magnetic leakage, i.e. when all the flux due to current in one coil is not linked with the other coil,

$$M = k\sqrt{(L_1 L_2)} \tag{2.10}$$

where k is termed the *coupling coefficient*. 'Coupling coefficient' is a term much used in radio work to denote the degree of coupling between two coils; thus, if the two coils are close together, most of the flux produced by current in one coil passes through the other and the coils are said to be *tightly* coupled. If the coils are well apart, only a small fraction of the flux is linked with the secondary, and the coils are said to be *loosely* coupled.

Example 2.16 A ferromagnetic ring of cross-sectional area 800 mm² and of mean radius 170 mm has two windings connected in series, one of 500 turns and one of 700 turns. If the relative permeability is 1200, calculate the self-inductance of each coil and the mutual inductance of each assuming that there is no flux leakage.

$$S = \frac{l}{\mu_0 \mu_r A} = \frac{2\pi \times 170 \times 10^{-3}}{4\pi \times 10^{-7} \times 1200 \times 800 \times 10^{-6}}$$

$$= 8.85 \times 10^5 \, \text{H}$$

$$L_1 = \frac{N_1^2}{S} = \frac{500^2}{8.85 \times 10^5} = 0.283 \, \text{H}$$

$$L_2 = \frac{N_2^2}{S} = \frac{700^2}{8.85 \times 10^5} = 0.552 \, \text{H}$$

$$M = k(L_1 L_2)^{\frac{1}{2}} = 1 \times (0.283 \times 0.552)^{\frac{1}{2}} = 0.395 \, \text{H}$$

Alternating voltage and current

Average and r.m.s. values of an alternating current

Most electrical energy is provided by rotating a.c. generators operating on the principles already described in this chapter. The e.m.f.s and the resulting voltages and currents are for the most part sinusoidal which is the waveform on which we have concentrated. However, the use of electronic switching has resulted in many circuits operating with waveforms which are anything but sinusoidal; square waveforms are especially common in communication circuits.

Let us first consider the general case of a current the waveform of which cannot be represented by a simple mathematical expression. For instance, the wave shown in Fig. 2.39 is typical of the current taken by a transformer on no load. If n equidistant mid-ordinates, i_1, i_2, etc. are taken over either the positive or the negative half-cycle, then *average* value of current over half a cycle is

$$I_{av} = \frac{i_1 + i_2 + \ldots + i_n}{n}$$ [2.11]

Or, alternatively, average value of current is

$$\frac{\text{Area enclosed over half-cycle}}{\text{Length of base over half-cycle}}$$ [2.12]

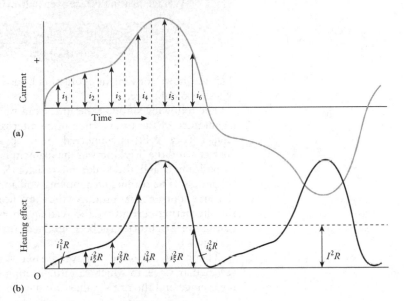

Fig. 2.39 Average and r.m.s. values

This method of expressing the average value is the more convenient when we come to deal with sinusoidal waves.

In a.c. work, however, the average value is of comparatively little importance. This is due to the fact that it is the power produced by the electric current that usually matters. Thus, if the current represented in Fig. 2.39(a) is passed through a resistor having resistance R ohms, the heating effect of i_1 is $i_1^2 R$, that of i_2 is $i_2^2 R$, etc. as shown in Fig. 2.39(b). The variation of the heating effect during the second half-cycle is exactly the same as that during the first half-cycle.

$\therefore \qquad$ Average heating effect $= \dfrac{i_1^2 R + i_2^2 R + \ldots + i_n^2 R}{n}$

Suppose I to be the value of *direct* current through the same resistance R to produce a heating effect equal to the average heating effect of the alternating current, then

$$I^2 R = \frac{i_1^2 R + i_2^2 R + \ldots + i_n^2 R}{n}$$

$\therefore \qquad$ $I = \sqrt{\left(\dfrac{i_1^2 + i_2^2 + \ldots + i_n^2}{n}\right)}$ [2.13]

$=$ square *root* of the *mean* of the *squares* of the current

$=$ root-mean-square (or r.m.s.) value of the current

This quantity is also termed the *effective* value of the current. It will be seen that the r.m.s. or *effective value of an alternating current is measured in terms of the* direct *current that produces the same heating effect in the same resistance*.

Alternatively, the average heating effect can be expressed as follows:

Average heating effect over half-cycle

$= \dfrac{\text{area enclosed by } i^2 R \text{ curve over half-cycle}}{\text{length of base}}$ [2.14]

This is a more convenient expression to use when deriving the r.m.s. value of a sinusoidal current.

The following simple experiment can be found useful in illustrating the significance of the r.m.s. value of an alternating current. A metal-filament lamp L (Fig. 2.40) is connected to an a.c. supply by closing switch S on contact a and the brightness of the filament is noted. Switch S is then moved to position b and the slider on resistor R is adjusted to give the same brightness. The reading on a moving-coil ammeter A then gives the value of the direct current that produces the same heating effect as that produced by the alternating current. If the reading on ammeter A is, say, 0.3 A when equality of brightness has been attained, the r.m.s. value of the alternating current is 0.3 A.

The r.m.s. value is always greater than the average except for a rectangular wave, in which case the heating effect remains constant so that the average and the r.m.s. values are the same.

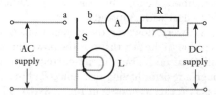

Fig. 2.40 An experiment to demonstrate the r.m.s. value of an alternating current

Form factor of a wave is

$$\frac{\text{RMS value}}{\text{Average value}} \qquad\qquad [2.15]$$

Peak or *crest factor* of a wave is

$$\frac{\text{Peak or maximum value}}{\text{RMS value}} \qquad\qquad [2.16]$$

Average and r.m.s. values of sinusoidal currents and voltages

If I_m is the maximum value of a current which varies sinusoidally as shown in Fig. 2.41(a), the instantaneous value i is represented by

$$i = I_m \sin \theta$$

where θ is the angle in radians from instant of zero current.

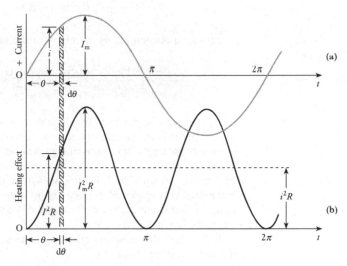

Fig. 2.41 Average and r.m.s. values of a sinusoidal current

For a very small interval $d\theta$ radians, the area of the shaded strip is $i \cdot d\theta$ ampere radians. The use of the unit 'ampere radian' avoids converting the scale on the horizontal axis from radians to seconds, therefore, total area enclosed by the current wave over half-cycle is

$$\int_0^\pi i \cdot d\theta = I_m \int_0^\pi \sin \theta \cdot d\theta = -I_m \Big[\cos \theta \Big]_0^\pi$$

$$= -I_m[-1 - 1] = 2I_m \text{ ampere radians}$$

From expression [2.12], average value of current over a half-cycle is

$$\frac{2I_m \text{ [ampere radians]}}{\pi \text{ [radians]}}$$

i.e. $I_{av} = 0.637 I_m$ amperes   [2.17]

If the current is passed through a resistor having resistance R ohms, instantaneous heating effect $= i^2R$ watts.

The variation of i^2R during a complete cycle is shown in Fig. 2.41(b). During interval $d\theta$ radians, heat generated is $i^2R \cdot d\theta$ watt radians and is represented by the area of the shaded strip. Hence heat generated during the first half-cycle is area enclosed by the i^2R curve and is

$$\int_0^\pi i^2R \cdot d\theta = I_m^2 R \int_0^\pi \sin^2\theta \cdot d\theta$$

$$= \frac{I_m^2 R}{2} \int_0^\pi (1 - \cos 2\theta) \cdot d\theta$$

$$= \frac{I_m^2 R}{2} \left[\theta - \tfrac{1}{2}\sin 2\theta\right]_0^\pi$$

$$= \frac{\pi}{2} I_m^2 R \text{ watt radians}$$

From expression [2.14], average heating effect is

$$\frac{(\pi/2)I_m^2 R \text{ [watt radians]}}{\pi \text{ [radians]}} = \tfrac{1}{2} I_m^2 R \text{ watts} \qquad [2.18]$$

This result can be observed from the equation $\sin^2\theta = \tfrac{1}{2} - \tfrac{1}{2}\cos 2\theta$. In words, this means that the square of a sine wave may be regarded as being made up of two components: (a) a constant quantity equal to half the maximum value of the $\sin^2\theta$ curve, and (b) a cosine curve having twice the frequency of the $\sin\theta$ curve. From Fig. 2.41 it is seen that the curve of the heating effect undergoes two cycles of change during one cycle of current. The average value of component (b) over a complete cycle is zero; hence the average heating effect is $\tfrac{1}{2}I_m^2 R$.

If I is the value of direct current through the same resistance to produce the same heating effect

$$I^2R = \tfrac{1}{2}I_m^2 R$$

$\therefore$ $I = \dfrac{I_m}{\sqrt{2}} = 0.707 I_m$ [2.19]

While I is I_{RMS} it is normal practice to omit the RMS subscript, as this is the most common current.

Since the voltage across the resistor is directly proportional to the current, it follows that the relationships derived for currents also apply to voltages.

Hence, in general, average value of a sinusoidal current or voltage is

$0.637 \times$ maximum value

$\therefore$ $I_{av} = 0.637 I_m$ [2.20]

r.m.s. value of a sinusoidal current or voltage is

0.707 × maximum value

$$\therefore \quad I = 0.707 I_m \tag{2.21}$$

From expressions [2.20] and [2.21], form factor of a sine wave is

$$\frac{0.707 \times \text{maximum value}}{0.637 \times \text{maximum value}}$$

$$k_f = 1.11 \tag{2.22}$$

and peak or crest factor of a sine wave is

$$\frac{\text{maximum value}}{0.707 \times \text{maximum value}}$$

$$\therefore \quad k_p = 1.414 \tag{2.23}$$

Example 2.17 An alternating current of sinusoidal waveform has an r.m.s. value of 10.0 A. What are the peak values of this current over one cycle?

$$I_m = \frac{I}{0.707} = \frac{10}{0.707} = 14.14 \text{ A}$$

The peak values therefore are **14.14 A** and **−14.14 A**.

Example 2.18 An alternating voltage has the equation $v = 141.4 \sin 377t$; what are the values of:

(a) r.m.s. voltage;
(b) frequency;
(c) the instantaneous voltage when $t = 3$ ms?

The relation is of the form $v = V_m \sin \omega t$ and, by comparison,

(a) $V_m = 141.4 \text{ V} = \sqrt{2} V$

hence $V = \dfrac{141.4}{\sqrt{2}} = 100 \text{ V}$

(b) Also by comparison

$$\omega = 377 \text{ rad/s} = 2\pi f$$

hence $f = \dfrac{377}{2\pi} = 60 \text{ Hz}$

(c) Finally

$$v = 141.4 \sin 377t$$

When $t = 3 \times 10^{-3}$ s

$$v = 141.4 \sin(377 \times 3 \times 10^{-3}) = 141.4 \sin 1.131$$

$$= 141.4 \times 0.904 = \mathbf{127.8 \text{ V}}$$

Note that, in this example, it was necessary to determine the sine of 1.131 rad, which could be obtained either from suitable tables, or from a calculator. Alternatively, 1.131 rad may be converted into degree measurement, i.e.

$$1.131 \text{ rad} \equiv 1.131 \times \frac{180}{\pi} = 64.8°$$

Example 2.19　A moving-coil ammeter, a thermal* ammeter and a rectifier are connected in series with a resistor across a 110 V sinusoidal a.c. supply. The circuit has a resistance of 50 Ω to current in one direction and, due to the rectifier, an infinite resistance to current in the reverse direction. Calculate:

(a) the readings on the ammeters;
(b) the form and peak factors of the current wave.

(a) Maximum value of the voltage

$$V_{\text{m}} = \frac{V}{0.707} = \frac{110}{0.707} = 155.5 \text{ V}$$

therefore maximum value of the current

$$I_{\text{m}} = \frac{V_{\text{m}}}{R} = \frac{155.5}{50} = 3.11 \text{ A}$$

During the positive half-cycle the current is proportional to the voltage and is therefore sinusoidal, as shown in Fig. 2.42(a); therefore average value of current over the positive half-cycle

$$I_{\text{av}} = 0.637 I_{\text{m}} = 0.637 \times 3.11 = 1.98 \text{ A}$$

During the negative half-cycle, the current is zero. Owing, however, to the inertia of the moving system, the moving-coil ammeter reads the average value of the current over the *whole* cycle, therefore reading on moving-coil ammeter is

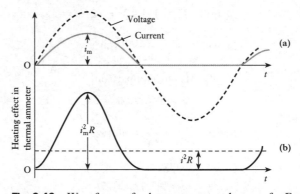

Fig. 2.42　Waveforms of voltage, current and power for Example 2.19

* A thermal ammeter is an instrument the operation of which depends upon the heating effect of a current.

$$\frac{1.98}{2} = 0.99 \, \text{A}$$

The variation of the heating effect in the thermal ammeter is shown in Fig. 2.42(b), the maximum power being $I_m^2 R$, where R is the resistance of the instrument.

From expression [2.18] it is seen that the average heating effect over the positive half-cycle is $\frac{1}{2}I_m^2 R$; and since no heat is generated during the second half-cycle, it follows that the average heating effect over a complete cycle is $\frac{1}{4}I_m^2 R$.

If I is the direct current which would produce the same heating effect

$$I^2 R = \tfrac{1}{4}I_m^2 R$$

$$\therefore \qquad I = \tfrac{1}{2}I_m = \frac{3.11}{2} = 1.555 \, \text{A}$$

i.e. reading on thermal ammeter = **1.56 A**.

A mistake that can very easily be made is to calculate the r.m.s. value of the current over the positive half-cycle as 0.707×3.11, namely 2.2 A, and then say that the reading on the thermal ammeter is half this value, namely 1.1 A. The importance of working out such a problem from first principles should now be evident.

(b) From equation [2.22], form factor is

$$k_f = \frac{I}{I_{av}} = \frac{1.555}{0.99} = 1.57$$

and from equation [2.23], peak factor is

$$k_p = \frac{I_m}{I} = \frac{3.11}{1.555} = 2.0$$

Average and r.m.s. values of non-sinusoidal currents and voltages

Having demonstrated the determination of average and r.m.s. values for sinusoidal currents and voltages, it is a relatively short step to consider non-sinusoidal quantities. This can easily be done by considering further examples.

Example 2.20

A current has the following steady values in amperes for equal intervals of time changing instantaneously from one value to the next (Fig. 2.43):

0, 10, 20, 30, 20, 10, 0, −10, −20, −30, −20, −10, 0, etc.

Calculate the r.m.s. value of the current and its form factor.

Because of the symmetry of the waveform, it is only necessary to calculate the values over the first half-cycle.

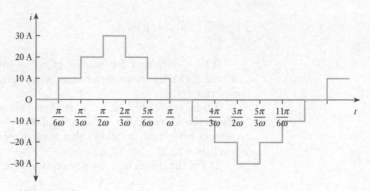

Fig. 2.43 Part of Example 2.20

$$I_{av} = \frac{\text{area under curve}}{\text{length of base}}$$

$$= \frac{0\left(\frac{\pi}{6\omega} - 0\right) + 10\left(\frac{2\pi}{6\omega} - \frac{\pi}{6\omega}\right) + 20\left(\frac{3\pi}{6\omega} - \frac{2\pi}{6\omega}\right) + 30\left(\frac{4\pi}{6\omega} - \frac{3\pi}{6\omega}\right) + 20\left(\frac{5\pi}{6\omega} - \frac{4\pi}{6\omega}\right) + 10\left(\frac{6\pi}{6\omega} - \frac{5\pi}{6\omega}\right)}{\frac{\pi}{\omega} - 0}$$

$$= 15.0 \text{ A}$$

$$I^2 = \frac{0^2\left(\frac{\pi}{6\omega} - 0\right) + 10^2\left(\frac{2\pi}{6\omega} - \frac{\pi}{6\omega}\right) + 20^2\left(\frac{3\pi}{6\omega} - \frac{2\pi}{6\omega}\right) + 30^2\left(\frac{4\pi}{6\omega} - \frac{3\pi}{6\omega}\right) + 20^2\left(\frac{5\pi}{6\omega} - \frac{4\pi}{6\omega}\right) + 10^2\left(\frac{6\pi}{6\omega} - \frac{5\pi}{6\omega}\right)}{\frac{\pi}{\omega} - 0}$$

$$= 316$$

$$I = \sqrt{316} = \mathbf{17.8 \text{ A}}$$

$$k_f = \frac{I}{I_{av}} = \frac{17.8}{15.0} = \mathbf{1.19}$$

Example 2.21 Calculate the form factor for each of the waveforms in Fig. 2.44.

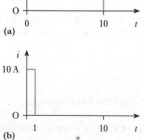

Fig. 2.44 Part of Example 2.21

For Fig. 2.44(a):

$$I_{av} = \frac{1(10 - 0)}{10 - 0} = 1.0 \text{ A}$$

$$I = \left(\frac{1^2(10 - 0)}{10 - 0}\right)^{\frac{1}{2}} = 1.0 \text{ A}$$

$$k_f = \frac{I}{I_{av}} = \frac{1.0}{1.0}$$

$$= \mathbf{1.0}$$

For Fig. 2.44(b):

$$I_{av} = \frac{10(1 - 0) + 0(10 - 1)}{10 - 0} = 1.0 \text{ A}$$

$$I = \left(\frac{10^2(1 - 0) + 0^2(10 - 1)}{10 - 0}\right)^{\frac{1}{2}} = 3.16 \text{ A}$$

$$k_f = \frac{I}{I_{av}} = \frac{3.16}{1.0}$$

$$= \mathbf{3.16}$$

It will be noted that the first waveform is that of direct current in which the r.m.s. current and the mean current have the same value. It is for this reason that the r.m.s. value of an alternating current may be equated to the mean value of a direct current.

Representation of an alternating quantity by a phasor

Suppose OA in Fig. 2.45(a) to represent to scale the maximum value of an alternating quantity, say, current, i.e. $OA = I_m$. Also, suppose OA to rotate anticlockwise about O at a uniform angular velocity. This is purely a conventional direction which has been universally adopted. An arrowhead is drawn at the outer end of the phasor, partly to indicate which end is assumed to move and partly to indicate the precise length of the phasor when two or more phasors happen to coincide.

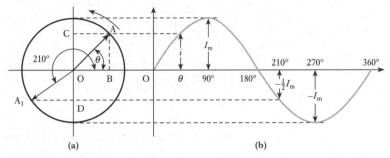

Fig. 2.45   Phasor representation of an alternating quantity

Figure 2.45(a) shows OA when it has rotated through an angle θ from the position occupied when the current was passing through its zero value. If AB and AC are drawn perpendicular to the horizontal and vertical axes respectively:

$$OC = AB = OA \sin \theta$$

$$= I_m \sin \theta$$

$$= i, \text{ namely the value of the current at that instant}$$

Hence the projection of OA on the vertical axis represents to scale the instantaneous value of the current. Thus when $\theta = 90°$, the projection is OA itself; when $\theta = 180°$, the projection is zero and corresponds to the current passing through zero from a positive to a negative value; when $\theta = 210°$, the phasor is in position OA_1, and the projection $= OD = \frac{1}{2}OA_1 = -\frac{1}{2}I_m$; and when $\theta = 360°$, the projection is again zero and corresponds to the current passing through zero from a negative to a positive value. It follows that OA rotates through one revolution or 2π radians in one cycle of the current wave.

If f is the frequency in hertz, then OA rotates through f revolutions of $2\pi f$ radians in 1 s. Hence the angular velocity of OA is $2\pi f$ radians per second and is denoted by the symbol ω (omega), i.e.

$$\omega = 2\pi f \quad \text{radians per second} \qquad [2.24]$$

If the time taken by OA in Fig. 2.45 to rotate through an angle θ radians is t seconds, then

$$\theta = \text{angular velocity} \times \text{time}$$

$$= \omega t = 2\pi f t \text{ radians}$$

We can therefore express the instantaneous value of the current thus:

$$i = I_m \sin \theta = I_m \sin \omega t$$

$$\therefore \qquad i = I_m \sin 2\pi f t \qquad [2.25]$$

Let us next consider how two quantities such as voltage and current can be represented by a phasor diagram. Figure 2.46(b) shows the voltage leading the current by an angle ϕ. In Fig. 2.46(a), OA represents the maximum value of the current and OB that of the voltage. The angle between OA and OB must be the same angle ϕ as in Fig. 2.46(b). Consequently when OA is along the horizontal axis, the current at that instant is zero and the value of the voltage is represented by the projection of OB on the vertical axis. These values correspond to instant O in Fig. 2.46(b).

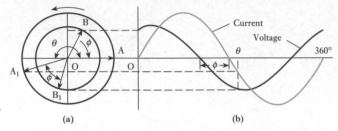

Fig. 2.46   Phasor representation of quantitites differing in phase

After the phasors have rotated through an angle θ, they occupy positions OA_1 and OB_1 respectively, with OB_1 still leading OA_1 by the same angle ϕ; and the instantaneous values of the current and voltage are again given by the projections of OA_1 and OB_1 on the vertical axis, as shown by the horizontal dotted lines.

If the instantaneous value of the current is represented by

$$i = I_m \sin \theta$$

then the instantaneous value of the voltage is represented by

$$v = V_m \sin(\theta + \phi)$$

where $I_m = OA$ and $V_m = OB$ in Fig. 2.46(a).

The current in Fig. 2.46 is said to *lag* the voltage by an angle ϕ which is the *phase difference* between the two phasors. The phase difference remains constant irrespective of the phasor positions. When one sine wave passes through the zero following another, it is said to lag. Thus in Fig. 2.46, the current lags the voltage.

Addition and subtraction of sinusoidal alternating quantities

Suppose OA and OB in Fig. 2.47 to be phasors representing to scale the maximum values of, say, two alternating voltages having the same frequency but differing in phase by an angle ϕ. Complete the parallelogram OACB and draw the diagonal OC. Project OA, OB and OC on to the vertical axis. Then for the positions shown in Fig. 2.47:

Instantaneous value of OA = OD

Instantaneous value of OB = OE

and   Instantaneous value of OC = OF

Since AC is parallel and equal to OB, DF = OE,

∴   OF = OD + DF = OD + OE

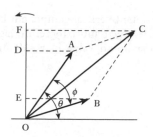

Fig. 2.47 Addition of phasors

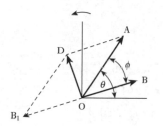

Fig. 2.48 Subtraction of phasors

i.e. the instantaneous value of OC equals the sum of the instantaneous values of OA and OB. Hence OC represents the maximum value of the resultant voltage to the scale that OA and OB represent the maximum values of the separate voltages. Therefore OC is termed the *phasor sum* of OA and OB; and it is evident that OC is less than the arithmetic sum of OA and OB except when the latter are in phase with each other. This is the reason why it is seldom correct in a.c. work to add voltages or currents together arithmetically.

If voltage OB is to be subtracted from OA, then OB is produced backwards so that OB_1 is equal and opposite to OB (Fig. 2.48). The diagonal OD of the parallelogram drawn on OA and OB_1 represents the *phasor differences* of OA and OB.

For simplicity, OA can be represented by **A** and OB as **B**, bold letters being used to indicate the appropriate phasors. It follows that

$$\mathbf{C} = \mathbf{A} + \mathbf{B} \quad \text{and} \quad \mathbf{D} = \mathbf{A} - \mathbf{B}$$

Example 2.22

The instantaneous values of two alternating voltages are represented respectively by $v_1 = 60 \sin \theta$ volts and $v_2 = 40 \sin(\theta - \pi/3)$ volts. Derive an expression for the instantaneous value of:

(a) the sum;
(b) the difference of these voltages.

(a) It is usual to draw the phasors in the position corresponding to $\theta = 0$,[*] i.e. OA in Fig. 2.49 is drawn to scale along the x-axis to represent 60 V, and OB is drawn $\pi/3$ radians or 60° behind OA to represent 40 V. The diagonal OC of the parallelogram drawn on OA and OB represents the phasor sum of OA and OB. By measurement, OC = 87 V and angle ϕ between OC and the x-axis is 23.5°, namely 0.41 rad; hence:

Instantaneous sum of the two voltages = $87 \sin(\theta - 23.5°)$ V

Alternatively, this expression can be found thus:

Horizontal component of OA = 60 V

Horizontal component of OB = OD = 40 cos 60° = 20 V

∴   Resultant horizontal component = OA + OD = 60 + 20

= 80 V = OE in Fig. 2.49

Vertical component of OA = 0

Vertical component of OB = BD = $-40 \sin 60°$

= -34.64 V

∴   Resultant vertical component = -34.64 V = CE

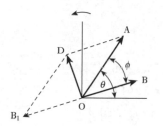

Fig. 2.49 Addition of phasors for Example 2.22

---

[*] The idea of a phasor rotating continuously serves to establish its physical significance, but its application in circuit analysis is simplified by *fixing* the phasor in position corresponding to $t = 0$, as in Fig. 2.49, thereby eliminating the time function. Such a phasor represents the magnitude of the sinusoidal quantity and its phase relative to a reference quantity, e.g. in Fig. 2.49 phasor OB lags the reference phasor OA by 60°.

The minus sign merely indicates that the resultant vertical component is *below* the horizontal axis and that the resultant voltage must therefore lag relative to the reference phasor OA. Hence maximum value of resultant voltage is

$$OC = \sqrt{\{(80)^2 + (-34.64)^2\}}$$

$$= 87.2 \text{ V}$$

If ϕ is the phase difference between OC and OA

$$\tan \phi = EC/OE = -\frac{34.64}{80} = -0.433$$

$$\therefore \qquad \phi = -23.4° = -0.41 \text{ rad}$$

and instantaneous value of resultant voltage is

$$87.2 \sin(\theta - 23.5°) \text{ V}$$

(b) The construction for subtracting OB from OA is shown in Fig. 2.50. By measurement, OC = 53 V and $\phi = 41° = 0.715$ rad. Therefore instantaneous difference of the two voltages is

$$53 \sin(\theta + 40.9°) \text{ V}$$

Alternatively, resultant horizontal component is

$$OA - OE = 60 - 20 = 40 \text{ V} = OD \text{ in Fig. 2.50}$$

and Resultant vertical component $= B_1E = 34.64$ V

$$= DC \text{ in Fig. 2.50}$$

therefore maximum value of resultant voltage is

$$OC = \sqrt{\{(40)^2 + (34.64)^2\}}$$

$$= 52.9 \text{ V}$$

and $$\tan \phi = DC/OD = \frac{34.64}{40}$$

$$= 0.866$$

$$\therefore \qquad \phi = 40.9° = 0.714 \text{ rad}$$

and instantaneous value of resultant voltage is

$$52.9 \sin(\theta + 40.9°) \text{ V}$$

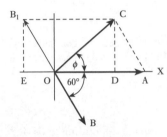

Fig. 2.50 Subtraction of phasors for Example 2.22

Phasor diagrams drawn with r.m.s. values instead of maximum values

It is important to note that when alternating voltages and currents are represented by phasors it is assumed that their waveforms are sinusoidal. It has already been shown that for sine waves the r.m.s. or effective value is 0.707 times the maximum value. Furthermore, ammeters and voltmeters are almost invariably calibrated to read the r.m.s. values. Consequently it is much more convenient to make the length of the phasors represent r.m.s. rather than maximum values. If the phasors of Fig. 2.50, for instance, were drawn to represent to scale the r.m.s. instead of the maximum values of the voltages, the shape of the diagram would remain unaltered and the phase relationships between the various quantities would remain unaffected.

Alternating system frequencies in practice

We have discussed alternating voltages, currents and frequencies at some length. Before progressing to the analysis of a.c. circuits, it would be appropriate to consider what values we are likely to meet in practice.

Most electrical supplies operate at 50 or 60 Hz, with domestic supplies at 110 V up to 230 V. However, the power is distributed at higher voltages such as 11 000 V and transmitted at such voltages as 275 kV. Currents can be anything up to a few thousand amperes.

The sounds we hear depend on frequency. We can produce sound by using electrical signals between 15 Hz and 20 kHz, although not many of us can hear the upper limit. As the frequencies increase, we find signals which can be used to transmit radio, television and other communications information. In particular most of us are familiar with identifying radio stations by a frequency between 88 and 108 MHz. Frequencies above and below this range are used for television signals.

Frequencies above 300 MHz are known as microwave frequencies. This range can rise up to 300 GHz, thus we can experience remarkably high values of frequency in practice. However, in most systems at high frequencies the voltages and currents are normally very small, e.g. millivolts and microamperes.

The ranges of frequency are indicated in Fig. 2.51.

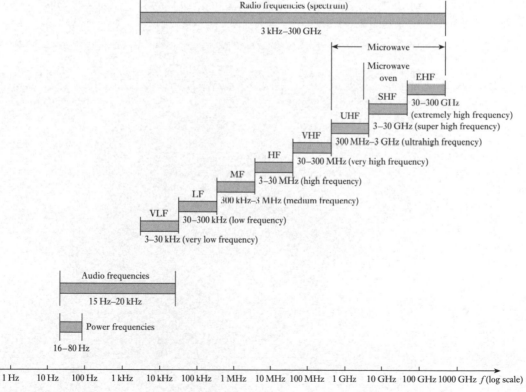

Fig. 2.51 Frequency ranges

Laplace transforms

Introduction

The *Laplace transform* is a method of transforming differential equations into more easily solved algebraic equations. This chapter introduces the Laplace transform and considers its use in solving problems which would otherwise require the solution of differential equations.

To help put the concept of mathematical transforms into perspective, a simple example of a mathematical transform is when the problem of multiplication is changed into the simpler operation of addition by means of the *logarithm transform* (Fig. 2.52). Thus the multiplication of B by C to give A,

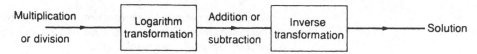

Fig. 2.52 The logarithm transformation

$$A = BC$$

can be transformed by using logarithms to

$$\log A = \log BC = \log B + \log C$$

We can then add $\log B$ and $\log C$ to give the number D. Then

$$\log A = D$$

To find A we have to carry out the inverse logarithm, or antilogarithm, operation.

$$A = \text{antilog } D$$

The *Laplace transform* is a similar type of mathematical operation to this logarithm transform (Fig. 2.53). Differential equations which describe how a circuit behaves with time are transformed into simple algebraic relationships, not involving time, where we can carry out normal algebraic manipulations of the quantities. We talk of the circuit behaviour in the *time domain* being transformed to the *s domain* in which the algebraic manipulations can be carried out. Then we use an inverse transform, like the antilogarithm, in order to obtain the solution describing how a signal varies with time, i.e. transform from the *s* domain back to the time domain.

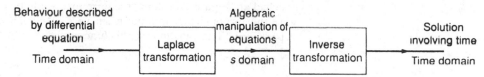

Fig. 2.53 The Laplace transformation

The Laplace transformation

The French mathematician P. S. de Laplace (1749–1827) discovered a means of solving differential equations: multiply each term in the equation by e^{-st} and then integrate each such term with respect to time from zero to infinity; *s* is a constant with the unit of 1/time. The result is what we now call the *Laplace transform*. Thus the Laplace transform of some term which is a function of time is

$$\int_0^\infty (\text{term})e^{-st}dt$$

Because the term is a function of time it is usually written as $f(t)$ with the Laplace transform, since it is a function of s, written as $F(s)$. It is usual to use a capital letter F for the Laplace transform and a lower-case letter f for the time-varying function $f(t)$. Thus

$$F(s) = \int_0^\infty f(t)e^{-st}dt \qquad [2.26]$$

To illustrate the use of the function notation, consider a resistor R with the current through it at some instant being i and the potential difference across it v. Generally, we would write

$$v = Ri$$

But since both v and i are functions of time, we should ideally indicate this by writing the equation to indicate this, i.e.

$$v(t) = Ri(t)$$

The (t) does not indicate that the preceding term should be multiplied by t but just that the preceding term is a function of time, i.e. its value depends on what time we are considering.

If we take the Laplace transforms of i and v the equation becomes

$$V(s) = RI(s)$$

$V(s)$ indicates that the term is the Laplace transform of $v(t)$, similarly $I(s)$ indicates that the term is the Laplace transform of $i(t)$. The (s) does not indicate that the preceding term should be multiplied by s.

The Laplace transform for a step function

As an illustration of how a Laplace transform can be developed from first principles, consider a step function. The step function describes an abrupt change in some quantity. This function is used frequently to describe the change in the input to a system when a sudden change in its value is made, e.g. the change in the voltage applied to a circuit when it is suddenly switched on. Figure 2.54 shows the form that would be taken by a step input when the abrupt change in input takes place at time $t = 0$ and the size of the step is 1 unit. The equation for this function is

$$f(t) = 1$$

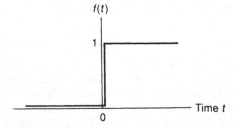

Fig. 2.54   A step function of height 1

for all values of t greater than 0. For values of t less than 0 the equation is

$$f(t) = 0$$

The Laplace transform of this step function, for values greater than 0, is thus

$$F(s) = \int_0^\infty 1\,e^{-st}dt$$

and so

$$F(s) = -\frac{1}{s}\left[e^{-st}\right]_0^\infty$$

Since when $t = \infty$ the value of e^∞ is 0 and when $t = 0$ the value of e^{-0} is -1, then

$$F(s) = \frac{1}{s} \tag{2.27}$$

Suppose now instead of a step input signal of height 1 unit we have one of height a units, as in Fig. 2.55. Then, for all values of t greater than 0 we have

$$(f)t = a$$

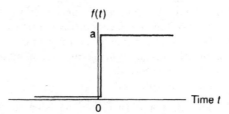

Fig. 2.55 A step function of height a

The Laplace transform of this function is

$$F(s) = \int_0^\infty ae^{-st}dt$$

$$= a\int_0^\infty e^{-st}dt$$

But this is just a multiplied by the transform of the unit step. Thus

$$F(s) = \frac{a}{s} \tag{2.28}$$

The multiplication of some function of time by a constant a gives a Laplace transform which is just the multiplication of the Laplace transform of that function by the constant.

Example 2.23

Determine, from first principles, the Laplace transform of the function e^{at}, where a is a constant.

Solution

The Laplace transform of this function is found as follows:

$$f(t) = e^{at}$$

$$\text{Laplace transform} = F(s) = \int_0^\infty e^{at} e^{-st} dt$$

This can be simplified to

$$F(s) = \int_0^\infty e^{-(s-a)t} dt$$

$$F(s) = -\frac{1}{s-a}\left[e^{-(s-a)t}\right]_0^\infty$$

When $t = \infty$ then the term in the brackets becomes 0 and when $t = 0$ it becomes -1. Thus

$$F(s) = \frac{1}{s-a}$$

Using Laplace transforms

Fortunately it is not usually necessary to evaluate the integrals obtained in carrying out the Laplace transformation since tables are available which give the Laplace transforms of all the commonly occurring functions and these combined with some basic rules for handling such transforms enable most problems to be solved.

The basic rules are:

1. The addition of two functions becomes the addition of their two Laplace transforms.

$$f_1(t) + f_2(t) \quad \text{becomes} \quad F_1(s) + F_2(s)$$

2. The subtraction of two functions becomes the subtraction of their two Laplace transforms.

$$f_1(t) - f_2(t) \quad \text{becomes} \quad F_1(s) - F_2(s)$$

3. The multiplication of some function by a constant becomes the multiplication of the Laplace transform of the function by the same constant.

$$af(t) \quad \text{becomes} \quad aF(s)$$

4. A function which is delayed by a time T, i.e. $f(t - T)$, becomes $e^{-Ts}F(s)$ for values of T greater than or equal to zero.
5. The first derivative of some function becomes s times the Laplace transform of the function minus the value of $f(t)$ at $t = 0$.

$$\frac{d}{dt}f(t) \quad \text{becomes} \quad sF(s) - f(0)$$

where $f(0)$ is the value of the function at $t = 0$.

6. The second derivative of some function becomes s^2 times the Laplace transform of the function minus s times the value of the function at $t = 0$ minus the value of the first derivative of $f(t)$ at $t = 0$.

$$\frac{d^2}{dt^2} f(t) \quad \text{becomes} \quad s^2 F(s) - sf(0) - \frac{df(0)}{dt}$$

where $sf(0)$ is s multiplied by the value of the function at $t = 0$ and $df(0)/dt$ is the first derivative of the function at $t = 0$.

7. The nth derivative of some function becomes s^n times the Laplace transform of the function minus terms involving the values of $f(t)$ and its derivatives at $t = 0$.

$$\frac{d^n}{dt^n} f(t) \quad \text{becomes} \quad s^n F(s) - s^{n-1} f(0)$$

$$- \ldots - \frac{d^{n-1} f(0)}{dt^{n-1}}$$

8. The first integral of some function, between zero time and time t, becomes $(1/s)$ times the Laplace transform of the function.

$$\int_0^t f(t) \quad \text{becomes} \quad \frac{1}{s} F(s)$$

Table 2.1 gives some of the more common Laplace transforms and their corresponding time functions.

Example 2.24	Determine, using Table 2.1, the Laplace transforms for:

(a) A step voltage of size 4 V which starts at $t = 0$.
(b) A step voltage of size 4 V which starts at $t = 2$ s.
(c) A ramp voltage which starts at $t = 0$ and increases at the rate of 3 V/s.
(d) A ramp voltage which starts at $t = 2$ s and increases at the rate of 3 V/s.
(e) An impulse voltage of size 4 V which starts at $t = 3$ s.
(f) A sinusoidal voltage of amplitude 2 V and angular frequency 10 Hz.

Solution

Figure 2.56 shows the form of the six functions, the six representing common forms of signals input to systems.

(a) The step voltage is a function of the form

$$f(t) = a$$

where a has the value, in this case, of 4 V. The Laplace transform of the step function of size 1 is $1/s$ and thus the step function of size a has the the Laplace transform of

$$F(s) = a \times \frac{1}{s}$$

Hence

$$F(s) = \frac{4}{s}$$

Table 2.1 Laplace transforms

Laplace transform	Time function	Description of time function
1		A unit impulse
$\dfrac{1}{s}$		A unit step function
$\dfrac{e^{-st}}{s}$		A delayed unit step function
$\dfrac{1-e^{-st}}{s}$		A rectangular pulse of duration T
$\dfrac{1}{s^2}$	t	A unit slope ramp function
$\dfrac{1}{s^3}$	$\dfrac{t^2}{2}$	
$\dfrac{1}{s+a}$	e^{-at}	Exponential decay
$\dfrac{1}{(s+a)^2}$	$t\,e^{-at}$	
$\dfrac{2}{(s+a)^3}$	$t^2\,e^{-at}$	
$\dfrac{a}{s(s+a)}$	$1-e^{-at}$	Exponential growth
$\dfrac{a}{s^2(s+a)}$	$t-\dfrac{(1-e^{-at})}{a}$	
$\dfrac{a^2}{s(s+a)^2}$	$1-e^{-at}-ate^{-at}$	
$\dfrac{s}{(s+a)^2}$	$(1-at)e^{-at}$	
$\dfrac{1}{(s+a)(s+b)}$	$\dfrac{e^{-at}-e^{-bt}}{b-a}$	
$\dfrac{ab}{s(s+a)(s+b)}$	$1-\dfrac{b}{b-a}e^{-at}+\dfrac{a}{b-a}e^{-bt}$	
$\dfrac{1}{(s+a)(s+b)(s+c)}$	$\dfrac{e^{-at}}{(b-a)(c-a)}+\dfrac{e^{-bt}}{(c-a)(a-b)}+\dfrac{e^{-ct}}{(a-c)(b-c)}$	
$\dfrac{\omega}{s^2+\omega^2}$	$\sin \omega t$	Sine wave
$\dfrac{s}{s^2+\omega^2}$	$\cos \omega t$	Cosine wave
$\dfrac{\omega}{(s+a)^2+\omega^2}$	$e^{-at}\sin \omega t$	Damped sine wave
$\dfrac{s+a}{(s+a)^2+\omega^2}$	$e^{-at}\cos \omega t$	Damped cosine wave
$\dfrac{\omega^2}{s(s^2+\omega^2)}$	$1-\cos \omega t$	
$\dfrac{\omega^2}{s^2+2\zeta\omega s+\omega^2}$	$\dfrac{\omega}{\sqrt{(1-\zeta^2)}}e^{-\zeta\omega t}\sin[\omega\sqrt{(1-\zeta^2)}t]$	
$\dfrac{\omega^2}{s(s^2+2\zeta\omega s+\omega^2)}$	$1-\dfrac{1}{\sqrt{(1-\zeta^2)}}e^{-\zeta\omega t}\sin[\omega\sqrt{(1-\zeta^2)}t+\phi]$	
with $\zeta<1$	with $\zeta=\cos\phi$	

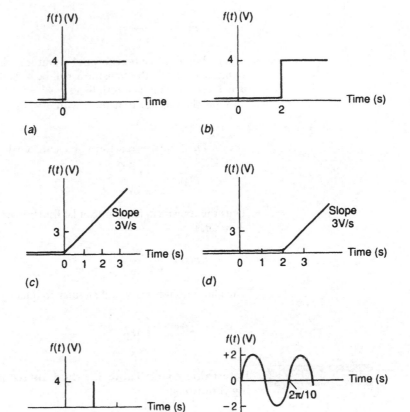

Fig. 2.56 (*a*) Step function, (*b*) delayed step function, (*c*) ramp function, (*d*) delayed ramp function, (*e*) delayed impulse, (*f*) sinusoidal function

(*b*) The step function in (*a*) is delayed by 2 s. For a delayed function the Laplace transform is that of the undelayed function, i.e. the function starting at $t = 0$, multiplied by e^{-sT}. Thus the Laplace transform is

$$F(s) = \frac{a}{s}e^{-sT} = \frac{4}{s}e^{-2s}$$

(*c*) The ramp function is of the form

$$f(t) = at$$

with a having the value 3 V/s. Because a is a constant then the Laplace transform of the function will be a multiplied by the transform of t which is $1/s^2$. Thus

$$F(s) = \frac{a}{s^2} = \frac{3}{s^2}$$

(*d*) The ramp voltage is delayed by a time T, where $T = 3$ s. For a delayed function the Laplace transform is that of the undelayed function, i.e. the function starting at $t = 0$, multiplied by e^{-sT}. Thus the Laplace transform is

$$F(s) = \frac{ae^{-T/s}}{s^2} = \frac{3e^{-2s}}{s^2}$$

(e) The Laplace transform of a unit impulse occurring at $t = 0$ is 1. For an impulse of 4 V the transform will be 4. Delaying the impulse means the undelayed function is multiplied by $e^{-T/s}$.

Thus the Laplace transform with $T = 3$ s is

$$F(s) = 4 e^{-3/s}$$

(f) The Laplace transform of a sinusoidal function $\sin \omega t$ is

$$F(s) = \frac{\omega}{s^2 + \omega^2}$$

Thus the transform for a sinusoidal function of amplitude A, i.e the function $A \sin \omega t$, is

$$F(s) = \frac{A\omega}{s^2 + \omega^2}$$

Thus for amplitude 2 V and angular frequency 10 Hz,

$$F(s) = \frac{20}{s^2 + 100}$$

Example 2.25   Determine, using Table 2.1, the Laplace transforms for the following functions:

(a) $t2$
(b) $t2e^{-at}$
(c) $t2(1 + e^{-at})$

Solution

(a) The table gives the Laplace transform of $\frac{1}{2}t^2$ as $1/s^3$. Thus to obtain the Laplace transform of t^2 we have to multiply the function in the table by 2. Since this is a constant, the Laplace transform of t^2 will be

$$F(s) = \frac{2}{s^3}$$

(b) Using the table, the transform is

$$F(s) = \frac{2}{(s+a)^3}$$

Note that the Laplace transform of two functions multiplied together is *not* the multiplication of their separate Laplace transforms.

(c) The Laplace transform of two functions added together is the addition of their separate Laplace transforms.

$$f(t) = t^2 + t^2e^{-at}$$

$$F(s) = \frac{2}{s^3} + \frac{2}{(s+a)^3}$$

Example 2.26	Determine, using Table 2.1, the inverse transformations of:

$$(a) \ \frac{2}{s}$$

$$(b) \ \frac{3}{2s+1}$$

$$(c) \ \frac{2}{s-5}$$

Solution

To use Table 2.1 to obtain the inverse transformations means looking through the table to find the Laplace transform which is of the same basic form.

(*a*) The table includes a Laplace transform of $1/s$ and thus since this is just multiplied by the constant 2 the inverse transformation will be the function which gives $1/s$, i.e. 1 multiplied by the same constant. The inverse transformation is thus 2.

(*b*) This transform can be rearranged to give

$$\frac{(3/2)}{s+(1/2)}$$

The table contains the transform $1/(s+a)$, the inverse of which is e^{-at}. Thus the inverse transformation is just this multiplied by the constant $(3/2)$ with $a = (1/2)$, i.e. $(3/2)\,e^{-t/2}$.

(*c*) This transform is of the same form as in (*b*) with $a = -5$. Thus the inverse transformation is $2\,e^{5t}$.

Using Laplace transforms to solve differential equations	In using Laplace transforms to obtain the solution to a differential equation, the procedure adopted is:

1. Transform each term in the differential equation into its Laplace transform, i.e. change the function of time into a function of (*s*).
2. Carry out all algebraic manipulations, e.g. considering what happens when a step input is applied to the system.
3. Convert the resulting Laplace function back into an equation giving a function of time, i.e. invert the Laplace transformation operation. In order to use tables of Laplace transforms to carry out the conversion, it is often necessary first to use partial fractions to get it into the standard forms given in tables.

Example 2.27	Use Laplace transforms to solve the following differential equation:

$$3\frac{dx}{dt} + 2x = 4$$

with $x = 0$ at $t = 0$.

Solution

The Laplace transform of $3\,dx/dt$ is 3 times the Laplace transform of dx/dt. The Laplace transform of $2x$ is 2 times the Laplace transform of x. The Laplace transform of 4 is, since this can be considered to be a step function of height 4, $4/s$. Thus

$$3[sX(s) - x(0)] + 2X(s) = 4/s$$

where $X(s)$ is the Laplace transform of x. Since $x(0) = 0$ then

$$3[sX(s) - 0] + 2X(s) = 4/s$$

and so

$$3s^2X(s) + 2sX(s) = 4$$

$$X(s) = \frac{4}{3s^2 + 2s} = \frac{2(2/3)}{s[s + (2/3)]}$$

We now need to find the functions which would give the Laplace transforms of this form in order to obtain the inverse transformation and obtain x. Since the inverse transformation of $a/[s(s + a)]$ is $(1 - e^{-at})$ then

$$x = 2(1 - e^{-2t/3})$$

Example 2.28 For a voltage step input of size V at $t = 0$ into a series CR circuit the differential equation for the potential difference across the capacitor v_C is given by

$$V = RC\frac{dv_C}{dt} + v_C$$

v_C is zero at $t = 0$. Use Laplace transforms to solve this equation.

Solution

The Laplace transform of a unit step input is $1/s$ and thus for one of size V it is V/s. The Laplace transform for dv_C/dt is $[sV_C(s) - 0]$, since the function v_C is zero at $t = 0$. Thus the Laplace transform for $RC\,dv_C/dt$ is $RCsV_C(s)$. The Laplace transform of v_C is $V_C(s)$. Thus the transform of the differential equation is

$$\frac{V}{s} = RCsV_C(s) + V_C(s)$$

Thus

$$V_C(s) = \frac{V}{(RCs + 1)s}$$

This can be rearranged to give

$$V_C(s) = \frac{V(1/RC)}{[s + (1/RC)]s}$$

The function $(1 - e^{-at})$ gives the Laplace transform

$$\frac{a}{(s + a)s}$$

Thus, with $a = (1/RC)$,

$$v_C = V(1 - e^{-t/RC}).$$

Figure 2.57 shows a graph of this equation. Such a form of equation and graph is typical of first-order systems subject to a step input. RC is the time constant τ.

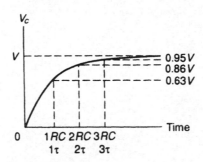

Fig. 2.57 Example 2.28

Example 2.29

For a step input at $t = 0$ of size V into a series LR circuit the current variation with time is described by the equation

$$\frac{L}{R}\frac{\mathrm{d}i}{\mathrm{d}t} + i = \frac{V}{R}$$

The current i is zero at $t = 0$. Using Laplace transforms solve this equation.

Solution

The Laplace transform of $\mathrm{d}i/\mathrm{d}t$ is $sI(s)$, since $i(0)$ is zero, and so for $(L/R)\mathrm{d}i/\mathrm{d}t$ it is $(L/R)sI(s)$. The Laplace transform for i is $I(s)$. The Laplace transform for a unit step input is $1/s$ and thus for one of size (V/R) it is $(V/R)/s$. Hence, the transform of the differential equation can be written as

$$(L/R)sI(s) + I(s) = \frac{(V/R)}{s}$$

Hence

$$I(s) = \frac{(V/R)}{[(L/R)s + 1]s}$$

This can be rearranged to give

$$I(s) = \frac{(V/R)[(R/L)]}{[s + (R/L)]s}$$

The function $(1 - e^{-at})$ gives the Laplace transform

$$\frac{a}{(s + a)s}$$

Thus, with $a = (R/L)$,

$$i = (V/R)(1 - e^{-Rt/L})$$

The graph of this equation is of a similar form to that given in Fig. 2.57, the time constant τ being L/R and the current reached eventually being V/R.

Dynamic system models

Introduction

This section considers the behaviour of control systems when changes with time are not ignored, i.e. the dynamic behaviour of systems.

Transfer functions of dynamic elements

Suppose we have a system where the input θ_i is related to the output θ_o by the differential equation

$$a_2\frac{d^2\theta_o}{dt^2} + a_1\frac{d\theta_o}{dt} + a_0\theta_o = b_1\theta_i$$

where a_2, a_1, a_0 and b_1 are constants. If all the initial conditions are zero then the Laplace transform of this equation is

$$a_2s^2\theta_o(s) + a_1s\theta_o(s) + a_0\theta_o(s) = b_1\theta_i(s)$$

$$\frac{\theta_o(s)}{\theta_i(s)} = \frac{b_1}{a_2s^2 + a_1s + a_0}$$

The *transfer function* $G(s)$ of a linear system which describes the dynamic behaviour is defined as the ratio of the Laplace transform of the output variable $\theta_o(s)$ to the Laplace transform of the input variable $\theta_i(s)$, with all initial conditions assumed to be zero.

$$G(s) = \frac{\theta_o(s)}{\theta_i(s)} \qquad\qquad [2.29]$$

Hence, for the system giving the above equation

$$G(s) = \frac{\theta_o(s)}{\theta_i(s)} = \frac{b_1}{a_2s^2 + a_1s + a_0}$$

Thus if we represent a system by a block diagram, then $G(s)$ is the 'function' in the box which takes an input of $\theta_i(s)$ and gives an output $\theta_o(s)$ (Fig. 2.58).

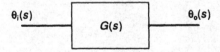

$\theta_i(s)$ $G(s)$ $\theta_o(s)$

Fig. 2.58 Block diagram representation

Example 2.30

Write down the transfer function $G(s)$ for systems giving the following input–output relationships:

(a) **A spring-dashpot-mass system, with input F and output x**

$$m\frac{d^2x}{dt^2} + c\frac{dx}{dt} + kx = F$$

(b) **A resistor-capacitor circuit, with input v and output v_C**

$$v = RC\frac{dv_C}{dt} + v_C$$

(c) A resistor-capacitor-inductor circuit, with input v and output v_C

$$v = RC\frac{dv_C}{dt} + LC\frac{d^2v_C}{dt^2} + v_C$$

(d) An electrical system, with input v and output v_C

$$v = \frac{R}{L}\int v_C dt + RC\frac{dv_C}{dt} + v_C$$

(e) A hydraulic system, with input q_1 and output h

$$q_1 = A\frac{dh}{dt} + \frac{\rho gh}{R}$$

(f) The elements in the armature controlled d.c. motor system:

Armature circuit: input $(v_a - v_b)$, output i_a

$$v_a - v_b = L_a\frac{di_a}{dt} + R_a i_a$$

Armature coil: input i_a, output T

$$T = k_4 i_a$$

Load: input T output ω

$$I\frac{d\omega}{dt} = T - \omega$$

Feedback loop: input ω, output v_b

$$v_b = k_3\omega$$

(g) Hydraulic system with load

$$\tau\frac{d^2x_o}{dt^2} + \frac{dx_o}{dt} = kx_i$$

Solution

(a) Carrying out the Laplace transform of the equation with all initial conditions zero gives

$$ms^2X(s) + csX(s) + kX(s) = F(s)$$

Hence

$$G(s) = \frac{X(s)}{F(s)} = \frac{1}{ms^2 + cs + k}$$

(b) Carrying out the Laplace transform of the equation with all initial conditions zero gives

$$RCsV_C(s) + V_C(s) = V(s)$$

Hence

$$G(s) = \frac{V_C(s)}{V(s)} = \frac{1}{RCs + 1}$$

(*c*) Carrying out the Laplace transform of the equation with all initial conditions zero gives

$$RCsV_C(s) + LCs^2V_C(s) + V_C(s) = V(s)$$

Hence

$$G(s) = \frac{V_C(s)}{V(s)} = \frac{1}{LCs^2 + RCs + 1}$$

(*d*) Carrying out the Laplace transform of the equation with all initial conditions zero gives

$$\frac{R}{L}\frac{1}{s}V_C(s) + RCsV_C(s) + V_C(s) = V(s)$$

Hence

$$G(s) = \frac{V_C(s)}{V(s)} = \frac{1}{(R/L)(1/s) + RCs + 1}$$

$$= \frac{s}{(R/L) + RCs^2 + s}$$

(*e*) Carrying out the Laplace transform of the equation with all initial conditions zero gives

$$AsH(s) + (\rho g/R)H(s) = Q_1(s)$$

Hence

$$G(s) = \frac{H(s)}{Q_1(s)} = \frac{1}{As + (\rho g/R)}$$

(*f*) Carrying out the Laplace transform of the equation with all initial conditions zero gives

Armature circuit

$$(V_a - V_b)(s) = L_a s I_a(s) + R_a I_a(s)$$

$$G(s) = \frac{I_a(s)}{(V_a - V_b)(s)} = \frac{1}{L_a s + R_a}$$

Armature coil

$$G(s) = \frac{T(s)}{i_a(s)} = k_4$$

Load

$$Is\omega(s) = T(s) - c\omega(s)$$

$$G(s) = \frac{\omega(s)}{T(s)} = \frac{1}{Is + c}$$

Feedback

$$G(s) = \frac{V_b(s)}{\omega(s)} = k_3$$

(g) Carrying out the Laplace transform of the equation with all initial conditions zero gives

$$\tau s^2 X_o(s) + s X_o(s) = k X_i(s)$$

$$G(s) = \frac{X_o(s)}{X_i(s)} = \frac{k}{s(\tau s + 1)}$$

First-order and second-order elements

The *order* of an element, or system, can be defined as being the highest power of derivative in the differential equation. Alternatively, the *order* of an element, or system, can be defined as being the highest power of s in the denominator. Thus a first-order element will only have s to the power 1 in the denominator, while a second-order element will have the highest power of s in the denominator being two.

For a *first-order element* the differential equation is of the form

$$a_1 \frac{d\theta_o}{dt} + a_0 \theta_o = b_0 \theta_i \qquad [2.30]$$

The corresponding Laplace transform of the equation is, if $\theta_o = 0$ at $t = 0$,

$$a_1 s \times \theta_o(s) + a_0 \times \theta_o(s) = b_0 \times \theta_i(s)$$

Hence

$$G(s) = \frac{b_0}{a_1 s + a_0}$$

This can be rearranged to give

$$G(s) = \frac{b_0 / a_0}{(a_1 / a_0)s + 1} \qquad [2.31]$$

b_0 / a_0 is the steady-state transfer function G of the system. a_1 / a_0 is the time constant τ of the system. Hence

$$G(s) = \frac{G}{\tau s + 1} \qquad [2.32]$$

This is the general form that is taken for the output input relationship in the s domain for a first-order system.

The relationship between the input θ_i and output θ_o for a *second-order* element is described by the differential equation

$$a_2 \frac{d^2\theta_o}{dt^2} + a_1 \frac{d\theta_o}{dt} + a_0 \theta_o = b_0 \theta_i \qquad [2.33]$$

where b_0, a_0, a_1 and a_2 are constants. If at $t = 0$ we have $\theta_o = 0$ and $d\theta_o/dt = 0$ then the Laplace transform is

$$a_2 s^2 \times \theta_o(s) + a_1 s \times \theta_o(s) + a_0 \times \theta_o(s) = b_0 \times \theta_i(s)$$

Hence

$$G(s) = \frac{\theta_o(s)}{\theta_i(s)} = \frac{b_0}{a_2 s^2 + a_1 s + a_0}$$

This can be rearranged to give

$$G(s) = \frac{(b_0/a_0)}{(a_2/a_0)s^2 + (a_1/a_0)s + 1}$$ [2.34]

The second-order differential equation can be written in terms of the natural frequency ω_n and the damping ratio ζ.

$$\frac{d^2\theta_o}{dt^2} + 2\zeta\omega_n\frac{d\theta_o}{dt} + \omega_n^2\theta_o = b_0\omega_n^2\theta_i$$ [2.35]

where ω_n is the angular frequency with which the system will freely oscillate in the absence of any damping and ζ is the *damping ratio*. The Laplace transform is

$$s^2\theta_o(s) + 2\zeta\omega_n s\theta_o(s) + \omega_n^2\theta_o(s) = b_0\omega_n^2\theta_i(s)$$

Hence

$$G(s) = \frac{\theta_o(s)}{\theta_i(s)} = \frac{b_0\omega_n^2}{s^2 + 2\zeta\omega_n s + \omega_n^2}$$ [2.36]

This is the general form taken by a second-order system in the *s* domain.

Example 2.31

What are the orders of the elements described by the transfer function answers in Example 2.30?

(a) $G(s) = \dfrac{1}{ms^2 + cs + k}$

(b) $G(s) = \dfrac{1}{RCs + 1}$

(c) $G(s) = \dfrac{1}{LCs^2 + RCs + 1}$

(d) $G(s) = \dfrac{s}{(R/L) + RCs^2 + s}$

(e) $G(s) = \dfrac{1}{As + (\varrho g/R)}$

Solution

(a) Second order since the denominator has the highest *s* term of s^2.
(b) First order since the denominator has the highest *s* term of *s*.
(c) Second order since the denominator has the highest *s* term of s^2.
(d) Second order since the denominator has the highest *s* term of s^2.
(e) First order since the denominator has the highest *s* term of *s*.

Step input to a first-order system

Consider the behaviour of a first-order system when subject to a step input. For a first-order system we can take the relationship to be of the form given by equation [2.32], namely

$$G(s) = \frac{G}{\tau s + 1}$$

The Laplace transform of the output is thus

$$G(s) \times \text{Laplace transform of input}$$

$$\frac{G}{\tau s + 1} \times \text{Laplace transform of input}$$

The Laplace transform for a one unit step input at $t = 0$ is $1/s$. Hence, for such an input

$$\text{Laplace transform of output} = \frac{G}{\tau s + 1} \times \frac{1}{s}$$

$$= G \times \frac{(1/\tau)}{s[s + (1/\tau)]}$$

The transform is of the form

$$\frac{a}{s(s + a)}$$

where $a = (1/\tau)$. Hence, for a unit step input,

$$\theta_o = G[1 - e^{-t/\tau}] \qquad [2.37]$$

Figure 2.59 is a graph of this equation. If the step has a size A then

$$\theta_o = AG[1 - e^{-t/\tau}] \qquad [2.38]$$

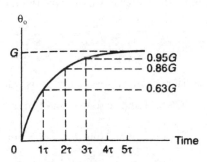

Fig. 2.59 $\theta_o = G[1 - e^{-t/\tau}]$ for a unit step input

| **Example 2.32** | A thermocouple has the transfer function linking its output in volts to its input θ_i in °C of |

$$G(s) = \frac{30 \times 10^{-6}}{10s + 1}$$

What will be (*a*) the time taken for the output of the thermocouple to reach 95% of its final value and (*b*) the final steady value when there is a step input of 100 °C?

Solution

(a) As the transfer function indicates, the thermocouple is a first-order system. Thus comparing the transfer function with equation [2.32], i.e.

$$G(s) = \frac{G}{\tau s + 1}$$

$G = 30 \times 10^{-6}$ V/°C and $\tau = 10$ s. The time taken to reach 95% of the output is 3τ and thus 30 s.

(b) We can use the final value theorem

$$\lim_{s \to 0} sF(s) = \lim_{t \to \infty} f(t)$$

For a step input of size θ_i the Laplace transform of the output is θ_i/s, hence

$$\text{Laplace transform of output} = \frac{G}{\tau s + 1} \times \frac{\theta_i}{s}$$

Thus

$$sF(s) = \frac{G\theta_i}{\tau s + 1}$$

As $s \to 0$ then $sF(s)$ tends to $G\theta_i$ and so this is the final steady value. This is thus $30 \times 10^{-6} \times 100 = 300 \times 10^{-6}$ V.

Ramp input to a first-order system

Consider the behaviour of a first-order system when subject to a step input. For a first-order system we can take the relationship to be of the form given by equation [2.32], namely

$$G(s) = \frac{G}{\tau s + 1}$$

The Laplace transform of the output is thus

$$G(s) \times \text{Laplace transform of input}$$

$$\frac{G}{\tau s + 1} \times \text{Laplace transform of input}$$

The Laplace transform for a one unit slope ramp input at $t = 0$ is $1/s^2$. Hence, for such an input

$$\text{Laplace transform of output} = \frac{G}{(\tau s + 1)s^2}$$

$$= G \times \frac{(1/\tau)}{[s + (1/\tau)]s^2}$$

This transform is of the form

$$\frac{a}{s^2(s + a)}$$

which has the solution

$$t - \frac{(1 - e^{-at})}{a}$$

Thus the output θ_o for a unit slope ramp is given by

$$\theta_o = G[t - \tau(1 - e^{-t/\tau})] \tag{2.39}$$

Figure 2.60 is a graph of this equation. It can be considered to be a graph of Gt minus a graph of $G\tau(1 - e^{-t/\tau})$. For a ramp input of slope A, i.e. $\theta_i = At$, then

$$\theta_o = GA[t - \tau(1 - e^{-t/\tau})] \tag{2.40}$$

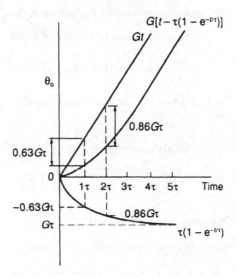

Fig. 2.60 $\theta_o = G[t - \tau(1 - e^{-t/\tau})]$ for unit ramp input

Example 2.33

A thermocouple has the transfer function linking its output in volts to its input θ_i in °C of

$$G(s) = \frac{30 \times 10^{-6}}{10s + 1}$$

When the thermocouple is subject to a steadily rising temperature input of 5 °C/s, what will be the thermocouple output after 12 s and how much will it lag behind the output it would have indicated if it had responded instantly to the input?

Solution

For a ramp input to a first-order system, equation [2.40] gives

$$\theta_o = GA[t - \tau(1 - e^{-t/\tau})]$$

and, since the time constant τ for the system is 10 s and G is 30×10^{-6} V/°C, then for a ramp of 5 °C/s

$$\theta_o = 30 \times 10^{-6} \times 5[12 - 10(1 - e^{-12/10})] = 7.5 \times 10^{-4} \text{ V}$$

As Fig. 2.60 indicates, the lag is the difference between the values of GAt and $GA[t - \tau(1 - e^{-t/\tau})]$. Since $GAt = 30 \times 10^{-6} \times 5 \times 12 = 18.0 \times 10^{-4}$ V, the lag is 10.5×10^{-4} V.

Impulse input to a first-order system

Consider the behaviour of a first-order system when subject to an impulse input. For a first-order system we can take the relationship to be of the form given by equation [2.32], namely

$$G(s) = \frac{G}{\tau s + 1}$$

The Laplace transform of the output is thus

$$G(s) \times \text{Laplace transform of input}$$

$$\frac{G}{\tau s + 1} \times \text{Laplace transform of input}$$

The Laplace transform for a unit impulse at $t = 0$ is 1. Hence, for such an input

$$\text{Laplace transform of output} = \frac{G}{\tau s + 1} \times 1$$

$$= G \times \frac{(1/\tau)}{[s + (1/\tau)]}$$

This transform is of the form

$$\frac{1}{s + a}$$

and this is given by the function e^{-at}. Thus

$$\theta_o = G(1/\tau)e^{-t/\tau} \tag{2.41}$$

Figure 2.61 is a graph of this equation. If the impulse has a size A, then

$$\theta_o = GA(1/\tau)e^{-t/\tau} \tag{2.42}$$

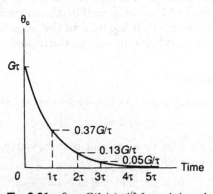

Fig. 2.61 $\theta_o = G(1/\tau)e^{-t/\tau}$ for unit impulse at $t = 0$

| Example 2.34 | A thermocouple has the transfer function linking its output in volts to its input θ_i in °C of |

$$G(s) = \frac{30 \times 10^{-6}}{10s + 1}$$

What will be the output of the thermocouple 5 s after it was subject to a temperature impulse of 100 °C by suddenly and very briefly coming into contact with a hot object?

Solution

The thermocouple is a first-order system subject to an impulse of size 100 °C. Thus equation [2.42] can be used

$$\theta_o = GA(1/\tau)e^{-t/\tau}$$

and since $G = 30 \times 10^{-6}$ V and $\tau = 10$ s (see Example 2.32) then

$$\theta_o = 30 \times 10^{-6} \times 100(1/10)e^{-5/10} = 1.8 \times 10^{-4} \text{ V}$$

| Step input to a second-order system | Consider the output from a second-order system when it is subject to a unit step input. |

Laplace transform of output
= $G(s) \times$ Laplace transform of input

Thus, using equation [2.36] to represent the general form of a second-order system in the s domain,

$$\theta_o(s) = \frac{b_0\omega_n^2}{s^2 + 2\zeta\omega_n s + \omega_n^2} \times \theta_i(s) \qquad [2.43]$$

Since, for a unit step, $\theta_i(s) = 1/s$ then

$$\theta_o(s) = \frac{b_0\omega_n^2}{(s^2 + 2\zeta\omega_n s + \omega_n^2)s} \qquad [2.44]$$

This can be rearranged as

$$\theta_o(s) = \frac{b_0\omega_n^2}{(s - m_1)(s - m_2)s} \qquad [2.45]$$

where m_1 and m_2 are the roots of the equation

$$s^2 + 2\zeta\omega_n s + \omega_n^2 = 0$$

Thus, since the roots are given for an equation of the form $ax^2 + bx + c = 0$ by

$$x = \frac{-b \pm \sqrt{(b^2 - 4ac)}}{2a}$$

then

$$m = \frac{-2\zeta\omega_n \pm \sqrt{(4\zeta^2\omega_n^2 - 4\omega_n^2)}}{2}$$

$$m_1 = -\zeta\omega_n + \omega_n\sqrt{(\zeta^2 - 1)} \qquad [2.46]$$

$$m_2 = -\zeta\omega_n + \omega_n\sqrt{(\zeta^2 - 1)} \qquad [2.47]$$

The type of response that occurs, i.e. the inverse transformation, depends on the value of the damping factor ζ. When $\zeta > 1$ then $\sqrt{(\zeta^2 - 1)}$ is a real number and the system is said to be *overdamped*. This means both the roots are real.

Using partial fractions equation [2.45] can be rearranged as

$$\theta_o(s) = \frac{1}{s} + \frac{A}{s - m_1} + \frac{B}{s - m_2} \qquad [2.48]$$

with

$$(s - m_1)(s - m_2) + As(s - m_2) + Bs(s - m_1) = b_0\omega^2 \qquad [2.49]$$

Hence when $s = m_1$, then

$$Am_1(m_1 - m_2) = b_0\omega_n^2$$

$$A = \frac{b_0\omega_n^2}{m_1(m_1 - m_2)}$$

Substituting for the values of m_1 and m_2 from equations [2.46] and [2.47],

$$A = \frac{b_0\omega_n^2}{[-\zeta\omega_n + \omega_n\sqrt{(\zeta^2 - 1)}][2\omega_n\sqrt{(\zeta^2 - 1)}]}$$

$$A = \frac{b_0}{[-\zeta + \sqrt{(\zeta^2 - 1)}]2\sqrt{(\zeta^2 - 1)}}$$

Multiplying the top and bottom of this fraction by $[-\zeta - \sqrt{(\zeta^2 - 1)}]$ gives

$$A = \frac{b_0[-\zeta - \sqrt{(\zeta^2 - 1)}]}{[1]2\sqrt{(\zeta^2 - 1)}}$$

Hence

$$A = -\frac{b_0\zeta}{2\sqrt{(\zeta^2 - 1)}} - \frac{b_0}{2} \qquad [2.50]$$

With equation [2.49] when $s = m_2$ then

$$Bm_2(m_2 - m_1) = b_0\omega_n^2$$

$$B = \frac{b_0\omega_n^2}{m_2(m_2 - m_1)}$$

and by a similar discussion to that above for A,

$$B = \frac{b_0\zeta}{2\sqrt{(\zeta^2 - 1)}} - \frac{b_0}{2} \qquad [2.51]$$

The response of the system is the inverse transformation of equation [2.48]. The inverse transformation for $1/s$ is 1, for $A/(s - m_1)$ is $A \exp m_1 t$, and for $B/(s - m_2)$ is $B \exp m_2 t$, then

$$\theta_o = 1 + A \exp(m_1 t) + B \exp(m_2 t) \qquad [2.52]$$

Substituting the values for A, B, m_1 and m_2 obtained above,

$$\theta_o = 1 + \left[-\frac{b_0\zeta}{2\sqrt{(\zeta^2 - 1)}} - \frac{b_0}{2} \right] \exp\{[-\zeta\omega_n + \omega_n\sqrt{(\zeta^2 - 1)}]t\}$$

$$+ \left[\frac{b_0\zeta}{2\sqrt{(\zeta^2 - 1)}} - \frac{b_0}{2} \right] \exp\{[-\zeta\omega_n - \omega_n\sqrt{(\zeta^2 - 1)}]t\} \quad [2.53]$$

When $\zeta = 1$ the system is said to be *critically damped*. For this condition $m_1 = m_2 = -\zeta\omega_n$. Equation [2.45] then becomes

$$\theta_o(s) = \frac{b_0\omega_n^2}{(s + \omega_n)^2 s}$$

The inverse transformation of this is (see Table 2.1)

$$\theta_o = b_0[1 - \exp(-\omega_n t) - \omega_n t \exp(-\omega_n t)] \quad [2.54]$$

When $\zeta < 1$ the roots are complex and the system is said to be *underdamped*. When this happens the roots, equations [2.46] and [2.47] can be written as

$$m_1 = -\zeta\omega_n + \omega_n\sqrt{(\zeta^2 - 1)}$$

$$m_1 = -\zeta\omega_n + \omega_n\sqrt{[(-1)(1 - \zeta^2)]}$$

and thus writing j for $\sqrt{(-1)}$

$$m_1 = -\zeta\omega_n + j\omega_n\sqrt{(1 - \zeta^2)} \quad [2.55]$$

Similarly since

$$m_2 = -\zeta\omega_n - \omega_n\sqrt{(\zeta^2 - 1)}$$

then

$$m_2 = -\zeta\omega_n - j\omega_n\sqrt{(1 - \zeta^2)} \quad [2.56]$$

The inverse transform for equation [2.44] with this condition is (see Table 2.1)

$$\theta_o(s) = \frac{b_0\omega^2}{s(s^2 + 2\zeta\omega s + \omega^2)}$$

$$\theta_o = b_0\left[1 - \frac{1}{\sqrt{(1 - \zeta^2)}} \exp(-\zeta\omega_n t)\sin[\omega_n\sqrt{(1 - \zeta^2)}t + \phi]\right] \quad [2.57]$$

where $\cos\phi = \zeta$. When $\zeta = 0$, i.e. there is no damping, then equation [2.56] gives

$$\theta_o = b_0\{1 - 1\,e^0\sin[\omega_n\sqrt{(1)}t + 0]\}$$

$$\theta_o = b_0\{1 - \sin\omega_n t\}$$

The output thus oscillates with the undamped frequency ω_n.

Example 2.35

A system has the following relationship, in the s domain, between its output θ_o and its input θ_i. What is the state of damping of the system when it is subject to a step input?

$$\frac{\theta_o(s)}{\theta_i(s)} = \frac{1}{s^2 + 8s + 16}$$

Solution

For a unit step input $\theta_i = 1/s$, hence

$$\theta_o = \frac{1}{s(s^2 + 8s + 16)}$$

This can be simplified to

$$\theta_o = \frac{1}{s(s+4)(s+4)}$$

The roots of the $s^2 + 8s + 16$ equation are thus $m_1 = m_2 = -4$. Both roots are real and the same. The system is thus critically damped.

Example 2.36

A second-order system is underdamped with a damping factor of 0.4 and a free angular frequency of 10 Hz. What is (*a*) the relationship between the output and the input in the *s* domain, (*b*) the relationship between the output and the input in the time domain when it is subject to a unit step input and (*c*) the percentage overshoot with such an input?

Solution

(*a*) In the *s* domain the second-order equation will be of the form given by equation [2.36]

$$G(s) = \frac{\theta_o(s)}{\theta_i(s)} = \frac{b_0 \omega_n^2}{s^2 + 2\zeta\omega_n s + \omega_n^2}$$

where b_0 is a constant, ω_n the natural angular frequency and ζ the damping constant. Thus

$$\frac{\theta_o(s)}{\theta_i(s)} = \frac{100b_0}{s^2 + 8s + 100}$$

(*b*) When subject to a unit step input

$$\theta_o(s) = \frac{100b_0}{s(s^2 + 8s + 100)}$$

This has the general solution, as given by Table 2.1 and discussed above (equation [2.56]), of

$$\theta_o = b_0 \left\{ 1 - \frac{1}{\sqrt{(1 - \zeta^2)}} \exp(-\zeta\omega_n t) \sin[\omega_n \sqrt{(1 - \zeta^2)} t + \phi] \right\}$$

where $\cos \phi = \zeta$. Thus, with $\omega_n = 10$ and $\zeta = 0.4$,

$$\theta_o = b_0 \left\{ 1 - \frac{1}{0.84} e^{-4t} \sin(9.2t + 66.4°) \right\}$$

(c) Percentage overshoot $= \exp\left[\dfrac{-\zeta\pi}{\sqrt{(1-\zeta^2)}}\right] \times 100\%$

and thus with $\zeta = 0.4$,

$$\text{Percentage overshoot} = \exp\left[\dfrac{-0.4\pi}{\sqrt{(1-0.4^2)}}\right] \times 100\%$$

$$= 25.4\%$$

Ramp input to a second-order system

Consider the output from a second-order system when it is subject to a unit ramp input.

Laplace transform of output $= G(s) \times$ Laplace transform of input

Thus, using equation [2.36] to represent the general form of a second-order system in the s domain,

$$\theta_o(s) = \frac{b_0\omega_n^2}{s^2 + 2\zeta\omega_n s + \omega_n^2} \times \theta_i(s)$$

Since, for a unit ramp, $\theta_i(s) = 1/s^2$, then

$$\theta_o(s) = \frac{b_0\omega_n^2}{(s^2 + 2\zeta\omega_n s + \omega_n^2)s^2} \qquad [2.58]$$

$$\theta_o(s) = \frac{b_0\omega_n^2}{(s-m_1)(s-m_2)s^2} \qquad [2.59]$$

where m_1 and m_2 are the roots of the quadratic expression. Since for an equation of the form $ax^2 + bx + c$ the roots are given by

$$m = \frac{-b \pm \sqrt{(b^2 - 4ac)}}{2a}$$

then

$$m_1 = \frac{-2\zeta\omega_n + \sqrt{(4\zeta^2\omega_n^2 - 4\omega_n^2)}}{2} = -\zeta\omega_n + \omega_n\sqrt{(\zeta^2 - 1)}$$

and

$$m_2 = -\zeta\omega_n - \omega_n\sqrt{(\zeta^2 - 1)}$$

Equation [2.59] can be rearranged using partial fractions into the form

$$\theta_o(s) = b_0\left(\frac{A}{s^2} + \frac{B}{s} + \frac{C}{s-m_1} + \frac{D}{s-m_2}\right) \qquad [2.60]$$

Evaluation of these constants A, B, C and D and substitution of the values of m_1 and m_2 derived above gives

$$A = 1$$

$$B = -\frac{2\zeta}{\omega_n}$$

$$C = \frac{\zeta}{\omega_0} + \frac{2\zeta^2 - 1}{2\omega_n \sqrt{(\zeta^2 - 1)}}$$

$$D = \frac{\zeta}{\omega_n} - \frac{2\zeta^2 - 1}{2\omega_n \sqrt{(\zeta^2 - 1)}}$$

The inverse transformation of equation [2.60] gives

$$\theta_o = b_0[At + B + C \exp(m_1 t) + D \exp(m_2 t)]$$

$$\theta_o = b_0\left[t - \frac{2\zeta}{\omega_n} + C \exp(m_1 t) + D \exp(m_2 t) \right] \qquad [2.61]$$

The C and D terms in the equation give the transient response. The form of this response depends on whether ζ is greater than, equal to or less than 1 and so consequently the roots are real and unequal, real and equal, or complex and unequal. The form the transient response takes is thus the same as that occurring with the step input discussed earlier in this chapter. The A and B terms give the steady-state response. With no damping, i.e. $\zeta = 0$, then the steady-state response is just $b_0 t$ and indicates that the output keeps up with the steadily changing unit ramp input signal of t. However, when there is damping the steady-state response lags behind the input signal by $2\zeta/\omega_n$ (Fig. 2.62). This is referred to as the *steady-state error*. Figure 2.63 shows the types of steady-state plus transient responses that can occur with different degrees of damping.

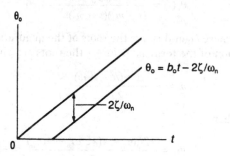

Fig. 2.62 Steady-state response of a second-order system to a unit ramp input

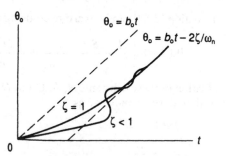

Fig. 2.63 Response of a second-order system to a unit ramp input

Example 2.37 The relationship between the input signal to a radiotelescope dish and the direction in which it points is given by the transfer function

$$G(s) = \frac{\omega_n^2}{s^2 + 2\zeta\omega_n + \omega_n^2}$$

with ζ having the value 0.4 and ω_n the value 10 Hz. What is (a) the steady-state error when the input signal to the telescope is a ramp signal, and (b) the 2% settling time?

Solution

(a) The steady-state error is the amount by which the steady-state position of the telescope lags behind the input ramp signal. This error has the value

$$\text{Steady-state error} = \frac{2\zeta}{\omega_n} = \frac{2 \times 0.4}{10} = 0.08 \text{ s}$$

(b) The settling time is the time taken for the response to settle down to within some fixed percentage of the steady-state value, in this case 2%. This time is given by

$$t_s = \frac{4}{\zeta\omega_n} = \frac{4}{0.4 \times 10} = 1 \text{ s}$$

Example 2.38 A robot arm has a transfer function given by

$$G(s) = \frac{K}{(s + 3)^2}$$

Derive the relationship between the output, i.e. the position of the arm, and time when the arm is subject to a unit ramp input.

Solution

When subject to a unit ramp input $(1/s^2)$ the output will be given by

$$\theta_o(s) = \frac{K}{s^2(s + 3)^2}$$

This can be rearranged in partial fractions as

$$\frac{A}{s^2} + \frac{B}{(s + 3)} + \frac{C}{(s + 3)^2}$$

Hence

$$A(s + 3)^2 + Bs^2(s + 3) + Cs^2 = K$$

When $s = -3$ then $9C = K$ and so $C = K/9$. When $s = 0$ then $9A = K$ and so $A = K/9$. When $s = 1$ then $16A + 4B + C = K$ and so $B = -2K/9$. Hence

$$\theta_o(s) = \frac{K}{9s^2} - \frac{2K}{9(s + 3)} + \frac{K}{9(s + 3)^2}$$

Using Table 2.1,

$$\theta_o = (K/9)t - (2K/9)\,e^{-3t} + (K/9)t\,e^{-3t}$$

Impulse input to a second-order system

Consider the output from a second-order system when it is subject to a unit impulse input at $t = 0$.

Laplace transform of output $= G(s) \times$ Laplace transform of input

Thus, using equation [2.36] to represent the general form of a second-order system in the s domain,

$$\theta_o(s) = \frac{b_0\omega_n^2}{s^2 + 2\zeta\omega_n s + \omega_n^2} \times \theta_i(s)$$

Since, for a unit impulse at $t = 0$, $\theta_i(s) = 1$ then

$$\theta_o(s) = \frac{b_0\omega_n^2}{(s^2 + 2\zeta\omega_n s + \omega_n^2)} \qquad [2.62]$$

This can be rearranged as

$$\theta_o(s) = \frac{b_0\omega_n^2}{(s - m_1)(s - m_2)} \qquad [2.63]$$

where m_1 and m_2 are the roots of the equation

$$s^2 + 2\zeta\omega_n s + \omega_n^2 = 0$$

Thus, since the roots are given for an equation of the form $ax^2 + bx + c = 0$ by

$$x = \frac{-b \pm \sqrt{(b^2 - 4ac)}}{2a}$$

then

$$m = \frac{-2\zeta\omega_n \pm \sqrt{(4\zeta^2\omega_n^2 - 4\omega_n^2)}}{2}$$

$$m_1 = -\zeta\omega_n + \omega_n\sqrt{(\zeta^2 - 1)}$$

$$m_2 = -\zeta\omega_n - \omega_n\sqrt{(\zeta^2 - 1)}$$

Using partial fractions equation [2.63] can be rearranged as

$$\theta_o(s) = \frac{A}{s - m_1} + \frac{B}{s - m_2} \qquad [2.64]$$

Hence

$$A(s - m_2) + B(s - m_1) = b_0\omega_n^2$$

and when $s = m_2$ then $B(m_2 - m_1) = b_0\omega_n^2$ and when $s = m_1$ then $A(m_1 - m_2) = b_0\omega_n^2$. Thus, substituting for the values of m_1 and m_2,

$$A = -B = \frac{b_0\omega_n}{2\sqrt{(\zeta^2 - 1)}}$$

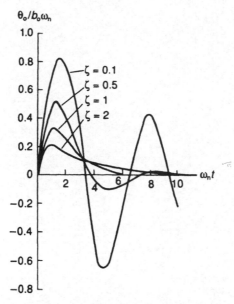

Fig. 2.64 Response of a second-order system to a unit impulse at $t = 0$

The inverse transform of equation [2.64] gives

$$\theta_o = A \exp m_1 t + B \exp m_2 t$$

and thus, substituting for the values of A and B,

$$\theta_o = \frac{b_0 \omega_n}{2\sqrt{(\zeta^2 - 1)}}[\exp{(m_1 t)} - \exp{(m_2 t)}] \qquad [2.65]$$

The form of response that occurs will depend on whether the roots m_1 and m_2 are real or complex, i.e. whether ζ is greater than or less than 1. When $\zeta > 1$ the roots are real and unequal and the result is just an increase in output which is followed by a slow decrease back to the zero value (Fig. 2.64). When $\zeta = 1$ the roots are real and equal and the system is critically damped. This means that following the initial increase in output the response dies back to the zero value in the minimum time with no oscillations. When $\zeta < 1$ the roots are complex quantities and following the initial increase in output oscillations of steadily decreasing amplitude occur until eventually the output goes back to the zero value.

When ζ is less than 1 the roots are complex. When this is the case equation [2.65] is often written in a different form. This form could have been obtained by using the inverse transformation, given in Table 2.1, of

$$\frac{\omega_n^2}{s^2 + 2\zeta\omega_n s + \omega_n^2}$$

as

$$\frac{\omega_n}{\sqrt{(1 - \zeta^2)}} \exp{(-\zeta\omega_n t)} \sin[\omega_n\sqrt{(1 - \zeta^2)}t]$$

then, for equation [2.62],

$$\theta_o = \frac{b_0 \omega_n}{\sqrt{(1 - \zeta^2)}} \exp{(-\zeta\omega_n t)} \sin[\omega_n\sqrt{(1 - \zeta^2)}t] \qquad [2.66]$$

CHAPTER 3
Mechanical Principles

Unit 4: Mechanical Principles

Unit code: F/601/1450

QCF level: 5

Credit value: 15

Aim

This unit aims to develop learners' understanding of an extended range of mechanical principles that underpin the design and operation of mechanical engineering systems.

Unit abstract

This unit will develop learners' understanding of complex loading systems and will provide an introduction to the concept of volumetric strain and the relationship between elastic constants. The expressions derived for linear and volumetric strain then form a basis for determining dimensional changes in loaded cylinders.

The unit will build upon learners' existing knowledge of the relationship between the distribution of shear force and bending moment in loaded beams, to include the relationship between bending moment, slope and deflection.

Learners will analyse the use of mechanical power transmission systems, both individually and in the combinations that are used in practical situations. Learners' knowledge of rotating system elements is further extended through an investigation of the dynamic characteristics of the slider-crank and four-bar linkage. The balancing of rotating systems is also investigated, together with the determination of flywheel mass and size to give sufficiently smooth operating conditions.

Learning outcomes

On successful completion of this unit a learner will:

1 Be able to determine the behavioural characteristics of materials subjected to complex loading systems
2 Be able to determine the behavioural characteristics of loaded beams and cylinders
3 Be able to determine the dynamic parameters of power transmission system elements
4 Be able to determine the dynamic parameters of rotating systems.

Unit content

1 Be able to determine the behavioural characteristics of materials subjected to complex loading systems

Relationship: definition of Poisson's Ratio; typical values of Poisson's Ratio for common engineering materials

Two- and three-dimensional loading: expressions for strain in the x, y and z-directions; calculation of changes in dimensions

Volumetric strain: expression for volumetric strain; calculation of volume change

Elastic constants: definition of Bulk Modulus; relationship between Modulus of Elasticity; Shear Modulus; Bulk Modulus and Poisson's Ratio for an elastic material

2 Be able to determine the behavioural characteristics of loaded beams and cylinders

$$\text{Relationships: slope } i = \frac{1}{E1} \int M dx$$

$$\text{deflection } y = \frac{1}{E1} \iint M dx dx$$

Loaded beams: slope and deflection for loaded beams eg cantilever beams carrying a concentrated load at the free end or a uniformly distributed load over the entire length, simply supported beams carrying a central concentrated load or a uniformly distributed load over the entire length

Stresses in thin-walled pressure vessels: circumferential hoop stress and longitudinal stress in cylindrical and spherical pressure vessels subjected to internal and external pressure eg compressed-air receivers, boiler steam drums, submarine hulls, condenser casings; factor of safety; joint efficiency

Stresses in thick-walled cylinders: circumferential hoop stress, longitudinal stress and radial stress in thick-walled cylinders subjected to pressure eg hydraulic cylinders, extrusion dies, gun barrels; Lame's theory; use of boundary conditions and distribution of stress in the cylinder walls

3 Be able to determine the dynamic parameters of power transmission system elements

Belt drives: flat and v-section belts; limiting coefficient friction; limiting slack and tight side tensions; initial tension requirements; maximum power transmitted

Friction clutches: flat single and multi-plate clutches; conical clutches; coefficient of friction; spring force requirements; maximum power transmitted by constant wear and constant pressure theories; validity of theories

Gear trains: simple, compound and epicycle gear trains; velocity ratios; torque, speed and power relationships; efficiency; fixing torques

4 Be able to determine the dynamic parameters of rotating systems

Plane mechanisms: slider crank and four bar linkage mechanisms; production of vector diagrams and determination of kinetic characteristics

Balancing: single plane and multi-plane rotating mass systems; Dalby's method for determination of out-of-balance forces and couples and the required balancing masses

Flywheels: angular momentum; kinetic energy; coefficient of fluctuation of speed; coefficient of fluctuation of energy; calculation of flywheel mass/dimensions to give required operating conditions

Effects of coupling: conservation of angular momentum; common final velocity and energy loss due to coupling of two freely rotating systems

Learning outcomes and assessment criteria

Learning outcomes On successful completion of this unit a learner will:	Assessment criteria for pass The learner can:
LO1 Be able to determine the behavioural characteristics of materials subjected to complex loading systems	1.1 apply the relationship between longitudinal and transverse strain to determine the dimensional effects of uniaxial loading on a given material 1.2 determine the effects of two-dimensional and three-dimensional loading on the dimensions of a given material 1.3 determine volumetric strain and change in volume due to three-dimensional loading 1.4 apply the relationship between elastic constants
LO2 Be able to determine the behavioural characteristics of loaded beams and cylinders	2.1 apply the relationship between bending moment, slope and deflection to determine the variation of slope and deflection along a simply supported beam 2.2 determine the principal stresses that occur in a thin-walled cylindrical pressure vessel 2.3 determine the distribution of the stresses that occur in a pressurised thick-walled cylinder
LO3 Be able to determine the dynamic parameters of power transmission system elements	3.1 determine the dynamic parameters of a belt drive 3.2 determine the dynamic parameters of a friction clutch 3.3 determine the holding torque and power transmitted through compound and epicyclic gear trains
LO4 Be able to determine the dynamic parameters of rotating systems	4.1 determine the parameters of a slider-crank and a four-bar linkage mechanism 4.2 determine the balancing masses required to obtain dynamic equilibrium in a rotating system 4.3 determine the energy storage requirements of a flywheel 4.4 determine the dynamic effects of coupling two freely rotating systems.

Guidance

Links

This unit can be linked with *Unit 1: Analytical Methods for Engineers, Unit 2: Engineering Science, Unit 35: Further Analytical Methods for Engineers and Unit 60: Dynamics of Machines.*

Essential requirements

Sufficient laboratory/test equipment will need to be available to support a range of practical investigations.

Employer engagement and vocational contexts

Liaison with employers would prove of benefit to centres, especially if they are able to offer help with the provision of suitable mechanical systems/equipment that can be used to demonstrate applications of the principles.

Machines

Belt drives

Figure 3.1(a) shows an open belt drive, Fig. 3.1(b) a crossed belt drive. In the open drive the pulleys rotate in the same direction, whereas in the crossed drive they rotate in opposite directions.

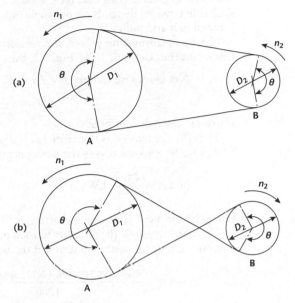

Fig. 3.1

The angle θ shown is the *angle of lap* or *contact*. For the crossed belt drive θ is the same for both pulleys. This is not necessarily the case for the open drive.

Velocity ratio

Consider pulley A of diameter D_1. In one revolution the length of belt unwrapped from one side is πD_1. Hence, in n_1 revolutions a length $n_1 \times \pi D_1$ is unwrapped. If pulley B, of diameter D_2, makes n_2 revolutions *in the same time* then the length of belt going on to it is $n_2 \times \pi D_2$.

If there is no slip or stretching of the belt the length unwrapped from A must equal the length wrapped on to B; thus

$$n_1 \pi D_1 = n_2 \pi D_2$$

or

$$n_1 D_1 = n_2 D_2$$

i.e.

$$\frac{n_1}{n_2} = \frac{D_2}{D_1}$$

Thus *the speeds of two pulleys connected by a belt are inversely proportional to their diameters.*

Power transmitted

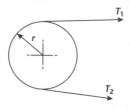

Fig. 3.2

If a driving torque is applied to pulley A the belt coming on to the pulley tightens, and the belt leaving the pulley slackens. The belt is mounted on the two pulleys with an initial tension so that, when driving, the tension on the tight side is greater than that on the slack side. The ratio of the tight and slack side tensions depends on the angle of lap and the coefficient of friction between belt and pulley.

If, when transmitting power, the tension on the tight side is T_1 and the tension on the slack side is T_2, Fig. 3.2, then

$$\text{Net clockwise torque, } T = T_1 r - T_2 r$$

$$= (T_1 - T_2)r$$

where r is the radius of pulley.

The *effective* tension is therefore $(T_1 - T_2)$.

At a pulley speed n revs/s the power is given by

$$\text{power} = \frac{2\pi n T}{1000} \text{ kW}$$

where the torque T is in newton metres.

Alternatively, since the effective tension in the belt is $(T_1 - T_2)$, the power transmitted may be written in terms of the belt speed v, thus:

$$\text{power} = \frac{\text{effective tension (N)} \times \text{speed (m/s)}}{1000}$$

$$= \frac{(T_1 - T_2)v}{1000} \text{ kW}$$

The relation between belt speed v and the speed of rotation n is

$$v = \omega r$$

where $\omega = 2\pi n$ radians per second and n is in revolutions per second.

Example 3.1

The ratio of the tensions in the two sides of a belt drive is 3:1. Find the tensions when 10 kW is being transmitted at 6 rev/s. The diameter of the driving pulley is 750 mm.

Solution

$$\text{Power} = \frac{2\pi n T}{1000} \text{ kW}$$

Therefore

$$\text{torque } T = \frac{10 \times 1000}{2\pi \times 6} = 265 \text{ N m}$$

so that

$$(T_1 - T_2)r = 265 \text{ N m}$$

and

$$T_1 - T_2 = \frac{265}{0.375} = 707 \text{ N}$$

Also

$$\frac{T_1}{T_2} = 3$$

Hence the tensions are

$$T_1 = \mathbf{1062} \text{ N and } T_2 = \mathbf{354} \text{ N}$$

Example 3.2 A compound belt and countershaft drive is shown in Fig. 3.3. The pulley diameters are: A, 72 cm; B, 27 cm; C, 54 cm; D, 24 cm. The power input to pulley A is 10 kW at a speed of 100 rev/min.

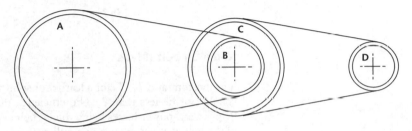

Fig. 3.3

If the belt drive is 85 per cent efficient, calculate:

(a) the output power (kW) at D,
(b) the speed of rotation of D,
(c) the torque exerted at D.

Solution

In this drive pulleys B and C form a compound pulley, rotating as one pulley on the countershaft. Since the diameters of the pulleys B and C are different, the belt speeds are different.

(a) $$\text{Efficiency} = \frac{\text{output}}{\text{input}}$$

Therefore,

$$\text{output kW at D} = \text{efficiency} \times \text{input kW at A}$$

$$= 0.85 \times 10$$

$$= \mathbf{8.5} \text{ kW}$$

(b)   Speed of A = 100 rev/min

$$\text{speed of B, C} = 100 \times \frac{72}{27} \text{ rev/min}$$

$$\text{speed of D} = \left(100 \times \frac{72}{27}\right) \times \frac{54}{24}$$

$$= 600 \text{ rev/min}$$

(c) $\text{Power} = \dfrac{2\pi n T}{1000} \text{ kW}$

At D, $n = \dfrac{600}{60} = 10 \text{ rev/s}$ and power = 8.5 kW

Therefore,

$$\text{torque } T = \frac{\text{power (kW)} \times 1000}{2\pi n}$$

$$= \frac{8.5 \times 1000}{2\pi \times 10}$$

$$= 136 \text{ N m}$$

Notes on belt drives

The tension ratio T_1/T_2 for a leather or solid woven belt is often about 5, and should not be less than 3. The efficiency of a good drive is usually about 97 per cent, power losses being due to belt slip, bearing friction and bending of the belt as it passes over the pulley.

The pulley face for a flat belt drive is usually cambered, Fig. 3.4. If the belt tends to wander from the centre-line joining two pulleys the camber ensures that there is a component of the belt tension acting towards the crown of the camber, thus tending to restore the belt to the centre.

The efficient transmission of large powers at high speeds is best performed by the Vee rope drive, Fig. 3.5. The vee-grooves cut in the pulley face ensure a higher friction force between belt and pulley and therefore higher driving torque. A number of ropes can be used on one drive with a tension ratio of up to 20.

Cambered face

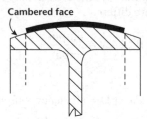

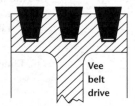

Vee belt drive

Fig. 3.4   **Fig. 3.5**

Belt drives are often used when it is required to prevent sudden changes of load and shocks from damaging the driving motor or engine. Sudden overloads are absorbed in belt slip or stretching of the belt.

Direct stress and strain 1

**Poisson's ratio:
lateral strain**

When a bar is loaded axially in tension by a force F it extends in length but at the same time the lateral dimensions contract, Fig. 3.6. The extension in the direction of the force is given by Hooke's law within the limit of proportionality. The ratio of the strain in the lateral direction to that in the longitudinal direction is found to be constant for a particular material and is called *Poisson's ratio*, denoted by v. Thus:

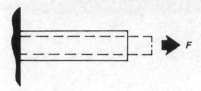

Fig. 3.6

$$v = \frac{\text{lateral strain}}{\text{longitudinal strain}}$$

If the longitudinal strain is ε then the lateral strain is $-v\varepsilon$.

In materials with high elasticity (elastomers) such as rubber, silicone and certain plastics, a large longitudinal extension is accompanied by appreciable reduction in cross-sectional area. In soft metals, the reduction within the elastic region is also significant but in stiff metals the lateral changes are very small.

Poisson's ratio applies in the same way to a bar loaded in compression.

Change in volume: volumetric strain

When a bar is pulled, its length increases and its transverse dimensions decrease, and there is an increase in volume. Let the length of the bar be L and the cross-section to be square of side B; then if σ is the stress produced,

$$\text{longitudinal strain } \varepsilon = \frac{\sigma}{E}$$

The lateral strain in the other two directions is $-v\varepsilon$. If V_1 and V_2 are the initial and final volumes respectively, then

$$V_1 = LB^2$$

and $\quad V_2 = (\text{final length}) \times (\text{final thickness})^2$

$$= (L + \varepsilon L)(B - v\varepsilon B)^2$$

$$= (1 - 2v\varepsilon + \varepsilon + \dots)LB^2$$

$$= (1 - 2v\varepsilon + \varepsilon)V_1$$

neglecting the terms involving ε^2. Therefore

$$\text{change in volume} = V_2 - V_1$$

$$= (1 - 2v\varepsilon + \varepsilon)V_1 - V_1$$

$$= \varepsilon(1 - 2v)V_1$$

The *volumetric strain* is the change in volume per unit volume, i.e.

$$\text{volumetric strain} = \frac{V_2 - V_1}{V_1}$$

$$= \frac{\varepsilon(1 - 2v)V_1}{V_1}$$

$$= \varepsilon(1 - 2v)$$

Since a bar in tension has an increase in volume, the change in volume must be positive, therefore $(1 - 2v)$ must be positive. Thus Poisson's ratio for any material is less than 0.5. For some rubbers $v = 0.5$, and for most metals v lies between that for tungsten and chromium, 0.21, and that for gold, 0.44.

Note: The formula in terms of linear strain and Poisson's ratio should always be used to find the *difference* of the two volumes. Calculation of V_2 directly is impracticable because of the minute changes in length involved.

Example 3.3

A bar of titanium alloy of length 120 mm and square cross-section, 7.5 mm × 7.5 mm, is pulled axially by a force of 15 kN. Find the percentage decrease in thickness if E = 106 GN/m² and v = 0.33.

Solution

$$\text{Stress } \sigma = \frac{15\,000}{7.5 \times 7.5 \times 10^{-6}} = 267 \times 10^6 \text{ N/m}^2$$

$$\text{Longitudinal strain } \varepsilon = \frac{\sigma}{E} = \frac{267 \times 10^6}{106 \times 10^9} = 0.0025$$

$$\text{Lateral strain} = v\varepsilon = 0.33 \times 0.0025 = 0.001$$

i.e.

$$\frac{\text{change in thickness}}{\text{original thickness}} = 0.001$$

i.e. percentage change in thickness $= 0.001 \times 100 = \mathbf{0.1}$

Example 3.4

A bar of aluminium alloy of rectangular section 75 mm × 20 mm and 800 mm long is stretched by an axial force of 150 kN. Find the volumetric strain, the actual change in volume and the percentage reduction in cross-sectional area of the bar. Take E = 70 GN/m² and v = 0.34.

Solution

$$\text{Stress } \sigma = \frac{150 \times 10^3}{75 \times 20 \times 10^{-6}} = 100 \times 10^6 \text{ N/m}^2$$

$$\text{Longitudinal strain } \varepsilon = \frac{\sigma}{E} = \frac{100 \times 10^6}{70 \times 10^9} = 0.00143$$

$$\text{Change in volume} = \text{volumetric strain} \times \text{original volume}$$
$$= \varepsilon(1 - 2v) \times (75 \times 20 \times 800)$$
$$= 0.00143(1 - 2 \times 0.34) \times 12 \times 10^5$$
$$= \mathbf{550 \ mm^3}$$

If B and b are the initial lengths of the sides of the section then the original area is Bb. The new lengths are $(B - v\varepsilon B)$ and $(b - v\varepsilon b)$, hence

$$\text{reduction in area} = Bb - (B - v\varepsilon B)(b - v\varepsilon b)$$
$$= 2v\varepsilon Bb, \text{ neglecting small quantities}$$
$$= 2v\varepsilon \text{ per unit area}$$

therefore percentage reduction in area $= 2v\varepsilon \times 100$
$$= 2 \times 0.34 \times 0.00143 \times 100$$
$$= \mathbf{0.1}$$

Mechanical properties of materials

Introduction

The general properties of any material forming an engineering component depend on its chemical make-up, how it is built up from atoms and molecules into crystals, grains and solid material, and on the manufacturing processes and treatments used to produce its final form and condition. When a material is selected for a particular engineering situation, a variety of these properties have to be considered including strength, machinability, corrosion resistance, electrical characteristics, thermal conductivity, melting point, etc. Often, however, these requirements have to be balanced, one against the other and the choice of a material therefore usually involves compromise.

In this chapter the emphasis is specifically on the mechanical properties of materials and their behaviour under load. The treatment is of necessity restricted because of the proliferation of metals and plastics now in use in modern industry and the range of testing machines and techniques available. For fuller information students should refer to more specialist texts, British Standards and manufacturers' publications.

Metals and alloys

Engineering metals can be divided into two groups based on their iron content; those consisting mainly of iron are called *ferrous metals* and all others *non-ferrous*. The 'light' metals include aluminium, magnesium and titanium, and the 'refractory' metals with heat-resisting properties include tungsten and molybdenum. Alloys are formed by adding quantities of various elements to a basic metal, in some cases very small quantities, and the resulting materials usually have markedly different properties from those of the individual constituents. The most commonly used alloys are those of iron with a small amount of carbon to produce steel or cast iron. The non-metallic content, less than 4 per cent by *weight*, is the primary factor in determining the nature and properties of the ferrous metal produced. Steels contain less than 1.5 per cent carbon; the 'plain' carbon steels, composed almost entirely of iron and carbon are termed low- (or mild), medium- or high-carbon steels depending on the proportion of carbon present. When a carbon steel is alloyed with other elements besides carbon, it is called an 'alloy steel' and is designated according to the predominant element added, e.g. manganese steel. Each alloying element is used to produce specific effects on the properties of the steel produced or on the manufacturing process involved, e.g. to give a tough, machinable material, to resist the effects of high temperatures, or to enable a steel to be hardened. A particular example is the use of cobalt, nickel and titanium, which together with ageing processes result in high-strength, very ductile 'maraging' steels, greatly used in rocket work. Cast irons have a higher carbon content than steels together with amounts of silicon, magnesium, sulphur and phosphorus. There is a great variety of modern cast irons but the most common is the traditional grey iron, very brittle, easily machinable, a good conductor of heat and useful in massive parts for damping down vibrations. Adding a small amount of magnesium in the production stages produces nodular or spheroidal iron, a strong, tough, ductile material.

Non-ferrous metals and their alloys are equally as important as the ferrous. Aluminium, a soft metal with a low melting point, is noted for its high-electrical and thermal conductivity as well as resistance to corrosion. It is the foremost metal in use after steel because of its excellent strength to weight ratio, giving light, stiff materials. Copper, alloyed with up to 40 per cent zinc and small quantities of other elements such as tin, is the basis of the various straight brasses, but when alloyed without zinc to tin, phosphorus, silicon or aluminium, it gives a range of bronzes. Phosphor-bronze, for example, is a tin bronze with added phosphorus and like manganese bronze is particularly resistant to sea water. Further examples of non-ferrous alloys are those based on nickel, magnesium and titanium, each of which has special properties. Nickel is noted for hardness and strength, titanium for lightness and rigidity as well as strength at high temperatures, and magnesium is the lightest of all the metals.

It is useful to define the mechanical properties of materials in general, plastics as well as metals, by considering in particular the behaviour of black mild steel when loaded in tension and compression.

Black mild steel in tension

Black mild steel is a low-carbon steel in a hot-rolled or annealed condition. A tension test on a typical specimen would give the graph of load against extension shown in Fig. 3.7.

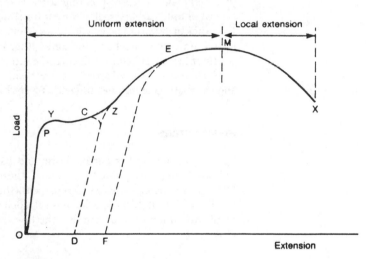

Fig. 3.7

Elastic stage

In the initial stage of the test the steel is elastic, i.e. when unloaded the test-piece returns to its original unstretched length. This is represented by the line OP, Fig. 3.7. Over the major portion of this stage the material obeys Hooke's law, i.e. the extension is proportional to the load and the strain is proportional to the stress.

Limit of proportionality

The point P represents the *limit of proportionality*. Beyond P the metal no longer obeys Hooke's law.

Elastic limit

The stress at which a permanent extension occurs is the *elastic limit stress* and the metal is no longer elastic. In black mild steel, the limit of proportionality and elastic limit are very close together and often cannot be distinguished. Elastic limit stress and limit of proportionality values have limited use today.

Permanent set

If the metal is loaded beyond the point P representing the elastic limit, and then unloaded, a permanent extension remains, called the *permanent set*.

Yield stress

At Y the metal stretches without further increase in load. Y is termed the *yield point* and the corresponding stress is the *yield stress*. This sharp yield is typical of mild carbon steel, wrought iron and some plastics, but occurs with few other materials. The graph shows a very slight dip at the yield point. For a medium carbon steel and for some other metals, depending on their heat treatment and mechanical working, the dip at point Y is sufficient to indicate an *upper* and *lower* yield stress, i.e. the yield point is reached at a certain load and the material continues to yield at a slightly lower load.

Plastic stage

Beyond Y, the steel is partly elastic and partly *plastic*. If the test piece is unloaded from any point C beyond Y the permanent extension would be OD, approximately, where CD represents the unloading line (approximately parallel with PO). If the specimen is reloaded immediately the load–extension graph would tend to traverse first the line DC and then continue from near C as before.

Work hardening

At the point Z, further extension requires an increase in load and the steel is said to *work harden* or increase in strength. If unloaded from any point E between Z and M, the unloading graph would be approximately the line EF. If reloaded, the graph would trace out approximately the same elastic line from F to E, after which it continues from E to M, as it would have done if not unloaded. The process of *cold working*, i.e. cold drawing or rolling, represents a work hardening or strengthening.

During the stage Z to M, the mill scale on an unmachined specimen of black steel is seen to flake off from the stretched metal. Furthermore, the extension is now no longer small but could be measured roughly with a simple rule.

Waisting

M represents the *maximum load* which the test-piece can carry. At this point the extension is no longer uniform along the length of the specimen but is localized at one portion. The test-piece begins to *neck down* or *waist*, the area at the waist decreasing rapidly. Local extension continues with a decrease of load until fracture occurs at point X.

Ultimate tensile stress

The *ultimate tensile stress* (UTS) is defined as:

$$\frac{\text{maximum load}}{\text{original area}}$$

Black mild steel has an UTS of about 400 MN/m². There are very few steels with a strength above 1500 MN/m² and only a limited number with a specified UTS above 1200 MN/m². One of the strongest is the wire used in musical instruments, a very hard-drawn, high-carbon steel, the highest grade of spring wire, with a strength in the range 1800–3000 MN/m².

Breaking stress

The *nominal fracture* or *breaking stress* is:

$$\frac{\text{load at fracture}}{\text{original area}}$$

and this is less than the UTS in a metal which necks down before fracture. This stress is seldom quoted today.

True fracture stress

The *true* or *actual fracture stress* is:

$$\frac{\text{load at fracture}}{\text{final area at fracture}}$$

and this is greater than either the nominal fracture stress or the UTS in a metal which necks down, due to the reduced area at fracture. The true stress may be as much as 100 per cent higher than the UTS for mild steel. Also, it may be noted that the true stress is found to be roughly constant for a given material whereas the UTS varies with the treatment of the specimen before testing.

Fracture

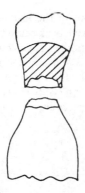

Fig. 3.8

The appearance of the fracture is shown in Fig. 3.8. It is described as a cup-and-cone fracture and is typical of a *ductile* material such as mild steel.

Failure: factor of safety

The term 'failure' applied to a material or element in a machine can mean fracture as we have discussed here, or it can mean that the member has deformed past the elastic limit, buckled or collapsed. Fracture can also be brought about by bending or cyclic stresses as well as by direct tension or compression. In practice, engineering parts are designed with a margin of safety, e.g. by assuming a working or *allowable* stress which is a fraction of the UTS or in some cases, the yield stress. A *factor of safety* based on the UTS is given by

$$\text{factor of safety} = \frac{\text{UTS}}{\text{allowable or working stress}}$$

The kind of loading is important in arriving at a factor of safety. The loading may be dynamic, static, fluctuating, suddenly applied or due to wind. Many other aspects must also be considered besides elasticity.

Ductility

Black mild steel is a *ductile* material since it can be drawn out into a fine wire and undergo considerable plastic deformation before fracture. Ductility in a member of a structure permits it to 'give' slightly under load, which is useful where errors in workmanship or non-uniform stresses occur. Ductility is of importance in manufacture where material is to be bent or formed to shape. Ductility is measured in two ways:

1. By the *percentage reduction in area*, which is

$$\frac{\text{reduction in area}}{\text{original area}} \times 100 \text{ per cent}$$

   where the reduction in area is the difference between the original area and the least area at the point of fracture.
2. By the *percentage elongation in length*. If a gauge length l is marked on the test-piece before testing and the extension of this length after fracture found to be x, then, provided fracture occurred between the gauge points,

$$\text{percentage elongation} = \frac{x}{l} \times 100$$

The percentage elongation depends on the dimensions of the test-piece so that, for the purposes of comparison, the dimensions have been standardized. It is found that for cylindrical test-pieces, if the ratio of gauge length to diameter is kept constant, the percentage elongation is constant for a given material. By international agreement, the gauge length is five diameters, i.e. $l = 5D$. The standard test piece for a round bar in tension (BSS 18) is shown in Fig. 3.9. The dimensions for a 10 mm diameter test-piece are shown below.

Gauge length, l (mm)	50
Diameter, D (mm)	10
Radius, R, minimum (mm)	9
Area (mm²)	78.5
P, minimum (mm)	55

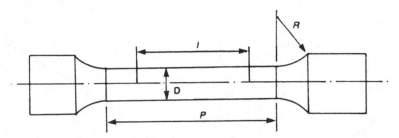

Fig. 3.9

There appears to be no simple relation between percentage elongation and percentage reduction in area for steels. To estimate ductility both ratios should be found as some steels show a high percentage elongation with a low percentage reduction in area.

Stress–strain curve

So far we have considered the load–extension diagram. However, since

$$\text{nominal stress} = \frac{\text{load}}{\text{original area}}$$

and

$$\text{strain} = \frac{\text{extension}}{\text{original gauge length}}$$

the curve of (nominal) stress against strain will be of the same shape as the load–extension graph up to the maximum load. At the point of maximum load, the test-piece begins to neck down and the cross-sectional area diminishes rapidly. Beyond this point the extension to gauge length no longer measures the true strain at any point. Similarly, the ratio of load to original area is an inaccurate measure of the *true stress* at the waist. Nevertheless it is convenient to sketch a *stress–strain curve* which illustrates some of the properties of the material independent of the size of the specimen.

Modulus of elasticity

The modulus of elasticity E is the ratio of stress to strain at a point on the initial straight-line portion of the load–extension diagram obtained from a tensile test on a standard test-piece.

Figure 3.10 represents, for a metal obeying Hooke's law, the best straight-line connecting load W and extension x obtained from the plotted experimental points. The modulus of elasticity E is determined directly from the slope of the graph as follows: If A is the cross-sectional area of the test-piece and l the gauge length, then

$$\text{strain, } \varepsilon = \frac{x}{l}$$

and

$$\text{stress, } \sigma = \frac{W}{A}$$

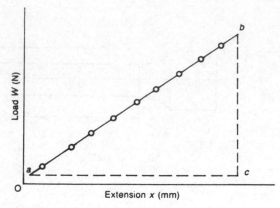

Fig. 3.10

and
$$E = \frac{\sigma}{\varepsilon}$$

$$= \frac{W/A}{x/l}$$

$$= \frac{l}{A} \times \frac{W}{x}$$

But W/x is the slope of the load–extension graph, i.e. bc/ac. Therefore

$$E = \frac{l}{A} \times \frac{bc}{ac}$$

The load–extension graph does not usually pass through the point of zero load for two reasons:

1. The specimen is lightly loaded on first gripping in the testing machine.
2. Initial extensometer readings are slightly inaccurate at light loads.

However, since only the slope of the graph is required the zero error is unimportant when calculating the elastic modulus.

The modulus gives a very quick and accurate indication of the *stiffness* of a material. When E is large, the slope of the elastic line is steep, i.e. a large load is required for a given extension. Stiffness is a measure of the amount of spring in a metal and must be distinguished from strength which is the force needed for fracture. Typical figures for E are given in Table 3.1. In practice, there is a wide spread of values around those given because of the effects of impurities, the different processes of manufacture, mechanical working and heat treatment. The stiffest of materials is the diamond, with an extremely high modulus, 1200 GN/m². The modulus for steel is in a fairly narrow range, 196–210 GN/m². For most metals, however, E lies between that of lead, 16 GN/m² and that of tungsten 360 GN/m². Where a material such as cast iron does not obey Hooke's law, the figures given in the table are very approximate. Plastics and rubbers have little rigidity and E for such materials may be as low as 1 GN/m², and even when reinforced with high-strength fibres, the modulus for reinforced plastic is only exceptionally more than 60 GN/m². The characteristics of rubber vary with time and temperature and this material does not have a properly defined value for E.

Table 3.1

Material	Young's modulus $(GN/m^2$ or $kN/mm^2)$	Relative density	Approximate specific modulus (GN/m^2)
Steel	196–210	7.8	25
Wrought iron	175	7.8	23
Cast iron: grey	105–125	7.2	16
spheroidal	180	7.2	25
Titanium alloys	110	4.5	25
Magnesium alloys	45	1.8	25
Tungsten	360	19.2	19
Aluminium alloy	70	2.7	25
Copper	80–140	8.9	9–16
Brass	84	8.4	10
Bronze	85–120	8.6	10–14
Gun-metal	80–100	8.7	9–12
Timber	7–20	0.5–0.8	14–30
Lead	16	11.3	–
Concrete	15–40	–	–
Rubber	<0.04	–	–
Unreinforced plastics	1.4	1.4	1
Glass fibre	50–85	2.5	20–34
Carbon fibre, high modulus	420	2	210
Reinforced plastic: glass fibre	7–60	1.9	5–30
carbon fibre	130–200	1.5	90–130

Specific modulus of elasticity

The denser a material, the heavier it will be for a given strength and rigidity. Where the strength-to-weight ratio is critical as in aircraft and transport vehicles, it is not the absolute value of E that is important but the *specific* value which takes into account the relative density or specific gravity of the material. Thus

$$\text{specific modulus of elasticity} = \frac{E}{\text{relative density}}$$

Relative density is the density of the material relative to that of water and since it is a ratio, the basic units of the specific modulus are the same as those of E, i.e. N/m^2.

Table 3.1 shows typical values of the specific modulus and it can be seen that for a surprising number of materials, the specific modulus is roughly the same as that of steel, about 25 GN/m^2.

Black mild steel in compression: malleability

Up to the limit of proportionality, tension and compression tests on black mild steel give roughly similar stress–strain graphs, the value of the modulus of elasticity being approximately the same in compression as in tension. A well-defined yield point occurs after which the stress continues to rise with

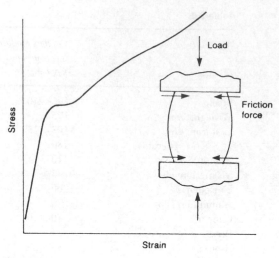

Fig. 3.11

increasing strain, no maximum load or stress being reached before destruc-tion. Owing to friction at the surfaces of contact between specimen and com-pression plattens the metal does not deform uniformly but develops a barrel shape, Fig. 3.11. To avoid buckling under load, the length of a cylindrical test-piece is usually less than twice the diameter.

Malleability is a very similar property to ductility and is the capacity of a metal to be forced, rolled or beaten into plates, i.e. to be shaped or deformed to a great extent when compressed. Of the common engineering metals, aluminium is the most malleable.

Bright drawn mild steel

Bright drawn mild steel is again low carbon steel but has been previously worked by cold drawing. The material is stronger but less ductile than the same steel in the form of black mild steel. A typical stress–strain curve in tension would follow the curve OPMX, Fig. 3.12(a). The sharp yield

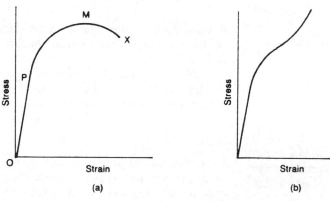

Fig. 3.12

point has disappeared but a limit of proportionality may be determined. If sufficiently cold-worked, fracture may occur without necking. In compression, the stress rises continuously and there is no fracture, Fig. 3.12(b). Bright drawn mild steel when annealed shows the same properties as black mild steel. The curve of Fig. 3.12(a) is typical of a number of other metals such as hard brass and most alloys of copper and aluminium. Hard alloy steels also have the same shape but with fracture occurring between P and M without prior necking.

Ductile metals

A ductile metal has a large percentage elongation and shows considerable deformation and necking before fracture. Black mild steel is a ductile metal but various non-ferrous metals such as soft aluminium or copper have even greater ductility. A tensile test of a highly ductile metal would give a stress–strain curve of the form shown in Fig. 3.13. The limit of proportionality and yield point are not defined. Work hardening of a ductile metal reduces its ductility. Gold is the most ductile and malleable metal but following on the noble metals, the *order* of ductility of the engineering metals is iron, copper, aluminium, zinc, tin, lead.

Proof stress

For engineering purposes it is desirable to know the stress to which a highly ductile material such as aluminium can be loaded safely before a large permanent extension takes place. This stress is known as the *proof* or *offset stress* and is defined as the stress at which a specified permanent extension has taken place in the tensile test. The extension specified may be 0.1, 0.2 or 0.5 per cent of gauge length, but the 0.2 per cent figure is becoming more common.

The proof stress is found from the stress–strain curve, Fig. 3.13, as follows. From the point on the strain axis representing 0.1 per cent strain draw a line parallel to the initial slope of the stress–strain diagram at O. The stress at the point where this line cuts the curve is the 0.1 per cent proof stress. The 0.2 per cent proof stress is found in a similar manner by starting from the point on the strain axis representing 0.2 per cent extension.

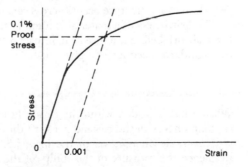

Fig. 3.13

Brittle materials

A material which has little ductility and does not neck down before fracture is termed *brittle*. The most obviously brittle materials are the ceramic, glasses and concrete, together with some cast irons and cold-rolled steel. Also, non-ferrous metals and alloys, when suitably worked, are brittle, as well as thermosetting plastics and some of the thermoplastics.

Figure 3.14 shows the stress–strain curve for grey cast iron in *tension*. The metal is elastic almost up to fracture but does not obey Hooke's law. Yielding is continuous and the total strain and elongation before fracture occurs is very small, less than 0.7 per cent elongation. Cast iron fractures straight across the specimen as distinct from the cup-and-cone fracture of a ductile material. The modulus of elasticity for cast iron is not a constant since there is no straight-line portion of the graph, but varies according to the point or small portion of the curve at which it is calculated.

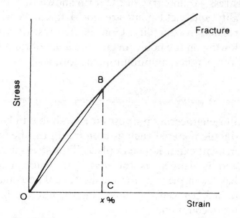

Fig. 3.14

A method of *estimating* the value of E used in rubber and plastics technology, employs the slope of the secant line OB; this gives a ratio of stress to strain at x per cent strain for the whole portion of the curve up to point B. This is called the *secant modulus*, and is given by BC/OC.

The stress–strain curve for cast iron in *compression* is similar to that for a tension test. The metal fractures across planes making 55° with the axis of the specimen, indicating failure by shearing, except when the specimen is very short when fracture occurs across several planes.

The brittleness of a material is often best measured by the energy which it will absorb before fracture in an impact test; the lower the energy absorbed by a standard specimen of a given material, the greater the brittleness.

Resilience and toughness

When a bar is loaded within its elastic limit, the work expended is stored as strain energy in the bar and is called the *resilience* of the bar. The energy is recoverable on removal of the load, i.e. the bar behaves like a spring. Resilience is a measure of the ability of the material to store energy and to withstand a blow without permanent distortion.

Toughness is the converse of brittleness, and describes the ability of a material to resist the propagation of cracks and to withstand shock loads without rupturing. Both resilience and toughness are important characteristics of metals, plastics and fibres. Toughness is usually measured by the amount of energy, in joules, required to fracture a notched test-piece held gripped in a vice and struck a single transverse blow by a heavy pendulum. The pendulum head strikes at a fixed height above the notch, and the 'notch-toughness' of the metal is measured by the loss of energy of the pendulum on impact and the machines are calibrated accordingly. The Izod and Charpy impact testing machines use this method. Results obtained from impact tests require care in interpretation and precise information is essential regarding the type of test, notch dimensions (which are critical) and the test conditions.

Mechanical properties of metals

Table 3.2 gives typical values of percentage elongation, yield or 0.1 per cent proof stress, and ultimate tensile strength. These values vary widely, however, not only for alloys where the precise mix of elements is crucial, but also because of the many factors already discussed.

Table 3.2

	Percentage elongation (total)	Yield stress (MN/m^2)	0.1% proof stress (MN/m^2)	Ultimate tensile stress (MN/m^2)
Copper, annealed	60	–	60	220
Copper, hard	4	–	320	400
Aluminium, soft	35	–	30	90
Aluminium, hard	5	–	140	150
Brass, soft (30% zinc)	70	–	80	320
Brass, high tensile	15	–	280	540
Phosphor bronze (cast)	10	–	150	310
Black mild steel	25–26	230–280	–	350–400
Bright mild steel	14–17	–	–	430
Structural steel	20	220–250	–	430–500
Stainless steel (cutlery)	8	1400	–	1560
Stainless steel (tool)	3	1870	–	1950
Maraging steel (high alloy)	12	1870	–	1800–3000
Cast iron, grey	–	–	120–240	280–340
Spheroidal graphite cast iron (annealed)	10–25	300–380	–	420–540
Cast iron, malleable	20	–	–	310–500

Example 3.5

In a tensile test on a specimen of black mild steel of 12 mm diameter, the following results were obtained for a gauge length of 60 mm.

Load W (kN)	5	10	15	20	25	30	35	40
Extension $\times (10^{-3}$ mm)	14	27.2	41	54	67.6	81.2	96	112

When tested to destruction, maximum load = 65 kN; load at fracture = 50 kN, diameter at fracture = 7.5 mm, total extension on gauge length = 17 mm. Find Young's modulus, specific modulus, ultimate tensile stress, breaking stress, true stress at fracture, limit of proportionality, percentage elongation, percentage reduction in area. The relative density of the steel is 7.8.

Solution

The load–extension graph is plotted in Fig. 3.15 and the slope of the straight line portion determined from the best straight line drawn through the experimental points. The gradient of the straight line portion is found to be 366×10^6 N/m.*

$$E = \frac{\sigma}{\varepsilon} = \frac{W}{A} \times \frac{l}{x} = \frac{l}{A} \times \frac{W}{x}$$

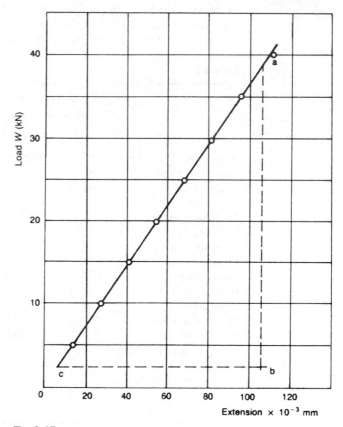

Fig. 3.15

---

* Gradient $\dfrac{W}{x} = \dfrac{ab}{bc} = \dfrac{38.75 - 2.5}{(106 - 7) \times 10^{-3}}$

$= \dfrac{36.25}{99 \times 10^{-3}} = 366$ kN/mm $= 366 \times 10^6$ N/m

$$\frac{W}{x} = 366 \times 10^6 \text{ N/m}$$

$$l = 60 \text{ mm}$$

and $\quad A = \dfrac{\pi}{4}(12 \times 10^{-3})^2 = 113 \times 10^{-6} \text{ m}^2$

Then $\quad E = \dfrac{0.06}{113 \times 10^{-6}} \times 366 \times 10^6$

$$= 195 \times 10^9 \text{ N/m}^2$$

$$= \mathbf{195 \ GN/m^2}$$

$$\text{Specific modulus} = \frac{E}{\text{relative density}} = \frac{195}{7.8} = \mathbf{25 \ GN/m^2}$$

$$\text{Ultimate tensile stress} = \frac{\text{maximum load}}{\text{area}}$$

$$= \frac{65}{113 \times 10^{-6}}$$

$$= 0.575 \times 10^6 \text{ kN/m}^2 = \mathbf{575 \ MN/m^2}$$

$$\text{Breaking stress} = \frac{50}{113 \times 10^{-6}}$$

$$= 0.442 \times 10^6 \text{ kN/m}^2 = \mathbf{442 \ MN/m^2}$$

$$\text{Area at fracture} \doteq \frac{\pi}{4}(7.5 \times 10^{-3})^2$$

$$= 44.2 \times 10^{-6} \text{ m}^2$$

$$\text{True stress at fracture} = \frac{\text{load at fracture}}{\text{area at fracture}} = \frac{50}{44.2 \times 10^{-6}}$$

$$= 1.13 \times 10^6 \text{ kN/m}^2 = \mathbf{1.13 \ GN/m^2}$$

$$\text{Percentage elongation} = \frac{\text{extension}}{\text{gauge length}} = \frac{17}{60} \times 100 \text{ per cent}$$

$$= \mathbf{28.3 \ per \ cent}$$

$$\text{Percentage reduction in area} = \frac{113 \times 10^{-6} - 44.2 \times 10^{-6}}{113 \times 10^{-6}} \times 100$$

$$= \mathbf{61 \ per \ cent}$$

The load at the limit of proportionality = 30 kN approximately, hence

$$\text{stress at limit of proportionality } \sigma = \frac{30}{113 \times 10^{-6}}$$

$$= 0.266 \times 10^6 \text{ kN/m}^2$$

$$= \mathbf{266 \ MN/m^2}$$

Direct stress and strain 2

Hoop stress in a cylinder

A cylinder containing fluid under pressure is subjected to a uniform radial pressure normal to the walls, Fig. 3.16. Since the cylinder tends to expand radially, there will be a tensile or *hoop stress* σ_h set up in the circumferential direction, i.e. tangential to the shell wall. This stress may be found by considering the equilibrium of forces acting on one-half of the shell. Imagine the cylinder to be cut across a diameter, Fig. 3.17. Then there is a uniform downward pressure p acting on the diametral surface section ABCD shown; this is balanced by the upward force due to the hoop stress σ_h along the two edges.

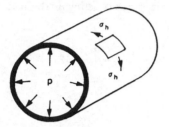

Fig. 3.16

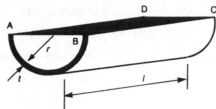

Fig. 3.17

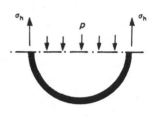

Force due to radial pressure on area $ABCD = p \times$ area ABCD

$$- p \times AB \times BC$$

$$= p \times 2r \times l$$

where r is the cylinder internal radius and l the length. If the thickness t of the shell wall is small compared to the internal radius r (e.g. if t is less than $r/10$), then the hoop stress may be taken as uniform across the wall section. Then

upward force on the two edges due to $\sigma_h = 2 \times \sigma_h \times$ area of one edge

$$= 2\sigma_h \times t \times l$$

Equating these two forces

$$2\sigma_h tl = 2\,prl$$

Therefore

$$\sigma_h = \frac{pr}{t}$$

This is the only stress due to pressure in a long open-ended seamless cylinder (e.g. a pipeline) provided that the section considered is distant from an end connection or flange.

Axial stress in a cylinder

In a closed pipe or cylinder, such as a pressure vessel there is, in addition to the hoop stress, a longitudinal or *axial stress* arising from the force due to pressure on the closed ends. Imagine the cylinder to be cut by a plane normal to the axis, Fig. 3.18. Then the pressure p acts on a cross-sectional area πr^2 and the corresponding axial force is:

$$p \times \pi r^2$$

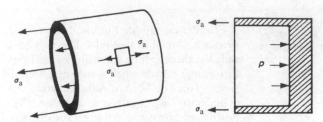

Fig. 3.18

This force is balanced by the force due to the axial stress σ_a acting on the area of the shell rim, which is approximately:

$$\text{circumference} \times \text{thickness} = 2\pi r \times t$$

hence

$$\sigma_a \times 2\pi r t = p \times \pi r^2$$

i.e.

$$\sigma_a = \frac{pr}{2t}$$

and

$$\sigma_h = \frac{pr}{t}$$

hence

$$\boldsymbol{\sigma_a = \tfrac{1}{2}\sigma_h}$$

i.e. the axial stress is one-half the hoop stress.

Tangential stress in a spherical shell

If a thin spherical shell is subject to internal pressure p, a tensile stress is set up in the shell wall due to the tendency of the shell to expand under pressure. Imagine the spherical shell to be cut across a diameter and consider the forces acting on one-half of the shell. Fig. 3.19. These are:

1. The diametral force due to the pressure $= p \times \pi r^2$.
2. The resisting force due to the tangential stress σ_t acting on the section of the rim. If t is small compared with the internal radius r, the area of the rim section is approximately $2\pi r t$ and σ_t is nearly uniform,

    i.e.   resisting force $= \sigma_t \times 2\pi r t$

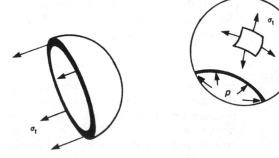

Fig. 3.19

Equating these two forces

$$\sigma_t \times 2\pi r t = p \times \pi r^2$$

i.e.

$$\sigma_t = \frac{pr}{2t}$$

This applies to any diametral section of the sphere and hence at any point there is a tangential stress σ_t acting in all directions tangential to the wall.

Effect of joints on stresses in thin shells

In many cases cylindrical shells are not seamless but are jointed, the joints being along a circumferential or longitudinal seam. The distribution of stress in a riveted joint is complex and the strength of such joints cannot be calculated with any great accuracy. The design of riveted joints is largely empirical and cannot be dealt with properly here. It is possible, however, to arrive at more accurate values for the stresses by making allowances for the efficiencies of the joints. The efficiency of a joint may be defined as the ratio:

$$\frac{\text{strength of joint of given width}}{\text{strength of solid plate of same width}}$$

For example, if the efficiency of a joint is 70 per cent it means in effect that the effective area of the perforated plate is 0.7 of that of the solid plate. The average stresses calculated using the thin cylinder formulae would therefore have to be increased in the ratio 1 : 0.7.

A circumferential joint has to resist the axial tension whereas the longitudinal joint has to resist the hoop tension. The axial tension is one-half the hoop tension so that the longitudinal joint is potentially the weakest part of the cylinder. Circumferential joints, therefore, do not have to be of the same efficiency as the longitudinal joint and are often permitted to have a much lower efficiency.

Example 3.6

Calculate the required thickness of the shell of an experimental pressure vessel of spherical shape and 450 mm diameter, which has to withstand an internal fluid pressure of 7 MN/m² without the stress in the material of the shell exceeding 70 MN/m². If the shell is to be made by bolting together two flanged halves using sixteen bolts what should be the root area of each bolt? The tensile stress in the bolts must not exceed 150 MN/m².

Solution

$$\text{Hoop stress} = \frac{pr}{2t}$$

thus

$$t = \frac{7 \times 10^6 \times 0.225}{2 \times 70 \times 10^6} = 0.01125 \text{ m}$$

$$= 11.25 \text{ mm}$$

$$\text{Diametral bursting force} = p \times \pi r^2$$

$$= 7 \times 10^6 \times \pi \times 0.225^2$$

$$= 1.114 \times 110^6 \text{ N}$$

$$\text{Force per bolt} = \frac{1.114 \times 10^6}{16}$$

$$= 69\,600 \text{ N}$$

Therefore $69\,600 = \text{stress in bolt} \times \text{root area}$

$$= 150 \times 10^6 \times A$$

Thus $A = 464 \times 10^{-6} \text{ m}^2 = \textbf{464 mm}^2$

(24 mm diameter bolts would be required.)

Example 3.7 A thin tube contains oil at a pressure of 6 MN/m². Each end is closed by a piston, the two pistons being free to move in the tube but rigidly connected by a rod as shown, Fig. 3.20. (a) Calculate the stresses in the tube if it has an inside diameter of 50 mm and a wall thickness 2.5 mm. (b) Calculate the tensile stress in the rod joining the pistons if it is of 25 mm diameter.

Fig. 3.20

Solution

(*a*) The axial force due to oil pressure is taken by the connecting rod. There is therefore no axial force or stress in the tube. The hoop stress in the tube is given by:

$$\text{hoop stress} = \frac{pr}{t}$$

$$= \frac{6 \times 10^6 \times 0.025}{0.0025}$$

$$= 60 \times 10^6 \text{ N/m}^2 = \textbf{60 MN/m}^2$$

(*b*) $\text{Inside area of piston} = \dfrac{\pi}{4} \times 0.05^2 - \dfrac{\pi}{4} \times 0.025^2$

$$= 1.47 \times 10^{-3} \text{ m}^2$$

$$\text{axial force on piston} = 6 \times 10^6 \times 1.47 \times 10^{-3}$$

$$= 8820 \text{ N}$$

$$\text{area of rod} = \frac{\pi}{4} \times 0.025^2 = 492 \times 10^{-6} \text{ m}^2$$

$$\text{tensile stress in rod} = \frac{8820}{492 \times 10^{-6}}$$

$$= 18 \times 10^6 \text{ N/m}^2 = \textbf{18 MN/m}^2$$

Example 3.8 A cylindrical boiler shell is 2 m internal diameter and is made of plate 20 mm thick. If the working pressure is 1.75 MN/m^2 and the efficiency of the longitudinal joint is 75 per cent, find the average hoop stress in the plate at the joint.

Solution

For the riveted plate, since the joint efficiency is 0.75,

$$\text{average hoop stress} = \frac{pr}{t} \times \frac{1}{0.75}$$

$$= \frac{1.75 \times 10^6 \times 1}{0.02} \times \frac{1}{0.75}$$

$$= 116.7 \times 10^6 \text{ N/m}^2$$

$$= 117 \text{ MN/m}^2$$

Example 3.9 A cylindrical pressure vessel has an internal diameter of 1600 mm and is subject to an internal fluid pressure of 30 bar. The plate is 15 mm thick with an ultimate tensile stress of 600 N/mm^2. The efficiencies of the circumferential and longitudinal joints are 50 and 80 per cent respectively. Determine the factor of safety. 1 bar = 10^5 N/m^2.

Solution

$$p = 30 \text{ bar} = 30 \times 10^5 \text{ N/m}^2 = 3 \text{ N/mm}^2$$

For the solid plate (working throughout in N and mm),

$$\text{hoop stress} = \frac{pr}{t}$$

$$= \frac{3 \times 800}{15}$$

$$= 160 \text{ N/mm}^2$$

$$\text{At the longitudinal joint, hoop stress} = \frac{160}{0.8}$$

$$= 200 \text{ N/mm}^2$$

$$\text{For the solid plate, axial stress} = \frac{160}{2}$$

$$= 80 \text{ N/mm}^2$$

$$\text{At the circumference joint, axial stress} = \frac{80}{0.5}$$

$$= 160 \text{ N/mm}^2$$

In this case, it is the ratio of the ultimate tensile stress to the *maximum* stress, which is the hoop stress at the longitudinal joint.

$$\text{Thus factor of safety} = \frac{600}{200}$$

$$= 3$$

Aircraft and rockets

Reaction propulsion

The principle of *reaction propulsion* whereby a jet of fluid is formed and expelled from an engine or pushed by a rotating rotor is the basis of working for propeller-driven ships and planes, jet planes, rockets, helicopters and satellite control. Apart from the mechanical aspects and body structure, each type of vehicle differs greatly in regard to the mass of fluid dealt with and the speed and form of the jet.

For any type of jet-propelled machine, the mass fluid flow, jet speed and flight speed, govern the magnitude of the propelling force or *thrust* as shown below.

Jet propulsion aircraft

The simplest form of jet propulsion is the *ramjet*, used for high-altitude, high-speed flight. The 'ram effect' is due to the forward speed of the plane or missile forcing the necessary air for combustion into the engine through a front duct and diffuser (a diverging chamber) which greatly slows it down, and then a jet of hot, extremely high-speed gas is ejected from the tail. A ramjet cannot be used on its own but must be launched at high speed or have an auxiliary power supply to bring it to its operating speed. In a *turbo-* or *straight*-jet, the incoming air has its pressure raised by a compressor followed by combustion and the issue of a jet through a nozzle in an exit jet pipe. Jet nozzles are designed according to the speed of flow required and the exit velocity usually exceeds the speed of sound. Some of the hot gas is utilized to drive a turbine which in turn drives the compressor. This is called *gas-turbine* propulsion and, as described, is the basic form of the jet engine, now superceded by the *turbofan* and *turboprop* (*see* below). The S/VTOL (Short/Vertical Take-Off and Landing) machines take off vertically or from short runways but overcome the drawback of their precursor, the helicopter, with its low forward speed. In some designs two engines are fitted, one for take-off and one for flight. The Harrier Jump Jet uses 'vectored thrust' whereby only one engine is required and the plane is propelled by several swivelling nozzles, controlling speed and direction of flight. Ramps with gradients upwards of 7° are used to assist take-off in situations of short run-up, e.g. ship's deck.

Notes on aircraft speeds

An aircraft has two speeds: (*a*) its *groundspeed*, over or relative to the ground, (*b*) its *indicated airspeed* through or relative to the air, equal to the forward speed. In still air, groundspeed and airspeed are the same and this is the speed of the intake air to a jet engine or approaching the blades of a propeller. Airspeed is not affected by wind but the groundspeed does alter and has to be calculated from a 'velocity diagram' using vectors for airspeed, windspeed and groundspeed.

The speed of sound in air is important in relation to airspeed. Speeds below the sonic velocity (at sea-level 340 m/s, 661 knots, 1224 km/h) are in general referred to as *subsonic* but for speeds approaching and passing through the 'sound barrier' the term *transonic* is used; *supersonic* covers speeds above sonic velocity and *hypersonic* (rocket driven) when the speed exceeds about five times the sonic speed. High speeds are denoted by *Mach numbers*, Mach 1 being the speed of sound at the altitude where the aircraft is flying. Transonic speeds are usually held only for brief periods; large airliners tend to cruise at about Mach 0.85 (880–950 km/h) whereas the exceptional Concorde at an altitude of 15 km maintains flight at Mach 2, the speed of sound at this altitude being 1065 km/h.

Thrust of a jet

The thrust of a jet depends on the rate of change of momentum given to the jet fluid. Let v be the air velocity relative to the engine at entry, Fig. 3.21, and v_e the velocity of the *gas* jet relative to the engine at exit. Then, *relative to the engine*, and neglecting the effect of the mass of fuel burnt (since the air to fuel ratio (by mass) is of the order 70:1)

Fig. 3.21

$$\text{initial momentum of } m \text{ kg of fluid} = mv$$

and
$$\text{final momentum} = mv_e$$

therefore
$$\text{change in momentum} = m(v_e - v)$$

If $\dot{m}$ is the mass of fluid passing through the engine per second, the force exerted *on* the jet of fluid equals the change of momentum per second, i.e.

$$\text{force} = \dot{m}(v_e - v)$$

From Newton's third law, the active force exerted by the engine expelling the gas through the exit nozzle at the tail must have an equal and opposite reactive force and this is the force due to the pressure of the combustion gases on the inside surfaces of the engine, i.e. there is a force or *thrust T* on the plane propelling it forward in reaction to the formation of the jet. When the engine is on a stationary rig, the thrust is taken by the supports. Thus

engine thrust $T = \dot{m}(v_e - v)$

The thrust (performance) of a jet engine is therefore directly proportional to the mass flow rate of air drawn into the engine and to the gain in velocity of the air passing through the engine. There is also a small thrust due to the burnt fuel leaving in the jet. The fuel is initially *at rest* relative to the plane and its exit velocity is v_e relative to the plane, hence the additional thrust is

$$\dot{m}_f v_e$$

where $\dot{m}_f$ is the mass of fuel consumed per second.

The above expression for thrust gives the *overall* thrust, i.e. the net effect of the separate thrusts (positive and negative) due to the varying pressures and speeds in the individual units making up the engine.

Modifications to the turbojet which is inefficient at low speeds, have produced more efficient engines with higher thrusts for lower jet velocities. In the turboprop, advantage has been taken of the high efficiency of propellers at low speeds; the core turbine supplies thrust from the hot gases expanding through a nozzle but also drives a propeller which deals with a large mass flow of air and contributes the greater part of the total thrust. Because of the limitations of the propeller, the jet alone with *by-pass* air is used in the turbofan (or ducted fan) engine thereby increasing the mass flow of air with more efficient use of fuel. In one arrangement, a second turbine drives a multi-bladed fan placed in front of the engine compressor and pushes the air to the rear in two streams. One stream enters the core engine via the compressor, acting as a supercharger, while the other, not compressed to the same extent, but several times greater in volume, by-passes the engine before exhausting. The by-pass ratio (BPR) is the ratio of the volume of by-pass air to that going through the engine. The two streams may issue from the same nozzle having been mixed together before reaching it, or from an annulus formed by the cold air tailpipe surrounding the hot gas pipe; both streams exhaust at roughly the same speed. A high proportion of the total thrust is derived from the by-pass air depending on the by-pass ratio; and the proportion of the thrust can be altered by a flow valve. The BPR is generally 5 or 6 to 1, or even higher. An example of a high by-pass engine is the Rolls–Royce RB211 (5.7:1).

For short bursts of extra power at take-off or for manoeuvres, an aircraft may be fitted with an *afterburner* or *reheat pipe* in the tailpipe into which fuel is injected directly. For example, the Concorde's Olympus engine (which is a *turbojet*) has a rated thrust of 170 kN with 17 per cent afterburning.

Incompressible and compressible flow

When air or gas flows through an engine (a 'control volume'), any change of pressure alters the density and there is always some degree of turbulence. Such effects increase with speed of flow but when dealing with aerodynamic forces it makes calculations easier in many subsonic problems and gives satisfactory results if certain assumptions are made to simplify the conditions of flow. These are

1. The air is *incompressible*, thus the density is constant.
2. The flow is *steady*, so that it follows from the Law of Conservation of Mass that the rate at which a mass of air enters an engine must equal the rate at which it leaves, and, since the density is constant, the volume rate of flow must also be constant. This is the *equation of continuity* which states that the velocity in steady flow is inversely proportional to the area of cross-section of flow.
3. *Bernoulli's equation* applies–derived from the application of the principle of conservation of energy to steady, frictionless, incompressible flow of fluid along a streamline. It means, ignoring potential energy, that the pressure energy and kinetic energy are interchangeable, i.e. a reduction in pressure is always accompanied by an increase in velocity and vice versa.

The assumptions are valid at low speeds; at higher speeds the density changes are more significant but they are still small enough to continue with the assumptions. At subsonic speed the air in front of the aircraft is pushed forwards and warns the air ahead of its coming. However, a critical speed is reached, approaching the speed of sound in air, where the behaviour of the air alters suddenly and it becomes compressible; the air in front of the aircraft is not 'alerted' to its approach and there is a sharp rise in pressure and density with the oncoming air to the nose of the aircraft becoming compressed. The abrupt rise in pressure and density is termed a *shock* and shock waves occur ahead of the nose. The waves form a cone with its vertex at the source of disturbance; this is called a *Mach cone*. Above the critical speed the effect of density change and Mach number must be taken into account. In the problems set here the air is assumed to be incompressible.

Mass flow rate of air

For the flow of air into a jet engine, making the assumptions listed above, the volume passing any section at the intake scoop per second is constant and given by

$$Q = \text{scoop area } (A) \times \text{airspeed } (v)$$

$$= Av$$

and the mass flow rate of air is

$$\dot{m} = \text{density} \times \text{volume passing per second}$$

$$= \rho A v$$

where ρ is the density of the air at intake. The standard density at any altitude may be found from tables as explained below. The *characteristic gas equation* may be used for the flow at any instant and this gives the relationship between the pressure p (absolute), temperature T (absolute)* and the mass m of a volume V of air. Thus

$$pV = mRT$$

where $R = 287$ J/kg K is the *gas constant* for air. Since we are dealing with flow rate, $\dot{m}$ may be substituted for m and Q for V and the equation becomes

$$pQ = \dot{m}RT$$

or $\qquad p = \rho RT$

For example, if 80 m³/s of air is drawn into an engine per second at absolute pressure 90 kN/m² and temperature 268 K, then

$$90 \times 10^3 \times 80 = \dot{m} \times 287 \times 268$$

i.e. $\qquad \dot{m} = 94$ kg/s

or, given the density of the intake air as 1.18 kg/m³, then

$$\dot{m} = \rho Q = 1.18 \times 80 = 94 \text{ kg/s}$$

When the flow through the engine is a mixture of air and gas the value of R alters, e.g. at exhaust pipe conditions R will have a higher value, over 300 J/kg K.

International standard atmosphere (ISA)

In fields of work such as aircraft, space vehicles and ballistics, which involve atmospheric properties, standard values are required at a range of altitudes to serve as a basis for engineering design, comparison of performances

---

* Symbol T is being used for both thrust and absolute temperature.

and calibration of instruments. Many obvious factors affect atmospheric conditions and assumptions have to be made, for example, that the air is still and dry, so that average or 'standard' figures can be tabulated for different parts of the world, corrections being included for off-standard conditions. For sea-level in Western Europe the ISA values are–pressure, 101.3 kN/m²; temperature, 288.2 K; density, 1.225 kg/m³; speed of sound in air, 340 m/s.

As the altitude increases in the lower atmosphere the temperature drops steadily at a rate taken to be 6.5 K per km, reaching 216.7 K at 11 km (the limit of the troposphere), then it remains constant before starting to rise again at a height of 20 km. The pressure falls irregularly and at a more rapid rate than temperature, the rate of fall slowing down as the air rarefies; at 11 km the pressure is 22.7 kN/m² and at 20 km, 5.5 kN/m². Density of the air and the speed of sound in air are important when dealing with aerodynamic forces; density falls with pressure and temperature, at a slower rate than pressure, the values being 0.365 kg/m³ at 11 km and 0.089 kg/m³ at 20 km. The speed of sound is proportional to the square root of the absolute temperature and reduces from the standard value to 295 m/s at 11 km, remains constant at this figure in the lower atmosphere, before rising again to 295 m/s at 20 km.

Power developed by a turbojet engine

If the thrust T is known for a particular flight speed v, then if the units are newton, metre and second

power output = thrust × flight speed

$$= \frac{Tv}{1000} \text{ kW}$$

Power is only developed by a thrust when the aircraft is moving, in flight or on the runway. When stationary on the runway or on a test rig the thrust is still exerted but resisted by friction forces or restraints; since there is no movement, there is no *output* power developed although some power is taken by the rotating parts of the engine.

The thrust of a jet in practice is fairly constant with flight speed and hence the power output varies directly with the flight speed, unlike the engines of a propeller-driven plane or motor car where the power output does not depend on the speed of the vehicle itself; this is called the 'shaft' or 'brake' power because work is done by a torque rotating the engine crankshaft. Shaft power may be measured when the engine is stationary by a brake resisting the crankshaft rotation. There is no shaft work for a jet engine, so its power output cannot be measured and thrust is used instead to assess propulsion performance. The 'static' thrust can be measured directly on a stationary test rig, usually at sea-level standard conditions with maximum power settings. An engine may be rated to static, sea-level thrust on a test rig at ISA conditions but there are other methods of rating an aero engine, e.g. at ambient conditions. Ratings may be classified as normal, cruise or take-off. The thrust of an engine on a rig is usually greater than when installed in an aircraft. In flight the thrust may be gauged by monitoring the engine pressure ratio (EPR), i.e. the ratio of turbine discharge pressure to compressor inlet pressure and this gives an indication of achieved power. A large airliner, such as a Boeing 747, for example, has a static thrust of 900 kN at full power settings for take-off registered by a particular EPR and the thrust lever can be set at this position.

Example 3.10

A Stationary jet engine under test is supplied with air at the rate of 80 m³/s. The air speed at entry to the engine is 50 m/s, at a pressure of 106 kN/m² (absolute) and temperature 292 K. If fuel is burned at the rate of 1.2 kg/s and the gases leave the tail at 400 m/s, find the specific thrust, i.e. the thrust per unit mass of fuel used in unit time. Characteristic gas constant for air, R = 287 J/kg K.

Solution

Applying the characteristic gas equation to the air at entry,

$$\dot{m} = \frac{pQ}{RT}$$

$$= \frac{106 \times 10^3 \times 80}{287 \times 292}$$

$$= 101.2 \text{ kg/s}$$

The speed of the air changes from 50 to 400 m/s in passing through the stationary engine, hence the thrust is

$$\dot{m}(v_e - v) = 101.2(400 - 50)$$

$$= 35\ 420 \text{ N}$$

The fuel has its speed increased from rest to 400 m/s, hence the additional thrust due to the fuel is

$$\dot{m}_f(v_e - 0) = 1.2 \times 400$$

$$= 480 \text{ N}$$

$$\text{Total thrust} = 35\ 420 + 480 \text{ N}$$

$$= 36 \text{ kN}$$

The additional thrust due to the effect of the fuel is only 1.3 per cent of the total thrust.

$$\text{Specific thrust} = \frac{\text{thrust}}{\text{mass flow rate of fuel}}$$

$$= \frac{T}{\dot{m}_f}$$

$$= \frac{36}{1.2}$$

$$= 30 \text{ kN s/kg}$$

Example 3.11

A jet plane flies at 500 knots, drawing in air at the rate of 80 m³/s and expelling a jetstream at 600 m/s, relative to the engine. The atmospheric conditions are 750 mbar and 260 K. Estimate the thrust and power output at this speed. Characteristic gas constant for air, R = 287 J/kg K; 1 mbar = 100 N/m²; 1 knot = 0.514 m/s.

Solution

Applying the gas equation to the air at entry to the engine,

$$\dot{m} = \frac{pQ}{RT}$$

$$= \frac{(750 \times 100) \times 80}{287 \times 260}$$

$$= 80.4 \text{ kg/s}$$

Forward speed, $v = 500$ knots $= 500 \times 0.514$ m/s

$$= 257 \text{ m/s}$$

Thrust $= \dot{m}(v_e - v)$

$$= 80.4(600 - 257)$$

$$= 27\,600 \text{ N}$$

$$= 27.6 \text{ kN}$$

Power output $=$ thrust $\times$ speed

$$= 27.6 \times 257 \text{ kW}$$

$$= \mathbf{7100 \text{ kW}}$$

Example 3.12

A ramjet has a flight speed of Mach 0.7 at an altitude where the density is 0.73 kg/m³ and the speed of sound in air is 320 m/s. The jet velocity relative to the ramjet is 550 km/s. What is the frontal area of the intake scoop required for a thrust of 18 kN? If the specific fuel consumption is 210 kg/kN of thrust/hour, what is the air to fuel ratio?

Solution

Airspeed $v = 0.7 \times 320 = 224$ m/s

Thrust $\quad\quad\quad T = \dot{m}(v_e - v)$

i.e. $\quad\quad\quad 18 \times 10^3 = \dot{m}(550 - 224)$

therefore $\quad\quad\quad \dot{m} = 55.2$ kg/s

If A is the area of cross-section of the intake scoop and Q the volume of air drawn in per second then

$$Q = \text{area of scoop} \times \text{flight speed}$$

$$= A \times 224 \text{ m}^3/\text{s}$$

and $\quad\quad\quad \dot{m} = \rho Q$

i.e. $\quad\quad\quad 55.2 = 0.73 \times A \times 224$

therefore $A = 0.34 \text{ m}^2$

Fuel used $= 210 \text{ kg/kN/h}$

$$= \frac{210 \times 18}{3600} \text{ kg/s}$$

$$= 1.05 \text{ kg/s}$$

Hence air:fuel $= \dfrac{55.2}{1.05} = \mathbf{52.6}$

Problems

(Characteristic gas constant for air, $R = 287 \text{ J/kg K}$; 1 knot $= 0.514 \text{ m/s}$; 1 mbar $= 100 \text{ N/m}^2$.)

3.1 An aircraft draws 45 kg of air per second into its engine and ejects it at a speed of 360 m/s relative to the engine. Find the thrust exerted by the jet, (*a*) when stationary, (*b*) at a forward speed of 800 km/h.
(16.2 kN; 6.2 kN)

3.2 A jet plane discharges at jet at the rate of 30 kg/s with a velocity of 1000 m/s relative to the plane. If the forward speed of the plane is 900 km/h, what is the thrust on the plane and the power developed at the jet? (22.5 kN; 5.625 MW)

3.3 A jet aircraft has a forward speed of 200 m/s at a height where the absolute pressure is 800 mbar and the temperature 280 K. At these conditions the air consumption is 70 m³/s. The jet speed is 500 m/s relative to the plane and the fuel used is 0.65 kg/s. Neglecting the effect of fuel in the jet, find the thrust. (20.9 kN)

3.4 The specific fuel consumption of a four-engined jet aircraft is stated as 72 kg/kN of thrust/hour for each engine. At a speed of 820 knots in level flight, the total thrust for all engines operating is estimated at 160 kN from static test results, and the jet speed is 1100 m/s relative to the aircraft. For each engine, find the airflow in kg/s, the air to fuel ratio and the power output. (59 kg/s; 74; 16.9 MW)

3.5 A ramjet has a forward speed of 290 m/s at an altitude where the density of the air is 0.6 kg/m³. The exhaust jet speed is 1.2 km/s relative to the ramjet. If the intake duct for the air has an area of 0.11 m², find the mass of air used per second and, neglecting the mass of fuel, the thrust exerted. If the fuel is consumed at the rate of 0.9 kg/s, what is the additional thrust? (19.1 kg/s; 17.4 kN; 1.08 kN)

3.6 A single-engined jet plane travels at 400 knots at an altitude of 5 km. The ISA figure for density at this altitude is 0.74 kg/m³ and the engine draws in air at the rate of 90 m³/s. The jet issues at 700 m/s, relative to the aircraft. Find the power output. (6.77 MW)

3.7 The engine of a jet plane is tested on a stationary rig with air being supplied at 120 m/s, at normal temperature and pressure (16°C, 101.3 kN/m² abs). The area of cross-section of the intake duct is 0.4 m², the speed of the exhaust jet is 600 m/s and the fuel consumption, 0.9 kg/s. Show that the density of the intake air is 1.22 kg/m² and allowing for the fuel in the jet, find the thrust, air/fuel ratio and the specific fuel consumption, i.e. the rate of fuel used per unit of thrust.
(28.7 kN; 65:1; 113 kg/h per kN)

3.8 A twin-engined turbofan draws in air to each engine at the rate of 45 kg/s and the exhaust jets are expelled at a mean speed of 1 km/s relative to the aircraft. Find the output power if the speed of flight is Mach 0.8 and the local speed of sound in air is 1188 km/h. (17.5 MW)

3.9 A jet plane travels at 900 km/h at an altitude where the air pressure is 470 mbar (abs.) and temperature −24°C. The total intake scoop area of cross-section is 0.28 m² and the exhaust jet velocity is 950 m/s relative to the aircraft. Find the density of the intake air, the mass flow rate of air through the scoop and the thrust. (0.66 kg/m³; 46 kg/s; 32 kN)

Propeller-driven aircraft

Aircraft driven solely by propellers are powered by piston engines, limited in output to about 3 MW. In a turboprop plane, a gas turbine supplies much greater power and the thrust is provided mainly by the propeller but also by the reaction to the exhaust jet. The propeller or 'airscrew' shaft is driven by the engine, rotating the blades, thereby drawing in a very large quantity of air and pushing it backwards with a moderate increase in speed (Fig. 3.22). The reaction to the formation of the propeller slipstream or race produces a thrust. Besides the speed of rotation, many other variables affect the performance of propellers, including the shape and diameter of the blades and the pitch, which may be fixed, adjustable by the pilot or automatically variable and speed controlled. The pitch is the distance travelled by the propeller through the air in each revolution, assuming there is no slip. Variable-pitch has several advantages, one of which is that adjustment of the blades to a negative angle enables the pilot to obtain a negative or reverse thrust by blowing the air forwards, for braking and taxying.

Besides the conventional propellers, there are high-speed designs which are ultra-light and uniquely shaped from composite materials and there are ducted and unducted fans with many more blades than the usual three to six. The unducted or propfan has very large, thin, fan-like blades rotating freely in the air, whereas the ducted fan has its blades shrouded in a casing, resulting in a different form of airflow. A single propeller causes a swirling action in the slipstream and to counteract this, a second propeller may be placed downstream on the same shaft, rotating in the opposite direction to the first. This contraflow arrangement reduces the loss of energy from turbulence and also serves to offset the torque reaction caused by a piston engine. We consider here only the thrust and power aspects of a propeller rotating freely in air and powered by a piston engine.

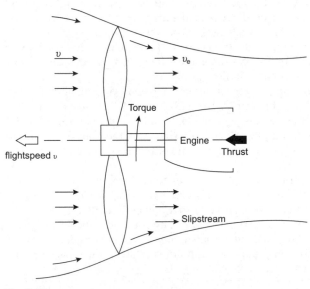

Fig. 3.22

Power

The power output for a propeller-driven aircraft (Fig. 3.22) is **thrust × forward speed,** as for a jet engine. The power supplied to the engine is the energy in the fuel consumed per second. Some of this energy is lost due to the inefficiency of the engine itself and there are further losses between engine brake shaft and propeller shaft as well as in the propulsive process of the propeller. The *overall efficiency* of the system is the ratio of the power output to the energy available in the fuel consumed. The *propulsive efficiency* of the propeller is the ratio of the power output to the power delivered at the propeller shaft. Thus

$$\text{overall efficiency} = \frac{\text{power output}}{\text{heat energy supplied per second}}$$

$$\text{and} \quad \text{propeller efficiency} = \frac{\text{power output}}{\text{power delivered to propeller shaft}}$$

The efficiency of propellers* may be up to 90 per cent at moderate speeds (below 600 km/h) but at higher speeds, the efficiency falls off rapidly. Propeller-driven aircraft, even with advanced propeller systems, are limited to about 800 km/h.

Thrust

The flow of air past rotating blades is complex because of the rotation and turbulence imported to the air. Several theorems are available to analyse a propeller's performance but to find the thrust, the simplest is the momentum theory as used previously for the jet engine. Simplifying assumptions are that the propeller is a thin disc, the flow is axial without rotation, the slip-stream is a uniform, continuous jet of constant density in steady flow and there is no change in velocity across the disc, Fig. 3.23. The approach velocity is v, relative to the aircraft, at a point where the pressure is atmospheric. A sharp rise in pressure occurs across the faces of the disc and the pressure

---

* The work input per second is the gain in kinetic energy of the mass airflow so that the *theoretical* efficiency in the ideal case is given by

$$\eta = \frac{\text{useful work done per second}}{\text{gain in kinetic energy of airflow/second}}$$

$$= \frac{Tv}{\frac{1}{2}\dot{m}(v_e^2 - v^2)}$$

$$= \frac{\dot{m}(v_e - v)v}{\frac{1}{2}\dot{m}(v_e^2 - v^2)}$$

$$= \frac{2}{1 + \dfrac{v_e}{v}}$$

i.e. for a high efficiency, for a given value of v, the increase in velocity $(v_e - v)$, should be as small as possible. The actual or conversion efficiency is less than the theoretical value because of drag force on the blades and turbulence in the jet stream. The same efficiency applies to a jet-propelled aircraft but in this case the propulsion is inefficient at low speeds (e. g. take-off) and becomes more efficient as the forward speed approaches the jet speed.

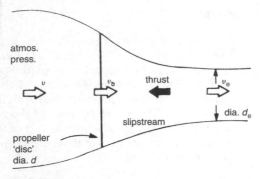

Fig. 3.23

returns to atmospheric in the straight and parallel part of the slipstream where the velocity is v_e, relative to the aircraft. From the 'equation of continuity', the area of cross-section of the jet varies inversely with the speed of flow and therefore the diameter of the jet where the speed is v_e reduces to some value d_e. If v_b is the velocity *across the disc*, relative to the aircraft, it can be shown by applying Bernoulli's theorem that v_b is the average of v_e and v, i.e.

$$v_b = \frac{v_e + v}{2}$$

The 'disc' area A swept out by the blades may be taken as $\pi d^2/4$, where d is the blade diameter. For flow across the disc, the volume of air passing per second is

$Q =$ area of section of jet $\times$ speed of flow across disc, relative
to aircraft

$\quad = A v_b$

or, for flow at the straight and parallel section,

$Q = A_e v_e$

where $A_e = \pi d_e^2/4$.

The mass flow rate of air is

$\dot{m} = \rho Q$

and the thrust is

$T = \dot{m}(v_e - v)$

as for a jet engine.

Example 3.13

A single-engined plane flies at 540 km/h in still air (density 1.15 kg/m³). The power supplied to the propeller shaft is 800 kW, the 'disc' area swept by the blades is 4 m² and the conversion efficiency is 85 per cent. Find the thrust and estimate the velocity of the jet well downstream of the blades.

Solution

$$v = 540 \text{ km/h} = 150 \text{ m/s}$$

$$\text{Thrust} \times \text{speed} = \text{power output}$$

i.e.

$$\text{thrust} = \frac{0.85 \times 800 \times 10^3}{150} = 4533 \text{ N}$$

Since

$$Q = Av_b$$

$$= 4 \times \frac{(v_e + v)}{2}$$

$$= 2(v_e + v) \text{ m}^3/\text{s}$$

and

$$\dot{m} = \rho Q = 1.15 \times 2(v_e + v)$$

$$= 2.3(v_e + v) \text{ kg/s}$$

then

$$\text{thrust} = \dot{m}(v_e - v)$$

$$= 2.3(v_e^2 - v^2) \text{ N}$$

i.e.

$$4533 = 2.3(v_e^2 - 150^2)$$

Therefore

$$v_e = \textbf{156 m/s} \text{ (relative to the plane)}$$

Example 3.14 A twin-engined aircraft cruises at 330 knots with the slipstream of each propeller moving at 180 m/s, relative to the aircraft, at a point well downstream where the jet diameter is 1.8 m. The density of the air is 1.23 kg/m^3 and the efficiency of each propeller is 85 per cent. Find the total brake power required. 1 knot = 0.514 m/s.

Solution

Fight speed, $v = 330 \times 0.514 = 170$ m/s.

For each engine, Q = area of cross-section of jet × speed of flow relative to aircraft (v_e)

$$= \frac{\pi \times 1.8^2}{4} \times 180$$

$$= 458 \text{ m}^3/\text{s}$$

and

$$\dot{m} = \rho Q = 1.23 \times 458 = 563 \text{ kg/s}$$

therefore

$$T = \dot{m}(v_e - v)$$

$$= 563(180 - 170)$$

$$= 5630 \text{ N}$$

$$= 5.63 \text{ kN}, \quad \text{for each engine}$$

$$\textit{Total} \text{ brake power required} = 2 \times \left(\frac{\text{thrust} \times \text{flight speed}}{\text{propeller efficiency}} \right)$$

$$= \frac{2 \times 5.63 \times 170}{0.85}$$

$$= \textbf{2250 kW}$$

Notes on lift and drag forces on an aircraft

To be airborne and fly, any type of machine must be provided with a lifting force equal to or greater than its deadweight, and this force is generated by the flow of air over the surface of wings or aerofoils when thrust forward. Alternatively it can be provided by rotating blades or downward-directed jets. When a fixed wing aircraft flies, the air flows over the wings in stream-lines and a resultant force is produced on the plane because of a slight difference in air pressure at the top and bottom skins of the wings.* This force has two components (i) a *lifting* force L, normal to the direction of airflow, counteracting the weight of the plane, (ii) a *drag* force D acting in the same direction as the flow of air, i.e. parallel to the line of flight opposing the motion of the plane. The drag is due to skin friction, turbulence and shock effects, and these components vary for different aircraft depending on their shape and speed, and particularly between subsonic and supersonic types. The forces L and D are shown in Fig. 3.24(a) for a plane in level flight. The lift depends on the density of the air and on the shape and angle of attack of the wings into the air. The lift acts at the centre of pressure C and the weight W acts through the centre of gravity G. The positions of C and G may vary because of the loading and also during flight but are not usually far apart; the centre of gravity must lie within specified limits. The line of action of the drag force is offset, above or below the line of resultant thrust which acts along the centre line of the propeller shaft or jet, in the case of a single engine, or central longitudinal axis of a multi-engined aircraft. The line of thrust is also affected by the location of the engines relative to the wings. Figure 3.24(a) shows (not to scale) the lift behind the line of action of the weight, and the drag force above the thrust. Figure 3.24(b) shows an aircraft climbing; the lift is normal to the line of flight and its magnitude is critical in regard to the *stalling* speed of the aircraft which occurs when there is a sudden loss of lift due to the streamline flow of the air over the wings becoming

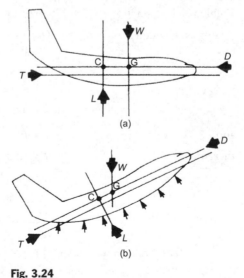

(a)

(b)

Fig. 3.24

---

* A full treatment of streamline flow, lift and drag forces, will be found in A.C. Kermode's 'Mechanics of Flight', Longman.

turbulent. At this point the angle of attack at which the airflow strikes the wings has exceeded a critical value and the main wings stall as the total lift is disrupted, the aircraft shakes and shudders, the drag increases sharply and the nose pitches downwards. Too low a speed for the conditions on flight sees the onset of stalling.

In practice, the lines of action of the resultant forces are determined largely by experiments on models, including full-scale rigs, using wind tunnels and other devices.

For a rocket, lift is supplied by downward-directed jets but there are also aerodynamic forces due to airflow. Helicopters with power-driven rotors obtain their lift from the blades pushing the air downwards but with propeller-driven autogyros the lift comes from 'auto-rotation' due to the *upward* flow of air through the horizontal rotor blades. Note that the lift and drag forces on wings may be expressed in terms of the density of the air, wing area, speed of airflow and coefficients of lift and drag. The aim of a designer is to achieve as high a lift/drag ratio as possible.

For every airborne vehicle, once the values of the four main forces – thrust, lift, drag and weight – are known, the principles of dynamics can be applied to finding the motion of the vehicle.

Forces on aircraft in flight

Level flight

For an aircraft to fly in straight and level flight at steady speed, the forces acting on it must balance and the net moment about any axis must be zero, Fig. 3.25(a). The aircraft is in equilibrium; this is not the same as being stable, since stability requires that the aircraft, if displaced slightly from its equilibrium position by wind buffeting or turbulence, must return to its original position without other controlling forces being applied. Natural stability in regard to pitching is brought about by maintaining the centre of gravity in front of the centre of pressure as shown in Fig. 3.24. Although aircraft are usually designed to be inherently stable,* there is always some degree of instability, more so in yawing and rolling than in pitching. Thus, for equilibrium

$$\text{thrust } T = \text{drag } D$$

and

$$\text{lift } L = \text{weight } W$$

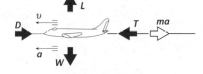

(a) Steady, level flight   (b) Accelerated, level flight

Fig. 3.25

---

* Ultra-modern fighter aircraft are aerodynamically unstable and are controlled in flight by computer systems. The limits of manoeuvrability in such aircraft are determined primarily by the gravity forces (g-forces) pilots can bear. Because of the aircrafts' instability they are able to make more extreme manoeuvres, such as fighter turns, than aircraft with inherent stability.

If the centres of gravity and pressure are assumed to coincide there will be no unbalanced moment. In practice, however, the lines of action of the forces are offset, as shown in Fig. 3.24, so that pitching moments are caused by thrust – drag and lift – weight couples forcing the aircraft to nose up or down. A correcting moment is supplied by a small force acting at a large moment-arm due to the airflow on the tailplane (horizontal stabilizer) and elevators. This force may be neglected in relation to the main forces.

When thrust exceeds drag, Fig. 3.25(b), the accelerating force is

$$F = T - D - ma$$

where m is the mass of the aircraft and a its acceleration. When drag exceeds thrust, the plane decelerates. In level flight, the nose of the aircraft is often pitched up slightly so that the exhaust jetstream is inclined downwards to the horizontal line of flight, thus affecting the forces on the plane.

Climbing and descending

In straight flight at an angle θ to the horizontal, the external forces acting along the longitudinal axis are: thrust T, drag D and a component of the weight $W \sin \theta$. These are shown in Fig. 3.26.

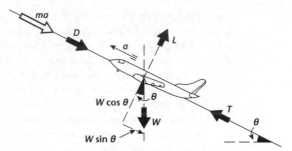

Fig. 3.26

At constant speed

$$T = D + W \sin \theta$$

Considering forces normal to the line of flight,

$$L = W \cos \theta$$

When accelerating

$$F = T - D - W \sin \theta = ma$$

and $L = W \cos \theta$ (as for constant speed)

When descending under power, the weight component *assists* the thrust. In a gliding descent with the engine cut out, there are only three forces D, L and W to be considered.

In all cases of climbing and descent, in straight flight, the lift is always less than the weight and equal to $W \cos \theta$.

Example 3.15

A twin-turbofan has an all-up weight of 88 kN at altitude of 6 km when climbing steadily at 25° to the horizontal in straight flight. For each engine, air is drawn in at the rate of 90 m³/s and the jet leaves the tailpipe at 590 m/s relative to the engine. The ISA value for the density at altitude 6 km is 0.66 kg/m³. Find the speed of climb in knots if the drag force is 14 kN. What is the lift force? 1 knot = 0.514 m/s.

Solution

For each engine, $\dot{m} = \rho Q$

$$= 0.66 \times 90$$

$$= 59.4 \text{ kg/s}$$

For two engines, $T = 2 \times \dot{m}(v_e - v)$

$$= 2 \times 59.4\,(590 - v) \times 10^{-3} \text{ kN}$$

$$= (70 - 0.12v) \text{ kN}$$

where v m/s is the airspeed.

In a straight climb at steady speed, (Fig. 3.27) we have

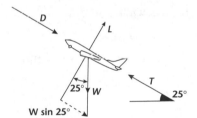

Fig. 3.27

$$T = D + W \sin 25°$$

i.e. $70 - 0.12v = 14 + 88 \times 0.42$

therefore $v = 159 \text{ m/s} = \dfrac{159}{0.514} = \textbf{309 knots}$

Resolving forces normal to the line of flight, the lift is given by

$$L = W \cos 25° = 88 \times 0.91 = \textbf{80 kN}$$

Example 3.16

A jet aeroplane of mass 4200 kg travels in level flight at a speed of 486 knots, drawing in air to the engine at the rate of 70 kg/s. The jet speed relative to the plane is 600 m/s. If the lift/drag ratio is 10, estimate the acceleration of the plane and the power output. If the plane climbs at 20° to the horizontal, what is then its acceleration, assuming the same thrust and drag as in level flight? 1 knot = 0.514 m/s.

Solution

$$\text{Forward speed, } v = 486 \text{ knots} = 486 \times 0.514 \text{ m/s}$$
$$= 250 \text{ m/s}$$

$$\text{Thrust} = \dot{m}(v_e - v)$$
$$= 70(600 - 250)$$
$$= 24\ 500 \text{ N}$$

$$\text{Lift} = \text{weight}$$
$$= 4200 \times 9.8 \text{ N}$$
$$= 41\ 160 \text{ N}$$

$$\text{Drag force} = \frac{\text{lift}}{10} = \frac{41\ 160}{10} = 4116 \text{ N}$$

Accelerating force

$$F = \text{thrust} - \text{drag}$$
$$= 24\ 500 - 4116$$
$$= 20\ 384 \text{ N}$$

and $F = ma$

i.e. $20\ 384 = 4200 \times a$

therefore $a = \mathbf{4.9 \ m/s^2}$

$$\text{Power output at 250 m/s} = \text{thrust} \times \text{speed}$$

$$= 24\ 500 \times 250 \times \frac{1}{1000} \text{ kW}$$

$$= \mathbf{6125 \ kW}$$

Referring to Fig. 3.26 the weight component opposing the thrust is $W \sin \theta =$ $41\ 160 \times \sin 20° = 14\ 080$ N. The accelerating force F is therefore reduced by this amount since the thrust and drag remain she same, i.e.

$$F = 20\ 384 - 14\ 080 = 6304 \text{ N,}$$

and $F = ma$

i.e. $6304 = 4200a$

i.e. $a = \mathbf{1.5 \ m/s^2}$

Mechanical properties of materials

Poisson's ratio

When the rubber block is compressed (negative strain) its sides will expand (positive strain). The ratio of these strains is constant.

When a deformable body is subjected to an axial tensile force, not only does it elongate but it also contracts laterally. For example, if a rubber band is stretched, it can be noted that both the thickness and width of the band are decreased. Likewise, a compressive force acting on a body causes it to contract in the direction of the force and yet its sides expand laterally. These two cases are illustrated in Fig. 3.28 for a bar having an original radius r and length L.

When the load **P** is applied to the bar, it changes the bar's length by an amount δ and its radius by an amount δ'. Strains in the longitudinal or axial direction and in the lateral or radial direction are, respectively,

$$\varepsilon_{\text{long}} = \frac{\delta}{L} \quad \text{and} \quad \varepsilon_{\text{lat}} = \frac{\delta'}{r}$$

In the early 1800s, the French scientist S. D. Poisson realized that within the *elastic range* the *ratio* of these strains is a *constant*, since the deformations δ and δ' are proportional. This constant is referred to as *Poisson's ratio*, v (nu), and it has a numerical value that is unique for a particular material that is both *homogeneous and isotropic*. Stated mathematically it is

$$v = -\frac{\varepsilon_{\text{lat}}}{\varepsilon_{\text{long}}} \qquad\qquad [3.1]$$

The negative sign is used here since *longitudinal elongation* (positive strain) causes *lateral contraction* (negative strain), and vice versa. Notice that this lateral strain is the *same* in all lateral (or radial) directions. Furthermore, this strain is caused only by the axial or longitudinal force; i.e., no force or stress acts in a lateral direction in order to strain the material in this direction.

Poisson's ratio is seen to be *dimensionless*, and for most nonporous solids it has a value that is generally between $\frac{1}{4}$ and $\frac{1}{3}$. Typical values of v for common materials are listed on the inside back cover. In particular, an ideal material having no lateral movement when it is stretched or compressed will have $v = 0$. Furthermore, the *maximum* possible value for Poisson's ratio is 0.5. Therefore $0 \le v \le 0.5$.

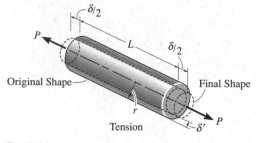

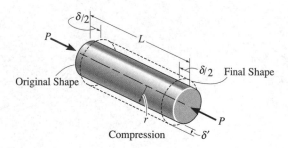

Fig. 3.28

| **Example 3.17** | A bar made of A-36 steel has the dimensions shown in Fig. 3.29. If an axial force of $P = 80$ kN is applied to the bar, determine the change in its length and the change in the dimensions of its cross section after applying the load. The material behaves elastically. |

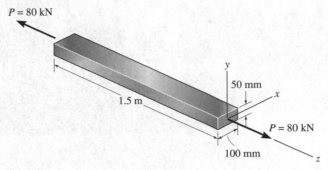

Fig. 3.29

Solution

The normal stress in the bar is

$$\sigma_z = \frac{P}{A} = \frac{80(10^3)\ \text{N}}{(0.1\ \text{m})(0.05\ \text{m})} = 16.0(10^6)\ \text{Pa}$$

For A-36 steel, $E_{st} = 200$ GPa, and so the strain in the z direction is

$$\varepsilon_z = \frac{\sigma_z}{E_{st}} = \frac{16.0(10^6)\ \text{Pa}}{200(10^9)\ \text{Pa}} = 80(10^{-6})\ \text{mm/mm}$$

The axial elongation of the bar is therefore

$$\delta_z = \varepsilon_z L_z = [80(10^{-6})](1.5\ \text{m}) = 120\ \mu\text{m}$$

Using Eq. 9–9, where $v_{st} = 0.32$ as found from the Appendix B, the contraction strains in *both* the x and y directions are

$$\varepsilon_x = \varepsilon_y = -v_{st}\varepsilon_z = -0.32[80(10^{-6})] = -25.6\ \mu\text{m/m}$$

Thus the changes in the dimensions of the cross section are

$$\delta x = \varepsilon x L x = -[25.6(10^{-6})](0.1\ \text{m}) = -2.56\ \mu\text{m}$$

$$\delta y = \varepsilon y L y = -[25.6(10^{-6})](0.05\ \text{m}) = -1.28\ \mu\text{m}$$

Stress and strain transformation

Plane-stress transformation

The general state of stress at a point is characterized by *six* independent normal and shear stress components, which act on the faces of an element of material located at the point, Fig. 3.30(a). This state of stress, however, is not often encountered in engineering practice. Instead, engineers frequently make approximations or simplifications of the loadings on a body in order that the stress produced in a structural member or mechanical element can be analyzed in a *single plane*. When this is the case, the material is said to be subjected to *plane stress*, Fig. 3.30(b). For example, if there is no load on the surface of a body, then the normal and shear stress components will be zero on the face of an element that lies on the surface. Consequently, the corresponding stress components on the opposite face will also be zero, and so the material at the point will be subjected to plane stress.

The general state of *plane stress* at a point is therefore represented by a combination of two normal-stress components, σ_x, σ_y, and one shear-stress component, τ_{xy}, which act on four faces of the element. For convenience, in this text we will view this state of stress in the x–y plane, Fig. 3.30(c). Realize that if the state of stress at a point is defined by the three stress components shown on the element in Fig. 3.31(a), then an element having a different

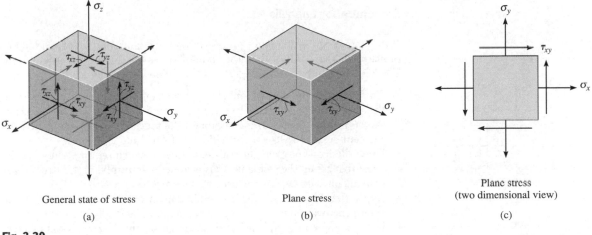

General state of stress

(a)

Plane stress

(b)

Plane stress
(two dimensional view)

(c)

Fig. 3.30

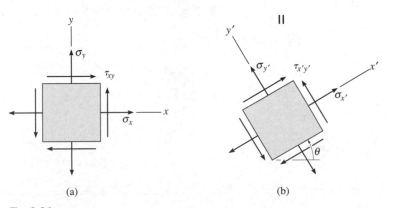

(a)

(b)

Fig. 3.31

orientation, such as in Fig. 3.31(b), will be subjected to three different stress components. In other words, *the state of plane stress at the point is uniquely represented by three components acting on an element that has a specific orientation at the point*.

In this section, by using numerical examples, we will show how to *transform* the stress components from one orientation of an element to an element having a different orientation. That is, if the state of stress is defined by the components σ_x, σ_y, τ_{xy}, oriented along the x, y axes, Fig. 3.31(a), we will show how to obtain the components $\sigma_{x'}$, $\sigma_{y'}$, $\tau_{x'y'}$, oriented along the x', y' axes, Fig. 3.31(b), so that they represent the *same* state of stress at the point. This is like knowing two force components, say, $\mathbf{F}_x$ and $\mathbf{F}_y$, directed along the x, y axes, that produce a resultant force $\mathbf{F}_R$, and then trying to find the force components $\mathbf{F}_{x'}$ and $\mathbf{F}_{y'}$, directed along the x', y' axes, so they produce the *same* resultant. The transformation of stress components, however, is more difficult than that of force components, since for *stress*, the transformation must account for the magnitude and direction of each stress component *and* the orientation of the area upon which each component acts. For force, the transformation must account only for the force component's magnitude and direction.

Procedure for analysis

If the state of stress at a point is known for a given orientation of an element of material, Fig. 3.32(a), then the state of stress for some other orientation, Fig. 3.32(b), can be determined using the following procedure.

- To determine the normal and shear stress components $\sigma_{x'}$, $\tau_{x'y'}$ acting on the x' face of the element, Fig. 3.32(b), section the element in 3.32(a) as shown in Fig. 3.32(c). If it is assumed the sectioned area is ΔA, then the adjacent areas of the segment will be $\Delta A \sin \theta$ and $\Delta A \cos \theta$.
- Draw the free-body diagram of the segment, which requires showing the *forces* that act on the element. This is done by multiplying the stress components on each face by the area upon which they act.
- Apply the equations of force equilibrium in the x' and y' directions to obtain the two unknown stress components $\sigma_{x'}$ and $\tau_{x'y'}$.
- If $\sigma_{y'}$, acting on the $+y'$ face of the element in Fig. 3.32(b), is to be determined, then it is necessary to consider a segment of the element as shown in Fig. 3.32(d) and follow the same procedure just described. Here,

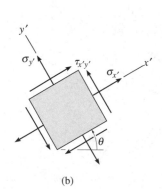

(a)

=

(b)

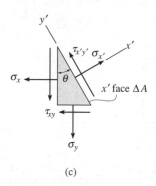

(c)

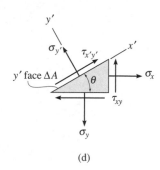

(d)

Fig. 3.32

however, the shear stress $\tau_{x'y'}$ does not have to be determined if it was previously calculated since it is complementary, that is, it has the same magnitude on each of the four faces of the element, Fig. 3.32(b).

Example 3.18

The state of plane stress at a point on the surface of the airplane fuselage is represented on the element oriented as shown in Fig. 3.33(a). Represent the state of stress at the point on an element that is oriented 30° clockwise from the position shown.

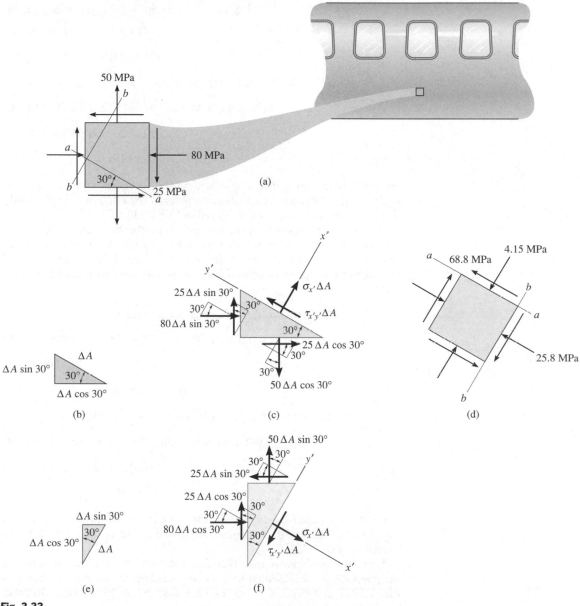

Fig. 3.33

Solution

The element is sectioned by the line a–a in Fig. 3.33(a), the bottom segment is removed, and assuming the sectioned (inclined) plane has an area ΔA, the horizontal and vertical planes have the areas shown in Fig. 3.33(b). The free-body diagram of the segment is shown in Fig. 3.33(c). Applying the equations of force equilibrium in the x' and y' directions to avoid a simultaneous solution for the two unknowns $\sigma_{x'}$ and $\tau_{x'y'}$, we have

$$+\nearrow\Sigma F_{x'} = 0; \quad \sigma_{x'}\Delta A - (50\ \Delta A \cos 30°)\cos 30°$$

$$+ (25\ \Delta A \cos 30°)\sin 30° + (80\ \Delta A \sin 30°)\sin 30°$$

$$+ (25\ \Delta A \sin 30°)\cos 30° = 0$$

$$\sigma_{x'} = -4.15\ \text{MPa}$$

$$+\nwarrow\Sigma F_{y'} = 0; \quad \tau_{x'y'}\Delta A - (50\ \Delta A \cos 30°)\sin 30°$$

$$- (25\ \Delta A \cos 30°)\cos 30° - (80\ \Delta A \sin 30°)\cos 30°$$

$$+ (25\ \Delta A \sin 30°)\sin 30° = 0$$

$$\tau_{x'y'} = 68.8\ \text{MPa}$$

Since $\sigma_{x'}$ is negative, it acts in the opposite direction of that shown in Fig. 3.33(c). The results are shown on the *top* of the element in Fig. 3.33(d), since this surface is the one considered in Fig. 3.33(c).

We must now repeat the procedure to obtain the stress on the *perpendicular* plane b–b. Sectioning the element in Fig. 3.33(a) along b–b results in a segment having sides with areas shown in Fig. 3.33(e). Orientating the $+x'$ axis outward, perpendicular to the sectioned face, the associated free-body diagram is shown in Fig. 3.33(f). Thus,

$$+\searrow\Sigma F_{x'} = 0; \quad \sigma_{x'}\Delta A - (25\ \Delta A \cos 30°)\sin 30°$$

$$+ (80\ \Delta A \cos 30°)\cos 30° - (25\ \Delta A \sin 30°)\cos 30°$$

$$- (50\ \Delta A \sin 30°)\sin 30° = 0$$

$$\sigma_{x'} = -25.8\ \text{MPa}$$

$$+\nearrow\Sigma F_{y'} = 0; \quad -\tau_{x'y'}\Delta A + (25\ \Delta A \cos 30°)\cos 30°$$

$$+ (80\ \Delta A \cos 30°)\sin 30° - (25\ \Delta A \sin 30°)\sin 30°$$

$$+ (50\ \Delta A \sin 30°)\cos 30° = 0$$

$$\tau_{x'y'} = 68.8\ \text{MPa}$$

Since $\sigma_{x'}$ is a negative quantity, it acts opposite to its direction shown in Fig. 3.33(f). The stress components are shown acting on the *right side* of the element in Fig. 3.33(d).

From this analysis we may therefore conclude that the state of stress at the point can be represented by choosing an element oriented as shown in Fig. 3.33(a), or by choosing one oriented as shown in Fig. 3.33(d). In other words, the states of stress are equivalent.

General equations of plane-stress transformation

The method of transforming the normal and shear stress components from the x, y to the x', y' coordinate axes, as discussed in the previous section, will now be developed in a general manner and expressed as a set of stress-transformation equations.

Sign convention

Before the transformation equations are derived, we must first establish a sign convention for the stress components. Briefly stated, once the x, y or x', y' axes have been established, a normal or shear stress component is *positive* provided it acts in the *positive* coordinate direction on the *positive* face of the element, or it acts in the *negative* coordinate direction on the *negative* face of the element, Fig. 3.34(a). For example, σ_x is positive since it acts to the right on the right-hand vertical face, and it acts to the left ($-x$ direction) on the left-hand vertical face. The shear stress in Fig. 3.34(a) is shown acting in the positive direction on all four faces of the element. On the right-hand face, τ_{xy} acts upward ($+y$ direction); on the bottom face, τ_{xy} acts to the left ($-x$ direction), and so on.

All the stress components shown in Fig. 3.34(a) maintain equilibrium of the element, and because of this, knowing the direction of τ_{xy} on one face of the element defines its direction on the other three faces. Hence, the above sign convention can also be remembered by simply noting that *positive normal stress acts outward from all faces and positive shear stress acts upward on the right-hand face of the element.*

Given the state of plane stress shown in Fig. 3.34(a), the orientation of the inclined plane on which the normal and shear stress components are to be determined will be defined using the angle θ. To show this angle properly, it is first necessary to establish a positive x' axis, *directed outward, perpendicular* or normal to the plane, and an associated y' axis, directed along the plane,

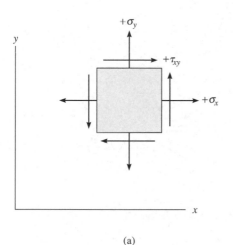

(a)

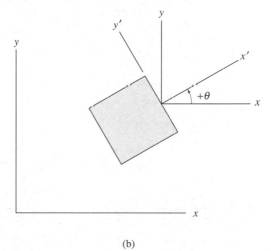

(b)

Positive Sign Convention

Fig. 3.34

Fig. 3.34(b). Notice that the unprimed and primed sets of axes both form right-handed coordinate systems; that is, the positive z (or z') axis is established by the right-hand rule. Curling the fingers from x (or x') toward y (or y') gives the direction for the positive z (or z') axis that points outward. The *angle* θ is measured from the positive x to the positive x' axis. It is *positive* provided it follows the curl of the right-hand fingers, i.e., counterclockwise as shown in Fig. 3.34(b).

Normal and shear stress components

Using the established sign convention, the element in Fig. 3.35(a) is sectioned along the inclined plane and the segment shown in Fig. 3.35(b) is isolated. Assuming the sectioned area is ΔA, then the horizontal and vertical faces of the segment have an area of $\Delta A \sin \theta$ and $\Delta A \cos \theta$, respectively.

The resulting *free-body diagram* of the segment is shown in Fig. 3.35(c). Applying the equations of force equilibrium to determine the unknown normal and shear stress components $\sigma_{x'}$ and $\tau_{x'y'}$, we obtain

$$+\nearrow\Sigma F_{x'} = 0; \quad \sigma_{x'}\Delta A - (\tau_{xy}\,\Delta A \sin \theta)\cos \theta - (\sigma_y\,\Delta A \sin \theta)\sin \theta$$
$$- (\tau_{xy}\,\Delta A \cos \theta)\sin \theta - (\sigma_x\,\Delta A \cos \theta)\cos \theta = 0$$
$$\sigma_{x'} = \sigma_x \cos^2 \theta + \sigma_y \sin^2 \theta + \tau_{xy}(2 \sin \theta \cos \theta)$$

$$+\nwarrow\Sigma F_{y'} = 0; \quad \tau_{x'y'}\,\Delta A + (\tau_{xy}\,\Delta A \sin \theta)\sin \theta - (\sigma_y\,\Delta A \sin \theta)\cos \theta$$
$$- (\tau_{xy}\,\Delta A \cos \theta)\cos \theta + (\sigma_x\,\Delta A \cos \theta)\sin \theta = 0$$
$$\tau_{x'y'} = (\sigma_y - \sigma_x)\sin \theta \cos \theta + \tau_{xy}(\cos^2 \theta - \sin^2 \theta)$$

These two equations may be simplified by using the trigonometric identities $\sin 2\theta = 2 \sin \theta \cos \theta$, $\sin^2 \theta = (1 - \cos 2\theta)/2$, and $\cos^2 \theta = (1 + \cos 2\theta)/2$, in which case,

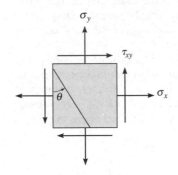

(a)

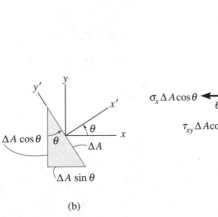

(b)

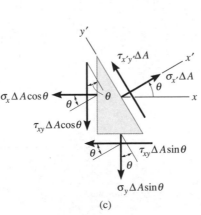

(c)

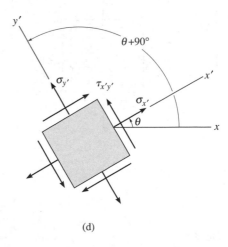

(d)

Fig. 3.35

$$\sigma_{x'} = \frac{\sigma_x + \sigma_y}{2} + \frac{\sigma_x - \sigma_y}{2} \cos 2\theta + \tau_{xy} \sin 2\theta \qquad [3.2]$$

$$\tau_{x'y'} = -\frac{\sigma_x - \sigma_y}{2} \sin 2\theta + \tau_{xy} \cos 2\theta \qquad [3.3]$$

If the normal stress acting in the y' direction is needed, it can be obtained by simply substituting ($\theta = \theta + 90°$) for θ into Equation [3.2], Fig. 3.35(d). This yields

$$\sigma_{y'} = \frac{\sigma_x + \sigma_y}{2} - \frac{\sigma_x - \sigma_y}{2} \cos 2\theta - \tau_{xy} \sin 2\theta \qquad [3.4]$$

If $\sigma_{y'}$ is calculated as a positive quantity, this indicates that it acts in the positive y' direction as shown in Fig. 3.35(d).

Procedure for analysis

To apply the stress transformation Equations [3.2] and [3.3], it is simply necessary to substitute in the known data for σ_x, σ_y, τ_{xy}, and θ in accordance with the established sign convention, Fig. 3.34. If $\sigma_{x'}$ and $\tau_{x'y'}$ are calculated as positive quantities, then these stresses act in the positive direction of the x' and y' axes.

For convenience these equations can easily be programmed on a pocket calculator.

Material-property relationships	Now that the general principles of multiaxial stress and strain have been presented, we will use these principles to develop some important relationships involving the material's properties. To do so we will assume that the material is homogeneous and isotropic and behaves in a linear-elastic manner.

Generalized Hooke's law

If the material at a point is subjected to a state of triaxial stress, σ_x, σ_y, σ_z, Fig. 3.36(a), associated normal strains ε_x, ε_y, ε_z are developed in the material. The stresses can be related to the strains by using the principle of super-position, Poisson's ratio, $\varepsilon_{lat} = -v\varepsilon_{long}$, and Hooke's law, as it applies in the uniaxial direction, $\varepsilon = \sigma/E$. To show how this is done we will first consider the normal strain of the element in the x direction, caused by separate application of each normal stress. When σ_x is applied, Fig. 3.36(b), the element elongates in the x direction and the strain ε_x' in this direction is

$$\varepsilon_x' = \frac{\sigma_x}{E}$$

Application of σ_y causes the element to contract with a strain ε_x'' in the x direction, Fig. 3.36(c). Here

$$\varepsilon_x'' = -v\frac{\sigma_y}{E}$$

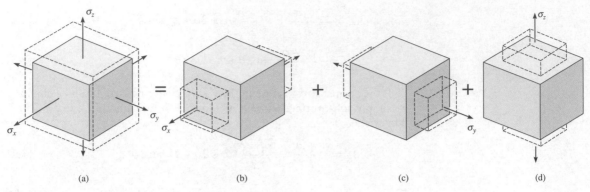

Fig. 3.36

Likewise, application of σ_z, Fig. 3.36(d), causes a contraction in the x direction such that

$$\varepsilon_x''' = -v\frac{\sigma_z}{E}$$

When these three normal strains are superimposed, the normal strain ε_x is determined for the state of stress in Fig. 3.36(a). Similar equations can be developed for the normal strains in the y and z directions. The final results can be written as

$$\varepsilon_x = \frac{1}{E}[\sigma_x - v(\sigma_y + \sigma_z)]$$

$$\varepsilon_y = \frac{1}{E}[\sigma_y - v(\sigma_x + \sigma_z)] \qquad\qquad [3.5]$$

$$\varepsilon_z = \frac{1}{E}[\sigma_z - v(\sigma_x + \sigma_y)]$$

These three equations express Hooke's law in a general form for a triaxial state of stress. As noted in the derivation, they are valid only if the principle of superposition applies, which requires a *linear-elastic* response of the material and application of strains that do not severely alter the shape of the material – i.e., small deformations are required. When applying these equations, note that tensile stresses are considered positive quantities, and compressive stresses are negative. If a resulting normal strain is *positive*, it indicates that the material *elongates*, whereas a *negative* normal strain indicates the material *contracts*.

Since the material is isotropic, the element in Fig. 3.36(a) will *remain a rectangular block* when subjected to the normal stresses; i.e., *no shear strains* will be produced in the material. If we now apply a shear stress τ_{xy} to the element, Fig. 3.37(a), experimental observations indicate that the material will deform *only* due to a shear strain γ_{xy}; that is, τ_{xy} will not cause other strains in the material. Likewise, τ_{yz} and τ_{xz} will only cause shear strains γ_{yz} and γ_{xz}, respectively. Hooke's law for shear stress and shear strain can therefore be written as

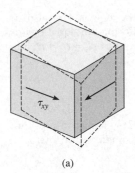

τ_{xy}

(a)

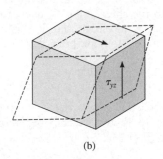

τ_{yz}

(b)

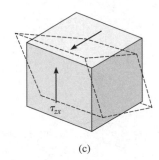

τ_{zx}

(c)

Fig. 3.37

$$\gamma_{xy} = \frac{1}{G}\tau_{xy} \qquad \gamma_{yz} = \frac{1}{G}\tau_{yz} \qquad \gamma_{xz} = \frac{1}{G}\tau_{xz} \qquad\qquad [3.6]$$

Relationship involving *E*, *v*, and *G*

The modulus of elasticity E is related to the shear modulus G as follows:

$$G = \frac{E}{2(1 + v)} \qquad\qquad [3.7]$$

One way to derive this relationship is to consider an element of the material to be subjected to pure shear ($\sigma_x = \sigma_y = \sigma_z = 0$), Fig. 3.38(a). This gives $\sigma_{max} = \tau_{xy}$ and $\sigma_{min} = -\tau_{xy}$. The element must be oriented $\theta_{p1} = 45°$ counterclockwise from the x axis in order to define the direction of the plane on which σ_{max} acts, Fig. 3.38(b). If the three principal stresses $\sigma_{max} = \tau_{xy}$, $\sigma_{int} = 0$, and $\sigma_{min} = -\tau_{xy}$ are substituted into the first of Equation [3.5], the principal strain ε_{max} can be related to the shear stress τ_{xy}. The result is

$$\varepsilon_{max} = \frac{\tau_{xy}}{E}(1 + v) \qquad\qquad [3.8]$$

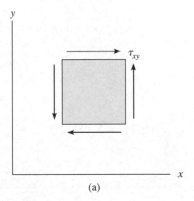

(a)

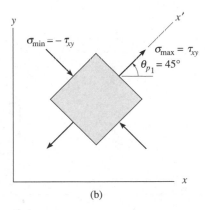

(b)

Fig. 3.38

This strain, which deforms the element along the x' axis, can also be related to the shear strain γ_{xy} using the strain transformation equations or Mohr's circle for strain. To do this, first note that since $\sigma_x = \sigma_y = \sigma_z = 0$, then from Equation [3.5] $\varepsilon_x = \varepsilon_y = 0$. This gives us

$$\varepsilon_1 = \varepsilon_{max} = \frac{\gamma_{xy}}{2}$$

By Hooke's law, $\gamma_{xy} = \tau_{xy}/G$, so that $\varepsilon_{max} = \tau_{xy}/2G$. Substituting into Equation [3.8] and rearranging terms gives the final result, namely, Equation [3.7].

Dilatation and bulk modulus

When an elastic material is subjected to normal stress, its volume will change. In order to compute this change, consider a volume element which is subjected to the principal stresses σ_x, σ_y, σ_z. The sides of the element are originally dx, dy, dz, Fig. 3.39(a); however, after application of the stress they become $(1 + \varepsilon_x)\,dx$, $(1 + \varepsilon_y)\,dy$, $(1 + \varepsilon_z)\,dz$, respectively, Fig. 3.39(b). The change in volume of the element is therefore

$$\delta V = (1 + \varepsilon_x)(1 + \varepsilon_y)(1 + \varepsilon_z)\,dx\,dy\,dz - dx\,dy\,dz$$

Neglecting the products of the strains since the strains are very small, we have

$$\delta V = (\varepsilon_x + \varepsilon_y + \varepsilon_z)\,dx\,dy\,dz$$

The change in volume per unit volume is called the "volumetric strain" or the *dilatation e*. It can be written as

$$e = \frac{\delta V}{dV} = \varepsilon_x + \varepsilon_y + \varepsilon_z \qquad [3.9]$$

By comparison, the shear strains will *not* change the volume of the element, rather they will only change its rectangular shape.

If we use the generalized Hooke's law, as defined by Equation [3.5], we can write the dilatation in terms of the applied stress. We have

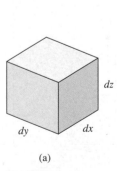

(a)

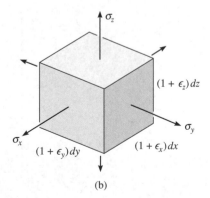

(b)

Fig. 3.39

$$e = \frac{1 - 2v}{E}(\sigma_x + \sigma_y + \sigma_z) \qquad [3.10]$$

When a volume element of material is subjected to the uniform pressure p of a liquid, the pressure on the body is the same in all directions and is always normal to any surface on which it acts. Shear stresses are *not present*, since the shear resistance of a liquid is zero. This state of 'hydrostatic' loading requires the normal stresses to be equal in any and all directions, and therefore an element of the body is subjected to principal stresses $\sigma_x = \sigma_y = \sigma_z = -p$, Fig. 3.40. Substituting into Equation [3.10] and rearranging terms yields

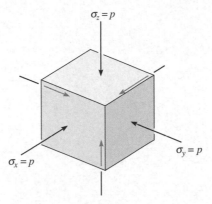

Hydrostatic stress

Fig. 3.40

$$\frac{p}{e} = \frac{E}{3(1 - 2v)} \qquad [3.11]$$

The term on the right consists *only* of the material's properties E and v. It is equal to the ratio of the uniform normal stress p to the dilatation or "volumetric strain." Since this ratio is *similar* to the ratio of linear-elastic stress to strain, which defines E, i.e., $\sigma/\varepsilon = E$, the terms on the right are called the *volume modulus of elasticity* or the **bulk modulus**. It has the same units as stress and will be symbolized by the letter k; that is,

$$k = \frac{E}{3(1 - 2v)} \qquad [3.12]$$

Note that for most metals $v \approx \frac{1}{3}$ so $k \approx E$. If a material existed that did not change its volume then $\delta V = 0$, and so k would have to be infinite. From Equation [3.12] the theoretical *maximum* value for Poisson's ratio is therefore $v = 0.5$. Also, during yielding, no actual volume change of the material is observed, and so $v = 0.5$ is used when plastic yielding occurs.

Important points

- When a homogeneous and isotropic material is subjected to a state of triaxial stress, the strain in one of the stress directions is influenced by the strains produced by *all* the stresses. This is the result of the Poisson effect, and results in the form of a generalized Hooke's law.

- A shear stress applied to homogeneous and isotropic material will only produce shear strain in the same plane.

- The material constants, E, G, and v, are related mathematically.

- *Dilatation*, or *volumetric strain*, is caused only by normal strain, not shear strain.

- The *bulk modulus* is a measure of the stiffness of a volume of material. This material property provides an upper limit to Poisson's ratio of $v = 0.5$, which remains at this value while plastic yielding occurs.

Internal loadings

Internal forces developed in structural members

The design of any structural or mechanical member requires an investigation of the loading acting within the member in order to be sure the material can resist this loading. These internal loadings can be determined by using the *method of sections*. To illustrate the procedure, consider the "simply supported" beam shown in Fig. 3.41(a), which is subjected to the forces F_1 and F_2 and the *support reactions* A_x, A_y, and B_y, Fig. 3.41(b). If the *internal loadings* acting on the cross section at C are to be determined, then an imaginary section is passed through the beam, cutting it into two segments. By doing this the internal loadings at the section become *external* on the free-body diagram of each segment, Fig. 3.41(c). Since both segments (AC and CB) were in equilibrium *before* the beam was sectioned, equilibrium of each segment is maintained provided rectangular force components N_C and V_C and a resultant couple moment M_C are developed at the section. Note that these loadings must be equal in magnitude and opposite in direction on each of the segments (Newton's third law). The magnitude of each of these loadings can now be determined by applying the three equations of equilibrium to either segment AC or CB. A *direct solution* for N_C is obtained by applying $\Sigma F_x = 0$; V_C is obtained directly from $\Sigma F_y = 0$; and M_C is determined by summing moments about point C, $\Sigma M_C = 0$, in order to eliminate the moments of the unknowns N_C and V_C.

In mechanics, the force components N, acting normal to the beam at the cut section, and V, acting tangent to the section, are termed the *normal or axial force* and the *shear force*, respectively. The couple moment M is referred to as the *bending moment*, Fig. 3.42(a). In three dimensions, a general internal force and couple moment resultant will act at the section. The x, y, z components of these loadings are shown in Fig. 3.42(b). Here N_y is the *normal force*, and V_x and V_z are *shear force components*. M_y is a *torsional or twisting moment*, and M_x and M_z are *bending moment components*. For most applications, these *resultant loadings* will act at the geometric center or centroid (C) of the section's cross-sectional area. Although the magnitude for each loading generally will be different at various points along the axis of the member, the method of sections can always be used to determine their values.

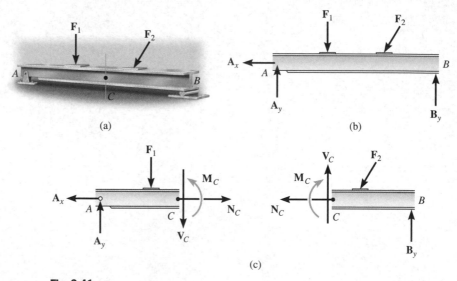

(a)

(b)

(c)

Fig. 3.41

To save on material the beams used to support the roof of this shelter were tapered since the roof loading will produce a larger internal moment at the beams' centers than at their ends.

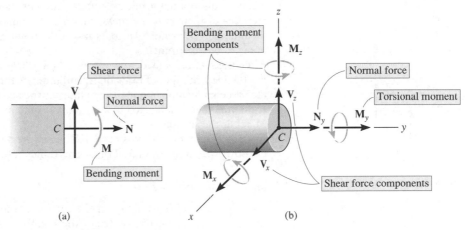

(a)

(b)

Fig. 3.42

Free-body diagrams

Since frames and machines are composed of *multiforce members*, each of these members will generally be subjected to internal normal, shear, and bending loadings. For example, consider the frame shown in Fig. 3.43(a). If the blue section is passed through the frame to determine the internal loadings at points *H*, *G*, and *F*, the resulting free-body diagram of the top portion of this section is shown in Fig. 3.43(b). At each point where a member is sectioned there is an unknown normal force, shear force, and bending moment. As a result, we cannot apply the *three* equations of equilibrium to this section in order to obtain these *nine unknowns*.* Instead, to solve this problem we must *first dismember* the frame and determine the reactions at the connections of the members. Once this is done, *each member* may then be sectioned at its

---

* This method of analysis worked well for trusses since truss members are *straight two-force members* which support only an axial or normal load.

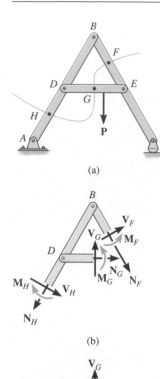

(a)

(b)

(c)

Fig. 3.43

appropriate point, and the three equations of equilibrium can be applied to determine N, V, and M. For example, the free-body diagram of segment DG, Fig. 3.43(c), can be used to determine the internal loadings at G provided the reactions of the pin, D_x and D_y, are known.

Procedure for analysis

The method of sections can be used to determine the internal loadings at a specific location in a member using the following procedure.

Support reactions

- Before the member is "cut" or sectioned, it may first be necessary to determine the member's support reactions, so that the equilibrium equations are used only to solve for the internal loadings when the member is sectioned.

Free-body diagram

- Keep all distributed loadings, couple moments, and forces acting on the member in their *exact locations*, then pass an imaginary section through the member, perpendicular to its axis at the point where the internal loading is to be determined.
- After the section is made, draw a free-body diagram of the segment that has the least number of loads on it, and indicate the x, y, z components of the force and couple moment resultants at the section.
- If the member is subjected to a *coplanar* system of forces, only N, V, and M act at the section.
- In many cases it may be possible to tell by inspection the proper sense of the unknown loadings; however, if this seems difficult, the sense can be assumed.

Equations of equilibrium

- Moments should be summed at the section about axes passing through the *centroid* or geometric center of the member's cross-sectional area in

In each case, the link on the backhoe is a two-force member. In the photo on the left it is subjected to both bending and axial load at its center. By making the member straight, as in the other photo, then only an axial force acts within the member.

order to eliminate the unknown normal and shear forces and thereby obtain direct solutions for the moment components.

• If the solution of the equilibrium equations yields a negative scalar, the assumed sense of the quantity is opposite to that shown on the free-body diagram.

Example 3.19

Determine the resultant internal loadings acting on the cross section at C of the beam shown in Fig. 3.44(a).

Solution

Support reactions   This problem can be solved in the most direct manner by considering segment CB of the beam, since then the support reactions at A do not have to be computed.

Free-body diagram   Passing an imaginary section perpendicular to the longitudinal axis of the beam yields the free-body diagram of segment CB shown in Fig. 3.44(b). It is important to keep the distributed loading exactly where it is on the segment until *after* the section is made. Only then should this loading be replaced by a single resultant force. Notice that the intensity of the distributed loading at C is found by proportion, i.e., from Fig. 3.44(a), $w/6 \text{ m} = (270 \text{ N/m})/9 \text{ m}$, $w = 180 \text{ N/m}$. The magnitude of the resultant of the distributed load is equal to the area under the loading curve (triangle) and acts through the centroid of this area. Thus, $F = \frac{1}{2}(180 \text{ N/m})(6 \text{ m}) = 540 \text{ N}$, which acts $1/3(6 \text{ m}) = 2 \text{ m}$ from C as shown in Fig. 3.44(b).

Equations of equilibrium   Applying the equations of equilibrium we have

$$\xrightarrow{+} \Sigma F_x = 0; \qquad\qquad -N_C = 0$$
$$N_C = 0$$

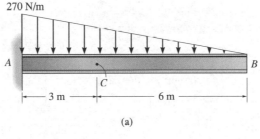

(a)

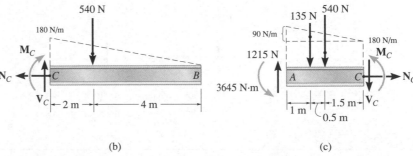

(b)   (c)

Fig. 3.44

$$+\uparrow \Sigma F_y = 0; \qquad V_C - 540 \text{ N} = 0$$
$$V_C = 540 \text{ N}$$
$$(+ \Sigma M_C = 0; \quad -M_C - 540 \text{ N}(2 \text{ m}) = 0$$
$$M_C = -1080 \text{ N} \cdot \text{m}$$

The negative sign indicates that $\mathbf{M}_C$ acts in the opposite direction to that shown on the free-body diagram. Try solving this problem using segment AC, by first obtaining the support reactions at A, which are given in Fig. 3.44(c).

Example 3.20

Determine the resultant internal loadings acting on the cross section at C of the machine shaft shown in Fig. 3.45(a). The shaft is supported by bearings at A and B, which exert only vertical forces on the shaft.

Solution

We will solve this problem using segment AC of the shaft.

Support reactions   A free-body diagram of the entire shaft is shown in Fig. 3.45(b). Since segment AC is to be considered, only the reaction at A has to be determined. Why?

$$(+ \Sigma M_B = 0; \quad -A_y(0.400 \text{ m}) + 120 \text{ N}(0.125 \text{ m}) - 225 \text{ N}(0.100 \text{ m}) = 0$$
$$A_y = -18.75 \text{ N}$$

The negative sign for A_y indicates that $\mathbf{A}_y$ acts in the *opposite sense* to that shown on the free-body diagram.

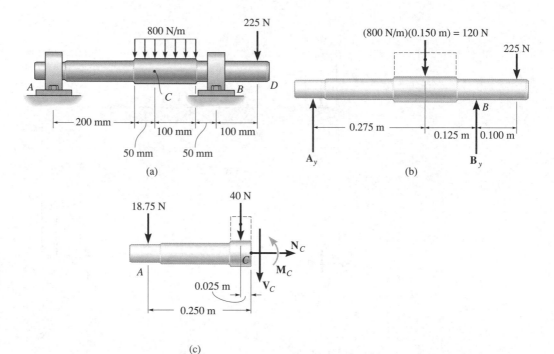

Fig. 3.45

Free-body diagram Passing an imaginary section perpendicular to the axis of the shaft through C yields the free-body diagram of segment AC shown in Fig. 3.45(c).

Equations of equilibrium

$$\xrightarrow{+} \Sigma F_x = 0; \qquad\qquad\qquad N_C = 0$$
$$+\uparrow \Sigma F_y = 0; \quad -18.75\ \text{N} - 40\ \text{N} - V_C = 0$$
$$V_C = -58.8\ \text{N}$$
$$\curvearrowleft + \Sigma M_C = 0; \quad M_C + 40\ \text{N}(0.025\ \text{m}) + 18.75\ \text{N}(0.250\ \text{m}) = 0$$
$$M_C = -5.69\ \text{N} \cdot \text{m}$$

What do the negative signs for V_C and M_C indicate? As an exercise, calculate the reaction at B and try to obtain the same results using segment CBD of the shaft.

Shear and moment equations and diagrams

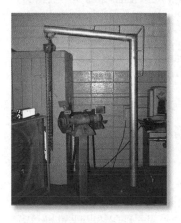

The designer of this shop crane realized the need for additional reinforcement around the joint in order to prevent severe internal bending of the joint when a large load is suspended from the chain hoist.

Beams are structural members which are designed to support loadings applied perpendicular to their axes. In general, beams are long, straight bars having a constant cross-sectional area. Often they are classified as to how they are supported. For example, a *simply supported beam* is pinned at one end and roller-supported at the other, Fig. 3.46, whereas a *cantilevered beam* is fixed at one end and free at the other. The actual design of a beam requires a detailed knowledge of the *variation* of the internal shear force V and bending moment M acting at *each point* along the axis of the beam. After this force and bending-moment analysis is complete, one can then use the theory of mechanics of materials and an appropriate engineering design code to determine the beam's required cross-sectional area.

The *variations* of V and M as functions of the position x along the beam's axis can be obtained by using the method of sections discussed at the beginning of this section. Here, however, it is necessary to section the beam at an arbitrary distance x from one end rather than at a specified point. If the results are plotted, the graphical variations of V and M as functions of x are termed the *shear diagram* and *bending-moment diagram*, respectively.

In general, the internal shear and bending-moment functions generally will be discontinuous, or their slopes will be discontinuous at points where a distributed load changes or where concentrated forces or couple moments

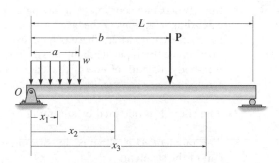

Fig. 3.46

are applied. Because of this, these functions must be determined for *each segment* of the beam located between any two discontinuities of loading. For example, sections located at x_1, x_2, and x_3 will have to be used to describe the variation of V and M throughout the length of the beam in Fig. 3.46. These functions will be valid *only* within regions from O to a for x_1, from a to b for x_2, and from b to L for x_3.

The internal normal force will not be considered in the following discussion for two reasons. In most cases, the loads applied to a beam act perpendicular to the beam's axis and hence produce only an internal shear force and bending moment. For design purposes, the beam's resistance to shear, and particularly to bending, is more important than its ability to resist a normal force.

Sign convention

Before presenting a method for determining the shear and bending moment as functions of x and later plotting these functions (shear and bending-moment diagrams), it is first necessary to establish a *sign convention* so as to define a "positive" and "negative" shear force and bending moment acting in the beam. [This is analogous to assigning coordinate directions x positive to the right and y positive upward when plotting a function $y = f(x)$.] Although the choice of a sign convention is arbitrary, here we will choose the one used for the majority of engineering applications. It is illustrated in Fig. 3.47. Here the positive directions are denoted by an internal *shear force* that causes *clockwise rotation* of the member on which it acts, and by an internal *moment* that causes *compression or pushing on the upper part* of the member. Also, positive moment would tend to bend the member if it were elastic, concave upward. Loadings that are opposite to these are considered negative.

Procedure for analysis

The shear and bending-moment diagrams for a beam can be constructed using the following procedure.

Support reactions

- Determine all the reactive forces and couple moments acting on the beam and resolve all the forces into components acting perpendicular and parallel to the beam's axis.

Shear and moment functions

- Specify separate coordinates x having an origin at the beam's *left end* and extending to regions of the beam *between* concentrated forces and/or couple moments, or where there is no discontinuity of distributed loading.
- Section the beam perpendicular to its axis at each distance x and draw the free-body diagram of one of the segments. Be sure **V** and **M** are shown acting in their *positive sense*, in accordance with the sign convention given in Fig. 3.47.
- The shear V is obtained by summing forces perpendicular to the beam's axis.
- The moment M is obtained by summing moments about the sectioned end of the segment.

Positive shear

Positive moment

Beam sign convention

Fig. 3.47

Shear and moment diagrams

- Plot the shear diagram (V versus x) and the moment diagram (M versus x). If computed values of the functions describing V and M are *positive*, the values are plotted above the x axis, whereas *negative* values are plotted below the x axis.
- Generally, it is convenient to plot the shear and bending-moment diagrams directly below the free-body diagram of the beam.

Example 3.21 Draw the shear and moment diagrams for the beam shown in Fig. 3.48(a).

Solution

Support reactions The support reactions have been determined, Fig. 3.48(d).

Shear and moment functions The beam is sectioned at an arbitrary distance x from the support A, extending within region AB, and the free-body diagram of the left segment is shown in Fig. 3.48(b). The unknowns **V** and **M** are indicated acting in the *positive sense* on the right-hand face of the segment according to the established sign convention. Applying the equilibrium equations yields

$$+\uparrow \Sigma F_y = 0; \quad V = \frac{P}{2} \qquad [3.13]$$

$$\zeta + \Sigma M = 0; \quad M = \frac{P}{2}x \qquad [3.14]$$

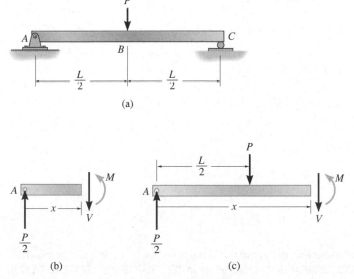

(a)

(b)

(c)

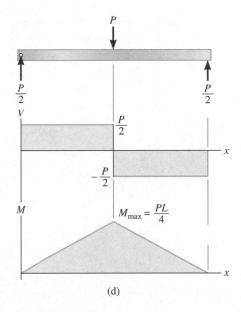

(d)

Fig. 3.48

A free-body diagram for a left segment of the beam extending a distance x within region BC is shown in Fig. 3.48(c). As always, **V** and **M** are shown acting in the positive sense. Hence,

$$+\uparrow \Sigma F_y = 0; \qquad \frac{P}{2} - P - V = 0$$

$$V = -\frac{P}{2} \qquad [3.15]$$

$$\zeta + \Sigma M = 0; \quad M + P\left(x - \frac{L}{2}\right) - \frac{P}{2}x = 0$$

$$M = \frac{P}{2}(L - x) \qquad [3.16]$$

The shear diagram represents a plot of equations [3.13] and [3.15], and the moment diagram represents a plot of equations [3.14] and [3.16], Fig. 3.48(d). These equations can be checked in part by noting that $dV/dx = -w$ and $dM/dx = V$ in each case.

Example 3.22   Draw the shear and moment diagrams for the beam shown in Fig. 3.49(a).

Solution

Support reactions   The support reactions have been determined in Fig. 3.49(d).

Shear and moment functions   This problem is similar to the previous example, where two x coordinates must be used to express the shear and moment in the beam throughout its length. For the segment within region AB, Fig. 3.49(b), we have

$$+\uparrow \Sigma F_y = 0; \quad V = -\frac{M_0}{L}$$

$$\zeta + \Sigma M = 0; \quad M = -\frac{M_0}{L}x$$

And for the segment within region BC, Fig. 3.49(c),

$$+\uparrow \Sigma F_y = 0; \quad V = -\frac{M_0}{L}$$

$$\zeta + \Sigma M = 0; \quad M = M_0 - \frac{M_0}{L}x$$

$$M = M_0\left(1 - \frac{x}{L}\right)$$

Shear and moment diagrams   When the above functions are plotted, the shear and moment diagrams shown in Fig. 3.49(d) are obtained. In this case, notice that the shear is constant over the entire length of the beam; i.e.,

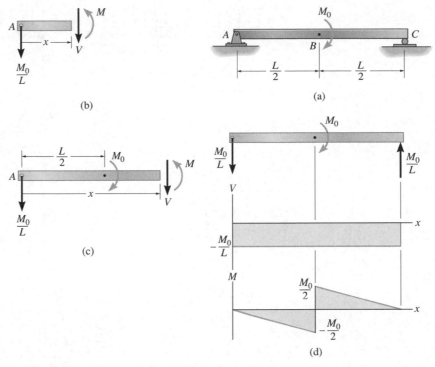

Fig. 3.49

it is not affected by the couple moment $\mathbf{M}_0$ acting at the center of the beam. Just as a force creates a jump in the shear diagram, Example 3.21, a couple moment creates a jump in the moment diagram.

Example 3.23   Draw the shear and moment diagrams for the beam shown in Fig. 3.50(a).

Solution

Support reactions   The support reactions have been computed in Fig. 3.50(c).

Shear and moment functions   A free-body diagram of the left segment of the beam is shown in Fig. 3.50(b). The distributed loading on this segment is represented by its resultant force only *after* the segment is isolated as a free-body diagram. Since the segment has a length x, the *magnitude* of the *resultant force* is wx. This force acts through the centroid of the area comprising the distributed loading, a distance of $x/2$ from the right end. Applying the two equations of equilibrium yields

$$+\uparrow \Sigma F_y = 0; \quad \frac{wL}{2} - wx - V = 0$$

$$V = w\left(\frac{L}{2} - x\right) \quad\quad\quad [3.17]$$

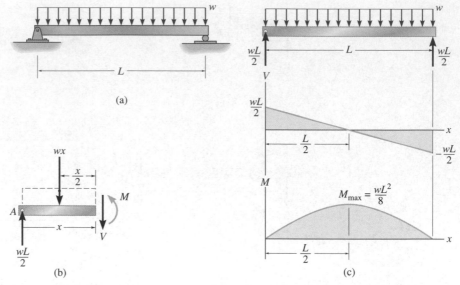

Fig. 3.50

$$\zeta + \Sigma M = 0; \quad -\left(\frac{wL}{2}\right)x + (wx)\left(\frac{x}{2}\right) + M = 0$$

$$M = \frac{w}{2}(Lx - x^2) \qquad\qquad [3.18]$$

These results for V and M can be checked by noting that $dV/dx = -w$. This is indeed correct, since positive w acts downward. Also, notice that $dM/dx = V$.

Shear and moment diagrams   The shear and moment diagrams shown in Fig. 7–13c are obtained by plotting equation [3.17] and [3.18]. The point of *zero shear* can be found from equation [3.17]:

$$V = w\left(\frac{L}{2} - x\right) = 0$$

$$x = \frac{L}{2}$$

From the moment diagram, this value of x happens to represent the point on the beam where the *maximum moment* occurs, since the slope $V = 0 = dM/dx$. From equation [3.18], we have

$$M_{max} = \frac{w}{2}\left[L\left(\frac{L}{2}\right) - \left(\frac{L}{2}\right)^2\right]$$

$$= \frac{wL^2}{8}$$

Combined loadings

Cylindrical or spherical vessels are commonly used in industry to serve as boilers or tanks. When under pressure, the material of which they are made is subjected to a loading from all directions. Although this is the case, the vessel can be analyzed in a simpler manner provided it has a thin wall. In general, '*thin wall*' refers to a vessel having an inner-radius-to-wall-thickness ratio of 10 or more ($r/t \geq 10$). Specifically, when $r/t = 10$ the results of a thin-wall analysis will predict a stress that is approximately 4% *less* than the actual maximum stress in the vessel. For larger r/t ratios this error will be even smaller.

When the vessel wall is 'thin,' the stress distribution throughout its thickness will not vary significantly, and so we will assume that it is *uniform* or *constant*. Using this assumption, we will now analyze the state of stress in thin-walled cylindrical and spherical pressure vessels. In both cases, the pressure in the vessel is understood to be the *gauge pressure*, since it measures the pressure *above* atmospheric pressure, which is assumed to exist both inside and outside the vessel's wall.

Cylindrical vessels

Consider the cylindrical vessel having a wall thickness t and inner radius r as shown in Fig. 3.51(a). A gauge pressure p is developed within the vessel by a contained gas or fluid, which is assumed to have negligible weight. Due to the uniformity of this loading, an element of the vessel that is sufficiently removed from the ends and oriented, as shown, is subjected to normal stresses σ_1 in the *circumferential or hoop direction* and σ_2 in the *longitudinal or axial direction*. Both of these stress components exert tension on the material. We wish to determine the magnitude of each of these components in terms of the vessel's geometry and the internal pressure. To do this requires using the method of sections and applying the equations of force equilibrium.

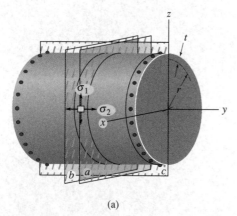

(a)

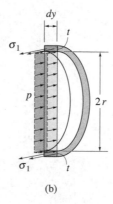

(b)

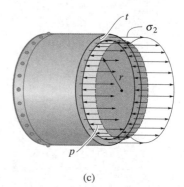

(c)

Fig. 3.51

For the hoop stress, consider the vessel to be sectioned by planes a, b, and c. A free-body diagram of the back segment along with the contained gas or fluid is shown in Fig. 3.51(b). Here only the loadings in the x direction are shown. These loadings are developed by the uniform hoop stress σ_1, acting throughout the vessel's wall, and the pressure acting on the vertical face of the sectioned gas or fluid. For equilibrium in the x direction, we require

$$\Sigma F_x = 0; \quad 2[\sigma_1(t\ dy)] - p(2r\ dy) = 0$$

$$\sigma_1 = \frac{pr}{t} \hspace{5cm} [3.19]$$

In order to obtain the longitudinal stress σ_2, we will consider the left portion of section b of the cylinder, Fig. 3.51(a). As shown in Fig. 3.51(c), σ_2 acts uniformly throughout the wall, and p acts on the section of gas or fluid. Since the mean radius is approximately equal to the vessel's inner radius, equilibrium in the y direction requires

$$\Sigma F_y = 0; \quad \sigma_2(2\pi rt) - p(\pi r^2) = 0$$

$$\sigma_2 = \frac{pr}{2t} \hspace{5cm} [3.20]$$

In the above equations,

> σ_1, σ_2 = the normal stress in the hoop and longitudinal directions, respectively. Each is assumed to be *constant* throughout the wall of the cylinder, and each subjects the material to tension
>
> p = the internal gauge pressure developed by the contained gas or fluid
>
> r = the inner radius of the cylinder
>
> t = the thickness of the wall ($r/t \geq 10$)

Comparing equations [3.19] and [3.20], it should be noted that the hoop or circumferential stress is twice as large as the longitudinal or axial stress. Consequently, when fabricating cylindrical pressure vessels from rolled-formed plates, the longitudinal joints must be designed to carry twice as much stress as the circumferential joints.

Shown is the barrel of a shotgun which was clogged with debris just before firing. Gas pressure from the charge increased the circumferential stress within the barrel enough to cause the rupture.

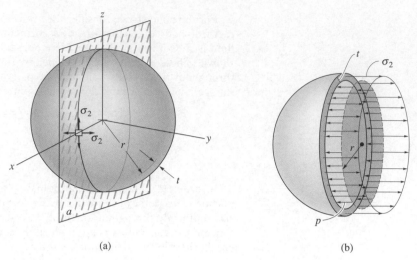

(a)   (b)

Fig. 3.52

Spherical vessels

We can analyze a spherical pressure vessel in a similar manner. For example, consider the vessel to have a wall thickness t and inner radius r and to be subjected to an internal gauge pressure p, Fig. 3.52(a). If the vessel is sectioned in half using section a, the resulting free-body diagram is shown in Fig. 3.52(b). Like the cylinder, equilibrium in the y direction requires

$$\Sigma F_y = 0; \qquad \sigma_2(2\pi r t) - p(\pi r^2) = 0$$

$$\sigma_2 = \frac{pr}{2t} \qquad\qquad\qquad\qquad\qquad [3.21]$$

By comparison, this is the *same result* as that obtained for the longitudinal stress in the cylindrical pressure vessel. Furthermore, from the analysis, this stress will be the same *regardless* of the orientation of the hemispheric free-body diagram. Consequently, an element of the material is subjected to the state of stress shown in Fig. 3.52(a).

The above analysis indicates that an element of material taken from either a cylindrical or a spherical pressure vessel is subjected to *biaxial stress*, i.e., normal stress existing in only two directions. Actually, material of the vessel is also subjected to a *radial stress*, σ_3, which acts along a radial line. This stress has a maximum value equal to the pressure p at the interior wall and decreases through the wall to zero at the exterior surface of the vessel, since the gauge pressure there is zero. For thin-walled vessels, however, we will *ignore* the radial-stress component, since our limiting assumption of $r/t = 10$ results in σ_2 and σ_1 being, respectively, 5 and 10 times *higher* than the maximum radial stress, $(\sigma_3)_{max} = p$. Lastly, realize that the above formulas should be used only for vessels subjected to an internal gauge pressure. If the vessel is subjected to an external pressure, the compressive stress developed within the thin wall may cause the vessel to become unstable, and collapse may occur by buckling.

Design of beams

Slope and displacement by integration

The elastic curve for a beam can be expressed mathematically as $v = f(x)$. To obtain this equation, we must first represent the curvature $(1/\rho)$ in terms of v and x. In most calculus books it is shown that this relationship is

$$\frac{1}{\rho} = \frac{d^2v/dx^2}{[1 + (dv/dx)^2]^{3/2}}$$

Substituting into Eq. 16–3, we get

$$\frac{d^2v/dx^2}{[1 + (dv/dx)^2]^{3/2}} = \frac{M}{EI} \tag{3.22}$$

This equation represents a nonlinear second-order differential equation. Its solution, which is called the *elastica*, gives the exact shape of the elastic curve, assuming, of course, that beam deflections occur only due to bending. Through the use of higher mathematics, elastica solutions have been obtained only for simple cases of beam geometry and loading.

In order to facilitate the solution of a greater number of deflection problems, equation [3.22] can be modified. Most engineering design codes specify *limitations* on deflections for tolerance or esthetic purposes, and as a result the elastic deflections for the majority of beams and shafts form a shallow curve. Consequently, the slope of the elastic curve which is determined from dv/dx will be *very small*, and its square will be negligible compared with unity. Therefore the curvature, as defined above, can be approximated by $1/\rho = d^2v/dx^2$. Using this simplification, equation [3.22] can now be written as

$$\frac{d^2v}{dx^2} = \frac{M}{EI} \tag{3.23}$$

It is also possible to write this equation in two alternative forms. If we differentiate each side with respect to x and substitute $V = dM/dx$, we get

$$\frac{d}{dx}\left(EI\frac{d^2v}{dx^2}\right) = V(x) \tag{3.24}$$

Differentiating again, using $-w = dV/dx$, yields

$$\frac{d^2}{dx^2}\left(EI\frac{d^2v}{dx^2}\right) = -w(x) \tag{3.25}$$

The moment of inertia of this bridge support varies along its length and this must be taken into account when computing its deflection.

For most problems the flexural rigidity will be constant along the length of the beam. Assuming this to be the case, the above results may be reordered into the following set of equations:

$$EI\frac{d^4v}{dx^4} = -w(x) \qquad\qquad [3.26]$$

$$EI\frac{d^3v}{dx^3} = V(x) \qquad\qquad [3.27]$$

$$EI\frac{d^2v}{dx^2} = M(x) \qquad\qquad [3.28]$$

Solution of any of these equations requires successive integrations to obtain the deflection v of the elastic curve. For each integration it is necessary to introduce a 'constant of integration' and then solve for all the constants to obtain a unique solution for a particular problem. For example, if the distributed load is expressed as a function of x and equation 3.26 is used, then four constants of integration must be evaluated; however, if the internal moment M is determined and equation 3.28 is used, only two constants of integration must be found. The choice of which equation to start with depends on the problem. Generally, however, it is easier to determine the internal moment M as a function of x, integrate twice, and evaluate only two integration constants.

If the loading on a beam is discontinuous, that is, consists of a series of several distributed and concentrated loads, then several functions must be written for the internal moment, each valid within the region between the discontinuities. Also, for convenience in writing each moment expression, *the origin* for each x coordinate can be *selected arbitrarily*. For example, consider the beam shown in Fig. 3.53(a). The internal moment in regions AB, BC, and CD can be written in terms of the x_1, x_2, and x_3 coordinates selected, as shown in either Fig. 3.53(b) or 3.53(c), or in fact in any manner that will yield $M = f(x)$ in as simple a form as possible. Once these functions are

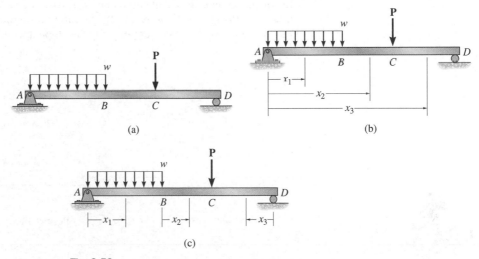

(a)

(b)

(c)

Fig. 3.53

integrated through the use of equation [3.28] and the constants of integration determined, the functions will give the slope and deflection (elastic curve) for each region of the beam for which they are valid.

Sign convention and coordinates

When applying equations [3.26] through [3.28], it is important to use the proper signs for M, V, or w as established by the sign convention that was used in the derivation of these equations. For review, these terms are shown in their *positive directions* in Fig. 3.54(a). Furthermore, recall that *positive deflection, v*, is *upward*, and as a result, the *positive slope angle* θ will be measured *counterclockwise* from the x axis when x is *positive to the right*. The reason for this is shown in Fig. 3.54(b). Here positive increases dx and dv in x and v create an increased θ that is counterclockwise. On the other hand, if *positive x* is directed to the *left*, then θ will be *positive clockwise*, Fig. 3.54(c).

It should be pointed out that by assuming dv/dx to be very small, the original horizontal length of the beam's axis and the arc of its elastic curve will be about the same. In other words, ds in Fig. 3.54(b) and 3.54(c) is approximately equal to dx, since $ds = \sqrt{(dx)^2 + (dv)^2} = \sqrt{1 + (dv/dx)^2}\, dx \approx dx$. As a result, points on the elastic curve are assumed to be *displaced vertically*, and not horizontally. Also, since the *slope angle* θ will be *very small*, its value in radians can be determined *directly* from $\theta \approx \tan \theta = dv/dx$.

Boundary and continuity conditions

The constants of integration are determined by evaluating the functions for shear, moment, slope, or displacement at a particular point on the beam where the value of the function is known. These values are called **boundary conditions**. Several possible boundary conditions that are often used to solve beam (or shaft) deflection problems are listed in Fig. 3.55. For example, if the beam is supported by a roller or pin (1, 2, 3, 4), then it is required that the displacement be *zero* at these points. Furthermore, if these supports are located at the *ends of the beam* (1, 2), the internal moment in the beam must also be zero. At the fixed support (5), the slope and displacement are both

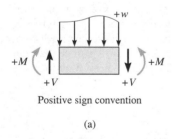

Positive sign convention

(a)

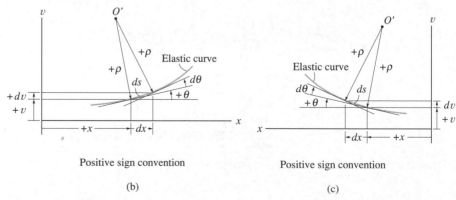

Positive sign convention

(b)

Positive sign convention

(c)

Fig. 3.54

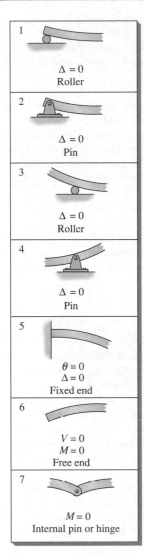

1

$\Delta = 0$
Roller

2

$\Delta = 0$
Pin

3

$\Delta = 0$
Roller

4

$\Delta = 0$
Pin

5

$\theta = 0$
$\Delta = 0$
Fixed end

6

$V = 0$
$M = 0$
Free end

7

$M = 0$
Internal pin or hinge

Fig. 3.55

The design of a roof system requires a careful consideration of deflection. For example, rain can accumulate on areas of the roof, which then causes ponding, leading to further deflection and possible failure of the roof.

zero, whereas the free-ended beam (6) has both zero moment and zero shear. Lastly, if two segments of a beam are connected by an 'internal' pin or hinge (7), the moment must be zero at this connection.

If a single x coordinate cannot be used to express the equation for the beam's slope or the elastic curve, then *continuity conditions* must be used to evaluate some of the integration constants. For example, consider the beam in Fig. 3.56(a). Here the x coordinates are both chosen with origins at A. Each is valid only within the regions $0 \le x_1 \le a$ and $a \le x_2 \le (a + b)$. Once the functions for the slope and deflection are obtained, they must give the *same values* for the slope and deflection at point B so the elastic curve is physically *continuous*. Expressed mathematically, this requires that $\theta_1(a) = \theta_2(a)$ and $v_1(a) = v_2(a)$. These equations can then be used to evaluate two constants of integration. On the other hand, if the elastic curve is expressed in terms of the coordinates $0 \le x_1 \le a$ and $0 \le x_2 \le b$, shown in Fig. 3.56(b), then the continuity of slope and deflection at B requires $\theta_1(a) = -\theta_2(b)$ and $v_1(a) = v_2(b)$. In this particular case, a *negative* sign is necessary to match the slopes at B since x_1 extends positive to the right, whereas x_2 extends positive to the left. Consequently, θ_1 is positive counterclockwise, and θ_2 is positive clockwise. See Fig. 3.54(b) and 3.54(c).

Procedure for analysis

The following procedure provides a method for determining the slope and deflection of a beam (or shaft) using the method of integration.

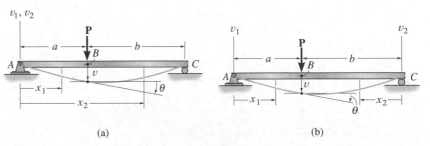

(a)

(b)

Fig. 3.56

Elastic curve

- Draw an exaggerated view of the beam's elastic curve. Recall that zero slope and zero displacement occur at all fixed supports, and zero displacement occurs at all pin and roller supports.
- Establish the x and v coordinate axes. The x axis must be parallel to the undeflected beam and can have an origin at any point along the beam, with a positive direction either to the right or to the left.
- If several discontinuous loads are present, establish x coordinates that are valid for each region of the beam between the discontinuities. Choose these coordinates so that they will simplify subsequent algebraic work.
- In all cases, the associated positive v axis should be directed upward.

Load or moment function

- For each region in which there is an x coordinate, express the loading w or the internal moment M as a function of x. In particular, *always* assume that M acts in the *positive direction* when applying the equation of moment equilibrium to determine $M = f(x)$.

Slope and elastic curve

- Provided EI is constant, apply either the load equation $EI \, d^4v/dx^4 = -w(x)$, which requires four integrations to get $v = v(x)$, or the moment equation $EI \, d^2v/dx^2 = M(x)$, which requires only two integrations. For each integration it is important to include a constant of integration.
- The constants are evaluated using the boundary conditions for the supports (Fig. 3.55) and the continuity conditions that apply to slope and displacement at points where two functions meet. Once the constants are evaluated and substituted back into the slope and deflection equations, the slope and displacement at *specific points* on the elastic curve can then be determined.
- The numerical values obtained can be checked graphically by comparing them with the sketch of the elastic curve. Realize that *positive* values for *slope* are *counterclockwise* if the x axis extends *positive* to the *right*, and *clockwise* if the x axis extends *positive* to the *left*. In either of these cases, *positive displacement* is *upward*.

Gearing

Gearing transmits rotary motion from one shaft to another at a fixed ratio of shaft angular velocities. The mating gear teeth acting against each other are actually cams which provide this constant ratio.

Spur gears are those gears with teeth parallel to the axis of the gear. Such gearing can transmit power between parallel shafts only. Other types of gears such as helical or bevel gears have teeth which are not parallel to the shaft. These other types are used for a range of special requirements, including nonparallel shafts.

The small gear in a pair of mating gears is termed the *pinion*.

Gear geometry

The shape of the gear tooth is a special curve known as an *involute*, though a few gears use curves other than the involute. As shown in Fig. 3.57, the involute is the curve traced by a point on a tight cord as the cord is unwound from a circle.

Certain definitions must be understood in order to comprehend the design and function of gears.

Pitch circle: A pinion and mating gear make contact at the pitch circle. The diameter of this circle is called the *pitch diameter*; this is the effective diameter of the gear. Pitch diameter is designated by D (Fig. 3.58).

Pitch: The pitch measures the size or the spacing of gear teeth around the pitch circle.

Circular pitch: The circular pitch, p_c, is the distance measured along the pitch circle between the same points on two adjacent teeth.

$$p_c = \frac{\text{pitch circle length}}{\text{number of teeth}} = \frac{\pi D}{N}$$

Diametral pitch: This is the number of teeth per inch of pitch diameter, symbolized by p_d. Any two mating gears must have the same diametral pitch. See Fig. 3.59 for sizes of teeth of varying diametral pitch. Note that a large diametral pitch indicates a small tooth size.

The product of the circular pitch and the diametral pitch is π.

Center distance: The center distance is the sum of the radii of the two mating gears. It can be expressed in terms of the number of teeth in the gears:

$$\text{Center distance} = C = \frac{D_1 + D_2}{2} = \frac{1}{2}\left(\frac{N_1}{pd} + \frac{N_2}{pd}\right) = \frac{N_1 + N_2}{2pd}$$

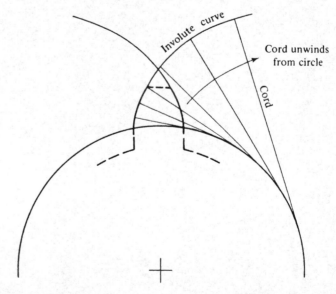

Fig. 3.57   The involute curve

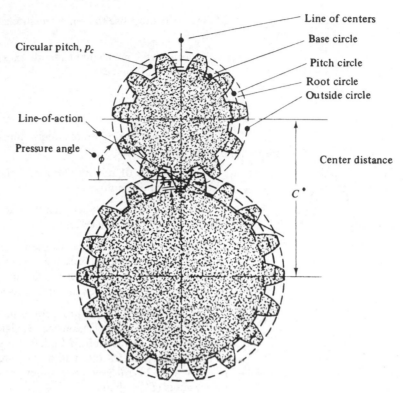

Fig. 3.58   Terminology for spur gears

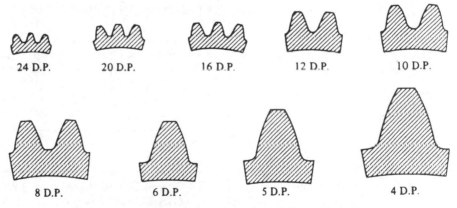

| 24 D.P. | 20 D.P. | 16 D.P. | 12 D.P. | 10 D.P. |

| 8 D.P. | 6 D.P. | 5 D.P. | 4 D.P. |

Fig. 3.59   Actual sizes of gear teeth in a range of diametral pitches

Velocity ratio: This is the ratio Z of angular velocities n_1 and n_2 rpm.

$$Z = \frac{n_1}{n_2} = \frac{D_2}{D_1} = \frac{N_2}{N_1}$$

Pressure angle: This is the angle the tooth profile makes with a radial line at the pitch circle. See Fig. 3.58. For power transmission gearing, the pressure angle is $14\frac{1}{2}$ or 20 degrees, for gear pumps it is often 28 degrees.

Mating gears must use the same pressure angle as well as the same diametral pitch.

Addendum: The height of a tooth, measured from the pitch radius to the outside radius of the gear.

$$\text{Addendum} = A = \frac{1}{p_d}$$

Dedendum: The depth of a tooth, measured from the pitch circle to the root circle of the gear.

Whole depth of tooth: The total height of the gear tooth; the sum of addendum and dedendum.

Clearance: The space between the outside circle of one mating gear and the root circle of the other gear.

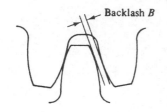

Fig. 3.60   Backlash

Backlash: The difference between a tooth space and the thickness of a tooth. See Fig. 3.60. Some backlash is needed to allow for thermal expansion, lubrication, and tooth and shaft deflection. Backlash may be designed into the gears or introduced by a slight increase in center distance.

Table 3.3 gives the tooth proportions for the standard systems adopted by the ASA (American Association Standards) and the AGMA (American Gear Manufacturers Association). Molded and sintered gears tend to adopt the 25-degree system. Gearing with higher pressure angle generates somewhat less noise than $14\frac{1}{2}$-degree systems but produce slightly higher forces against the bearings of the shaft.

The fine pitches are used in instrument systems such as computers and timers.

The following are the commonly used and preferred diametral pitches.

Coarse			*Fine*		
$\frac{1}{2}$	3	12	20	64	128
1	4	14	24	72	150
2	6	16	32	80	180
2.25	8	18	40	96	200
2.5	10		48	120	

Table 3.3   Standard gear systems

	$14\frac{1}{2}°$ and $20°$ Full-depth (ASA B.6)	$20°$ Stub (ASA B.6)	$20°$ and $25°$ Full-depth Coarse-pitch 19.99 and Coarser (AGMA 201.03)	$14\frac{1}{2}°$, $20°$ and $25°$ Full-depth, 20-pitch and Finer (AGMA 207.05)
Addendum	$\dfrac{1.000}{p_d}$	$\dfrac{0.800}{p_d}$	$\dfrac{1.000}{p_d}$	$\dfrac{1.000}{p_d}$
Dedendum	$\dfrac{1.157}{p_d}$	$\dfrac{1.000}{p_d}$	$\dfrac{1.250}{p_d}$	$\dfrac{1.200}{p_d} + 0.002$
Clearance	$\dfrac{0.157}{p_d}$	$\dfrac{0.200}{p_d}$	$\dfrac{0.250}{p_d}$	$\dfrac{0.200}{p_d} + 0.002$

Example 3.24   Consider a 12-DP spur pinion of 15 teeth rotating at 1725 rpm driving a gear rotating at 720 rpm. Find:

   (a) the number of teeth in the gear.
   (b) the pitch diameter of the pinion.
   (c) the pitch diameter of the gear.
   (d) the center distance of the two gears.
   (e) the O.D. of the larger gear.

Solution

   (a) $\dfrac{1725}{720} \times 15$ teeth $= 36$ teeth in gear

   (b) Diametral pitch $= \dfrac{N}{D}$

$$12 = \frac{15}{D}$$

$$D = 1.250 \text{ in.}$$

   (c) $D = \dfrac{36}{12} = 3.000$ in.

   (d) Center distance $= \dfrac{1}{2}$(sum of pitch diameters) $= \dfrac{3.000 + 1.250}{2} = 2.125$ in.

   (e) O.D. $=$ pitch diameter plus two addendums

$$A = \frac{1}{P_d} = \frac{1}{12}\ 0.0833 \text{ in.}$$

O.D. $= 3.000 + 2 \times 0.0833 = 3.167$ in.

Example 3.25   A 20-tooth 6-DP pinion meshes with a 72-tooth gear. The pinion has an angular velocity of 1200 rpm. Find:

   (a) the angular velocity of the gear.
   (b) the center distance.
   (c) the pitch diameter of the mating gears.

Solution

   (a) Gear rpm $= 20/72 \times 1200 = 333$ rpm

   (b) Center distance $= \dfrac{1}{2}\left(\dfrac{N_1 + N_2}{p_d}\right) = \dfrac{1}{2}\left(\dfrac{20 + 72}{6}\right) = 7.667$

   (c) $D = \dfrac{N}{p_d}$ $\dfrac{N_1}{p_d} = \dfrac{20}{6} = 3.333$ in.

$$\frac{N_2}{p_d} = \frac{72}{6} = 12.000 \text{ in.}$$

When a pinion has fewer than a certain number of teeth there is interference between the meshing teeth of the gears. Such interference occurs at the bottom of the pinion teeth as shown in Fig. 3.61. The least number of teeth that provides no interference or required undercutting of the teeth is 32 for a $14\frac{1}{2}°$ pressure angle and 18 for a 20° pressure angle. For a 20° pressure angle and stub teeth the minimum number is 14 teeth. If fewer teeth than these minimums must be used, then the teeth of the pinion must be undercut in manufacture.

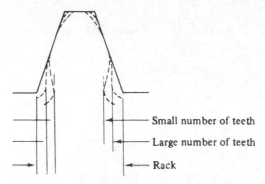

Fig. 3.61   Interference

If a gear must be keyed to a shaft, the minimum pitch diameter must be twice the shaft diameter.

In order to mate, the two gears must meet the following requirements:

1. Identical pitch.
2. Identical pressure angle.
3. Identical addendum and dedendum.

Metric gearing

In the S.I. system the module m is used rather than the diametral pitch p_d.

$$\text{Module} = m = \frac{1}{p_d} = \frac{D}{N} \text{ millimeters}$$

For diametral pitch, p_d is replaced by $25.4/m$.

The following formulas, based on m, then become reasonably obvious and therefore need not be discussed. Refer back to the earlier definitions in this section where necessary.

$$\text{Pitch diameter} = D = mN$$

$$\text{Circular pitch} = m\pi = \frac{\pi D}{N}$$

$$\text{Number of teeth} = N = \frac{D}{M}$$

From previous definitions:

$$\text{Addendum} = \frac{1}{p_d} = m$$

$$\text{O.D. of gear} = D + 2m = m(N + 2) \text{ mm}$$

$$\text{Center distance} = C = \frac{1}{2}m(N_1 + N_2) \text{ mm}$$

Example 3.26 **A pair of mating metric gears of module 1.25 have 28 and 38 teeth. Find the center distance, the pitch diameters, and the addendum.**

Solution

$$C = \frac{1}{2}\,m(N_1 + N_2)$$

$$= \frac{1}{2}(1.25)(28 + 38) = 41.25 \text{ mm}$$

$$D = 1.25 \times 28 \text{ and } 1.25 \times 38 \text{ or } 35 \text{ and } 47.5 \text{ mm}$$

$$A = m = 1.25$$

Forces in gears

Forces in gears may be resolved into three components:

1. A tangential component of force, tangential to the pitch circle.
2. A radial force tending to separate the gears.
3. A thrust force axial to the shaft. For straight spur gears there is no thrust.

These forces must be known in order to select suitable bearings for the shaft.

Figure 3.62 shows a mating gear and pinion. The forces between the mating teeth occur at the pitch circle along the pressure line at angle θ, the pressure angle. The force F, equal to the force between mating teeth, is transmitted to the bearings of the shaft.

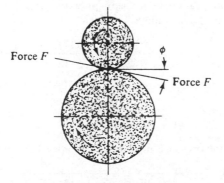

Force F ϕ Force F

Fig. 3.62 Pressure force between mating gear and pinion

In Fig. 3.63 the forces F and W are resolved into tangential and radial components. The torque transmitted by gear or pinion is

$$T = W_t R$$

Where R = radius of the pitch circle

If V is the pitch circle velocity in fpm, then

$$HP = \frac{W_t V}{33,000}$$

from which W_t may be calculated if the horsepower is known.

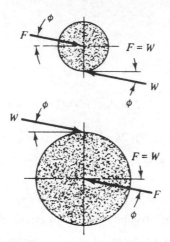

Fig. 3.63   Gear forces

| **Example 3.27** | Suppose the two gears of Example 3.25 transmit 5 HP. Determine the pitch line velocity and the force between the mating teeth. It is assumed that only one tooth of each gear transmits power at any instant. |

Solution

Both gears have the same pitch line velocity. For ease of calculation, use the gear to determine this velocity.

$$V = \frac{\pi D (\text{rpm})}{12} = \frac{\pi (12) 333}{12} = 1043 \text{ fpm}$$

$$HP = 5 = \frac{W_t V}{33,000} = \frac{1043}{33,000} W_t$$

$$W_t = 158 \text{ lb}$$

If the pressure angle is 20°, then the force between gear teeth is

$$\frac{W_t}{\cos 20°} = \frac{158}{0.94} = 168 \text{ lb}$$

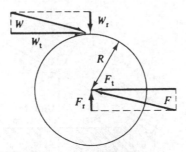

Fig. 3.64 Radial and tangential components of gear forces

Helical gears

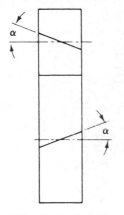

Fig. 3.65 Mating helical gears, one left hand, the other right hand

Helical gears, like spur gears, are cut from a cylindrical gear blank, but with teeth at some helix angle to the axis of the gear. This helix angle is measured at the pitch circle. Helical gears may substitute for spur gears driving parallel shafts, but may also be applied to shafts at an angle to each other. For shafts at 90 degrees they provide only a point contact between the two gears and therefore can transmit only small amounts of power. Helical gears are preferred if the width of the gear is large, since in the case of helical gears the whole width of the tooth does not engage at once. This action reduces shock and makes such gearing adaptable to heavy loads, high speeds, and low noise levels. Helical gears use the involute tooth shape and the usual pressure angles.

The hand of the helix must be selected correctly. If the two mating helical gears drive parallel shafts, one of the pair must have a left-hand helix and the other a right-hand helix, as in Fig. 3.65. The two gears must have identical helix angles.

Because of the helix, there is an axial force component parallel to the shaft. A double helical gear or herringbone gear is the equivalent of two helical gears of opposite hand mounted together to produce opposing thrusts which cancel each other out.

Bevel gears

The two shafts of a bevel gear drive are at an angle to each other, usually 90 degrees, and intersect (Fig. 3.66). The point of intersection of the two shafts is usually the apex of both pitch cones. If two spur tooth bevel gears intersect at right angles and both gears have the same number of teeth, they are referred to as miter gears. Terminology for bevel gears is given in Fig. 3.66.

The tooth section gradually becomes smaller as the apex of the pitch cone is approached. Only a length of cone close to its base is used for the teeth, actually not more than one-third of the full length of the cone. All such dimensions as pitch diameter, diametral pitch, addendum, and dedendum are measured at the large diameter of the bevel gear.

Besides the straight-tooth bevel gear, other variants are used, including helical bevel gears, hypoid, skew, and zerol types. Spiral or helical bevel gears are selected when low noise levels are a requirement. Hypoid gears resemble spiral bevel gears but the two shafts of the drive do not intersect. Hence the two shafts can be extended beyond the gears without interfering with each other. The hypoid gear was originally developed for automobile

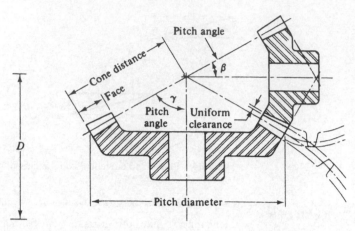

Fig. 3.66   Right-angle bevel gear drive

Fig. 3.67   Spiral bevel gears   **Fig. 3.68**   Zero–bevel gears

rear ends, because it allowed the drive shaft to be lower than the rear axle and permitted a lower floor level in the vehicle. Because there is less taper, hypoid drives are better suited to high horsepower requirements, but since this gear slides as well as rolls, it requires an extreme pressure lubricant.

The spiroid gear uses a tapered worm for a pinion (Fig. 3.70). It has the advantage of backlash control (by axial movement of the pinion) and shock

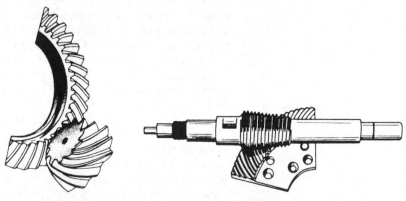

Fig. 3.69   Hypoid gears   **Fig. 3.70**   Spiroid gearing

resistance. Several teeth are simultaneously in contact. The spiroid gear is found in many portable power tools, including hedge trimmers, portable grinders, portable drills, electric can openers, etc.

Worm drives

The terminology for worm drives is given in Fig. 3.71. These drives are used to obtain large speed reductions up to a maximum of perhaps 80:1 in a small space. Higher reductions, however, are less efficient than smaller reduction ratios. The two shafts are usually at right angles to each other. The worm is a special case of a helical or spiral gear in that the helix wraps completely around the worm like a screw thread. Indeed, the worm teeth are referred to as threads.

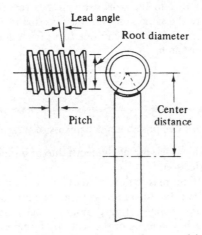

Fig. 3.71   Terminology of a worm drive

Because of considerable sliding friction there is the problem of heat generation in a worm drive. Selection of the lubricant is more critical than in other types of gearing. While most types of mating gears have efficiencies from 96 to 99%, the efficiency of a worm drive is much lower. To prevent seizure of worm to gear, the worm is usually a hardened steel and the gear a bronze.

For a single thread worm the speed reduction is the number of teeth in the gear. A double-thread worm will give a speed reduction of half the teeth in the gear. The number of threads also determines whether the drive is self-locking. A single-thread worm has the smallest helix angle and is always self-locking, that is, the worm cannot be turned by the gear. Multithread worms however are more common than single-threads because of higher efficiency. Self-locking worms do not require brakes.

The American Gear Manufacturers Association (AGMA) recommends the following relationships in worm drives:

$$p_d \text{ of worm} = \frac{C}{2.2}$$

where C = the center distance between shafts.

Face width of gear = 0.72 × worm pitch diameter approximately

Axial length of worm = $(4.5 + N_g/50)p_c$

where N_g = the number of gear teeth

The maximum input horsepower of a worm gear unit is limited by the problem of dissipating the friction heat that is generated. This maximum input horsepower can be estimated from

$$HP = \frac{9.50^{1.7}}{R + 5}$$

where R = the reduction ratio

C = the center distance

Note that in the worm the *pitch* is the axial distance from a point on a thread to the same point on the next thread. The *lead* is the distance a screw thread advances axially in one turn; for a double-threaded worm the lead is twice the pitch.

Gear lubrication

There are five possible mechanisms of wear in gear teeth:

1. Seizing: welding of the teeth due to high local pressure in the absence of lubrication.
2. Scuffing: plastic flow of material near the pitch line.
3. Pitting: due to compressive fatigue stress resulting from repeated applications of force. A hard tooth surface reduces scuffing.
4. Abrasion: scoring of the teeth by foreign matter.
5. Scoring: due to sharp edges on the teeth; not a problem in quality gearing.

Scuffing and seizing are prevented by proper lubrication. The type of gear and the loading conditions dictate the type of lubricant. A spur gear rolls, but a hypoid or worm gear also slides, and different lubricants are needed for these different conditions. Most gears with moderate loads will perform satisfactorily with a rust and oxidation inhibited (R & O) mineral oil; for heavier loads extreme pressure lubricants are preferred. Sliding gears such as worm gears require lubricants with special additives to reduce friction and supply resistance to scoring.

Five groups of gear lubricant are in common use:

1. R & O oil: rust and oxidation inhibited mineral oil.
2. EP (extreme pressure) oil: contains chemical additives that react with gear materials at high contact temperatures to produce a protective film that reduces metal-to-metal contact.
3. Compounded oil: usually a cylinder oil with a few percent of animal fat to reduce friction.
4. Heavy-bodied open-gear oil: these are heavy, sticky oils, applied by hand, dip, or intermittent spray. They are available with or without an EP additive.
5. Grease: a grease is a fluid thickened by an agent to reduce the tendency to flow away from the region being lubricated.

Lubrication requirements for spur, helical, and bevel gearing are identical. R & O oils are used, but EP oils are substituted for heavy and shock loads. For worm gears, EP and compounded oils are preferred. Hypoid gears require EP oils.

Gear trains

A power transmission system consisting only of gears is called a gear train or gear transmission. Gear trains are of several types: simple, compound, reverted, and planetary (epicyclic). In the planetary train at least one of the gear axes must rotate.

In a *simple gear train* each shaft carries only one gear. The compound gear train contains one or more shafts carrying more than one gear. Consider the simple gear train of Fig. 3.72, where gear A is the driving gear. Speed ratios are set by the number of teeth, hence

$$\frac{\omega_B}{\omega_A} = \frac{N_A}{N_B} \qquad \frac{\omega_C}{\omega_B} = \frac{N_B}{N_C} \qquad \frac{\omega_D}{\omega_C} = \frac{N_C}{N_D}$$

$$\frac{\omega_B}{\omega_A} = \left(\frac{\omega_B}{\omega_A}\right)\left(\frac{\omega_C}{\omega_B}\right)\left(\frac{\omega_D}{\omega_C}\right) = \frac{N_A N_B N_C}{N_B N_C N_D} = \frac{N_A}{N_D}$$

where ω = rpm or angular velocity

N − number of teeth.

Thus the intermediate gears, called idler gears, do not influence the overall velocity ratio. Such a simple gear train may be used to fill up a large center distance between driving and driven shafts, to reverse the direction of rotation of the driven shaft, or for taking power off the intermediate gears.

A compound gear train is illustrated in Fig. 3.73. Speed ratios are:

$$\frac{\omega_B}{\omega_A} = \frac{N_A}{N_A} \qquad \frac{\omega_D}{\omega_C} = \frac{N_C}{N_D} \qquad \frac{\omega_F}{\omega_E} = \frac{N_E}{N_F}$$

$$\text{Overall speed ratio} = \frac{\omega_F}{\omega_A} = \frac{\omega_B}{\omega_A}\frac{\omega_D}{\omega_C}\frac{\omega_F}{\omega_E}$$

where $\omega_B = \omega_C$ and $\omega_D = \omega_E$

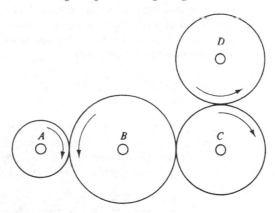

Fig. 3.72   Simple gear train of four gears

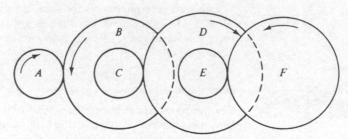

Fig. 3.73 Compound gear train

Substituting tooth numbers:

$$\frac{\omega_F}{\omega_A} = \left(\frac{N_A}{N_B}\right)\left(\frac{N_C}{N_D}\right)\left(\frac{N_E}{N_F}\right)$$

All the gears influence the overall speed ratio. Note that in this speed ratio equation the numerator is the product of all the driver teeth $(N_A \times N_C \times N_E)$ and the denominator is the product of all the driven teeth $(N_B \times N_D \times N_F)$. These same relationships apply to belt drives and chain drives as well as to gears, using the pitch diameters of pulleys and sprockets.

Design of a compound gear train

To understand the design of a compound gear train, consider the following example.

A small precision compound gear train requires a speed reduction of 1:15. Standard 20-degree full-depth spur gears with a diametral pitch of 24 are selected. A maximum pitch diameter of 3 in. is desired, and to avoid under-cutting, not less than 18 teeth should be used.

Given the requirements, it is clear that a single pair of gears cannot be used, because the number of teeth on the large gear would be 18×15, giving too large a pitch diameter. Eighteen is the smallest number of teeth allowed in the pinion, and 15 is the reduction ratio. Therefore to begin the design, try two equal speed reductions:

$$\frac{\omega_{\text{out}}}{\omega_{\text{in}}} = \frac{1}{15} = \frac{1}{3.88}\,\frac{1}{3.88}$$

where $3.88^2 = 15$, and each reduction is to be 1:3.88

Next change one of the 3.88's to a number close to 3.88 but which can be converted into a reasonably simple fraction. Change 3.88 to 3.875, which is $31/8$. This alters the speed ratio equation to:

$$\frac{1}{15} = \left(\frac{1}{\frac{31}{8}}\right)\left(\frac{\frac{31}{8}}{15}\right) = \frac{8}{31}\left[\frac{31}{8 \times 15}\right] = \frac{8}{31} \times \frac{31}{120}$$

A reduction of 8:31 then 31:120 (tooth numbers) will give the required ratio of 1:15, but the last gear would have 120 teeth and a pitch diameter of 5 in. The first gear would have only 8 teeth, an insufficient number. If the number of teeth in the first reduction is doubled to 16:62, then 16 teeth are still too few.

Try a larger reduction in the first pair of gears, say 1:4.

$$\frac{1}{15} = \frac{1}{4} \times \frac{4}{15} = \frac{18}{72} \times \frac{20}{75}$$

Eighteen teeth is the smallest number of teeth allowable and is acceptable, however 75 teeth gives a pitch diameter slightly over 3 in., but is probably acceptable.

For a second case, consider a gear reducer which is to reduce an electric motor speed of 1725 rpm to 200 rpm. No gear is to have less than 20 or more than 50 teeth. Determine the number of gear pairs and the tooth numbers.

The speed ratio is $^{1725}/_{200}$ or 8.625. Using the smallest and largest gears allowed, 20 and 50 teeth, the maximum speed reduction is 50/20 or 2.50. Using two pairs it is 50/20 × 50/20 or 6.25. This is still less than the required 8.625. Therefore three combinations of gears will be required.

Since three combinations are needed, first take the cube root of 8.625, which is 2.05. Ideally, the reductions would be

$$\frac{2.05}{1} \times \frac{2.05}{1} \times \frac{2.05}{1} = 8.625$$

Suppose we change two of the three ratio to 2/1 and then alter the third ratio to suit:

$$2.0 \times 2.0 \times 2.15625 = 8.625$$

For the first two reductions use tooth numbers of 40 and 20. For the last reduction, if 20 teeth are given to the driving gear, then the final driven gear will have 43 teeth (20×2.15).

The reverted gear train

A reverted gear train is a compound train in which both input and output shafts have the same line as axis. With this requirement, it will be seen that the center distance must be the same for all pairs of gears in the train. See Fig. 3.74.

If C is the center distance, then

$$2C = D_A + D_B = D_C + D_D$$

But since

$$D = \frac{N}{p_d} \qquad \text{then} \qquad 2C = \frac{N_A}{p_1} + \frac{N_B}{p_1} = \frac{N_C}{p_2} + \frac{N_D}{p_2}$$

where p_1 and p_2 are two diametral pitches. If a single diametral pitch is used in the reverted gear train, then

$$2Cp_d = N_A + N_B = N_C + N_D$$

and thus the same number of teeth must be used in each pair of gears.

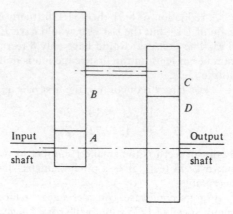

Fig. 3.74 Reverted gear train of four gears

To design a reverted gear train, the following example can be used. The speed ratio between input and output shafts is to be a reduction of 1:6. No gear is to have less than 18 teeth or more than 96, and a uniform diametral pitch will be used.

The maximum ratio for one pair of gears is $^{18}/_{96}$ or $^{3}/_{16}$, and for two pairs $^{9}/_{64}$. A ratio of 1:6 falls between these two numbers, so two reductions are required. Begin as with previous gear train designs by taking the square root of 1/6, which is $(1/2.45) \times (1/2.45)$.

Try $^{1}/_{2.5}$ for the first ratio and alter the second ratio to suit:

$$\frac{1}{6} = \frac{1}{2.5}\frac{2.5}{6}$$

But the sums of numerator and denominator are $(1 + 2.5)$ and $(2.5 + 6)$; these sums are not equal and therefore neither will the number of teeth be equal in the two combination.

$$\frac{1}{2.5}\frac{2.5}{6} = \frac{2}{5}\frac{5}{12}$$

with sums of 7 and 17. Now multiply the first fraction by $^{17}/_{7}$, the sum of $5 + 12$, and the second fraction by $^{7}/_{7}$, the sum of $2 + 5$:

$$\left(\frac{2}{5} \times \frac{17}{17}\right)\left(\frac{5}{12} \times \frac{7}{7}\right) = \frac{34}{85}\frac{35}{84}$$

The tooth totals are now equal. Neither too large nor too small a number of teeth has been used.

The planetary or epicyclic gear train

A simple type of planetary gear train is shown in Fig. 3.75. The distinguishing characteristic of this type of gear train is the rotating arm or planet carrier. If we assume the sun gear to be stationary and the arm to rotate clockwise about its axis O, then the planet gear also rotates clockwise about its center C. Alternatively, the ring gear could be the stationary member. If

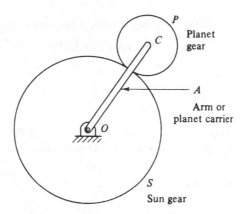

Fig. 3.75 Simple planetary gear train

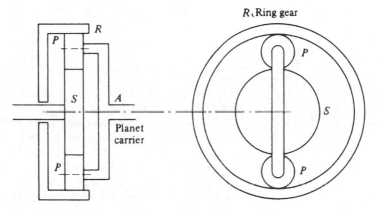

Fig. 3.76 Epicyclic gear train with two planetary pinions

the arm is stationary and both sun and planet gear rotate, then the planetary train becomes a standard gear train. In an epicyclic or planetary gear train one or more gears rotate about a moving axis.

Figure 3.76 shows a planetary train with two planet pinions. The number of pinions has no influence on the speed ratio, but allows more torque to be transmitted through an increased number of planet gears.

The gear speeds of the epicyclic train of Fig. 3.76 can be determined from the equation

$$\omega_S = \left(1 + \frac{N_R}{N_S}\right)\omega_A - \left(\frac{N_R}{N_S}\right)\omega_R$$

where ω_S = rpm of sun gear

ω_A = rpm of planet carrier arm

ω_R = rpm of ring gear

N_R = number of teeth on the ring gear

N_S = number of teeth on the sun gear

Example 3.28

The following information applies to the train of Fig. 3.76:

$$\omega_S = 1200 \text{ rpm clockwise}$$
$$N_S = 96$$
$$N_P = 24$$
$$N_R = 144$$

Find the planet carrier shaft speed if the sun gear is the input, the ring gear is fixed, and the planet carrier is the ouput.

Solution

$$\omega_S = \left(1 + \frac{N_R}{N_S}\right)\omega_A - \left(\frac{N_R}{N_S}\right)\omega_R$$

$$1200 = \left(1 + \frac{144}{96}\right)\omega_A - 0$$

$$= 2.5\omega_A$$

$$\omega_A = +480 \text{ rpm}$$

The direction of rotation of the carrier is the same as that of the sun gear, since the answer is positive.

A useful method of analyzing planetary trains requires a tabulation of separate motions. The former example will be worked by this tabular method.

In this method we lock the planetary train so that the gears cannot rotate, and rotate the arm and the whole train one positive turn. Then the arm, the sun, the planet, and the ring gear have all been rotated one positive turn. But in the above example the ring gear is actually fixed and should not have turned. This correction is made by rotating the ring gear one negative turn to bring it back to zero rotation. In doing so the planet and sun gears must also rotate the required number of turns given by their tooth numbers. All this tabulated as follows:

	Arm	Ring	Planet	Sun
Lock train and rotate arm	$+1$	$+1$	$+1$	$+1$
Rotate ring one negative turn	0	-1	$-\dfrac{144}{24}$	$+\dfrac{144}{46}$
Total rotations	$+1$	0	-5	$+2.5$

Then the sun gear to arm speed ratio is 2.5:1, and the arm rotates $^2/_5 \times 1200$ or 480 rpm in the same direction as the sun gear.

Example 3.29

In the planetary train of Fig. 3.77, the internal gear A is fixed. Find the ratio of turns of gear D to the arm.

Solution

As in the previous case, the gear train is first assumed to be locked and the whole train, including A, is rotated one positive turn. This rotates the arm

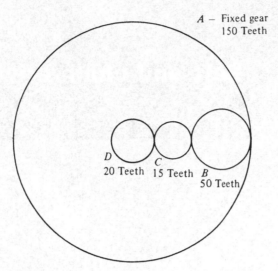

Fig. 3.77 Epicyclic example

one turn, but the gears have not rotated and A, actually a fixed gear, has made a rotation. Next A is given a negative turn to cancel out the positive turn, with the arm fixed and the gears rotating.

	Arm	A	B	C	D
Train locked, one positive turn	$+1$	$+1$	$+1$	$+1$	$+1$
Arm fixed, gear A one negative turn	0	-1	$-\dfrac{150}{50}$	$+\dfrac{150}{50} \times \dfrac{50}{15}$	$-\dfrac{150}{50} \times \dfrac{50}{15} \times \dfrac{15}{20}$
Relationship of turns	$+1$	0	-2	$+11$	$-6\frac{1}{2}$

Belt and chain drives

Belting materials

Flat belts have been used in power transmission for many centuries. Belts of earlier times were either leather or rope. While the rope belt no longer has a role in modern power transmission, the leather belt is still a most successful power transmission device and it is not easy to develop synthetic belting materials that can match leather's range of useful characteristics and its versatility. Synthetic rubber belting has been the most successful competitor to leather.

A belt is subject to tension, bending, and centrifugal forces. A suitable belt must be strong in tension, yet pliable for bending about pulleys, light in weight, and must provide sufficient friction against pulleys. Many belts are subject to shock loadings when drive motors are started, and a successful belt must have elasticity to absorb such shocks without breaking. Four classes of belting materials have suitable characteristics: leather, fabric, rubber, or synthetics (plastics).

Leather has a high coefficient of friction against pulleys, excellent flexibility, long life, and outstanding ability to hold belt splices. Leather belts are available in single-, double-, or triple-ply, and in light, medium, or heavy weights. Since leather is not a woven material but a hide, it does not unravel or become frayed. The absence of a weave also makes it more receptive to belt fasteners. A leather belt has a higher capacity for overloading than other belting materials. If installed with excessive tension, it stretches somewhat to reduce such tension.

Leather belts are tanned by immersion in solutions that are termed 'tan liquors.' Tan liquors are extracts of vegetable tanning materials such as oak bark, quebracho, and others. A belt tanned in such materials is termed 'vegetable-tanned' or 'oak-tanned.' This is the treatment given to most belts. An alternative is to use tanning solutions that contain mineral salts, usually chromic acid. Such a belt is termed 'mineral-tanned' or 'chrome-tanned.' Oak-tanned leather is firmer and less pliable than a chrome-tanned leather, but has a lower friction coefficient and a lower resistance to water.

A leather belt must be lubricated occasionally with a suitable belt dressing, otherwise its life is shortened due to hardening and cracking on the pulley side of the belt. Also, since the belt dressing maintains the leather in pliable condition, a high coefficient of friction with pulleys is maintained. Suitable belt dressings contain beef tallow, vegetable waxes, fish oils, or stearines, but the mineral oils and waxes that lubricate other power transmission devices such as bearings are not suitable for leather.

Rubber has become a commonly used belting material. It has a lower coefficient of friction than leather and thus requires more tension. Rubber belts, however, do not stretch as much as leather. The rubber belt has a core of canvas, cotton duck, or cords enveloped in rubber. The core material takes the tension stress in the belt, while the rubber provides resilience, elasticity, and surface friction against pulleys. Basic types of construction for such belts are raw-edge, folded-edge, and cord: these are illustrated in Fig. 3.78.

Woven cotton and canvas, often impregnated with rubber, is available in various grades. Synthetic materials have become more widely used in belting including polyester and nylon. Various combinations are in use, such as a nylon core with a leather surface for good grip.

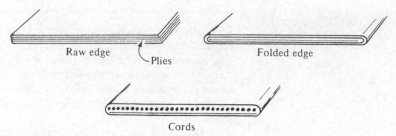

Fig. 3.78 Types of rubber belting for power transmission

Flat-belt drives

Power transmission by a flat belt is possible only with sufficient friction between the belt and its pulleys. As a result of friction effects, there will be a difference between the tight-side tension T_1 and the slack-side tension T_2. If the belt is on the verge of slipping the relationship between these two belt tensions is given by

$$\frac{T_1}{T_2} - e^{\mu\beta}$$

where $e = 2.718$
μ = coefficient of friction between belt and pulley
β = contact angle of belt in radians (1 radian = 57.3°)
$T_1 T_2$ = tight-side and slack-side tension forces in the belt, in units of force, usually pounds. Values of c^x are given in Table 3.4.

At high velocities the belt will tend to leave the pulley due to centrifugal effects, thus reducing friction force. To take account of such centrifugal effects, the above equation is thus modified:

$$\frac{T_1 \quad T_c}{T_2 \quad T_c} = e^{\mu\beta}$$

$$T_c = \frac{wV^2}{3600g}$$

where w = belt weight in pounds per lineal foot
V = belt speed in fpm
g = gravitational acceleration = 32.2 fps/s

The difference between tight-side and slack-side tensions in the belt produces a torque T:

$$T = (T_1 - T_2)r$$

or if centrifugal force is significantly large

$$T = [(T_1 - T_c) - (T_2 - T^c)]R = (T_1 - T_2)r$$

where r = pitch radius of the belt.

Horsepower and belt torque T are related by the equation

$$\mathrm{HP} = \frac{TV}{33,000r} = \frac{(T_1 - T_2)V}{33,000}$$

Table 3.4

x	c^x	x	c^x	x	c^x
0.02	1.0202	0.25	1.2840	0.45	1.5683
0.04	1.0408	0.26	1.2969	0.46	1.5841
0.06	1.0618	0.27	1.3100	0.47	1.6000
0.08	1.0833	0.28	1.3231	0.48	1.6161
		0.29	1.3364	0.49	1.6323
0.10	1.1052	0.30	1.3499	0.50	1.6487
0.11	1.1163	0.31	1.3634	0.56	1.8221
0.12	1.1275	0.32	1.3771	0.57	2.0138
0.13	1.1388	0.33	1.3910	0.58	2.2255
0.14	1.1505	0.34	1.4050	0.59	2.4596
0.15	1.1618	0.35	1.4191	1.0	2.7183
0.16	1.1735	0.36	1.4333	1.1	3.0042
0.17	1.1835	0.37	1.4477	1.2	3.3201
0.18	1.1972	0.38	1.4623	1.3	3.6693
0.19	1.2092	0.39	1.4770	1.4	4.0552
0.20	1.2214	0.40	1.4918	1.5	4.4817
0.21	1.2337	0.41	1.5068	1.6	4.9530
0.22	1.2461	0.42	1.5220	1.7	5.4739
0.23	1.2586	0.43	1.5373	1.8	6.0497
0.24	1.2712	0.44	1.5527	1.9	6.6859
				2.0	7.3891

where V = the belt speed in fpm
         r = the pitch radius of the belt in feet

Example 3.30   A flat belt with 200 degrees of wrap on the driving pulley transmits 25 HP to the driven shaft at a lower speed. Diameter of driving pulley is 18 in., coefficient of friction between belt and pulleys is 0.35, and belt speed is 100 fpm. Determine the tight-side force T_1.

Solution

$$\frac{T_1}{T_2} = e^{\mu\beta} = e^{0.35}$$

$$\beta = 200^0 = \frac{200}{57.3} \text{ radians}$$

Then

$$\mu\beta = e^{0.35 \times 3.49} = e^{1.22} = 3.39$$

$$T_1 = 3.39 \, T_2$$

$$\text{HP} = \frac{(T_1 - T_2)V}{32,000} = \frac{\left(T_1 - \frac{T_1}{3.39}\right)}{33,000}1000 = 25$$

$$T_1 = 1190 \text{ lb}$$

Note that these relationships hold only if the belt is on the verge of slipping and if the stated horsepower is actually being transmitted – not merely a rated horsepower.

For an approximation, the tension in the tight side of the belt can be taken as twice the tension in the slack side. Since the effective tension for power transmission equals the tight-side tension minus the slack-side tension, the driving force is equal to the slack-side tension, using this approximation.

Angle of wrap and belt length

A belt transmits power by means of friction against its pulley. Therefore the two most important factors in determining the maximum power that can be transmitted are the coefficient of friction and the angle of wrap or contact angle. Suppose we compare two angles of wrap, one of 40° and one of 180°, with the smaller angle of wrap transmitting 1 HP. If all other conditions are the same, the larger angle of 180° can transmit 2.73 HP. Small angles therefore are undesirable, such as are produced by mounting a small pulley very close to a large pulley.

Belt length is determined from the center distance and diameter of the pulleys. For the open-belt drive of Fig. 3.79 the length of the belt is computed as follows:

$$\sin \theta = \frac{D - d}{2C}$$

$$\beta_1 = 180° + 2\theta = 180° - 2 \sin^{-1} \frac{D - d}{2C}$$

$$\beta_2 = 180° - 2\theta = 180° - 2 \sin^{-1} \frac{D - d}{2C}$$

$$\text{Exact length} = 2C \cos \theta + \frac{\pi}{2}(D + d) + \frac{\pi \theta°}{180°}(D + d)$$

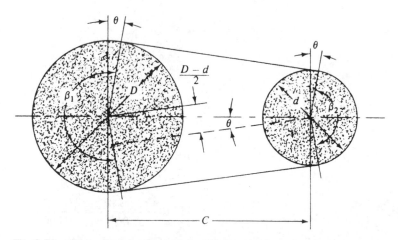

Fig. 3.79   Dimensions for determining the length of an open belt drive

$$\text{Approximate length} = 2C + 1.57(D + d) + \frac{(D - d)^2}{4C}$$

For the crossed belts of Fig. 3.80, β_1, β_2 and length L are given by

$$\sin \theta = \frac{D + d}{2C}$$

$$\beta_1 = \beta_2 = 180° + 2\theta = 180° + 2 \sin^{-1} \frac{D + d}{2C}$$

$$L \text{ exact} = 2C \cos \theta + \frac{(90° + \theta°)(D + d)}{180°}$$

Example 3.31

In the open-belt drive of Fig. 3.79, $D = 40$ in., $d = 10$ in., and $C = 30$ in. Find (a) the contact angles β_1 and β_2; (b) the difference in the calculated belt lengths for the exact and the approximate formulas.

Solution

(a) $\dfrac{\frac{D - d}{2}}{C} = \sin \theta = \dfrac{\frac{40 - 10}{2}}{30} = 0.5 \qquad \theta = 30°$

$\beta_1 = 180° + 2\theta = 240° \qquad \beta_2 = 180° - 2\theta = 120°$

(b) $L_{\text{exact}} = 2C \cos \theta + \dfrac{\pi}{2}(D + d) + \dfrac{\pi}{180}\theta(D - d)$

$= 2 \times 30 \times 0.866 + 1.57(40 + 10) + \dfrac{\pi 30}{180}(40 - 10)$

$= 146.2$ in.

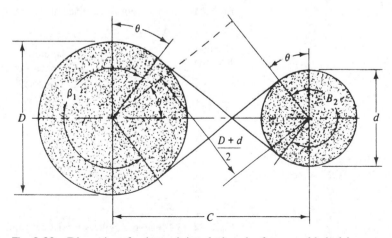

Fig. 3.80 Dimensions for determining the length of a crossed belt drive

$$L_{approx} = 2C + 1.57(D+d) + \frac{(D-d)^2}{4C}$$

$$= 60 + 1.57 \times 50 + \frac{30^2}{120} = 146.0 \text{ in.}$$

The difference in length by these two calculations is 0.2 in.

Note that in this belt drive that the angle of wrap for the large pulley is twice that for the small pulley. A larger center distance would make the angle θ smaller and therefore increase the angle of wrap of the small pulley.

Belt installations

The use of an idler pulley located near the small-diameter pulley will increase the angle of wrap and reduce the belt tension required for a given horsepower. If idlers are not used, then one set of bearings must be adjustable to allow for taking up slack as the belt stretches and to slack off the belt when it must be repaired, spliced, or replaced.

A flat belt on a conical pulley tends to move higher and higher up the cone. This tendency is put to use to keep the belt in position by crowning the pulley as shown in Fig. 3.82. A crown of $\frac{1}{8}$ inch per foot of pulley width

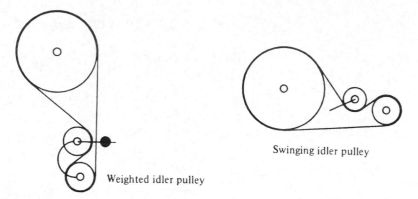

Weighted idler pulley

Swinging idler pulley

Fig. 3.81 Two idler pulley arrangements

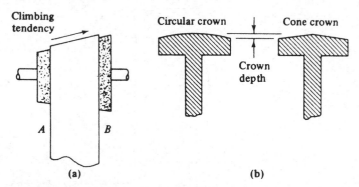

Fig. 3.82 Crowning of pulleys for flat belts: (a) the belt tends to move to the high point of the pulley; (b) circular and cone crown

is usual. The crowning of only one pulley is sufficient, and idlers are not usually crowned.

Speed ratios in belt drives rarely exceed 6:1. Large ratios require long center distances to obtain sufficiently large angles of wrap in the small pulley. The belt is flexed more severely when passing around a small pulley, and the result is a drastic reduction in belt life.

Belt speed should not exceed 5000 fpm. Above this speed centrifugal force causes excessive slippage of the belt.

Belts are preferably made of endless construction. An endless belt is uniform in strength, and the noise, wear, and jarring of fasteners passing over pulleys is avoided. However, it is not always possible to employ an endless belt, and belt fasteners are necessary to join the ends of the belt. Both belt lacing and hinges are in use for joining lighter sizes of belt, while plates are used for heavier loads.

The link belt of Fig. 3.84 should be considered for belt drives subject to slippage. In this type of belt the grain of the leather is at right angles to the face of the belt. This characteristic together with the many linkages gives a flexible belt that can use smaller pulleys, has excellent resistance to wear, and can slip without burning. It does not require a crowned pulley.

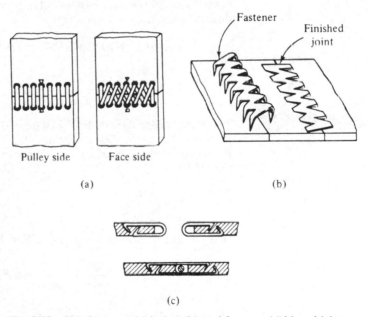

Fig. 3.83   Belt fasteners: (a) lacing; (b) steel fastener; (c) hinged joint

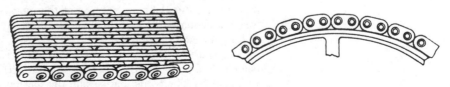

Fig. 3.84   Link belt

Service factors for flat belts

When selecting a flat belt for an application at a rated horsepower or design horsepower, the service factors of Table 3.5 are applied to the given horsepower as in the example below. For certain special conditions, these service factors are increased as follows:

Continuous operation	0.2
Frequent starts, stops, and reverses	0.1
Speed-up drives	0.2
Wet conditions	0.1

Example 3.32

A hammermill used in the preparation of animal feeds is rated at 5 HP. Operation is continuous. Determine the required horsepower rating for the belt driving the hammermill. The prime mover is a squirrel-cage motor.

Solution

From Table 3.4 the service factor is 1.4, to which must be added 0.2 for continuous operation.

$$\text{Required horsepower rating} = 5 \times 1.6 = 8 \text{ HP}$$

V-belt drives

The peculiar advantage of the V-belt drive is the wedging effect produced by the rubber belt in the sheave or pulley. The wedge increases the normal force P_n between the belt and the groove in the pulley by an amount equal to (see Fig. 3.85):

$$P_n = \frac{P}{2 \sin \theta}$$

Here θ is one half of the wedge angle. For the friction force F

$$F = 2\mu \, P_n = \frac{2\mu P}{2 \sin \theta} = \frac{\mu P}{\sin \theta} = \mu_e P$$

where $\mu_e = \dfrac{\mu}{\sin \theta}$, the equivalent coefficient of friction.

The flat-belt-drive equations previously given may be applied to V-belts if μ_e is substituted for μ. Because of the increased friction resulting from wedging action, V-belts can operate successfully on short center distances and small angles of wrap.

    The construction of a V-belt requires fabric, cords, and rubber compounds. Fabric is a woven material used for the cover stock and impregnated with rubber. The cords that sustain the tension in the belt in one or more plies are made of synthetic textiles such as polyester or nylong.

Table 3.5 Flat-belt service factors

FLAT BELT SERVICE FACTORS

Driven machine		Driver						Engines Gas or diesel
		A-C motors						
		Squirrel cage			Wound rotor (slip ring)	Synchronous		
		Normal torque		High torque		Normal torque (150% to 249%)	High torque (250% to 400%)	
General type	Specific type	Line start	Compensator start					
Agitators	for liquids	1.0	1.0	1.2	–	–	–	–
	for semi-liquids	1.2	1.0	1.4	1.2	–	–	–
Bakery machinery	–	1.2	–	–	–	–	–	–
Brick and clay machinery	de-airing machine, granulator auger, cutting table, rolls	–	1.2	1.4	1.4	–	–	–
	mixer, dry press	–	1.2	1.6	1.4	–	–	–
	pug mill	1.5	1.3	1.8	1.5	–	–	–
Compressors	centrifugal, rotary	1.2	1.2	–	1.4	1.4	–	–
	reciprocating, 1 or 2 cyl.	1.4	1.4	–	1.5	1.5	–	–
	reciprocating, 3 or more cyl.	1.2	1.2	–	1.4	1.4	–	–
Conveyors	apron, bucket, pan, elevator	–	1.4	1.6	–	–	–	–
	belt (ore, coal, sand, etc.)	–	1.2	1.4	–	–	–	–
	flight	–	1.6	1.8	–	–	–	–
	oven, belt (light package)	–	1.0	1.1	–	–	–	–
Crushing machinery	jaw, cone crushers, crushing rolls gyratory, ball, pebble, tube mills	–	1.4	1.6	1.4	1.4	1.6	1.4
Fans, blowers	centrifugal, induced draft, exhausters	1.2	1.2	–	1.4	–	–	1.4
	propeller, mine fans	1.6	1.6	1.6	1.6	–	1.8	1.6
	positive blowers	1.6	1.6	–	2.0	2.0	1.8	1.6
Flour, feed, cereal mill machinery	bolters, sifters, separators grinders, purifiers, reels	1.0	1.0	–	–	–	–	–
	mainline shaft, hammermills	1.4	1.4	1.6	1.4	1.4	–	1.8
Generators, exciters	–	1.2	–	–	–	–	–	1.2
Line shafts	–	1.4	1.4	–	1.4	1.4	2.0	1.6
Machine tools	grinders, milling machines boring mills, planers, shears	1.2	–	–	1.4	–	–	–
	lathes, screw machines, cam cutters shapers, drill press, drop hammers	1.0	–	–	1.2	–	–	–
Mills	pebble, rod, ball, roller	–	1.4	1.6	1.4	–	–	–
	flaking mills, tumbling barrels	–	1.6	1.6	1.4	–	–	–
Oil-field machinery	–	1.2	1.2	1.4	–	–	–	1.4
Paper machinery	jordan engines	1.5	1.3	1.8	1.5	1.6	1.8	–
	beaters, paper machines	1.4	1.4	–	1.5	–	–	–
	calenders, agitators, dryers	1.2	1.2	1.4	1.2	–	–	–
Printing machinery	–	1.2	1.2	–	1.2	–	–	–
Pumps	centrigual, gear, rotary	1.2	1.2	1.4	1.4	–	–	1.2
	reciprocating, 1 or 2 cyl	1.4	1.4	–	1.6	1.6	1.8	2.0
	3 or more	1.2	1.2	–	1.4	1.4	1.6	1.8
Rubber plant machinery	–	1.4	1.4	1.4	1.4	–	1.8	–
Sawmill machinery	log canter, log jack, cutoff saws trimmers, slashers, swing saws	1.4	1.4	–	1.4	–	–	–
	brand mill, circular, hogs, resaw	2.0	1.6	–	1.8	–	1.6	–
	planers	1.2	1.2	–	1.2	–	–	–
	edgers	1.6	1.6	–	1.6	–	1.6	–

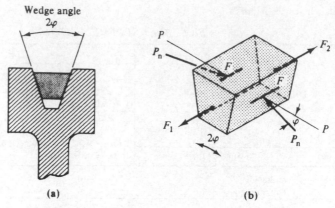

Fig. 3.85   V-belt and sheave

Industry standards for V-belts

V-belts are made in industrial, automotive, agricultural, and fractional horsepower types. The Rubber Manufacturers Association (RMA) and the Mechanical Power Transmission Association (MPTA) have developed standards for dimensions, tolerances, sheaves, and horsepower ratings for the convenience of users of V-belts.

Figure 3.86 gives the nominal dimensions of the five industrial V-belt sections A to E and their recommended tight-side tensions. Table 3.6 provides standard groove dimensions for sheaves. The pitch diameter is measured to that plane in the belt that does not change in length as the belt is bent around the sheave. Pitch diameter must be used in any calculations involving belt length and contact angle.

The following equations are used to calculate belt length if center distance is known and center distance if belt length is known:

$$L = 2C + 1.57(D' + d') + \frac{(D' - d')^2}{4C}$$

$$C = \frac{b + \sqrt{b^2 - 32(D' - d')^2}}{16}$$

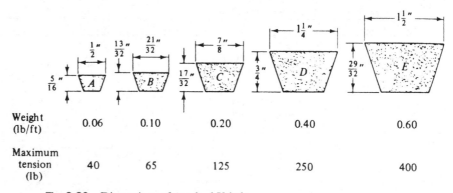

Fig. 3.86   Dimensions of standard V-belts

Table 3.6 V–belt pulley dimensions

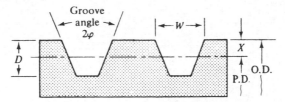

Belt	Pitch diameter (inches)		Groove angle ($\pm\frac{1}{2}°$)	Standard groove dimensions			Deep groove†† dimensions		
	Minimum	Range		W	D (±0.031)	X†	W	D (±0.031)	X†
A	3.0	2.6 to 5.4	34°	0.494 ± 0.005	0.490	0.125	0.589 ± 0.005	0.645	0.280
		Over 5.4	38°	0.504 ± 0.005			0.611 ± 0.005		
B	5.4	4.6 to 7.0	34°	0.637 ± 0.005	0.580	0.175	0.747 ± 0.005	0.760	0.355
		Over 7.0	38°	0.650 ± 0.005			0.774 ± 0.005		
C	9.0	7.0 to 7.99	34°	0.879 ± 0.007	0.780	0.200	1.066 ± 0.007	1.085	0.505
		8.0 to 12.0	36°	0.887 ± 0.007			1.085 ± 0.007		
		Over 12.0	38°	0.895 ± 0.007			1.105 ± 0.007		
D	13.0	12.0 to 12.99	34°	1.259 ± 0.007	1.050	0.300	1.513 ± 0.007	1.465	0.715
		13.0 to 17.0	36°	1.271 ± 0.007			1.541 ± 0.007		
		Over 17.0	38°	1.283 ± 0.007			1.569 ± 0.007		
E	21.0	18.0 to 24.0	36°	1.527 ± 0.010	1.300	0.400	1.816 ± 0.010	1.745	0.845
		Over 24.0	38°	1.542 ± 0.010			1.849 ± 0.010		

†Add 2 X to pd to get OD.
††Deep groove sheaves are intended for quarter-turn drives and for long center vertical shaft drives. They may also be necessary for such applications as car shakers, vibrating screens and certain types of crushers where oscillations in the center distance may occur.

where
$b = 4L - 6.28(D' + d')$
D' = pitch diameter of large sheave in inches
d' = pitch diameter of small sheave in inches
L = pitch length of belt
C = center distance in inches

In a multiple V-belt drive the belts of two different manufacturers must not be combined. Industry standards permit plus and minus tolerances, and if two brands of belts are installed in a multiple drive, some of the belts will be shorter than the others and will be forced to carry the full horsepower.

Narrow V-belts have a different cross-section from the industrial belts. Dimensions of narrow V-belts are given in Fig. 3.87.

Since these have different profile, they also require a different type of sheave. As with industrial V-belts, all 3V, 5V, and 8V belts and sheaves of all manufacturers are interchangeable, but as usual different brands of these belts must not be combined in a multiple V-belt drive.

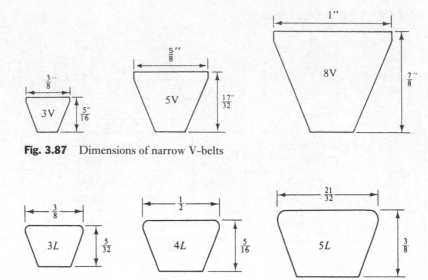

Fig. 3.87 Dimensions of narrow V–belts

Fig. 3.88 Dimensions of light-duty V–belts

For light-duty applications, the fractional horsepower belts of Fig. 3.88 may be used. The L in the designation stands for 'light duty,' and the number indicates the top width of the belt in eighths of an inch. Belt length is designated in tenths of an inch. Thus a 4L215 belt has a top width of ½ in. and a length of 21.5 in.

V–belts made to metric standards will presumably be designated using the following code:

$$00 \text{ X } 0000 \qquad \text{that is, 2 digits, 1 letter, 4 digits.}$$

The first two digits will designate the top width of the belt in millimeters and will be followed by a letter giving the type of belt. The last four digits will be the pitch length of the belt in millimeters.

MATHEMATICS FOR ENGINEERS

Outcome 1

Algebraic Methods

Algebraic methods

Introduction

It is often helpful to break down a complicated fraction into the sum of simpler fractions. For example, it can be shown that $\frac{4x+7}{x^2+3x+2}$ has the same value as $\frac{1}{x+2}+\frac{3}{x+1}$ for any value of x. We say that

$$\frac{4x+7}{x^2+3x+2} \text{ is identically equal to } \frac{1}{x+2}+\frac{3}{x+1}$$

and that the **partial fractions** of $\frac{4x+7}{x^2+3x+2}$ are $\frac{1}{x+2}$ and $\frac{3}{x+1}$. The ability to express a fraction as its partial fractions is particularly useful in the study of Laplace transforms, and in control theory. In this block we explain how partial fractions are found.

Proper and improper fractions

Frequently we find that an algebraic fraction appears in the form

$$\text{algebraic fraction} = \frac{\text{numerator}}{\text{denominator}} = \frac{\text{polynomial}}{\text{polynomial}}$$

that is as the ratio of two polynomials. For example,

$$\frac{x^3+x^2+3x+7}{x^2+1}, \quad \frac{3x^2-2x+5}{x^2-7x+2}, \quad \text{and} \quad \frac{x}{x^4+1}$$

The procedure for finding partial fractions depends critically upon the form of the denominator, as we shall see. The **degree** of the numerator, n say, is the highest power occurring in the numerator. The degree of the denominator, d say, is the highest power occurring in the denominator. If $d > n$ the fraction is said to be **proper**. If $d \leq n$ the fraction is said to be **improper**. Before calculating the partial fractions of an algebraic fraction it is important to decide whether the fraction is proper or improper.

Example 4.1

For each of the following fractions state the degrees of the numerator and denominator. Hence classify the fractions as proper or improper.

(a) $\dfrac{x^3+x^2+3x+7}{x^2+1}$ $\qquad$ (b) $\dfrac{3x^2-2x+5}{x^2-7x+2}$

(c) $\dfrac{x}{x^4+1}$ $\qquad$ (d) $\dfrac{s^2+4s+5}{(s^2+2s+4)(s+3)}$

Solution

(a) The degree of the numerator, n, is 3. The degree of the denominator, d, is 2. Because $d \leq n$ the fraction is improper.

(b) Here $n = 2$ and $d = 2$. State whether this fraction is proper or improper.

$d \leq n$; the fraction is improper

(c) Noting that $x = x^1$ we see that $n = 1$ and $d = 4$. State whether this fraction is proper or improper.

$d > n$; the fraction is proper

(d) Removing the brackets in the denominator we see that it has degree 3. The degree of the numerator is 2 and so this fraction is proper.

The denominator of an algebraic fraction can be factorised into a product of linear and quadratic factors. Linear factors are those of the form $ax + b$, for example $2x + 7$, $3x - 2$ and $4 - x$. Quadratic factors are those of the form $ax^2 + bx + c$ such as $x^2 + x + 1$, and $4x^2 - 2x + 3$, which cannot be factorised into linear factors.

Exercises

1 For each fraction state the degrees of the numerator and denominator, and hence determine which are proper and which are improper:

(a) $\dfrac{x + 1}{x}$ (b) $\dfrac{x^2}{x^3 - x}$

(c) $\dfrac{(x - 1)(x - 2)(x - 3)}{x - 5}$

Solutions

1 (a) $n = 1$, $d = 1$, improper (b) $n = 2$, $d = 3$, proper
(c) $n = 3$, $d = 1$, improper

Proper fractions with linear factors

First we describe how to calculate partial fractions of proper fractions where the denominator may be written as a product of linear factors. The steps needed to calculate the partial fractions are as follows:

1. Factorise the denominator.
2. Each factor will produce a partial fraction. A factor such as $3x + 2$ will produce a partial fraction of the form $\dfrac{A}{3x + 2}$ where A is an unknown constant. In general a linear factor $ax + b$ will produce a partial fraction $\dfrac{A}{ax + b}$.
   The unknown constants for each partial fraction may be different and so we shall call them A, B, C and so on.
3. Evaluate the unknown constants by equating coefficients or substituting specific values of x.

The sum of the partial fractions is identical in value to the original algebraic fraction for any value of x.

Key point

A linear factor $ax + b$ produces a partial fraction of the form $\dfrac{A}{ax + b}$.

The steps involved are illustrated in the following example.

Example 4.2 Express $\dfrac{7x + 10}{2x^2 + 5x + 3}$ as its partial fractions.

Solution

Note that this fraction is proper. The denominator is factorised to give $(2x + 3)(x + 1)$. It has been written as the product of two linear factors. Each factor produces a partial fraction. The factor $2x + 3$ produces a partial fraction of the form $\frac{A}{2x+3}$. The factor $x + 1$ produces a partial fraction $\frac{B}{x+1}$, where A and B are unknown constants which we now try to find. We write

$$\frac{7x + 10}{(2x + 3)(x + 1)} = \frac{A}{2x + 3} + \frac{B}{x + 1}$$

By multiplying both sides by $(2x + 3)(x + 1)$ we obtain

$$7x + 10 = A(x + 1) + B(2x + 3) \qquad\qquad [4.1]$$

We may now let x take any value we choose. By an appropriate choice we can simplify the right-hand side. Let $x = -1$ because this choice eliminates A. We find

$$7(-1) + 10 = A(0) + B(-2 + 3)$$
$$3 = B$$

so that the constant B must equal 3. The constant A can be found by substituting other values for x or alternatively by equating coefficients. Observe that, by rearranging the right-hand side, equation [4.1] can be written as

$$7x + 10 = (A + 2B)x + (A + 3B)$$

Comparing the coefficients of x on both sides we see that $7 = A + 2B$. We already know $B = 3$ and so

$$7 = A + 2(3)$$
$$= A + 6$$

from which $A = 1$. We can therefore write

$$\frac{7x + 10}{2x^2 + 5x + 3} = \frac{1}{2x + 3} + \frac{3}{x + 1}$$

We have succeeded in expressing the given fraction as the sum of its partial fractions. The result can always be checked by adding the fractions on the right.

Example 4.3 Express $\dfrac{9 - 4x}{3x^2 - x - 2}$ in partial fractions.

Solution

First factorise the denominator:

$$3x^2 - x - 2 = \boxed{(3x + 2)(x - 1)}$$

Because there are two linear factors we write

$$\frac{9 - 4x}{3x^2 - x - 2} = \frac{9 - 4x}{(3x + 2)(x - 1)}$$
$$= \frac{A}{3x + 2} + \frac{B}{x - 1}$$

Multiply both sides by $(3x + 2)(x - 1)$ to obtain the equation from which we can find values for A and B.

$9 - 4x = $ $\qquad A(x - 1) + B(3x + 2)$

By substituting an appropriate value for x obtain B.

 $\qquad$ substitute $x = 1$ and get $B = 1$

Finally by equating coefficients of x obtain the value of A.

 $\qquad -4 = A + 3B, A = -7$ since $B = 1$

Finally, write down the partial fractions:

$$\frac{9 - 4x}{3x^2 - x - 2} = \qquad\qquad \frac{-7}{3x + 2} + \frac{1}{x - 1}$$

Exercises

1 (a) Find the partial fractions of

$$\frac{5x - 1}{(x + 1)(x - 2)}$$

(b) Check your answer by adding the partial fractions together again.

(c) Express in partial fractions

$$\frac{7x + 25}{(x + 4)(x + 3)}$$

(d) Check your answer by adding the partial fractions together again.

2 Find the partial fractions of $\dfrac{11x + 1}{(x - 1)(2x + 1)}$.

Express each of the following as the sum of partial fractions:

3 $\dfrac{3}{(x + 1)(x + 2)}$

4 $\dfrac{5}{x^2 + 7x + 12}$

5 $\dfrac{-3}{(2x + 1)(x - 3)}$

Solutions

1 (a) $\dfrac{2}{x + 1} + \dfrac{3}{x - 2}$ (c) $\dfrac{3}{x + 4} + \dfrac{4}{x + 3}$

2 $\dfrac{4}{x - 1} + \dfrac{3}{2x + 1}$

3 $\dfrac{3}{x + 1} - \dfrac{3}{x + 2}$

4 $\dfrac{5}{x + 3} - \dfrac{5}{x + 4}$

5 $\dfrac{6}{7(2x + 1)} - \dfrac{3}{7(x - 3)}$

Proper fractions with repeated linear factors

As before, the denominator is factorised first. Sometimes a linear factor appears more than once. For example, in

$$\frac{1}{(x + 1)(x + 1)} \quad \text{which equals} \quad \frac{1}{(x + 1)^2}$$

the factor $(x + 1)$ occurs twice. We call it a **repeated linear factor**. The repeated linear factor $(x + 1)^2$ produces two partial fractions of the form

$\frac{A}{x+1} + \frac{B}{(x+1)^2}$. In general, a repeated linear factor of the form $(ax+b)^2$ generates two partial fractions of the form

$$\frac{A}{ax+b} + \frac{B}{(ax+b)^2}$$

Key point

> Repeated linear factors $(ax+b)^2$ produce partial fractions of the form
>
> $$\frac{A}{ax+b} + \frac{B}{(ax+b)^2}$$

Once again the unknown constants are found by a mixture of equating coefficients and substituting specific values for x.

Example 4.4   **Express**

$$\frac{10x+18}{4x^2+12x+9}$$

in partial fractions.

Solution

First the denominator is factorised.

$4x^2 + 12x + 9 = $ $(2x+3)(2x+3) = (2x+3)^2$

You should have found a repeated linear factor. The repeated linear factor $(2x+3)^2$ gives rise to two partial fractions of the form

$$\frac{10x+18}{(2x+3)^2} = \frac{A}{2x+3} + \frac{B}{(2x+3)^2}$$

Multiply both sides through by $(2x+3)^2$ to obtain the equation that must be solved to find A and B.

 $10x + 18 = A(2x+3) + B$

Now evaluate the constants A and B by equating coefficients. Equating coefficients of x gives

 $10 = 2A, A = 5$

Equating constant terms gives $18 = 3A + B$, from which $B = 3$. So, finally, we may write

$$\frac{10x+18}{(2x+3)^2} = \frac{5}{2x+3} + \frac{3}{(2x+3)^2}$$

Exercises

Express the following in partial fractions:

1 $\dfrac{3 - x}{x^2 - 2x + 1}$

2 $-\dfrac{7x - 15}{(x - 1)^2}$

3 $\dfrac{3x + 14}{x^2 + 8x + 16}$

4 $\dfrac{5x + 18}{(x + 4)^2}$

5 $\dfrac{2x^2 - x + 1}{(x + 1)(x - 1)^2}$

6 $\dfrac{5x^2 + 23x + 24}{(2x + 3)(x + 2)^2}$

7 $\dfrac{6x^2 - 30x + 25}{(3x - 2)^2(x + 7)}$

8 $\dfrac{s + 2}{(s + 1)^2}$

9 $\dfrac{2s + 3}{s^2}$

Solutions

1 $-\dfrac{1}{x - 1} + \dfrac{2}{(x - 1)^2}$

2 $-\dfrac{7}{x - 1} + \dfrac{8}{(x - 1)^2}$

3 $\dfrac{3}{x + 4} + \dfrac{2}{(x + 4)^2}$

4 $\dfrac{5}{x + 4} - \dfrac{2}{(x + 4)^2}$

5 $\dfrac{1}{x + 1} + \dfrac{1}{x - 1} + \dfrac{1}{(x - 1)^2}$

6 $\dfrac{3}{2x + 3} + \dfrac{1}{x + 2} + \dfrac{2}{(x + 2)^2}$

7 $-\dfrac{1}{3x - 2} + \dfrac{1}{(3x - 2)^2} + \dfrac{1}{x + 7}$

8 $\dfrac{1}{s + 1} + \dfrac{1}{(s + 1)^2}$

9 $\dfrac{2}{s} + \dfrac{3}{s^2}$

Proper fractions with quadratic factors

Sometimes a denominator is factorised producing a quadratic factor that cannot be factorised into linear factors. One such quadratic factor is $x^2 + x + 1$. This factor would produce a partial fraction of the form $\frac{Ax + B}{x^2 + x + 1}$. In general a quadratic factor of the form $ax^2 + bx + c$ produces a single partial fraction of the form $\frac{Ax + B}{ax^2 + bx + c}$.

Key point

A quadratic factor of the form $ax^2 + bx + c$ produces a partial fraction of the form

$$\frac{Ax + B}{ax^2 + bx + c}$$

Example 4.5 Express as partial fractions

$$\frac{3x+1}{(x^2+x+10)(x-1)}$$

Solution

Note that the quadratic factor cannot be factorised further. We have

$$\frac{3x+1}{(x^2+x+10)(x-1)} = \frac{Ax+B}{x^2+x+10} + \frac{C}{x-1}$$

Multiplying both sides by $(x^2+x+10)(x-1)$ gives

$$3x+1 = \rule{5cm}{0.5cm}$$

$$(Ax+B)(x-1) + C(x^2+x+10)$$

To evaluate C we can let $x = 1$, which eliminates the first term on the right. This gives

$$4 = 12C, \text{ so that } C = \frac{1}{3}$$

Equate coefficients of x^2 and hence find A. Finally substitute any other value for x or equate coefficients of x to find B.

$$A = -\frac{1}{3}, B = \frac{7}{3}$$

Finally

$$\frac{3x+1}{(x^2+x+10)(x-1)} = \frac{-\frac{1}{3}x + \frac{7}{3}}{x^2+x+10} + \frac{\frac{1}{3}}{x-1}$$

$$= \frac{1}{3}\frac{7-x}{x^2+x+10} + \frac{1}{3(x-1)}$$

Example 4.6 **Electrical Engineering – Admittance**

Admittance, Y, is a quantity that is used in analysing electronic circuits. A typical expression for admittance might take the form

$$Y(s) = \frac{s^2+4s+5}{(s^2+2s+4)(s+3)}$$

where s can be thought of as representing frequency. To calculate the behaviour of the circuit it is often necessary to express the admittance as the sum of its partial fractions and find the effect of each part separately. Express $Y(s)$ in partial fractions.

Solution

The fraction is proper. The denominator contains a quadratic factor that cannot be factorised further, and also a linear factor. Thus

$$\frac{s^2 + 4s + 5}{(s^2 + 2s + 4)(s + 3)} = \frac{As + B}{s^2 + 2s + 4} + \frac{C}{s + 3}$$

Multiplying both sides by $(s^2 + 2s + 4)(s + 3)$ we obtain

$$s^2 + 4s + 5 = (As + B)(s + 3) + C(s^2 + 2s + 4)$$

To find the constant C we can let $s = -3$ to eliminate A and B. Thus

$$(-3)^2 + 4(-3) + 5 = C[(-3)^2 + 2(-3) + 4]$$

so that

$$2 = 7C$$

and so $C = \frac{2}{7}$.

Equating coefficients of s^2 we find

$$1 = A + C$$

so that $A = 1 - C = 1 - \frac{2}{7} = \frac{5}{7}$.

Equating constant terms gives

$$5 = 3B + 4C$$

so that

$$3B = 5 - 4C$$

$$= 5 - 4\left(\frac{2}{7}\right)$$

$$= 5 - \frac{8}{7}$$

$$= \frac{27}{7}$$

so $B = \frac{9}{7}$

Finally

$$Y(s) = \frac{s^2 + 4s + 5}{(s^2 + 2s + 4)(s + 3)} = \frac{\frac{5}{7}s + \frac{9}{7}}{s^2 + 2s + 4} + \frac{\frac{2}{7}}{s + 3}$$

which can be written as

$$Y(s) = \frac{5s + 9}{7(s^2 + 2s + 4)} + \frac{2}{7(s + 3)}$$

Exercises

Express each of the following as the sum of its partial fractions:

1 $\dfrac{3}{(x^2 + x + 1)(x - 2)}$

2 $\dfrac{27x^2 - 4x + 5}{(6x^2 + x + 2)(x - 3)}$

3 $\dfrac{2x + 4}{4x^2 + 12x + 9}$

4 $\dfrac{6x^2 + 13x + 2}{(x^2 + 5x + 1)(x - 1)}$

Solutions

1 $\dfrac{3}{7(x-2)} - \dfrac{3(x+3)}{7(x^2+x+1)}$

2 $\dfrac{3x+1}{6x^2+x+2} + \dfrac{4}{x-3}$

3 $\dfrac{1}{2x+3} + \dfrac{1}{(2x+3)^2}$

4 $\dfrac{3x+1}{x^2+5x+1} + \dfrac{3}{x-1}$

Improper fractions

When calculating the partial fractions of improper fractions an extra term needs to be included. The extra term is a polynomial of degree $n - d$ where d is the degree of the denominator and n is the degree of the numerator. Recall that

- a polynomial of degree 0 is a constant, A say,
- a polynomial of degree 1 has the form $Ax + B$,
- a polynomial of degree 2 has the form $Ax^2 + Bx + C$,

and so on. For example, if the numerator has degree 5 and the denominator has degree 3, then $n - d = 2$, the fraction is improper, and we need to include an extra term of the form $Ax^2 + Bx + C$.

Key points

If a fraction is improper an additional term is included taking the form of a polynomial of degree $n - d$, where n is the degree of the numerator and d is the degree of the denominator.

Example 4.7

Express as partial fractions

$$\frac{2x^2 - x - 2}{x+1}$$

Solution

The fraction is improper because $n = 2$, $d = 1$ and so $d \leq n$. Further, note that $n - d = 1$. We therefore need to include an extra term: a polynomial of the form $Ax + B$, in addition to the usual partial fractions. So

$$\frac{2x^2 - x - 2}{x+1} = Ax + B + \frac{C}{x+1}$$

where the final term arises from the linear factor in the denominator. Multiplying both sides by $x + 1$ we find

$$2x^2 - x - 2 = (Ax + B)(x + 1) + C$$
$$= Ax^2 + (A + B)x + (B + C)$$

Equating coefficients of x^2 gives $A = 2$. Equating coefficients of x gives $-1 = A + B$ and so $B = -1 - A = -3$. Equating the constant terms gives $-2 = B + C$ and so $C = -2 - B = -2 - (-3) = 1$. Finally we have

$$\frac{2x^2 - x - 2}{x+1} = 2x - 3 + \frac{1}{x+1}$$

Exercises

Express the following in partial fractions:

1 $\dfrac{x+3}{x+2}$

2 $\dfrac{3x-7}{x-3}$

3 $\dfrac{x^2+2x+2}{x+1}$

4 $\dfrac{2x^2+7x+7}{x+2}$

5 $\dfrac{3x^5+4x^4-21x^3-40x^2-24x-29}{(x+2)^2(x-3)}$

6 $\dfrac{4x^5+8x^4+23x^3+27x^2+25x+9}{(x^2+x+1)(2x+1)}$

Solutions

1 $1+\dfrac{1}{x+2}$

2 $3+\dfrac{2}{x-3}$

3 $1+x+\dfrac{1}{x+1}$

4 $2x+3+\dfrac{1}{x+2}$

5 $\dfrac{1}{(x+2)^2}+\dfrac{1}{x+2}+\dfrac{1}{x-3}+3x^2+x+2$

6 $2x^2+x+7+\dfrac{1}{2x+1}+\dfrac{1}{x^2+x+1}$

End of section exercises

1 Express in partial fractions:

(a) $\dfrac{2x-4}{x(x-1)(x-3)}$

(b) $\dfrac{1+x}{(x+3)^2(x+1)}$

(c) $\dfrac{x^2+1}{(2x+1)(x-1)(x-3)}$

(d) $\dfrac{4s-3}{2s+1}$

(e) $\dfrac{3s+1}{s(s-2)}$

2 Express in partial fractions

$$\dfrac{K(1+\alpha s)}{(1+\tau s)s}$$

where K, α and τ are constants.

3 Express in partial fractions

(a) $\dfrac{2s+1}{s^5(s+1)}$ (b) $\dfrac{2s^3+6s^2+6s+3}{s+1}$

4 Express in partial fractions

$$\dfrac{2x+1}{(x-2)(x+1)(x-3)}$$

Solutions

1 (a) $-\dfrac{4}{3x}+\dfrac{1}{x-1}+\dfrac{1}{3(x-3)}$

(b) $\dfrac{1}{(x+3)^2}$

(c) $\dfrac{5}{21(2x+1)}-\dfrac{1}{3(x-1)}+\dfrac{5}{7(x-3)}$

(d) $2-\dfrac{5}{2s+1}$

(e) $\dfrac{7}{2(s-2)}-\dfrac{1}{2s}$

2 $\dfrac{K}{s}+\dfrac{K(\alpha-\tau)}{1+\tau s}$

3 (a) $\dfrac{1}{s^5}+\dfrac{1}{s^4}-\dfrac{1}{s^3}+\dfrac{1}{s^2}-\dfrac{1}{s}+\dfrac{1}{s+1}$

(b) $\dfrac{1}{s+1}+2s^2+4s+2$

4 $-\dfrac{5}{3(x-2)}-\dfrac{1}{12(x+1)}+\dfrac{7}{4(x-3)}$

Exponential, trigonometric and hyperbolic functions

Introduction

The exponential function has widespread application in many areas of science and engineering. Areas that utilise the exponential function include expansion of materials, laws of cooling, radioactive decay, and the discharge of a capacitor. This block details some properties of the exponential function and includes some of its applications.

The hyperbolic functions are also introduced. These functions are defined in terms of the exponential function. Identities involving the hyperbolic functions are tabulated.

Exponential expressions

An **exponent** is another name for a power or index. Expressions involving exponents are called **exponential expressions**. For example, 3^4 and a^b are exponential expressions. In the exponential expression a^x, a is called the **base** and x is the exponent. Exponential expressions can be simplified and manipulated using the laws of indices.

Laws of indices

$$a^m a^n = a^{m+n}, \quad \frac{a^m}{a^n} = a^{m-n}, \quad (a^m)^n = a^{mn}$$

In this section we shall be dealing with exponential expressions in which the base will always be a particular constant called the **exponential constant**. This has the symbol e and is approximately equal to 2.718. Exponential expressions with this base dominate engineering applications.

Example 4.8

Most calculators have powers of the exponential constant preprogrammed; these can be calculated, probably with a button marked e^x. Check that you can use your calculator by calculating the following:

(a) $e^{3.7}$ (b) $e^{-1.6}$ (c) $2e^{1.5}$

Solution

(a) $e^{3.7} =$ 40.4473

(b) $e^{-1.6} =$ 0.2019

(c) $2e^{1.5} =$ 8.9634

Simplifying exponential expressions

The laws of indices and the rules of algebra apply to exponential expressions. The following examples illustrate this.

Example 4.9 Simplify (a) $e^{2x}e^{3x}$, (b) $\dfrac{e^{4x}}{e^{7x}}$, (c) $(e^{2x})^3$.

Solution

(a) $e^{2x}e^{3x} = e^{2x+3x} = e^{5x}$.

(b) $\dfrac{e^{4x}}{e^{7x}} = e^{4x-7x} = e^{-3x}$. This may be written as $\dfrac{1}{e^{3x}}$.

(c) $(e^{2x})^3 = e^{2x\times3} = e^{6x}$.

Example 4.10 **Expand the brackets and simplify where possible:**

(a) $e^x(e^{-x}+1)$
(b) $(e^x+1)^2 - 1$
(c) $(e^x+e^{-x})^2 - 2$

Solution

(a) $e^x(e^{-x}+1) = e^xe^{-x} + e^x$

$\qquad\qquad\qquad = e^0 + e^x$

$\qquad\qquad\qquad = 1 + e^x$

(b) $(e^x+1)^2 - 1 = \boxed{}$ $\qquad\qquad\qquad e^xe^x + 2e^x + 1 - 1$

$\qquad\qquad\quad = e^{2x} + 2e^x$

(c) $(e^x+e^{-x})^2 - 2 = \boxed{}$ $\qquad\qquad e^xe^x + 2e^xe^{-x} + e^{-x}e^{-x} - 2$

$\qquad\qquad\qquad = \boxed{}$ $\qquad\qquad\qquad\qquad e^{2x} + 2 + e^{-2x} - 2$

$\qquad\qquad\qquad = e^{2x} + e^{-2x}$

Exercises

1 Simplify each expression as far as possible:

(a) $e^{2x}e^{7x}$
(b) $(3e^x)(2e^{-x})$
(c) $e^{2x}(e^{-2x} + e^{-x} + 1) - e^x(1 + e^x)$
(d) $\dfrac{e^{-3x}}{2e^{-x}}$

2 Expand the brackets of the following expressions:

(a) $(e^x+2)^2$
(b) $(e^x+1)(e^{-x}-1)$
(c) $(e^{2x}+e^x)(e^{-2x}+e^{-x})$
(d) $(1+e^{2x}+e^{-2x})(1-e^x)$

3 Simplify as far as possible:

(a) $\dfrac{e^x+e^{-x}}{2} + \dfrac{e^x-e^{-x}}{2}$

(b) $e^x + \dfrac{1}{e^x} - e^{-x}$

(c) $\dfrac{e^{2x}+e^x}{e^x} - 1$

(d) $e^{3x}(e^{-2x}-e^{-3x}) + 1$

Solutions

1 (a) e^{9x} (b) 6   (c) 1   (d) $\dfrac{e^{-2x}}{2}$

2 (a) $e^{2x} + 4e^x + 4$ (b) $e^{-x} - e^x$

(c) $2 + e^x + e^{-x}$
(d) $1 - e^x + e^{2x} - e^{3x} + e^{-2x} - e^{-x}$

3 (a) e^x (b) e^x (c) e^x (d) e^x

The exponential function and its graph

Key point

An exponential function has the form

$$y = a^x$$

where a is a positive constant called the **base**.

Hence $y = (0.4)^x$, $y = 2.5^x$ and $y = 10^x$ are all exponential functions. Note that, in an exponential function, the independent variable appears as a power.

Key point

The most commonly used exponential function, commonly called the **exponential function**, is

$$y = e^x$$

where the base e is the exponential constant whose value is e = 2.71828182 . . .

Table 4.1 gives values of the exponential function e^x for various x values and Fig. 4.1 illustrates a graph of $y = e^x$ for $-3 \le x \le 3$.

Table 4.1   Values of e^x.

x	e^x	x	e^x
−3	0.05	0.5	1.65
−2.5	0.08	1.0	2.72
−2.0	0.14	1.5	4.48
−1.5	0.22	2.0	7.39
−1.0	0.37	2.5	12.18
−0.5	0.61	3.0	20.09
0	1.00		

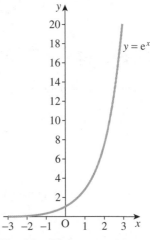

Fig. 4.1   The exponential function, $y = e^x$.

From Fig. 4.1 we note some properties of the exponential function:

1. As x becomes large and positive, e^x increases without bound. We express this mathematically as $e^x \to \infty$ as $x \to \infty$.
2. As x becomes large and negative, e^x approaches 0. We write $e^x \to 0$ as $x \to -\infty$.
3. e^x is never negative.

The property that e^x increases as x increases is referred to as **exponential growth**.

Fig. 4.2 shows a graph of the related function $y = e^{-x}$ for $-3 \le x \le 3$ and Table 4.2 lists appropriate values of e^{-x}.

From Fig. 4.2 we see that e^{-x} decreases as x increases: this is referred to as **exponential decay**.

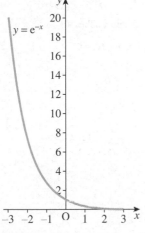

Fig. 4.2   The function $y = e^{-x}$ exhibits exponential decay.

Table 4.2   Values of e^{-x}.

x	e^{-x}	x	e^{-x}
−3	20.09	0.5	0.61
−2.5	12.18	1.0	0.37
−2.0	7.39	1.5	0.22
−1.5	4.48	2.0	0.14
−1.0	2.72	2.5	0.08
−0.5	1.65	3.0	0.05
0	1.00		

Example 4.11   Plot $y = e^{0.5x}$ and $y = e^{0.7x}$ for $0 \le x \le 3$. Comment on your graphs.

Solution

Table 4.3 shows values of $e^{0.5x}$ and $e^{0.7x}$ for $0 \le x \le 3$. Fig. 4.3 illustrates the graphs.

From Fig. 4.3 we see that $y = e^{0.7x}$ grows more rapidly than $y = e^{0.5x}$.

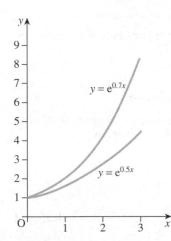

Fig. 4.3 $y = e^{0.7x}$ grows more rapidly than $y = e^{0.5x}$.

Table 4.3   Values of $e^{0.5x}$ and $e^{0.7x}$.

x	$e^{0.5x}$	$e^{0.7x}$
0	1.00	1.00
0.5	1.28	1.42
1.0	1.65	2.01
1.5	2.12	2.86
2.0	2.72	4.06
2.5	3.49	5.75
3.0	4.48	8.17

Exercises

1 Evaluate (a) $e^{2.7}$, (b) $e^{-1.6}$, (c) $3e^{0.7}$, (d) $-1.9e^{0.5}$.

2 Plot

$x = 3 + 2e^{-t}$ $0 \le t \le 4$

Which value does x approach as t increases?

3 Plot

$R(t) = 4 - 2e^{-1.5t}$ $0 \le t \le 3$

Which value does R approach as t increases?

4 State the domain and range of (a) $y = e^x$, (b) $y = e^{-x}$.

Solutions

1 (a) 14.8797   (b) 0.2019   (c) 6.0413   (d) −3.1326

2 See Fig. 4.4. As t increases, x approaches 3.

3 See Fig. 4.5. As t increases R approaches 4.

4 (a) $(-\infty, \infty)$, $(0, \infty)$ (b) $(-\infty, \infty)$, $(0, \infty)$

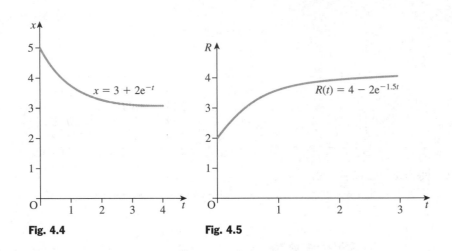

Fig. 4.4   **Fig. 4.5**

Applications of the exponential function

The following examples illustrate some of the applications of the exponential function.

Example 4.12

Electrical Engineering – Discharge of a capacitor

The charge, $q(t)$, stored on a capacitor having a capacitance C, discharging through a resistor of resistance R, is given by

$$q(t) = Qe^{-\frac{t}{CR}}$$

where Q is the initial charge.

(a) Find the value of the charge when $t = 1$ given $Q = 50$, $C = 0.25$ and $R = 2$.
(b) If the value of R is doubled calculate the new value of the charge when $t = 1$.

Solution

(a) $q(1) = 50e^{-\frac{1}{(0.25)(2)}}$

$\quad\quad\quad = 50e^{-2}$

$\quad\quad\quad = 6.77$

(b) $q(1) = 50e^{-\frac{1}{(0.25)(4)}}$

$\quad\quad\quad = 50e^{-1}$

$\quad\quad\quad = 18.39$

Example 4.13   **Electrical Engineering – Decay of a current in a circuit**

Consider a circuit with resistance R, inductance L and an initial current of i_0. The current $i(t)$ will decay with time, t, according to the law

$$i(t) = i_0 e^{-\frac{Rt}{L}}$$

(a) Calculate the current when $t = 1.5$ given $i_0 = 12$, $R = 2$ and $L = 6$.
(b) If L is increased from 6 to 9 calculate the new value of $i(1.5)$.

Solution

(a) $i(1.5) = 12e^{-\frac{2(1.5)}{6}}$

$\quad\quad\quad = 12e^{-0.5}$

$\quad\quad\quad = 7.28$

(b) $i(1.5) = $ $\quad\quad\quad\quad\quad\quad\quad\quad\quad\quad$ $12e^{-\frac{2(1.5)}{9}} = 12e^{-\frac{1}{3}} = 8.60$

Example 4.14   **Chemical Engineering – Newton's law of cooling**

Newton's law of cooling states that the rate at which a body cools is proportional to the excess of its temperature above the temperature of the environment in which it is placed. Let $\Theta(t)$ be the temperature of a body at time t, Θ_0 its initial temperature and Θ_e the temperature of the environment. Newton's law of cooling can be stated mathematically as

$$\Theta(t) = \Theta_e + (\Theta_0 - \Theta_e)e^{-kt}$$

where k is a positive constant that depends upon the material of the body. From this equation we see that the temperature is dropping exponentially owing to the term e^{-kt}: that is, the temperature follows an exponential decay curve. In this example we take $k = 1$, $\Theta_e = 20$ and $\Theta_0 = 120$, so

$$\Theta(t) = 20 + 100e^{-t}$$

(a) Plot $\Theta(t)$ for $t = 0$ to $t = 6$.
(b) Use your graph to find the temperature that the body approaches as t increases.

Solution

(a) Table 4.4 gives values of $\Theta(t)$ for various values of t from 0 to 6. Fig. 4.6 shows the graph of $\Theta(t)$.
(b) From Fig. 4.6 we see that the temperature, $\Theta(t)$, approaches 20 as t increases. This is to be expected: the temperature of the body approaches the temperature of the environment.

The result stated in Example 4.14(b) can be seen for the general case by considering the equation

$$\Theta(t) = \Theta_e + (\Theta_0 - \Theta_e)e^{-kt}$$

We have already noted that e^{-x} approaches 0 as x increases; clearly e^{-t} and e^{-kt} approach 0 as t increases since k is positive. Hence $(\Theta_0 - \Theta_e)e^{-kt}$ approaches 0 as t increases. Finally $\Theta_e + (\Theta_0 - \Theta_e)e^{-kt}$ approaches Θ_e as t increases.

Table 4.4

t	$\Theta(t) = 20 + 100e^{-t}$	t	$\Theta(t) = 20 + 100e^{-t}$
0	120.0	3.5	23.0
0.5	80.7	4.0	21.8
1.0	56.8	4.5	21.1
1.5	42.3	5.0	20.7
2.0	33.5	5.5	20.4
2.5	28.2	6.0	20.2
3.0	25.0		

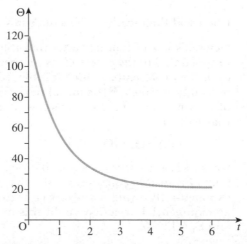

Fig. 4.6 Temperature decays exponentially with time.

Exercises

1 The number of particles, $N(t)$, emitted by a radioactive substance varies with time, t, according to the law

$$N(t) = 9.63 \times 10^{17} e^{-0.6t} \quad t \geq 0$$

(a) Calculate the number of particles emitted when $t = 0$.

(b) Calculate the number of particles emitted when $t = 2$.

2 The length, $l(T)$, of a bar depends upon the temperature, T, according to the law

$$l(T) = l_0 e^{\alpha T}$$

where l_0 is the length of the bar when $T = 0$, and α is a positive constant.

(a) Calculate the percentage change in length when T increases from $T = 20$ to $T = 100$, given $\alpha = 0.001$.

(b) Calculate the percentage change in length when T decreases from $T = 150$ to $T = 50$.

3 Atmospheric pressure, $P(h)$ atmospheres, varies according to the height, h metres, above the surface of the Earth. Given

$$P(h) = e^{-0.000016h}$$

calculate the pressure at a height of

(a) 2 km

(b) 10 km

above the Earth.

Solutions

1 (a) 9.63×10^{17} (b) 2.90×10^{17}

2 (a) 8.33% increase (b) 9.52% decrease

3 (a) 0.9685 atmospheres

(b) 0.8521 atmospheres

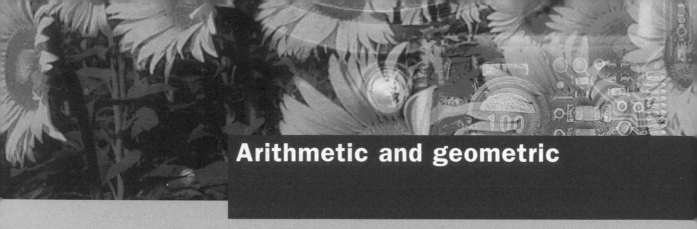

Arithmetic and geometric

Introduction

A **sequence** is a set of numbers written down in a specific order. For example, 1, 3, 5, 7, 9 and −1, −2, −3, −4, −5 are both sequences. Each number in the sequence is called a **term** of the sequence. Sometimes we use the symbol . . . to indicate that the sequence continues. For example, 1, 2, 3, . . . , 20 is the sequence of integers from 1 to 20 inclusive. The sequence 1, 3, 5, 7, 9, . . . can be assumed to continue indefinitely.

It is necessary to introduce a notation for handling sequences. Consider again the sequence of odd numbers 1, 3, 5, 7, 9, ... Suppose we let $x[1]$ stand for the first term, $x[2]$ stand for the second term and so on. Then

$$x[1] = 1, \quad x[2] = 3, \quad x[3] = 5 \text{ and so on}$$

Clearly $x[k]$ will stand for the kth term. Note that by inspection we can write down a formula for the kth term. It is $x[k] = 2k − 1$. Substitute some values of k for yourself to check this.

To denote the full sequence concisely we write

$$x[k] = 2k − 1 \text{ where } k = 1, 2, 3, \ldots$$

Some books use the alternative notation $x_1 = 1$, $x_2 = 3$, $x_3 = 5$ and $x_k = 2k − 1$.

Example 4.15

Consider the sequence of even numbers 2, 4, 6, 8, ... By inspection find a formula for the kth term of this sequence.

Solution

$$x[k] = 2k, \text{ where } k = 1, 2, 3, \ldots$$

Example 4.16

Write down the first five terms of the sequence given by $x[k] = (−1)^{k+1} \frac{1}{k}$ where $k = 1, 2, 3, \ldots$.

Solution

$$x[1] = (−1)^2 \tfrac{1}{1} = 1$$

$$x[2] = (−1)^3 \tfrac{1}{2} = −\tfrac{1}{2}$$

Write down the third, fourth and fifth terms.

$$\frac{1}{3}, -\frac{1}{4}, \frac{1}{5}$$

A **series** is obtained when the terms of a sequence are added. For example, if we add the terms of the sequence 1, 3, 5, 7, 9 we obtain the series

$$1 + 3 + 5 + 7 + 9$$

We use **sigma notation** to write a series concisely. For example, the sum of the first 10 odd numbers can be written

$$\sum_{k=1}^{10} 2k - 1$$

where the lowermost and uppermost values of k are placed below and above the sigma sign respectively. Similarly, the sum of the first six even numbers can be written

$$\sum_{k=1}^{6} 2k$$

Example 4.17   Write out explicitly the terms of the series $\sum_{k=1}^{5} \dfrac{1}{k}$.

Solution

$$1 + \frac{1}{2} + \frac{1}{3} + \frac{1}{4} + \frac{1}{5}$$

In this section we start by discussing the behaviour of sequences and series that have an infinite number of terms. Then two particular types of sequence are described — the arithmetic sequence and the geometric sequence. These are particularly straightforward, and there are simple formulae for finding their sums.

Exercises

1 Explain carefully the distinction between a sequence and a series.

2 Write out fully the following sums:

(a) $\sum_{k=1}^{6} k$ (b) $\sum_{k=1}^{k=4} k^2$ (c) $\sum_{k=1}^{k=5} k^3$

3 A sequence is defined by

$$x[k] = \frac{k^2}{2} + k, \quad k = 0, 1, 2, 3, \ldots$$

State the first five terms.

4 A sequence is given by $5, \dfrac{5}{8}, \dfrac{5}{27}, \dfrac{5}{64}, \ldots$. Write down an expression to denote the full sequence.

5 Write out explicitly the series

$$\sum_{k=1}^{4} \frac{1}{(2k+1)(2k+3)}$$

Solutions

2 (a) $1 + 2 + 3 + 4 + 5 + 6$
(b) $1^2 + 2^2 + 3^2 + 4^2$
(c) $1^3 + 2^3 + 3^3 + 4^3 + 5^3$

3 $0, \dfrac{3}{2}, 4, \dfrac{15}{2}, 12$

4 $x[k] = \dfrac{5}{k^3}$, $k = 1, 2, 3, \ldots$, for example

5 $\dfrac{1}{(3)(5)} + \dfrac{1}{(5)(7)} + \dfrac{1}{(7)(9)} + \dfrac{1}{(9)(11)}$

The limit of an infinite sequence

Some sequences stop after a finite number of terms. These are called **finite sequences**. Others continue indefinitely, and these are called **infinite sequences**. Sometimes the terms of an infinite sequence get closer and closer to a fixed value. For example, the terms of the sequence $x[k] = \dfrac{1}{k}$, for $k = 1, 2, 3, \ldots$, are

$$1, \frac{1}{2}, \frac{1}{3}, \frac{1}{4}, \frac{1}{5}, \ldots$$

The terms appear to be getting smaller. What do you think will be the eventual behaviour of the sequence as k gets large?

terms approach the value 0

We say that 'as k tends to infinity, $x[k]$ tends to zero', or 'the **limit** of $x[k]$ as k tends to infinity is zero' and write this as

$$\lim_{k \to \infty} x[k] = 0$$

When a sequence possesses a limit as k tends to infinity, it is said to **converge**.

Example 4.18 Write down the first four terms of the sequence $x[k] = \frac{1}{k^2}$, for $k = 1, 2, 3, \ldots$. What is the behaviour of the sequence as k tends to infinity?

Solution

The first four terms are

$$1, \frac{1}{4}, \frac{1}{9}, \frac{1}{16}$$

As k tends to infinity, $\dfrac{1}{k^2}$ tends to zero.

Example 4.19 Explore the behaviour of the sequence $x[k] = \sqrt{2 + \frac{1}{k}}$, $k = 1, 2, 3, \ldots$ as $k \to \infty$.

Solution

Write down the first few terms of this sequence:

$$\sqrt{3}, \sqrt{2\tfrac{1}{2}}, \sqrt{2\tfrac{1}{3}}, \ldots$$

As k tends to infinity the term $\dfrac{1}{k}$ tends to zero. So $\lim_{k \to \infty} x[k] = \sqrt{2}$.

When a sequence does not possess a limit it is said to **diverge**. The sequence of odd numbers diverges because the terms of the sequence get larger and larger and so the sequence does not possess a limit. The oscillating sequence $-1, 1, -1, 1, -1, 1, \ldots$ is divergent because it does not possess a limit.

Example 4.20 (a) Write out the first four terms of the sequence $x[k] = \sqrt{k}$, $k = 1, 2, 3, \ldots$.
(b) Find $\lim_{k \to \infty} x[k]$.

Solution

(a) 1, $\sqrt{2}$, $\sqrt{3}$, $\sqrt{4}$.

(b) The terms of this sequence increase indefinitely. The sequence therefore diverges.

Example 4.21   **Find the limit of the sequence** $x[k] = \dfrac{3k^2 + 2k - 7}{9k^2 - 7k}$ **as** $k \to \infty$.

Solution

The approach to tackling a problem like this is to rewrite $x[k]$ in a form in which we can sensibly let $k \to \infty$. Dividing both numerator and denominator by the highest power of k, that is k^2, gives

$$x[k] = \frac{3 + \frac{2}{k} - \frac{7}{k^2}}{9 - \frac{7}{k}}$$

Now because $\dfrac{1}{k}$ and $\dfrac{1}{k^2}$ both tend to zero as k tends to infinity it follows that

$$\lim_{k \to \infty} x[k] = \lim_{k \to \infty} \frac{3 + \frac{2}{k} - \frac{7}{k^2}}{9 - \frac{7}{k}}$$

$$= \frac{3}{9}$$

$$= \frac{1}{3}$$

Exercises

1 Find if possible the limit of each of the following sequences:

(a) $x[k] = \dfrac{1}{k+1}$, $k = 1, 2, 3, \ldots$

(b) $x[k] = k^2$, $k = 1, 2, 3, \ldots$

(c) $x[k] = \dfrac{k-1}{k+1}$, $k = 1, 2, 3, \ldots$

(d) $x[k] = \left(\dfrac{1}{3}\right)^k$, $k = 1, 2, 3, \ldots$

(e) $x[k] = \dfrac{2k+3}{4k+2}$, $k = 1, 2, 3, \ldots$

Solutions

1 (a) 0   (b) diverges   (c) 1   (d) 0   (e) $\dfrac{1}{2}$

The sum of an infinite series

When the terms of an infinite sequence are added we obtain an **infinite series**. It may seem strange to try to add together an infinite number of terms but under some circumstances their sum is finite and can be found. For example,

consider the infinite series formed from the sequence $x[k] = \dfrac{1}{2^k}$, $k = 0, 1, 2, .$
$. . .$

$$1 + \frac{1}{2} + \frac{1}{4} + \frac{1}{8} + . . .$$

We can calculate the sum of n terms, S_n, for various values of n. For example, the sum of just the first term is

$$S_1 = 1$$

The sum of the first two terms is

$$S_2 = 1 + \frac{1}{2}$$

$$= 1.5$$

Similarly $S_3 = 1.75$, $S_4 = 1.875$, . . . , $S_{10} = 1.9980$. The sequence S_1, S_2, S_3, . . . is called the **sequence of partial sums**. As we calculate S_n for larger and larger values of n, we note that S_n gets nearer and nearer to 2. We write S to stand for the sum of an infinite number of terms, so

$$S = \sum_{k=0}^{\infty} \frac{1}{2^k}$$

$$= 2$$

For any infinite series, say $\sum_{k=1}^{\infty} x[k]$, we can form the sequence of partial sums:

$$S_1 = x[1], \; S_2 = x[1] + x[2], \; S_3 = x[1] + x[2] + x[3], \; . . .$$

If the sequence S_n converges to a limit S we say that the infinite series has sum S, or that it has converged to S.

In general it is difficult to determine whether or not an infinite series has a finite sum. It is possible to establish tests or **convergence criteria** to help decide whether or not a given series converges or diverges, but for these you must refer to a more advanced book.

Example 4.22　Calculate the first six partial sums of the series

$$\sum_{k=1}^{\infty} (-1)^{k+1} \frac{1}{k}$$

Solution

The first six terms of the series are

$$1 - \frac{1}{2} + \frac{1}{3} - \frac{1}{4} + \frac{1}{5} - \frac{1}{6}$$

Form the first six partial sums for yourself working to 4 d.p.

$1, 0.5000, 0.8333, 0.5833, 0.7833, 0.6167$

If you proceed to calculate many more terms you will see that the sequence of partial sums converges to 0.6931, which is in fact ln 2.

Exercises

1 Calculate the first four partial sums of the series $\sum_{k=0}^{\infty} \frac{1}{k!}$. (Recall $0! = 1$.)

2 Calculate the first four partial sums of the series $\sum_{k=0}^{\infty} (-1)^k \frac{1}{(2k)!}$.

Solutions

1 1, 2, 2.5, 2.6667 (in fact this converges to e = 2.7183)

2 1, 0.5, 0.5417, 0.5403 (this converges to cos 1 = 0.5403).

Arithmetic sequences

An **arithmetic sequence** is a sequence of numbers where each new term after the first is formed by adding a fixed amount called the **common difference** to the previous term in the sequence. For example, the sequence

$$3, 5, 7, 9, 11, \ldots$$

is an arithmetic sequence. Note that having chosen the first term to be 3, each new term is found by adding 2 to the previous term, so the common difference is 2.

The common difference can be negative: for example, the sequence

$$2, -1, -4, -7, \ldots$$

is an arithmetic sequence with first term 2 and common difference -3.

In general we can write an arithmetic sequence as follows:

Key point

Arithmetic sequence

$$a, a + d, a + 2d, a + 3d, \ldots$$

where the first term is a and the common difference is d. Some important results concerning arithmetic sequences now follow:

Key point

The nth term of an arithmetic sequence is given by

$$a + (n - 1)d$$

Key point

The sum of the first n terms of an arithmetic sequence is

$$S_n = \frac{n}{2}[2a + (n - 1)d]$$

The sum of the terms of an arithmetic sequence is known as an **arithmetic series**.

Example 4.23 Find the 17th term of an arithmetic sequence with first term 5 and common difference 2.

Solution

The nth term is $a + (n - 1)d$.
   Hence

17th term = | $5 + (17 - 1)2 = 5 + 32 = 37$

Example 4.24 Find the sum of the first 23 terms of the arithmetic sequence

$$4, -3, 10, \ldots$$

Solution

First identify a and d.

| $a = 4, d = -7$

Then, using $S_n = \dfrac{n}{2}[2a + (n - 1)d]$, find the sum of 23 terms:

| $\dfrac{23}{2}[2(4) + (23 - 1)(-7)] = -1679$

Exercises

1 Find the 23rd term of an arithmetic sequence with first term 2 and common difference 7.

2 Find the sum of the first five terms of the arithmetic sequence with first term 3 and common difference 5.

3 Write down the 10th and 19th terms of the arithmetic sequence

(a) $8, 11, 14, \ldots$ (b) $8, 5, 2, \ldots$

4 An arithmetic sequence is given by

$$b, \frac{2b}{3}, \frac{b}{3}, 0, \ldots$$

(a) State the sixth term.
(b) State the kth term.
(c) If the 20th term has a value of 15, find b.

Solutions

1 156

2 65

3 (a) $35, 62$ (b) $-19, -46$

4 (a) $-\dfrac{2b}{3}$ (b) $\dfrac{b(4 - k)}{3}$ (c) $-\dfrac{45}{16}$

Geometric sequences

A **geometric sequence** is a sequence of numbers where each term after the first is found by multiplying the previous term by a fixed number called the **common ratio**. For example, the sequence

$$1, 3, 9, 27, \ldots$$

is a geometric sequence with first term 1 and common ratio 3. Each term after the first is found by multiplying the preceding term by 3.

The common ratio could be a fraction and it might be negative.

Example 4.25 Write down the first few terms of the geometric sequence with first term 2 and common ratio $-\frac{1}{3}$.

Solution

$$2, -\frac{2}{3}, \frac{2}{9}, -\frac{2}{27}, \ldots$$

In general we can write a geometric sequence as follows:

Key point

Geometric sequence

$$a, ar, ar^2, ar^3, \ldots$$

where the first term is a and the common ratio is r.

Some important results concerning geometric sequences now follow:

Key point

The nth term of a geometric sequence is given by

$$ar^{(n-1)}$$

Key point

The sum of the first n terms of a geometric sequence is

$$S_n = \frac{a(1-r^n)}{1-r} \text{ (valid only if } r \neq 1)$$

The sum of the terms of a geometric sequence is known as a **geometric series**.

Example 4.26 Find the seventh term of the geometric sequence

$$2, -6, 18, \ldots$$

Solution

First identify a and the common ratio r.

$$a = 2, r = -3$$

Then, the nth term is ar^{n-1}, so the seventh term is

$$(2)(-3)^6 = 1458$$

If the common ratio in a geometric series is less than 1 in modulus (i.e. $-1 < r < 1$), the sum of an infinite number of terms converges and can be calculated. This is known as the **sum to infinity**, S_∞.

Key point

$$S_\infty = \frac{a}{1-r} \text{ provided } -1 < r < 1$$

Example 4.27 **Find the sum to infinity of the geometric sequence with first term 3 and common ratio $\frac{1}{2}$.**

Solution

$$S_\infty = \frac{a}{1-r}$$

$$= \blacksquare$$

6

Exercises

1 Find the seventh term of a geometric sequence with first term 2 and common ratio 3.

2 Find the sum of the first five terms of the geometric sequence with first term 3 and common ratio 2.

3 Find the sum of the infinite geometric series with first term 2 and common ratio $\frac{1}{2}$.

4 A geometric sequence has first term 1. The ninth term exceeds the fifth term by 240. Find possible values for the eighth term.

5 The sum to infinity of a geometric sequence is four times the first term. Find the common ratio.

6 A geometric series has $S_3 = \frac{37}{8}$ and $S_6 = \frac{3367}{512}$. Find the first term and the common ratio.

7 A geometric sequence is given by $1, \frac{1}{2}, \frac{1}{4}, \ldots$ What is its common ratio?

Solutions

1 1458

2 93

3 4

4 ± 128

5 $\frac{3}{4}$

6 $2, \frac{3}{4}$

7 $\frac{1}{2}$

End of section exercises

1 State whether the following sequences are arithmetic, geometric or neither:

(a) $1, -1, -3, -5, \ldots$ (b) $4, 2, 1, 0.5, \ldots$
(c) $6, 7, 8, 9, \ldots$ (d) $4, 5, 7, 10, \ldots$
(e) $1, 0.1, 0.01, 0.001, \ldots$
(f) $1, -1, 1, -1, 1, \ldots$ (g) $1, 1, 1, 1, \ldots$

2 An arithmetic sequence has first term -3 and common difference 4. State (a) the 10th term, (b) the 300th term.

3 An arithmetic series has first term 4 and common difference $\frac{1}{2}$. Find (a) the sum of the first 20 terms, (b) the sum of the first 100 terms.

End of section exercises continued

4 A geometric sequence has first term -2 and common ratio $-\frac{3}{4}$. State the 20th term.

5 A geometric series has first term equal to 3 and a common ratio of 1.5. Calculate the sum of

(a) the first 10 terms, (b) the first 50 terms,
(c) the 30th to the 49th terms inclusive.

6 Find the limit as $k \to \infty$, if it exists, of each of the following:

(a) $x[k] = k^5$ (b) $x[k] = \sin k$

(c) $x[k] = \dfrac{k^2 + k}{k^2 + k + 1}$

(d) $x[k] = \dfrac{3k^2 + k}{k^2 + k + 1}$

7 Show that the sum of the first n terms of an arithmetic sequence, S_n, can be expressed as

$$S_n = \frac{n}{2}(\text{first term} + \text{last term})$$

Solutions

1 (a) arithmetic (b) geometric (c) arithmetic
(d) neither (e) geometric (f) geometric
(g) arithmetic and geometric

2 (a) 33 (b) 1193

3 (a) 175 (b) 2875

4 8.4566×10^{-3}

5 (a) 339.99 (b) 3.8257×10^{9} (c) 2.5497×10^{9}

6 (a) diverges (b) diverges (c) 1 (d) 3

Outcome 2

Sinusoidal Functions

Trigonometrical functions and their graphs

Introduction

Having introduced the trigonometrical ratios of sine, cosine and tangent we are ready to consider the three trigonometrical functions $y = \sin x$, $y = \cos x$ and $y = \tan x$. A number of properties and graphs of these functions are considered. Extensions are made to include the functions $y = \sin kx$, $y = \cos kx$ and $y = \tan kx$ for various values of k.

The function y = sin x

Table 4.5 gives values of x and the corresponding values of sin x found using a scientific calculator.

Table 4.5

x	0	30	60	90	120	150	180
$\sin x$	0	0.500	0.866	1	0.866	0.500	0

x	210	240	270	300	330	360
$\sin x$	−0.500	−0.866	−1	−0.866	−0.500	0

Plotting these values produces the graph shown in Fig. 4.7.

Note that the maximum value of sin x is 1; the minimum value of sin x is −1.

If we had been working in radians, then $0° \le x \le 360°$ would be replaced by $0 \le x \le 2\pi$. The shape of the sine function is often referred to as a **sine wave** or a **cycle**.

Sin $x = \sin(x + 360°) = \sin(x + 720°)$ and sin $x = \sin(x − 360°) = \sin(x − 720°)$ and so on. In other words, adding or subtracting multiples of 360° to an angle does not alter the sine of the angle. Hence the graph in Fig. 4.7 can be extended to the left and to the right by repeating cycles of the same shape every 360°. Fig. 4.8 illustrates this.

When using radian measure, cycles are repeated every 2π radians.

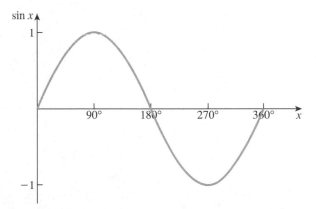

Fig. 4.7 A graph of $y = \sin x$ for $0° \le x \le 360°$.

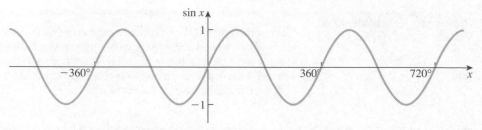

Fig. 4.8   Cycles are repeated every 360°.

Exercises

Use the graphs in Figs 4.7 and 4.8 to answer the following questions:

1 What is the maximum possible domain of the function $y = \sin x$?

2 What is the range of $y = \sin x$?

3 Is the function $y = \sin x$ one-to-one or many-to-one?

Solutions

1 all x

2 [−1, 1]

3 many-to-one

The function $y = \cos x$

Using a scientific calculator values of $\cos x$ are found for various values of x. These are recorded in Table 4.6.

The values are graphed in Fig. 4.9.

Table 4.6

x	0	30	60	90	120	150	180
$\cos x$	1	0.866	0.500	0	−0.500	−0.866	−1

x	210	240	270	300	330	360
$\cos x$	−0.866	−0.500	0	0.500	0.866	1

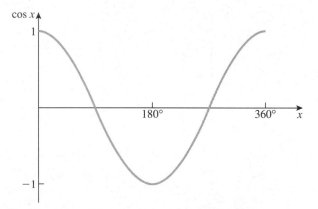

Fig. 4.9   The function $y = \cos x$ for $0° \leq x \leq 360°$.

As with $y = \sin x$, the function $y = \cos x$ may be extended to the left and to the right. Since adding or subtracting multiples of 360° to an angle leaves its cosine unchanged, then full cycles will be repeated every 360°. Fig. 4.10 illustrates this.

Note that $y = \cos x$ completes a full cycle every 360° or 2π radians. The maximum value of $\cos x$ is 1; the minimum value is −1.

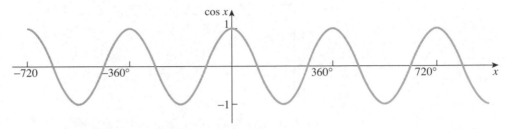

Fig. 4.10   The function $y = \cos x$ completes a full cycle every 360°.

Exercises

Use the graphs in Figs 4.9 and 4.10 to answer the following questions:

1 What is the maximum possible domain of the function $y = \cos x$?

2 What is the range of $y = \cos x$?

3 Is the function $y = \cos x$ one-to-one or many-to-one?

Solutions

1 all x

2 [−1, 1]

3 many-to-one

The function $y = \tan x$

Table 4.7 gives values of x and corresponding values of $\tan x$.

Table 4.7

x	0	30	60	90	120	150	180
$\tan x$	0	0.577	1.732	−	−1.732	−0.577	0

x	210	240	270	300	330	360
$\tan x$	0.577	1.732	−	−1.73	−0.577	0

Fig. 4.11 shows a graph of $y = \tan x$ for $0° \le x \le 360°$.

Note that the graph is radically different from those of $y = \sin x$ and $y = \cos x$. The function $y = \tan x$ has no maximum or minimum value.

Adding or subtracting multiples of 180 to an angle leaves its tangent unchanged we; see that extending the graph in Fig. 4.11 to the left and right produces that shown in therefore Fig. 4.12.

Note that the function is discontinuous at $x = \cdots -270°, -90°, 90° \; 270°, \ldots$

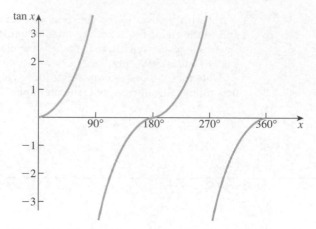

Fig. 4.11   The function $y = \tan x$ for $0° \leq x \leq 360°$.

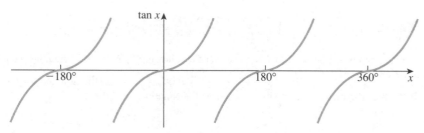

Fig. 4.12   For $y = \tan x$, cycles are repeated every $180°$ or π radians.

Exercises

Use the graphs in Figs 4.11 and 4.12 to answer the following questions:

1 What is the maximum possible domain of the function $y = \tan x$?

2 What is the range of $y = \tan x$?

3 Is the function $y = \tan x$ one-to-one or many-to-one?

Solutions

1 All values except $x = \cdots -270° -90°, 90°, 270°, \ldots$ These values must be excluded from the domain.

2 $(-\infty, \infty)$

3 many-to-one

The amplitude of $y = A \sin x$ and $y = A \cos x$

Consider the function $y = A \sin x$, where A is a positive constant, that is $A > 0$. The number A is called the **amplitude**. It is the maximum value of y. The minimum value of y is $-A$. Thus $y = 3 \sin x$ has an amplitude of 3. The maximum value of $3 \sin x$ is 3; the minimum value is -3. Note that the amplitude of $y = \sin x$ is 1. Fig. 4.13 shows graphs of $y = \sin x$ and $y = 3 \sin x$ for $0° \leq x \leq x$ 360°.

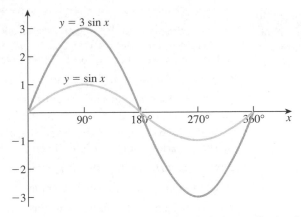

Fig. 4.13   The amplitude of $y = \sin x$ is 1; the amplitude of $y = 3 \sin x$ is 3.

Note that a full cycle of $y = 3 \sin x$ is completed in $360°$. The amplitude does not affect the periodic properties of $\sin x$: that is, it takes $360°$ for both $y = \sin x$ and $y = 3 \sin x$ to complete a full cycle. In general, $y = A \sin x$ completes a cycle every $360°$.

Similar comments apply to $y = A \cos x$. The amplitude of $A \cos x$ is A. It takes $360°$ for a full cycle of $A \cos x$ to be completed.

| Key point | The amplitude of $y = A \sin x$ and $y = A \cos x$ is A. |

Example 4.28   State the amplitude of each of the following functions:

(a) $y = 2 \sin x$
(b) $y = 4.7 \cos x$
(c) $y = \dfrac{2 \sin x}{3}$
(d) $y = 0.8 \cos x$

Solution

(a) 2   (b) 4.7   (c) $\frac{2}{3}$ (d) 0.8

Exercises

1 State the amplitude of

(a) $10 \sin x$ (b) $7.3 \cos x$ (c) $0.01 \sin t$
(d) $1.2 \cos \theta$

Solutions

1 (a) 10   (b) 7.3   (c) 0.01   (d) 1.2

The functions
$y = A \sin kx$ **and**
$y = A \cos kx$

We have already seen that A is the amplitude and this is the maximum value of y. We now consider the effect of the parameter k in $A \sin kx$. To allow us to focus on k we take A to be 1. Thus we examine the function $y = \sin kx$ for various values of k, for example $y = \sin 2x$, $y = \sin 3x$, $y = \sin \frac{x}{2}$ and $y = \sin \frac{3}{2x}$. We can deduce the graphs of these functions by reference to the graph of $y = \sin x$.

We begin by looking at $y = \sin 2x$. Recall that $y = \sin x$ completes one full cycle as x varies from $0°$ to $360°$. Then $y = \sin 2x$ completes one full cycle as $2x$ varies from $0°$ to $360°$, that is as x varies from $0°$ to $\frac{360°}{2} = 180°$. If x is measured in radians then $y = \sin 2x$ completes a full cycle as x varies from 0 to π radians. A graph of the function is illustrated in Fig. 4.14.

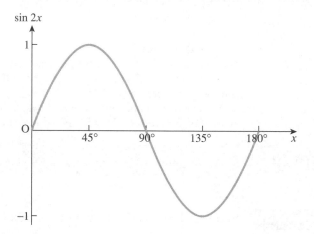

Fig. 4.14   The function $y = \sin 2x$ completes a full cycle every $180°$ or π radians.

We have noted previously that the amplitude does not affect the periodic property of $y = \sin x$. Since $y = \sin 2x$ completes a cycle every $180°$, then in general $y = A \sin 2x$ completes a cycle every $180°$ also. Note that the amplitude of $y = \sin 2x$ is 1.

As another example consider $y = \sin \frac{3x}{2}$. A full cycle is completed as $\frac{3x}{2}$ varies from $0°$ to $360°$: that is, as x varies from $0°$ to $\frac{360°}{3/2} = 240°$. A graph of $y = \sin \frac{3x}{2}$ is illustrated in Fig. 4.15.

Similarly, $y = A \sin \frac{3x}{2}$ completes a cycle every $240°$.

In general, $y = A \sin kx$ completes a full cycle in $\frac{360°}{k}$ or $\frac{2\pi}{k}$ radians.

The function $y = A \cos kx$ also has these properties. We have

Key point

The functions $y = A \sin kx$ and $y = A \cos kx$ complete a cycle every $\dfrac{360°}{k}$ or $\dfrac{2\pi}{k}$ radians.

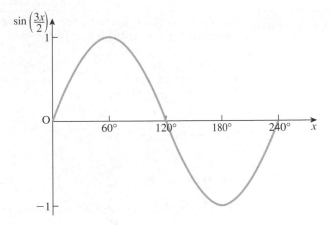

Fig. 4.15 $y = \sin \dfrac{3x}{2}$ completes a cycle every 240° or $\dfrac{4\pi}{3}$ radians.

Example 4.29 State the number of cycles of y in 360° given

(a) $y = 3 \sin 4x$
(b) $y = 4 \cos 3x$
(c) $y = \dfrac{1}{2} \cos \dfrac{x}{2}$
(d) $y = 5 \sin \dfrac{3x}{4}$

Solution

(a) $y = 3 \sin 4x$ completes a cycle every $\dfrac{360°}{4} = 90°$. In 360°, four cycles are completed.

(b) $y = 4 \cos 3x$ completes a cycle every $\dfrac{360°}{3} = 120$. In 360° three cycles are completed.

(c) $y = \dfrac{1}{2} \cos \dfrac{x}{2}$ completes a cycle every $\dfrac{360°}{1/2} = 720°$. In 360°, 0.5 of a cycle is completed.

(d) $y = 5 \sin \dfrac{3x}{4}$ completes a cycle every $\dfrac{360°}{3/4} = 480°$. In 360°, 0.75 of a cycle is completed.

Example 4.29 illustrates the following general statement.

Key point The functions $y = A \sin kx$ and $y = A \cos kx$ complete k cycles every 360° or every 2π radians.

Example 4.30   For each function, state (i) the minimum value (ii) the increase in x required for y to complete a full cycle.

(a) $y = 3 \sin 5x$
(b) $y = 0.65 \cos 6x$
(c) $y = \dfrac{4}{5} \sin \dfrac{x}{3}$
(d) $y = -2 \cos \dfrac{5x}{3}$

Solution

(a) The amplitude is 3 and so the minimum value is -3. A full cycle requires x to increase by $\dfrac{360°}{5} = 72°$.

(b) The minimum value is -0.65. A full cycle requires x to increase by $\dfrac{360°}{6} = 60°$.

(c) The minimum value is $-\dfrac{4}{5}$. A full cycle requires x to increase by $\dfrac{360°}{1/3} = 1080°$.

(d) The minimum value is -2. A full cycle requires x to increase by $\dfrac{360°}{5/3} = 216°$.

Example 4.31   State the maximum value, the minimum value and the number of cycles completed in 720° for the function $y = \dfrac{3}{2} \cos \dfrac{5x}{2}$.

Solution

The amplitude of $y = \dfrac{3}{2} \cos \dfrac{5x}{2}$ is $\dfrac{3}{2}$. Hence the maximum value is $\boxed{\dfrac{3}{2}}$

and the minimum value is $\boxed{}$ $-\dfrac{3}{2}$

The function $y = \dfrac{3}{2} \cos \dfrac{5x}{2}$ completes $\boxed{}$ cycles every 360°. $\dfrac{5}{2}$

Hence in 720° the function completes $\boxed{}$ cycles. 5

**The function
$y = A \tan kx$**

We consider the function $y = A \tan kx$. As with $y = A \sin kx$ and $y = A \cos kx$, the factor A does not affect the periodic properties of the tangent function. Recall that $y = \tan x$ completes a cycle as x increases by 180° or π radians. Hence $\tan kx$ completes a cycle as kx increases through 180°, that is as x increases through $\frac{180°}{k}$. So, for example, $y = A \tan 2x$ completes a cycle every $\frac{180°}{2} = 90°$, $y = A \tan 3x$ completes a cycle every $\frac{180°}{2} = 60°$, and $y = A \tan \frac{2x}{3}$ completes a cycle every $\frac{180°}{2/3} = 270°$. A graph of $y = 2 \tan 3x$ for $-30° \leq x \leq 150°$ is shown in Fig. 4.16.

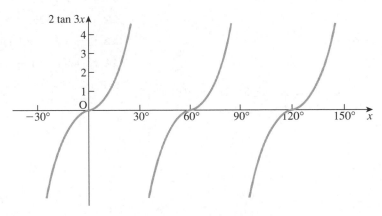

Fig. 4.16 $y = 2 \tan 3x$ completes a cycle every $60°$.

In general $y = A \tan kx$ completes a cycle every $\dfrac{180°}{k}$. In other words, k cycles are completed every $180°$.

Example 4.32 | **State the number of cycles completed every 360° for**

(a) $y = 3 \tan x$
(b) $y = 7 \tan 2x$
(c) $y = -\dfrac{1}{2} \tan \dfrac{3x}{2}$

Solution

(a) For $y = 3 \tan x$, the '3' does not affect the periodic properties.

Now $y = 3 \tan x$ completes ▓ cycles every 180° and so in 360°, | 1

▓ cycles are completed. | 2

(b) $y = 7 \tan 2x$ completes ▓ cycles every 180° and hence | 2

completes ▓ cycles every 360°. | 4

(c) $y = -\dfrac{1}{2} \tan \dfrac{3x}{2}$ completes ▓ cycles every 180° and so | $\dfrac{3}{2}$

completes ▓ cycles every 360°. | 3

End of section exercises

State the amplitude of the functions given in questions 1–6.

1 $y = 3 \sin 4x$

2 $y = \frac{3}{7} \cos 2x$

3 $y = 0.96 \sin x$

4 $y = -2 \cos 7x$

5 $y = -0.6 \sin 3x$

6 $y = \frac{4 \cos x}{7}$

State the number of cycles completed every 360° for the functions given in questions 7–12.

7 $y = 2 \sin 3x$

8 $y = -2 \sin 3x$

9 $y = 4 \cos \frac{5x}{6}$

10 $y = 0.5 \cos 0.5x$

11 $y = 6 \tan 6x$

12 $y = -3 \tan 9x$

13 Sketch $y = \sin(-x)$ for $0° \le x \le 360°$

14 Sketch $y = \tan \frac{x}{2}$ for $0° \le x \le 360°$

15 State two properties that are common to both $y = A \sin kx$ and $y = A \cos kx$.

Solutions

1 3

2 $\frac{3}{7}$

3 0.96

4 2

5 0.6

6 $\frac{4}{7}$

7 3

8 3

9 $\frac{5}{6}$

10 0.5

11 12

12 18

Applications

Introduction

Often voltages and currents vary with time, and can be modelled by sine and cosine functions. Important parameters such as amplitude, frequency, period and phase are used in the description of these waves. These terms are described in the following sections.

Two or more waves may be added together, producing a new single wave. The method of doing this is explained and illustrated.

Time-varying waves

The functions $y = \sin \theta$ and $y = \cos \theta$ were described in Block 4. There we saw that the graphs of these functions look like waves. The angle θ may be measured in degrees or radians.

Voltages and currents encountered in electrical circuits usually vary with time, t. Hence we consider sine and cosine waves in which the independent variable is t. For example, consider $y = \sin t$. As t increases from 0 seconds to 2π seconds, one complete cycle is produced. This is illustrated in Fig. 4.17.

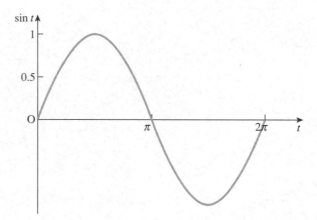

Fig. 4.17   As time t varies from 0 to 2π seconds one complete cycle is produced.

Amplitude of a wave

Consider the function $y = A \sin t$ for $A > 0$. Then A is the amplitude of the wave. This is the highest value attained by the wave. Similarly the amplitude of $y = A \cos t$ is A.

Key point

The **amplitude** of both $y = A \sin t$ and $y = A \cos t$ is A.

Example 4.33

State the amplitude of each of the following functions:

(a) $y = 3 \sin t$

(b) $y = \frac{2}{3} \cos t$

(c) $y = -\sin t$

Solution

(a) amplitude $= 3$

(b) amplitude $= \dfrac{2}{3}$

(c) Noting that the amplitude of a wave is the largest value attained, the amplitude of $-\sin t$ is 1.

Angular frequency of a wave

Consider the wave $y = A \sin \omega t$. We call ω the **angular frequency** of the wave. The units of ω are radians per second. Noting that t is measured in seconds, then ωt has units of radians. For example, $y = \sin 4t$ has an angular frequency of 4 radians per second. Note that $y = \sin t$ has an angular frequency of 1 radian per second. In like manner the angular frequency of $y = A \cos \omega t$ is ω radians per second.

Key point

> The **angular frequency** of $y = A \sin \omega t$ and $y = A \cos \omega t$ is ω radians per second.

Note that the amplitude, A, has no effect upon the angular frequency of a function.

Example 4.34 State the angular frequency of each of the following waves:

(a) $y = 5 \sin 3t$

(b) $y = 7 \cos \dfrac{t}{2}$

(c) $y = \cos \dfrac{2t}{3}$

Solution

(a) Comparing $5 \sin 3t$ with $A \sin \omega t$, we see that $\omega = 3$: that is, the angular frequency is 3 radians per second.

(b) angular frequency $=$ ⬚ $\dfrac{1}{2}$ radian per second

(c) angular frequency $=$ ⬚ $\dfrac{2}{3}$ radians per second

---

Exercises

1 State (i) the amplitude and (ii) the angular frequency of the following waves:

(a) $y = 2 \sin 5t$

(b) $y = 3 \cos 6t$

(c) $y = \sin \dfrac{t}{2}$

(d) $y = \cos \dfrac{4t}{3}$

(e) $y = \dfrac{3}{2} \sin \dfrac{2t}{3}$

(f) $y = -4 \sin \pi t$

Solutions

1 (a) 2, 5   (b) 3, 6   (c) 1, $\dfrac{1}{2}$ (d) 1, $\dfrac{4}{3}$ (e) $\dfrac{3}{2}, \dfrac{2}{3}$ (f) 4, π

Period of a wave

The time taken to complete one full cycle is called the **period** of the wave. It is closely connected to the angular frequency of the wave.

Consider $y = A \sin \omega t$. When $t = 0$ seconds, then $\omega t = 0$ radians. When $t = \frac{2\pi}{\omega}$ seconds, then $\omega t = \omega(\frac{2\pi}{\omega}) = 2\pi$ radians. Hence as t increases by $\frac{2\pi}{\omega}$ seconds, the angle, ωt, increases by 2π radians. A sine function completes one full cycle as the angle increases by 2π radians. Hence $y = A \sin \omega t$ completes a full cycle as t increases by $\frac{2\pi}{\omega}$ seconds: that is, the period of y is $\frac{2\pi}{\omega}$ seconds. Similarly the period of $y = A \cos \omega t$ is also $\frac{2\pi}{\omega}$ seconds. The period is denoted by T.

Key point

The **period** of both $y = A \sin \omega t$ and $y = A \cos \omega t$ is given by $T = \frac{2\pi}{\omega}$.

Example 4.35

State the period of each of the following functions:

(a) $y = 3 \sin 6t$
(b) $y = 5.6 \cos 6\pi t$
(c) $y = 50 \sin 100\pi t$

Solution

(a) Here $\omega = 6$ and so

$$T = \frac{2\pi}{6}$$

$$= \frac{\pi}{3}$$

The period is $\frac{\pi}{3}$ seconds.

(b) Here $\omega = \pi$ and so

$$T = \boxed{} \qquad\qquad \frac{2\pi}{\pi} = 2$$

The period is 2 seconds.

(c) Here $\omega = \boxed{}$ and so $\qquad\qquad 100\pi$

$$T = \boxed{} \qquad\qquad \frac{2\pi}{100\pi} = 0.02$$

The period is 0.02 seconds.

| **Example 4.36** | **Electrical Engineering – Oscilloscope trace** |

Fig. 4.18 shows an oscilloscope trace of a sine wave. State the equation of the wave.

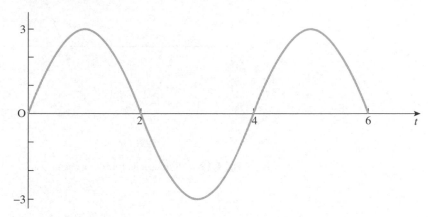

Fig. 4.18   Oscilloscope trace.

Solution

The wave has an equation of the form

$$y = A \sin \omega t$$

The maximum value of the wave is 3: that is, the amplitude, A, is 3. A full cycle is completed in 4 seconds: that is, $T = 4$. So

$$T = \frac{2\pi}{\omega}$$

$$= 4$$

from which

$$\omega = \frac{\pi}{2}$$

The equation of the wave is $y = 3 \sin \dfrac{\pi t}{2}$.

| **Example 4.37** | **Electrical Engineering – Oscilloscope trace** |

Fig. 4.19 shows an oscilloscope trace of a cosine wave. State the equation of the wave.

Solution

The wave has an equation of the form

$$y = A \cos \omega t$$

The highest value of the wave is ▮   4.2

Hence the value of the amplitude is 4.2.

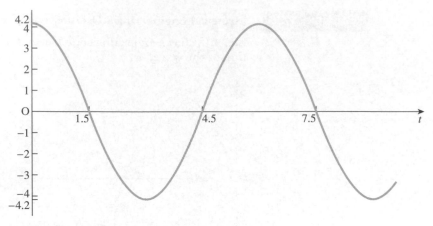

Fig. 4.19   Oscilloscope trace of a cosine wave.

A cycle is completed in ▢ seconds, and so   6

$$T = \frac{2\pi}{\omega}$$

$$= 6$$

Hence

$$\omega = \boxed{}$$ $\dfrac{2\pi}{6} = \dfrac{\pi}{3}$

The equation of the wave is therefore ▢ $4.2 \cos \dfrac{\pi t}{3}$

The frequency of a wave

The **frequency**, f, of a wave is the number of cycles completed in 1 second. It is measured in hertz (Hz). One hertz is one cycle per second.

Consider again the function $y = A \sin \omega t$. The period is $\frac{2\pi}{\omega}$ seconds: that is, one cycle is completed in $\frac{2\pi}{\omega}$ seconds. Hence ω cycles are completed in 2π seconds and $\frac{\omega}{2\pi}$ cycles are completed in 1 second. Thus we have

Key point

$$\text{frequency } f = \frac{\omega}{2\pi}$$

We note that

$$\text{period } T = \frac{2\pi}{\omega}, \text{ frequency } f = \frac{\omega}{2\pi}$$

and so

Key point

$$T = \frac{1}{f}$$

Example 4.38

State the period and frequency of the following waves:

(a) $y = 2 \sin 4t$
(b) $y = 3 \cos 2t$
(c) $y = \sin \pi t$

Solution

(a) Comparing $2 \sin 4t$ with $A \sin \omega t$ we see that $\omega = 4$. Hence the frequency, f, is found from

$$f = \frac{\omega}{2\pi}$$

$$= \frac{4}{2\pi}$$

$$= \frac{2}{\pi}$$

$$= 0.6366 \text{ Hz}$$

So 0.6366 cycles are completed every second. The period, T, is found from

$$T = \frac{1}{f}$$

$$= \frac{\pi}{2}$$

$$= 1.5708$$

It takes 1.5708 seconds to complete one cycle.

(b) Here $\omega = 2$ and so

$$f = \qquad\qquad\qquad \frac{\omega}{2\pi} = \frac{2}{2\pi} = \frac{1}{\pi} = 0.3183 \text{ Hz}$$

Thus, 0.3183 of a cycle is completed every second. The period, T, is found using

$$T = \qquad\qquad\qquad \frac{1}{f} = \pi = 3.1416$$

It takes π seconds to complete one cycle.

(c) Here $\omega = \pi$ and so

$$f = \qquad\qquad\qquad \frac{\omega}{2\pi} = \frac{\pi}{2\pi} = \frac{1}{2} \text{ Hz}$$

and

$$T = \qquad\qquad \frac{1}{f} = 2$$

Thus, 0.5 of a cycle is completed each second. It takes 2 seconds to complete one full cycle.

Exercises

1 State (i) the period and (ii) the frequency of the following waves:

(a) $y = 6 \sin 4t$ (b) $y = \cos 3t$

(c) $y = -4 \sin t$ (d) $y = \frac{1}{2} \cos 100\pi t$

(e) $y = \pi \sin 1.5t$

Solutions

1 (a) $\dfrac{\pi}{2}, \dfrac{2}{\pi}$ (b) $\dfrac{2\pi}{3}, \dfrac{3}{2\pi}$ (c) $2\pi, \dfrac{1}{2\pi}$ (d) $0.02, 50$ (e) $\dfrac{4\pi}{3}, \dfrac{3}{4\pi}$

Phase and time displacement of a wave

We now introduce waves of the form $y = A \sin(\omega t + \alpha)$ and $y = A \cos(\omega t + \alpha)$. Introducing α has the effect of moving the wave to either the left or the right. Fig. 4.20 shows graphs of $y = \sin 2t$ and $y = \sin(2t + 1)$.

From Fig. 4.20 we note that the peak of $y = \sin(2t + 1)$ occurs 0.5 seconds before the peak of $y = \sin 2t$. We say $\sin(2t + 1)$ **leads** $\sin 2t$ by 0.5 seconds. The quantity, 0.5 seconds, is known as the **time displacement** of $y = \sin(2t + 1)$.

Fig. 4.21 shows graphs of $y = \sin 2t$ and $y = \sin(2t - 1)$.

The peak of $y = \sin(2t - 1)$ is reached 0.5 seconds after the peak of $y = \sin 2t$. We say $\sin(2t - 1)$ **lags** $\sin 2t$ by 0.5 seconds. The time displacement of $\sin(2t - 1)$ is -0.5 seconds.

These examples lead us to the following general treatment.

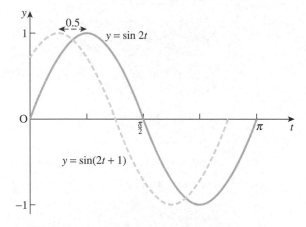

Fig. 4.20   The waves $y = \sin 2t$ and $y = \sin(2t + 1)$.

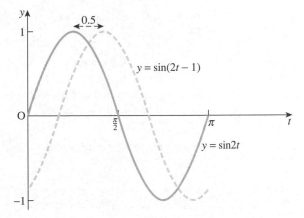

Fig. 4.21 The waves $y = \sin 2t$ and $y = \sin(2t - 1)$.

Consider the wave $y = A \sin(\omega t + \alpha)$. The angle α is called the **phase angle**, or simply the **phase**. We note that y may be written as

$$y = A \sin\left[\omega\left(t + \frac{\alpha}{\omega}\right)\right]$$

We call $\dfrac{\alpha}{\omega}$ the **time displacement** of the wave.

Key point

> The phase of $y = A \sin(\omega t + \alpha)$ is α radians.
>
> The **time displacement** of $y = A \sin(\omega t + \alpha)$ is $\dfrac{\alpha}{\omega}$ seconds.

In similar manner the phase and time displacement of $y = A \cos(\omega t + \alpha)$ are α radians and $\dfrac{\alpha}{\omega}$ seconds.

Example 4.39 State the phase and time displacement of each of the following waves:

(a) $y = \sin(2t + 1)$
(b) $y = \sin(2t - 1)$
(c) $y = 3 \cos\left(\dfrac{t}{2} + 3\right)$

Solution

(a) Here $\omega = 2$, $\alpha = 1$ and so the phase is 1 radian and the time displacement is

$$\frac{\alpha}{\omega} = \frac{1}{2} = 0.5 \text{ seconds}$$

This wave is illustrated in Fig. 4.20.

(b) Here $\omega = 2$, $\alpha = -1$ and so the phase is -1 radian and the time displacement is

$$\frac{\alpha}{\omega} = \frac{-1}{2} = -0.5 \text{ seconds}$$

This wave is illustrated in Fig. 4.21.

(c) Here $\omega = \boxed{}$ and $\alpha = \boxed{}$ $\qquad$ 0.5, 3

and so the phase is 3 radians and the time displacement is $\dfrac{3}{(0.5)} = 6$ seconds.

Exercises

1 State (i) the phase and (ii) the time displacement of the following waves:

(a) $y = 4 \sin(3t + 12)$
(b) $y = \sin(4t - 6)$
(c) $y = 2 \cos(t + 0.5)$

(d) $y = \sin(0.5t - 2)$
(e) $y = 3 \cos\left(\dfrac{t + 4}{3}\right)$

Solutions

1 (a) 12, 4 (b) $-6, -1.5$ (c) 0.5, 0.5 (d) $-2, -4$ (e) $\frac{4}{3}, 4$

Adding waves of the same frequency

Waves of the same angular frequency may be added together to form a new wave. The new wave has the same angular frequency as the original waves. The trigonometrical identities (see next section) are used, especially the formulae for $\sin(A \pm B)$ and $\cos(A \pm B)$. The following examples illustrate the technique.

Example 4.40

Express $2 \sin 3t + 6 \cos 3t$ in the form $A \cos(\omega t + \alpha)$, $\alpha \geq 0$.

Solution

The angular frequency of both $2 \sin 3t$ and $6 \cos 3t$ is 3 radians per second. Hence, on adding the waves, the angular frequency of the sum is also 3 radians per second and so $\omega = 3$. Use the trigonometrical identity from the next section:

$$\cos(A + B) = \cos A \cos B - \sin A \sin B$$

and so

$$2 \sin 3t + 6 \cos 3t = A \cos(\omega t + \alpha)$$
$$= A \cos(3t + \alpha)$$
$$= A(\cos 3t \cos \alpha - \sin 3t \sin \alpha)$$
$$= (A \cos \alpha) \cos 3t - (A \sin \alpha) \sin 3t$$
$$= -(A \sin \alpha) \sin 3t + (A \cos \alpha) \cos 3t$$

We now compare the coefficients of sin $3t$ and cos $3t$ on the left-hand and right-hand sides.
Comparing the sin $3t$ coefficients we have

$$2 = -A \sin \alpha \qquad\qquad [4.2]$$

Comparing the cos $3t$ coefficients we have

$$6 = A \cos \alpha \qquad\qquad [4.3]$$

Equations [4.2] and [4.3] must be solved for A and α. To find A, α is eliminated. This is accomplished by squaring equations [4.2] and [4.3] and then adding the results.
Squaring equation [4.2] gives

$$4 = A^2 \sin^2 \alpha \qquad\qquad [4.4]$$

Squaring equation [4.3] gives

$$36 = A^2 \cos^2 \alpha \qquad\qquad [4.5]$$

Adding equations [4.4] and [4.5] gives

$$40 = A^2 \sin^2 \alpha + A^2 \cos^2 \alpha$$
$$= A^2(\sin^2 \alpha + \cos^2 \alpha)$$
$$= A^2 \text{ using } \sin^2 \alpha + \cos^2 \alpha = 1$$

Hence $A = \sqrt{40}$.

To find α, A is eliminated from equations [4.2] and [4.3]. This is achieved by dividing equation [4.2] by equation [4.3] and using the identity $\dfrac{\sin \alpha}{\cos \alpha} = \tan \alpha$.
Dividing equation [4.2] by equation [4.3] gives

$$\frac{2}{6} = -\frac{A \sin \alpha}{A \cos \alpha} = -\tan \alpha$$

Hence

$$\tan \alpha = -\frac{1}{3}$$

Since $\tan \alpha < 0$, then α lies in either the second quadrant or the fourth quadrant. Noting from equation [4.2] that $\sin \alpha < 0$, then α must be in the fourth quadrant.
Solving $\tan \alpha = -\dfrac{1}{3}$ with α in the fourth quadrant gives $\alpha = 5.9614$. So finally

$$2 \sin 3t + 6 \cos 3t = \sqrt{40} \cos(3t + 5.9614)$$

The resulting wave has an amplitude of $\sqrt{40}$, an angular frequency of 3 radians per second and a phase of 5.9614 radians.

Example 4.41 Express $2 \sin 5t - 5 \cos 5t$ in the form $A \sin(\omega t - \alpha)$, $\alpha \geq 0$.

Solution

The angular frequency of both $2 \sin 5t$ and $5 \cos 5t$ is 5, and so the resultant wave has an angular frequency of 5, that is $\omega = 5$.

Recall the trigonometrical identity for $\sin(A - B)$:

$$\sin(A - B) = \sin A \cos B - \sin B \cos A$$

Hence

$$2 \sin 5t - 5 \cos 5t = A \sin(\omega t - \alpha)$$
$$= A \sin(5t - \alpha)$$
$$= A(\sin 5t \cos \alpha - \sin \alpha \cos 5t)$$
$$= (A \cos \alpha) \sin 5t - (A \sin \alpha) \cos 5t$$

Comparing the $\sin 5t$ terms on both sides gives

$$2 = A \cos \alpha \qquad\qquad [4.6]$$

Comparing the $\cos 5t$ terms on both sides gives

$$5 = A \sin \alpha \qquad\qquad [4.7]$$

To eliminate α from equations [4.6] and [4.7], the equations are squared and then added. Squaring the equations gives

$$4 = A^2 \cos^2 \alpha$$
$$25 = A^2 \sin^2 \alpha$$

and then adding gives

$$29 = A^2 \cos^2 \alpha + A^2 \sin^2 \alpha$$
$$= A^2(\cos^2 \alpha + \sin^2 \alpha)$$
$$= A^2$$

Hence $A = \sqrt{29}$.

To eliminate A, equation [4.7] is divided by equation [4.6] to give

$$\frac{5}{2} = \frac{A \sin \alpha}{A \cos \alpha}$$
$$= \tan \alpha$$
$$\tan \alpha = 2.5$$

We note that $\tan \alpha > 0$ and from equation [4.6] that $\cos \alpha > 0$ and so α must be in the first quadrant.

$$\alpha = \tan^{-1} 2.5 = 1.1903$$

So

$$2 \sin 5t - 5 \cos 5t = \sqrt{29} \sin(5t - 1.1903)$$

Example 4.42   Express $\cos 2t - 2 \sin 2t$ in the form $A \sin(\omega t + \alpha)$, $\alpha \geq 0$.

Solution

The angular frequency of both $\cos 2t$ and $2 \sin 2t$ is

Hence the angular frequency of the resulting wave is also 2, that is $\omega = 2$.

Recall from Block 5 the trigonometrical identity

$\sin(A + B) =$ ▮▮▮▮▮▮▮▮▮▮▮ $\sin A \cos B + \sin B \cos A$

Hence

$\cos 2t - 2 \sin 2t = A \sin(\omega t + \alpha)$

$\qquad\qquad = A \sin(2t + \alpha)$

$\qquad\qquad = $ ▮▮▮▮▮▮▮▮ $A(\sin 2t \cos \alpha + \sin \alpha \cos 2t)$

$\qquad\qquad = $ ▮▮▮ $\sin 2t + $ ▮▮▮ $\cos 2t$ $A \cos \alpha, A \sin \alpha$

So we have

$\qquad \cos 2t - 2 \sin 2t = A \cos \alpha \sin 2t + A \sin \alpha \cos 2t$

Comparing the $\sin 2t$ terms on both sides of the equation gives

$-2 = $ ▮▮▮▮   [4.8] $A \cos \alpha$

Comparing the $\cos 2t$ terms on both sides of the equation gives

$1 = $ ▮▮▮▮   [4.9] $A \sin \alpha$

Squaring equations [4.8] and [4.9] and then adding gives

$A^2 = $ ▮▮   5

and so $A = \sqrt{5}$.

To determine α, equation [4.9] is divided by equation [4.8]. This gives

$\tan \alpha = $ ▮▮▮▮ -0.5

Recognising that α is in the ▮▮▮ quadrant we see that   second

$\alpha = $ ▮▮▮▮▮▮ $\tan^{-1}(-0.5) = 2.6779$

Hence

$\cos 2t - 2 \sin 2t = $ ▮▮▮▮▮▮ $\sqrt{5} \sin(2t + 2.6779)$

Exercises

1 Express $6 \sin 3t - 7 \cos 3t$ in the form $A \cos(\omega t + \alpha)$, $\alpha \geq 0$.

2 Express $2 \cos t + 6 \sin t$ in the form $A \sin(\omega t - \alpha)$, $\alpha \geq 0$. State the maximum value of $2 \cos t + 6 \sin t$.

3 Express $5 \sin 2t + \cos 2t$ in the form $A \cos(\omega t - \alpha)$, $\alpha \geq 0$.

4 Show that the maximum value of

$a \sin \omega t + b \cos \omega t$ is $\sqrt{a^2 + b^2}$.

Solutions

1 $\sqrt{85} \cos(3t + 3.8502)$

2 $\sqrt{40} \sin(t - 5.9614)$, $\sqrt{40}$

3 $\sqrt{26} \cos(2t - 1.3734)$

End of section exercises

State the amplitude of the functions in questions 1–5.

1 $y = 3 \sin 2t$

2 $y = 2 \cos 3t$

3 $y = \dfrac{4}{3} \sin\left(\dfrac{t}{2}\right)$

4 $y = \cos\left(\dfrac{2t}{3}\right)$

5 $y = \dfrac{5 \cos 3t}{3}$

For questions 6–10 state the angular frequency of the functions given in questions 1–5.

For questions 11–15 state the period of the functions in questions 1–5.

For questions 16–20 state the frequency of the functions in questions 1–5.

State the phase of the functions in questions 21–25.

21 $y = 3 \sin(t + 2)$

22 $y = 2.3 \cos(4t - 2)$

23 $y = \cos\left(\dfrac{3t - 1}{2}\right)$

24 $y = \sin(0.5t + 3)$

25 $y = \sin\left(\dfrac{2t}{3} - \dfrac{\pi}{2}\right)$

For questions 26–30 state the time displacement of the functions in questions 21–25.

31 Express $3 \sin 5t + 6 \cos 5t$ in the form $A \sin(\omega t + \alpha)$, $\alpha \geq 0$.

32 Express $2 \cos 3t - \sin 3t$ in the form $A \sin(\omega t + \phi)$, $\phi \geq 0$.

33 Express $\sin 4t + 3 \cos 4t$ in the form $A \cos(\omega t + \phi)$, $\phi \geq 0$.

34 Express $\cos t - 7 \sin t$ in the form $A \cos(\omega t + \alpha)$, $\alpha \geq 0$.

35 Express $4 \sin 2t + 5 \cos 2t$ in the form $A \sin(\omega t - \phi)$, $\phi \geq 0$.

36 Express $5 \sin 3t - 3 \cos 3t$ in the form $A \sin(\omega t - \alpha)$, $\alpha \geq 0$.

37 Express $\sin t - 3 \cos t$ in the form $A \cos(\omega t - \phi)$, $\phi \geq 0$.

38 Express $-2 \sin 2t + 4 \cos 2t$ in the form $A \cos(\omega t - \alpha)$, $\alpha \geq 0$.

Solutions

1 3

2 2

3 $\dfrac{4}{3}$

4 1

5 $\dfrac{5}{3}$

6 2

7 3

8 $\dfrac{1}{2}$

9 $\dfrac{2}{3}$

10 3

11 π

12 $\dfrac{2\pi}{3}$

13 4π

14 3π

15 $\dfrac{2\pi}{3}$

16 $\dfrac{1}{\pi}$

17 $\dfrac{3}{2\pi}$

18 $\dfrac{1}{4\pi}$

19 $\dfrac{1}{3\pi}$

20 $\dfrac{3}{2\pi}$

21 2

22 -2

23 $-\dfrac{1}{2}$

24 3

Solutions continued

25 $-\dfrac{\pi}{2}$

26 2

27 $-\dfrac{1}{2}$

28 $-\dfrac{1}{3}$

29 6

30 $-\dfrac{3\pi}{4}$

31 $\sqrt{45}\sin(5t + 1.1071)$

32 $\sqrt{5}\sin(3t + 2.0344)$

33 $\sqrt{10}\cos(4t + 5.9614)$

34 $\sqrt{50}\cos(t + 1.4289)$

35 $\sqrt{41}\sin(2t - 5.3871)$

36 $\sqrt{34}\sin(3t - 0.5404)$

37 $\sqrt{10}\cos(t - 2.8198)$

38 $\sqrt{20}\cos(2t - 5.8195)$

Trigonometrical identities

Introduction

Consider the two expressions $\sin 2x$ and $2 \sin x \cos x$. These two expressions have the same value for every value of x. Try evaluating the expressions for, say, $x = 25°$, $60°$, 1.2 radians.

If two expressions are equal for all values of the variables used, then we say the expressions are **identical**. Hence $\sin 2x$ and $2 \sin x \cos x$ are identical, that is equal for all values of x. A statement such as $\sin 2x = 2 \sin x \cos x$ is known as an **identity**. In this section we provide a table of important identities and show how expressions involving the trigonometrical ratios can be simplified using them.

Common trigonometrical identities

There are several commonly used trigonometrical identities. These are listed in Table 4.8.

Table 4.8

$$\sin^2 A + \cos^2 A = 1$$

$$\frac{\sin A}{\cos A} = \tan A$$

$$\sin(A + B) = \sin A \cos B + \sin B \cos A$$

$$\sin(A - B) = \sin A \cos B - \sin B \cos A$$

$$\cos(A + B) = \cos A \cos B - \sin A \sin B$$

$$\cos(A - B) = \cos A \cos B + \sin A \sin B$$

$$\sin 2A = 2 \sin A \cos A$$

$$\cos 2A = 1 - 2 \sin^2 A = 2 \cos^2 A - 1 = \cos^2 A - \sin^2 A$$

$$\tan(A + B) = \frac{\tan A + \tan B}{1 - \tan A \tan B}$$

$$\tan(A - B) = \frac{\tan A - \tan B}{1 + \tan A \tan B}$$

$$2 \sin A \cos B = \sin(A + B) + \sin(A - B)$$

$$2 \cos A \cos B = \cos(A + B) + \cos(A - B)$$

$$2 \sin A \sin B = \cos(A - B) - \cos(A + B)$$

$$\sin^2 A = \frac{1}{2}(1 - \cos 2A)$$

$$\cos^2 A = \frac{1}{2}(1 + \cos 2A)$$

Note that we write $\sin^2 A$ to mean $(\sin A)^2$. Similarly, $\cos^2 A$ is the accepted notation for $(\cos A)^2$. The identities can be used to simplify trigonometrical expressions.

The first entry in the table is particularly important and should be remembered.

Key point

$$\sin^2 A + \cos^2 A = 1$$

Choose any angle A for yourself and verify that this identity is true.

Example 4.43   Use trigonometrical identities to simplify $\cos A \tan A$.

Solution

We note that $\tan A = \dfrac{\sin A}{\cos A}$ and so

$$\cos A \tan A = \cos A \frac{\sin A}{\cos A}$$

$$= \sin A$$

Hence $\cos A \tan A$ is identical to $\sin A$.

Example 4.44   (a) Show that $\sin 2A = 2 \sin A \cos A$.
(b) Show that $\cos 2A = \cos^2 A - \sin^2 A$.

Solution

(a) We use the identity

$$\sin(A + B) = \sin A \cos B + \sin B \cos A$$

A special case of this identity occurs when $B = A$. We then have

$$\sin 2A = \sin A \cos A + \sin A \cos A$$

that is

$$\sin 2A = 2 \sin A \cos A$$

(b) We use the identity

$$\cos(A + B) = \cos A \cos B - \sin A \sin B$$

A special case of this identity occurs when $B = A$. We then have

$$\cos 2A = \cos A \cos A - \sin A \sin A$$

that is

$$\cos 2A = \cos^2 A - \sin^2 A$$

Example 4.45   Show that $\cos(-\theta) = \cos \theta$.

Solution

We use the identity for $\cos (A - B)$ with $A = 0$ and $B = \theta$.
Now from Table 4.8

$$\cos(A - B) = \cos A \cos B + \sin A \sin B$$

With $A = 0$ and $B = 0$ this becomes

$$\cos(-\theta) = \qquad\qquad\qquad\qquad \cos 0 \cos \theta + \sin 0 \sin \theta$$

Noting that $\sin 0 = 0$ and $\cos 0 = 1$ this simplifies to

$$\qquad\qquad\qquad\qquad\qquad\qquad\qquad \cos \theta$$

Hence $\cos(-\theta) = \sin \theta$ as required.

Example 4.46   Show that

$$\tan(\theta + 45°) = \frac{1 + \tan\theta}{1 - \tan\theta}$$

Solution

We use the identity

$$\tan(A + B) = \frac{\tan A + \tan B}{1 - \tan A \tan B}$$

Putting $A = \theta$ and $B = 45°$ gives

$$\tan(\theta + 45°) = \frac{\tan\theta + \tan 45°}{1 - \tan\theta \tan 45°}$$

Now $\tan 45° = 1$ and so

$$\tan(\theta + 45°) = \frac{\tan\theta + 1}{1 - \tan\theta}$$

$$= \frac{1 + \tan\theta}{1 - \tan\theta}$$

Example 4.47   Simplify

$$\frac{\sin^3 A}{\cos A} + \sin A \cos A$$

Solution

We write the expression with a common denominator of $\cos A$:

$$\frac{\sin^3 A}{\cos A} + \sin A \cos A = \frac{\sin^3 A + \sin A \cos^2 A}{\cos A}$$

Now

$$\frac{\sin^3 A + \sin A \cos^2 A}{\cos A} = \frac{\sin A(\sin^2 A + \cos^2 A)}{\cos A}$$

$$= \frac{\sin A}{\cos A} \text{ since } \sin^2 A + \cos^2 A = 1$$

$$= \tan A$$

Hence $\dfrac{\sin^3 A}{\cos A} + \sin A \cos A$ simplifies to $\tan A$.

Example 4.48   Simplify

$$\frac{\sin 2A \sin A}{2 \cos A} + \cos 2A$$

Solution

From Example 4.44, $\sin 2A = 2 \sin A \cos A$ and so

$$\frac{\sin 2A \sin A}{2 \cos A} = \qquad\qquad\qquad\qquad \frac{2 \sin A \cos A \sin A}{2 \cos A} = \sin^2 A$$

Also from Example 4.44, $\cos 2A = \cos^2 A - \sin^2 A$. Hence

$$\frac{\sin 2A \sin A}{2 \cos A} + \cos 2A$$

$$= \qquad\qquad\qquad\qquad\qquad \sin^2 A + \cos^2 A - \sin^2 A = \cos^2 A$$

Example 4.49

Electrical Engineering – Amplitude modulation
Amplitude modulation is a technique which allows a signal of a certain frequency (the signal frequency) to be transmitted at a different frequency (the carrier frequency). (Note that the term frequency was explained in the previous section; see p. 469.)

The signal can be represented by the cosine wave $y_s = S \cos \omega_s t$. The carrier can be represented by $y_c = C \cos \omega_c t$. The modulated signal is given by the product $y_c y_s$. Use a trigonometrical identity to show that the modulated signal can be written as the sum of two cosine waves.

Solution

The modulated signal is

$$y_c y_s = (C \cos \omega_c t) \times (S \cos \omega_s t)$$

$$= CS(\cos \omega_c t \cos \omega_s t)$$

Using the identity $2 \cos A \cos B = \cos(A + B) + \cos(A - B)$ (Table 4.8), we can write

$$y_c y_s = \frac{1}{2} CS(\cos(\omega_c + \omega_s)t + \cos(\omega_c - \omega_s)t)$$

which is the sum of two cosine waves, oscillating at different frequencies from the original signal. This result enables the design of an antenna which can be used to transmit the original signal efficiently.

End of section exercises

1 From Table 4.8 we have
$\cos(A - B) = \cos A \cos B + \sin A \sin B$
Verify this identity when $A = 80°$ and $B = 30°$.

2 Verify the identity
$2 \sin A \sin B = \cos(A - B) - \cos(A + B)$
with $A = 50°$ and $B = 15°$.

3 Verify
$$\tan(A - B) = \frac{\tan A - \tan B}{1 + \tan A \tan B}$$
with $A = 65°$ and $B = 30°$.

4 Show $\sin(-\theta) = -\sin \theta$.

5 Show $\sin\left(\dfrac{\pi}{2} - \theta\right) = \cos \theta$.

End of section exercises continued

6 Show $\cos\left(\dfrac{\pi}{2} - \theta\right) = \sin\theta$.

7 Show $\sin\left(\theta + \dfrac{\pi}{2}\right) = \cos\theta$.

8 Show $\cos\left(\theta + \dfrac{\pi}{2}\right) = -\sin\theta$.

9 Show $\sin(180° - \theta) = \sin\theta$.

10 Show $\cos(180° - \theta) = -\cos\theta$.

11 Show $\tan(180° - \theta) = -\tan\theta$.

12 Show $\sin(180° + \theta) = -\sin\theta$.

13 Show $\cos(180° + \theta) = -\cos\theta$.

14 Show $\tan(180° + \theta) = \tan\theta$.

15 Show $\sin(360° - \theta) = -\sin\theta$.

16 Show $\cos(360° - \theta) = \cos\theta$.

17 Show $\tan(360° - \theta) = -\tan\theta$.

18 Show $\sin 3A = 3\sin A\cos^2 A - \sin^3 A$.

19 Show $\cos 3A = 4\cos^3 A - 3\cos A$.

20 Show $\sin 4A = 4\sin A\cos A(\cos^2 A - \sin^2 A)$.

21 Show $\cos 4A = 8\cos^4 A - 8\cos^2 A + 1$.

22 Simplify

$$\sin A\cos A\tan A + \frac{2\sin A\cos^3 A}{\sin 2A}$$

23 Simplify

$$\tan A + \frac{1}{\tan A}$$

24 Show

$$\frac{\sin 3A}{\sin 2A} = 2\cos A - \frac{1}{2\cos A}$$

Solutions

22 1

23 $\dfrac{1}{\cos A\sin A}$ which may be written as $\dfrac{2}{\sin 2A}$

OUTCOME 3
The Calculus

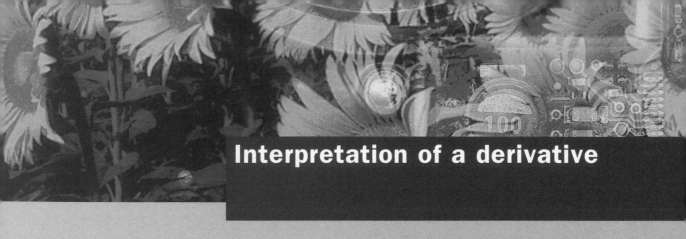

Interpretation of a derivative

Introduction

Engineers are often interested in the rate at which some variable is changing. For example, an engineer needs to know the rate at which the pressure in a vessel is changing, the rate at which the voltage across a capacitor is changing, or the rate at which the temperature is changing in a chemical reaction. Rapid rates of change of a variable may indicate that a system is not operating normally and is approaching critical values. Alarms may be triggered.

Rates of change may be positive, negative or zero. A positive rate of change means that the variable is increasing; a negative rate of change means that the variable is decreasing. A zero rate of change means that the variable is not changing.

Consider Fig. 4.22, which illustrates a variable, $y(x)$.

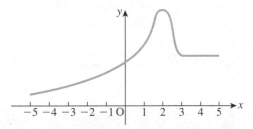

Fig. 4.22 The function $y(x)$ changes at different rates for different values of x.

Between $x = -5$ and $x = -3$, y is increasing slowly. Across this interval the rate of change of y is small and positive. Between $x = -3$ and $x = 1$, y is increasing more rapidly; the rate of change of y is positive and fairly large. Between $x = 1$ and $x = 2$, y is increasing very rapidly and so the rate of change is positive and large. From $x = 2$ to $x = 3$, y decreases rapidly; the rate of change is large and negative. From $x = 3$ to $x = 5$, y is constant and so the rate of change on this interval is zero.

The technique for calculating rate of change is called **differentiation**. Often it is not sufficient to describe a rate of change as, for example, 'positive and large' or 'negative and quite small'. A precise value is needed. Use of differentiation provides a precise value or expression for the rate of change of a function.

Average rate of change across an interval

We see from Fig. 4.22 that a function can have different rates of change at different points on its graph. We begin by defining and then calculating the **average rate of change** of a function across an interval. Fig. 4.23 shows a function, $y(x)$, and values x_1, x_2, $y(x_1)$ and $y(x_2)$.

Consider x increasing from x_1 to x_2. The change in x is $x_2 - x_1$. As x increases from x_1 to x_2, then y increases from $y(x_1)$ to $y(x_2)$. The change in y is $y(x_2) - y(x_1)$. Then the average rate of change of y across the interval is

$$\frac{\text{change in } y}{\text{change in } x} = \frac{y(x_2) - y(x_1)}{x_2 - x_1}$$

$$= \frac{\text{BC}}{\text{AC}}$$

From Fig. 4.23 we see that $\frac{BC}{AC} = \tan \theta$, which is also the gradient of the straight line or **chord** AB. Hence we see that the average rate of change across an interval is identical to the gradient of the chord across that interval.

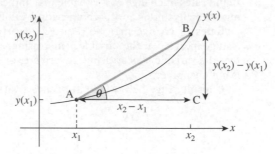

Fig. 4.23 Average rate of change $= \dfrac{y(x_2) - y(x_1)}{x_2 - x_1}$.

Key point

$$\text{average rate of change of } y = \frac{\text{change in } y}{\text{change in } x}$$

$$= \text{gradient of chord}$$

Example 4.50 **Calculate the average rate of change of $y = x^2$ across the interval**

(a) $x = 1$ to $x = 4$
(b) $x = -2$ to $x = 0$

Solution

(a) Change in $x = 4 - 1 = 3$.
When $x = 1$, $y = 1^2 = 1$. When $x = 4$, $y = 4^2 = 16$. Hence the change in y is $16 - 1 = 15$. So

$$\text{average rate of change across interval } [1, 4] = \frac{15}{3}$$

$$= 5$$

This means that across the interval $[1, 4]$, on average the y value increases by 5 for every 1 unit increase in x.

(b) Change in $x = 0 - (-2) = 2$. We have $y(-2) = 4$ and $y(0) = 0$ so the change in y is $0 - 4 = -4$. Hence

$$\text{average rate of change} = \frac{-4}{2}$$

$$= -2$$

On average, across the interval $x = -2$ to $x = 0$, y decreases by 2 units for every 1 unit increase in x.

Example 4.51

Electrical Engineering – Voltage across a capacitor

The voltage, $v(t)$, across a capacitor varies with time, t, according to

$$v(t) = 3 + 2e^{-t}$$

Find the average rate of change of voltage as time varies

(a) from $t = 0$ to $t = 2$
(b) from $t = 1$ to $t = 3$

Solution

(a) Change in $t = 2 - 0 = 2$.
When $t = 0$, $v = 3 + 2e^0 = 5$.

When $t = 2$, $v = $ $3 + 2e^{-2} = 3.2707$

So

average rate of change of $v(t) = $

$$\frac{3.2707 - 5}{2} = -0.8647$$

(b) Change in $t = $ $3 - 1 = 2$

$v(1) = 3 + 2e^{-1}$
$\quad = 3.7358$

$v(3) = $ $3 + 2e^{-3} = 3.0996$

So

average rate of change of $v(t)$ across $[1, 3] = $

$$\frac{3.0996 - 3.7358}{2} = -0.3181$$

Across the interval from $t = 1$ to $t = 3$, the voltage is decreasing but at a slower rate than across the interval from $t = 0$ to $t = 2$.

Exercises

1 Calculate the average rate of change of $y = x^2 + 2x$ from $x = 1$ to $x = 4$.

2 Calculate the average rate of change of $h(t) = 2t^2 - 2t + 1$ from $t = 0$ to $t = 2$.

3 Calculate the average rate of change of $i(t) = 50 \sin t$ from $t = 0$ to $t = \pi$.

4 Calculate the average rate of change of $r(x) = \dfrac{1}{x + 1}$ from $x = -3$ to $x = -2$.

Exercises continued

5 Calculate the average rate of change of $z(t) = 4 + 2t^2$ across (a) $t = 1$ to $t = 3$, (b) $t = -1$ to $t = 0$.

6 The temperature, T, of a vessel varies with time, t, according to

$$T(t) = 320 + \frac{65}{t^2}$$

Calculate the average rate of change of T from $t = 2$ to $t = 4$.

Solutions

1 7

2 2

3 0

4 −0.5

5 (a) 8   (b) −2

6 −6.094

Rate of change at a point

As mentioned earlier, we often need to know the rate of change of a function at a point, and not simply an average rate of change across an interval.

Refer again to Fig. 4.23. Suppose we wish to find the rate of change of y at the point A. The average rate of change across the interval from $x = x_1$ to $x = x_2$ is given by the gradient of the chord AB. This provides an approximation to the rate of change at A.

Suppose the chord AB is extended on both sides, as shown in Fig. 4.24. As B is moved closer to A, the gradient of the chord provides a better approximation to the rate of change at A.

Ultimately B is made coincident with A and then the chord AB becomes a tangent to the curve at A. The gradient of this tangent gives the rate of change of y at A:

Key point

rate of change at a point = gradient of tangent to the curve at that point

Calculating the rate of change of a function at a point by measuring the gradient of a tangent is usually not an accurate method. Consequently we develop an exact, algebraic way of finding rates of change.

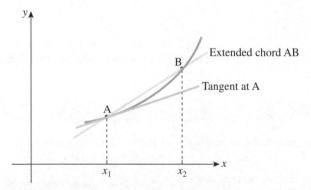

Fig. 4.24   The extended chord ultimately becomes the tangent at A.

Consider the function $y(x)$ as shown in Fig. 4.25.

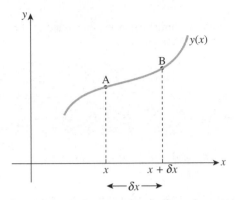

Fig. 4.25　As B approaches A, $\delta x \to 0$.

Let A be a point on the curve with coordinates $(x, y(x))$. B is a point on the curve near to A. The x coordinate of B is $x + \delta x$. The term δx is pronounced 'delta x'. It represents a small change in the x direction. The y coordinate of B is $y(x + \delta x)$. We calculate the gradient of the chord AB:

$$\text{gradient of AB} = \frac{\text{change in } y}{\text{change in } x}$$

$$= \frac{y(x + \delta x) - y(x)}{x + \delta x - x}$$

$$= \frac{y(x + \delta x) - y(x)}{\delta x}$$

The change in y, that is $y(x + \delta x) - y(x)$, is also written as δy. So

$$\text{gradient of AB} = \frac{y(x + \delta x) - y(x)}{\delta x}$$

$$= \frac{\delta y}{\delta x}$$

The gradient of AB gives the average rate of change of $y(x)$ across the small interval from x to $x + \delta x$. To calculate the rate of change of $y(x)$ at A we require the gradient of the tangent at A.

Consider A as a fixed point and let B move along the curve towards A. At each position of B we can calculate the gradient of the chord AB. As B gets closer to A, the chord AB approximates more closely to the tangent at A. Also, as B approaches A, the distance δx decreases. To find the gradient of the tangent at A we calculate the gradient of the chord AB and let δx get smaller and smaller. We say δx tends to zero and write this as $\delta x \to 0$.

As B approaches A, the x difference between A and B gets smaller, that is $\delta x \to 0$, and likewise the y difference, δy, also gets smaller, so $\delta y \to 0$. However, the gradient of AB, given by the ratio $\frac{\delta y}{\delta x}$, approaches a definite value, called a limit. So we seek the limit of $\frac{\delta y}{\delta x}$ as $\delta x \to 0$. We write this as

$$\lim_{\delta x \to 0} \frac{\delta y}{\delta x}$$

Note that 'limit' has been shortened to 'lim'.
    In summary we have

Key point

> rate of change of y = gradient of tangent
>
> $$= \lim_{\delta x \to 0} \frac{\delta y}{\delta x}$$

Let us see this applied to an example.

Example 4.52   Find the rate of change of $y(x) = x^2$.

Solution

Suppose A is the fixed point with coordinates (x, x^2) as shown in Fig. 4.26.
B is a point on the curve near to A with coordinates $(x + \delta x, (x + \delta x)^2)$. We
calculate the gradient of the chord AB.

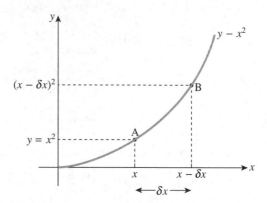

Fig. 4.26   The gradient of the tangent at A is approximated by the gradient of the
chord AB.

$$\text{change in } x = \delta x$$

$$\text{change in } y = \delta y$$

$$= (x + \delta x)^2 - x^2$$

$$= x^2 + 2x\delta x + (\delta x)^2 - x^2$$

$$= 2x(\delta x) + (\delta x)^2$$

$$\text{gradient of chord AB} = \frac{\delta y}{\delta x}$$

$$= \frac{2x(\delta x) + (\delta x)^2}{\delta x}$$

$$= 2x + \delta x$$

This is the average rate of change of $y(x)$ across the small interval from x to $x + \delta x$. To obtain the gradient of the tangent at A, we let $\delta x \to 0$.

$$\text{gradient of tangent a A} = \lim_{\delta x \to 0} (2x + \delta x)$$

$$= 2x$$

Hence the rate of change of x^2 is $2x$.

For example, if $x = 3$, then A is the point (3, 9) and the rate of change of y at this point is 6. Similarly if $x = -1$, A is the point (−1, 1) and the rate of change of $y = -2$.

Exercises

1 Find the rate of change of $y(x) = x^2 + 1$. Calculate the rate of change of y when x is

(a) 6 (b) 3 (c) −2 (d) 0

2 Find the rate of change of $y(x) = x^2 + 2x$. Calculate the rate of change of y when x is

(a) 6 (b) −5 (c) 0

Solutions

1 $2x$, (a) 12 (b) 6 (c) −4 (d) 0

2 $2x + 2$, (a) 14 (b) −8 (c) 2

Terminology and notation

The process of finding the rate of change of a given function is called **differentiation**. The function is said to be **differentiated**. If y is a function of the independent variable x, we say that y is differentiated with respect to (w.r.t.) x. The rate of change of a function is also known as the **derivative** of the function.

There is a notation for writing down the derivative of a function. If the function is $y(x)$, we denote the derivative of y by

$$\frac{dy}{dx}$$

pronounced 'dee y by dee x'. Hence

Key point

$$\lim_{\delta x \to 0} \frac{\delta y}{\delta x} = \frac{dy}{dx}$$

Another notation for the derivative is simply y', pronounced y dash. Similarly if the function is $z(t)$ we write the derivative as $\frac{dz}{dt}$ or z'. When the independent variable is t, the derivative may also be denoted using the dot notation. Thus, for example, $\frac{dz}{dt}$ may be written as $\dot{z}$, pronounced 'z dot'. Sometimes, instead of writing y, a function is written in full: for example, to show the derivative of $\sin 5x$ we write

$$\frac{d(\sin 5x)}{dx}$$

Exercises

1 If x is a function of the independent variable t, write down two ways in which the derivative can be written.

2 If f is a function of x, write down two ways in which the derivative can be written.

Solutions

1 $\dfrac{\mathrm{d}x}{\mathrm{d}t}$ or $\dot{x}$

2 $\dfrac{\mathrm{d}f}{\mathrm{d}x}$ or f'

End of section exercises

1 Calculate the average rate of change of $y = x^3 - 1$ from

   (a) $x = 1$ to $x = 3$
   (b) $x = 0$ to $x = 2$
   (c) $x = -2$ to $x = 2$

2 The pressure, P atmospheres, in a vessel varies with temperature, T (degrees Celsius), according to

$$P(T) = 120 - 20e^{-T/20}$$

Calculate the average rate of change of pressure as T varies from 10°C to 100°C.

3 The current, $i(t)$, in a circuit decays exponentially with time, t, according to the equation

$$i(t) = 5 + 2e^{-t}$$

Calculate the average rate of change of current as t varies from 0 to 3.

4 Explain the meaning of the expression $\dfrac{\mathrm{d}y}{\mathrm{d}x}$.

5 (a) Calculate the rate of change of

$$y(x) = 5 - x^2.$$

   (b) Calculate the rate of change of y when

$$x = -4.$$

6 (a) Calculate $\dfrac{\mathrm{d}R}{\mathrm{d}x}$ when $R(x) = 2x^2$.

   (b) Calculate $\dfrac{\mathrm{d}R}{\mathrm{d}x}$ when $x = 0.5$.

Solutions

1 (a) 13   (b) 4   (c) 4

2 0.13

3 −0.63

5 (a) $-2x$ (b) 8

6 (a) $4x$ (b) 2

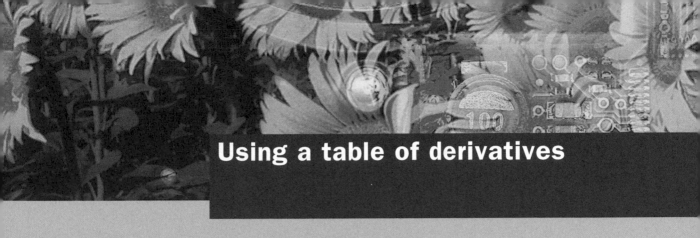

Using a table of derivatives

Introduction

The previous section gave a brief introduction to the meaning of a derivative. A derivative is the rate of change of a function. Geometrically we saw that this is given by the gradient of a tangent. If we consider a typical function, as illustrated in Fig. 4.27 it is clear that the gradient of a tangent depends upon where the tangent is drawn. For example, tangent A, drawn where x has a value x_1, has a different gradient from tangent B, drawn where x has a value x_2. In other words, the gradient of the tangent is itself a function of x. This was seen in Example 4.52, where the gradient was found to be $2x$.

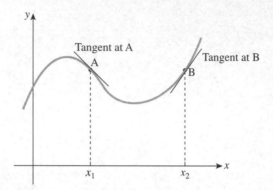

Fig. 4.27   The gradient of a tangent varies along the curve.

Rather than calculate the derivative of a function as explained in the previous section, it is common practice to use a table of derivatives. This block shows how to use such a table.

Table of derivatives

Table 4.9 lists some of the common functions used in engineering and their corresponding derivatives.

Example 4.53   Use Table 4.9 to find $\dfrac{\mathrm{d}y}{\mathrm{d}x}$ when y is given by

(a) $3x$ (b) 3   (c) $3x^2$ (d) $4x^7$

Solution

(a) We note that $3x$ is of the form kx where $k = 3$. Using Table 4.9 we then have $\dfrac{\mathrm{d}y}{\mathrm{d}x} = 3$.

(b) Noting that 3 is a constant we see that $\dfrac{\mathrm{d}y}{\mathrm{d}x} = 0$.

(c) We see that $3x^2$ is of the form kx^n, with $k = 3$ and $n = 2$. The derivative, knx^{n-1}, is then $6x^1$, or more simply, $6x$. So if $y = 3x^2$, then $\dfrac{\mathrm{d}y}{\mathrm{d}x} = 6x$.

(d) We see that $4x^7$ is of the form kx^n, with $k = 4$ and $n = 7$. Hence the derivative, $\dfrac{\mathrm{d}y}{\mathrm{d}x}$, is given by $28x^6$.

Table 4.9 Common functions and their derivatives

Function	Derivative
constant	0
x	1
kx	k
x^n	nx^{n-1}
kx^n	knx^{n-1}
e^x	e^x
e^{kx}	ke^{kx}
$\ln x$	$\dfrac{1}{x}$
$\ln kx$	$\dfrac{1}{x}$
$\sin x$	$\cos x$
$\sin kx$	$k \cos kx$
$\sin(kx + \alpha)$	$k \cos(kx + \alpha)$
$\cos x$	$-\sin x$
$\cos kx$	$-k \sin kx$
$\cos(kx + \alpha)$	$-k \sin(kx + \alpha)$
$\tan x$	$\sec^2 x$
$\tan kx$	$k \sec^2 kx$
$\tan(kx + \alpha)$	$k \sec^2(kx + \alpha)$
$\sinh x$	$\cosh x$
$\sinh kx$	$k \cosh kx$
$\cosh x$	$\sinh x$
$\cosh kx$	$k \sinh kx$
$\tanh x$	$\operatorname{sech}^2 x$
$\tanh kx$	$k \operatorname{sech}^2 kx$
$\sin^{-1} x$	$\dfrac{1}{\sqrt{1 - x^2}}$
$\sin^{-1} kx$	$\dfrac{k}{\sqrt{1 - k^2 x^2}}$
$\cos^{-1} x$	$\dfrac{-1}{\sqrt{1 - x^2}}$
$\cos^{-1} kx$	$\dfrac{-k}{\sqrt{1 - k^2 x^2}}$
$\tan^{-1} x$	$\dfrac{1}{1 + x^2}$
$\tan^{-1} kx$	$\dfrac{k}{1 + k^2 x^2}$

k, n and α are constants, and all angles are in radians

Example 4.54 Find $\dfrac{dy}{dx}$ when y is (a) $\sqrt{x}$, (b) $\dfrac{3}{x^2}$, (c) $\dfrac{2}{x}$.

Solution

(a) We write $\sqrt{x}$ as $x^{\frac{1}{2}}$, and use the result for x^n with $n = \frac{1}{2}$. So

$$\frac{dy}{dx} = nx^{n-1}$$

$$= \tfrac{1}{2}x^{\frac{1}{2}-1}$$

$$= \tfrac{1}{2}x^{-\frac{1}{2}}$$

This may be written as $\dfrac{1}{2\sqrt{x}}$.

(b) We write $\dfrac{3}{x^2}$ as $3x^{-2}$. Using the result of kx^n we see that

$$\frac{dy}{dx} = knx^{n-1}$$

$$= \rule{3cm}{0.6cm}$$ $\qquad$ $3(-2)x^{-2-1} = -6x^{-3}$

(c) We write $\dfrac{2}{x}$ as $2x^{-1}$. Then we see that

$$\frac{dy}{dx} = \rule{3cm}{0.6cm}$$ $\qquad$ $2(-1)x^{-1-1} = -2x^{-2}$

Example 4.55 Use Table 4.9 to find $\dfrac{dz}{dt}$ given z is (a) e^t, (b) e^{3t}, (c) e^{-5t}.

Solution

Although Table 4.9 is written using x as the independent variable, it can be used for any variable.

(a) From Table 4.9, if $y = e^x$, then $\dfrac{dy}{dx} = e^x$. Hence if $z = e^t$ then $\dfrac{dz}{dt} = e^t$.

(b) From Table 4.9 we see that when $y = e^{3x}$ then

$$\frac{dy}{dx} = \rule{1.5cm}{0.6cm}$$ $\qquad$ $3e^{3x}$

Hence $\dfrac{dz}{dt} = \rule{1.5cm}{0.6cm}$ $\qquad$ $3e^{3t}$

(c) Using the result for e^{kx} in Table 4.9 we see that when $z = e^{-5t}$,

$$\frac{dz}{dt} = \rule{1.5cm}{0.6cm}$$ $\qquad$ $-5e^{-5t}$

Example 4.56   Find the derivative, $\dfrac{dy}{dx}$, when y is (a) sin $3x$, (b) cos $\dfrac{x}{2}$, (c) tan $2x$.

Solution

(a) Using the result for sin kx, and taking $k = 3$, we see that

$$\frac{dy}{dx} = 3 \cos 3x$$

(b) From the result for cos kx, and taking $k = \frac{1}{2}$, we see that

$$\frac{dy}{dx} = \qquad\qquad \qquad\qquad -\frac{1}{2} \sin \frac{x}{2}$$

(c) From the result for tan kx, we see that

$$\frac{dy}{dx} = \qquad\qquad \qquad\qquad 2 \sec^2 2x$$

Exercises

1 Find the derivative of the following functions:

   (a) $9x$ (b) $4x$ (c) $6x^3$ (d) $-3x^2$ (e) ln $3t$

2 Find $\dfrac{dz}{dt}$ when z is given by

   (a) $\dfrac{4}{t^3}$ (b) $\sqrt{t^3}$ (c) $5t^{-2}$ (d) $-\dfrac{3}{2}t^{3/2}$

3 Find the derivative of each of the following functions:

   (a) sin $5x$ (b) cos $4t$ (c) tan $3r$ (d) e^{2v} (e) $\dfrac{1}{e^{3t}}$

4 Find the derivative of the following:

   (a) cos $\dfrac{2x}{3}$ (b) sin$(-2x)$ (c) tan πx (d) $e^{x/2}$

Solutions

1 (a) 9   (b) 4   (c) $18x^2$ (d) $-6x$ (e) $\dfrac{1}{t}$

2 (a) $-12t^{-4}$ (b) $\dfrac{3}{2}t^{1/2}$ (c) $-10t^{-3}$ (d) $-\dfrac{9}{4}t^{1/2}$

3 (a) 5 cos $5x$ (b) -4 sin $4t$ (c) 3 sec^2 $3r$ (d) $2e^{2v}$
   (e) $-3e^{-3t}$

4 (a) $-\dfrac{2}{3}$ sin $\dfrac{2x}{3}$ (b) -2 cos$(-2x)$ (c) π sec^2 πx (d) $\dfrac{1}{2}e^{x/2}$

Extending the table of derivatives

We introduce two simple rules that enable us to extend the range of functions that we can differentiate.

Key point

The derivative of $f(x) \pm g(x)$ is

$$\frac{df}{dx} \pm \frac{dg}{dx}$$

This rule says that to find the derivative of the sum (difference) of two functions, we simply calculate the sum (difference) of the derivatives of each function.

Key point

The derivative of $kf(x)$ is

$$k\frac{\mathrm{d}f}{\mathrm{d}x}$$

This rule tells us that if a function is multiplied by a constant, k, then the derivative is likewise multiplied by the same constant, k.

Example 4.57

Find the derivative of each of the following functions:

(a) $y = 6\sin 2x$ (b) $y = 6\sin 2x + 3x^2$ (c) $y = 6\sin 2x + 3x^2 - 5e^{3x}$

Solution

(a) From Table 4.9, the derivative of $\sin 2x$ is $2\cos 2x$. Hence the derivative of $6\sin 2x$ is $6(2\cos 2x)$, that is $12\cos 2x$.

$$y = 6\sin 2x, \frac{\mathrm{d}y}{\mathrm{d}x} = 6(2\cos 2x)$$

$$= 12\cos 2x$$

(b) The function comprises two parts: $6\sin 2x$ and $3x^2$. We have already differentiated $6\sin 2x$ in part (a), so we consider the derivative of $3x^2$. The derivative of x^2 is $2x$ and so the derivative of $3x^2$ is $3(2x)$, that is $6x$. These derivatives are now summed.

$$y = 6\sin 2x + 3x^2, \frac{\mathrm{d}y}{\mathrm{d}x} = 12\cos 2x + 6x$$

(c) We differentiate each part of the function in turn.

$$y = 6\sin 2x + 3x^2 - 5e^{3x}$$

$$\frac{\mathrm{d}y}{\mathrm{d}x} = 6(2\cos 2x) + 3(2x) - 5(3e^{3x})$$

$$= 12\cos 2x + 6x - 15e^{3x}$$

Example 4.58

Find $\dfrac{\mathrm{d}y}{\mathrm{d}x}$ where y is defined by

(a) $\dfrac{x^6}{2} - 3e^{-2x}$ (b) $4\cos\dfrac{x}{2} + 9 - 9x^3$

Solution

(a) The derivative of x^6 is $6x^5$. Hence the derivative of $\dfrac{x^6}{2}$ is

$$\frac{6x^5}{2} = 3x^5$$

The derivative of e^{-2x} is $-2e^{-2x}$

Hence the derivative of $3e^{-2x}$ is

$3(-2)e^{-2x} = -6e^{-2x}$

So given

$$y = \frac{x^6}{2} - 3e^{-2x}$$

then

$$\frac{dy}{dx} = \qquad\qquad 3x^5 + 6e^{-2x}$$

(b) The derivative of $\cos \dfrac{x}{2}$ is

$$-\frac{1}{2} \sin \frac{x}{2}$$

The derivative of 9 is zero. The derivative of $9x^3$ is

$27x^2$

So given

$$y = 4 \cos \frac{x}{2} + 9 - 9x^3$$

then

$$\frac{dy}{dx} = \qquad\qquad -2 \sin \frac{x}{2} - 27x^2$$

Exercises

1 Find $\dfrac{dy}{dx}$ when y is given by

(a) $4x^6 + 8x^3$ (b) $-3x^4 + 2x^{1.5}$

(c) $\dfrac{9}{x^2} + \dfrac{14}{x} - 3x$ (d) $\dfrac{3 + 2x}{4}$ (e) $(2 + 3x)^2$

2 Find the derivative of each of the following functions:

(a) $z(t) = 5 \sin t + \sin 5t$

(b) $h(v) = 3 \cos 2v - 6 \sin \dfrac{v}{2}$

(c) $m(n) = 4e^{2n} + \dfrac{2}{e^{2n}} + \dfrac{n^2}{2}$

(d) $H(t) = \dfrac{e^{3t}}{2} + 2 \tan 2t$

(e) $S(r) = (r^2 + 1)^2 - 4e^{-2r}$

3 Differentiate the following functions:

(a) $A(t) = (3 + e^t)^2$

(b) $B(s) = \pi e^{2s} + \dfrac{1}{s} + 2 \sin \pi s$

(c) $V(r) = \left(1 + \dfrac{1}{r}\right)^2 + (r + 1)^2$

(d) $M(\theta) = 6 \sin 2\theta - 2 \cos \dfrac{\theta}{4} + 2\theta^2$

(e) $H(t) = 4 \tan 3t + 3 \sin 2t - 2 \cos 4t$

Solutions

1 (a) $24x^5 + 24x^2$ (b) $-12x^3 + 3x^{0.5}$

(c) $-\dfrac{18}{x^3} - \dfrac{14}{x^2} - 3$ (d) $\dfrac{1}{2}$ (e) $12 + 18x$

2 (a) $5 \cos t + 5 \cos 5t$ (b) $-6 \sin 2v - 3 \cos \dfrac{v}{2}$

(c) $8e^{2n} - 4e^{-2n} + n$ (d) $\dfrac{3e^{3t}}{2} + 4 \sec^2 2t$

(e) $4r^3 + 4r + 8e^{-2r}$

3 (a) $6e^t + 2e^{2t}$

(b) $2\pi e^{2s} - \dfrac{1}{s^2} + 2\pi \cos(\pi s)$

(c) $-\dfrac{2}{r^2} - \dfrac{2}{r^3} + 2r + 2$

(d) $12 \cos 2\theta + \dfrac{1}{2} \sin \dfrac{\theta}{4} + 4\theta$

(e) $12 \sec^2 3t + 6 \cos 2t + 8 \sin 4t$

Evaluating a derivative

Engineers may need to find the rate of change of a function at a particular point: that is, find the derivative of a function at a specific point. We do this by finding the derivative of the function, and then evaluating the derivative at the given value of x. When evaluating, all angles are in radians. Consider a function, $y(x)$. We use the notation $\dfrac{dy}{dx}(0.7)$ or $y'(0.7)$ to denote the derivative of y evaluated at $x = 0.7$.

Example 4.59

Find the value of the derivative of $y = 3x^2$ where $x = 4$. Interpret your result.

Solution

We have $y = 3x^2$ and so $\dfrac{dy}{dx} = 6x$. We now evaluate the derivative.

When $x = 4$, $\dfrac{dy}{dx} = 6(4) = 24$, that is

$$\frac{dy}{dx}(4) = 24$$

The derivative is positive when $x = 4$ and so y is increasing at this point. Thus when $x = 4$, y is increasing at a rate of 24 vertical units per horizontal unit.

Example 4.60

Electrical Engineering

Find the rate of change of current, $i(t)$, given by

$$i(t) = 3e^{-t} + 2 \quad t \geq 0$$

when $t = 0.7$ seconds.

Solution

The rate of change of a function is the same as the derivative of the function, that is $\dfrac{di}{dt}$.

$$\frac{di}{dt} = \boxed{} \qquad\qquad \boxed{-3e^{-t}}$$

When $t = 0.7$

$$\frac{di}{dt} = \boxed{} \qquad\qquad \boxed{-3e^{-0.7} = -1.4898}$$

The derivative is negative and so we know that $i(t)$ is decreasing when $t = 0.7$. Thus, when $t = 0.7$, the current is decreasing at a rate of $1.49 \ \text{As}^{-1}$.

Exercises

1 Calculate the derivative of $y = 3x^2 + e^x$ when $x = 0.5$.

2 Calculate the rate of change of $i(t) = 4 \sin 2t + 3t$ when

(a) $t = \dfrac{\pi}{3}$ (b) $t = 0.6$.

3 Evaluate the rate of change of $H(t) = 5 \sin t - 3 \cos 2t$ when (a) $t = 0$ (b) $t = 1.3$.

Solutions

1 4.6487

2 (a) -1 (b) 5.8989

3 (a) 5 (b) 4.4305

End of section exercises

1 Find $\dfrac{dy}{dx}$ when y is given by

(a) $7x^5 + 6x^{-2} + \sin 2x$

(b) $3 \cos 4x - 6 \sin 5x$

(c) $e^{3x} + e^{-3x} + 2e^x + 1$

(d) $4 \tan \dfrac{x}{2} + \dfrac{1}{\sqrt{x}}$

(e) $3\sqrt{x} + \dfrac{9}{x} + \dfrac{1}{2} \sin 6x + \ln x$

2 Find the rate of change of the following functions:

(a) $e^t + e^{-t}$ (b) $2 \sin 3t + \ln 2t$ (c) $-3 \cos x$

(d) $\sqrt{r} + 2r^2$ (e) $2e^{-0.5v} + v^3$

3 Find $\dot{x}$ when x is given by

(a) $2t^4 - 3t + 1 + 2 \ln t$

(b) $\sin \pi t - 2 \cos \pi t$

(c) $3 \tan 2t - e^t$ (d) $e^{2t} - e^{-2t} + t$

(e) $t^{3/2} - t^{2/3}$

4 Find the rate of change of each function when $t = 1.2$:

(a) $3t^2 - 2t^3$ (b) $\dfrac{e^{4t}}{2} + 3e^{-t}$

(c) $6 \sin \dfrac{t}{2} + 3 \cos \dfrac{t}{2}$

(d) $2 \tan t - \tan 2t$

(e) $\dfrac{4}{t} + 4 \ln t$

5 Find the derivative of the following:

(a) $e^{2t}(e^t + e^{-t})$ (b) $\dfrac{2t^2 + 1}{t}$

(c) $(2t + 1)(2t - 1)$

(d) $\sin^2 2x + \cos^2 2x + \sin 2x + \cos 2x$

(e) $\dfrac{1}{e^x}$ (f) $\dfrac{\sin x}{\cos x}$

Solutions

1 (a) $35x^4 - 12x^{-3} + 2\cos 2x$
   (b) $-12\sin 4x - 30\cos 5x$
   (c) $3e^{3x} - 3e^{-3x} + 2e^x$

   (d) $2\sec^2\dfrac{x}{2} - \dfrac{1}{2}x^{-3/2}$

   (e) $\dfrac{3}{2}x^{-1/2} - \dfrac{9}{x^2} + 3\cos 6x + \dfrac{1}{x}$

2 (a) $e^t - e^{-t}$ (b) $6\cos 3t + \dfrac{1}{t}$ (c) $3\sin x$

   (d) $\dfrac{1}{2}r^{-1/2} + 4r$ (e) $-e^{-0.5v} + 3v^2$

3 (a) $8t^3 - 3 + \dfrac{2}{t}$ (b) $\pi\cos\pi t + 2\pi\sin\pi t$

   (c) $6\sec^2 2t - e^t$ (d) $2e^{2t} + 2e^{-2t} + 1$

   (e) $\dfrac{3}{2}t^{1/2} - \dfrac{2}{3}t^{-1/3}$

4 (a) -1.44 (b) 242.12 (c) 1.6290 (d) 11.5538
   (e) 0.5556

5 (a) $3e^{3t} + e^t$ (b) $2 - \dfrac{1}{t^2}$ (c) $8t$

   (d) $2\cos 2x - 2\sin 2x$ (e) $-e^{-x}$ (f) $\sec^2 x$

The product rule and the quotient rule

Introduction

The last two sections introduced the concept of differentiation and the use of a table of derivatives. Clearly every possible function cannot be listed in a table. We need a set of rules, used in conjunction with the table of derivatives, to extend the range of functions that we can differentiate. The product rule and the quotient rule are two such rules.

The product rule

As its name tells us, the product rule helps us to differentiate a product of functions. Consider the function $y(x)$, where $y(x)$ is the product of two functions, $u(x)$ and $v(x)$, that is

$$y(x) = u(x)v(x)$$

For example, if $y(x) = x^2 \sin x$ then $u(x) = x^2$ and $v(x) = \sin x$. The product rule states:

Key point

If

$$y(x) = u(x)v(x)$$

then

$$\frac{dy}{dx} = \frac{du}{dx}v + u\frac{dv}{dx}$$
$$= u'v + uv'$$

Example 4.61

Find $\dfrac{dy}{dx}$ where $y = x^2 \sin x$.

Solution

We have

$$y = x^2 \sin x = uv$$

and so $u = x^2$ and $v = \sin x$. Hence

$$\frac{du}{dx} = 2x, \quad \frac{dv}{dx} = \cos x$$

Applying the product rule we have

$$\frac{dy}{dx} = \frac{du}{dx}v + u\frac{dv}{dx}$$
$$= 2x(\sin x) + x^2(\cos x)$$
$$= x(2\sin x + x\cos x)$$

Example 4.62

Find y' where $y = e^x \cos x$.

Solution

We have

$$y = e^x \cos x = uv$$

So

$$u = \boxed{} \,, \quad v = \boxed{} \qquad\qquad\qquad e^x, \cos x$$

and hence

$$\frac{du}{dx} = \boxed{} \,, \quad \frac{dv}{dx} = \boxed{} \qquad\qquad\qquad e^x, -\sin x$$

Applying the product rule yields:

$$\frac{dy}{dx} = \frac{du}{dx}v + u\frac{dv}{dx}$$

$$= e^x \cos x + \boxed{} \qquad\qquad\qquad e^x(-\sin x)$$

$$= e^x(\cos x - \sin x)$$

Example 4.63 Find $\dfrac{d^2 y}{dx^2}$ where $y = x^2 \ln x$.

Solution

We have

$$y = x^2 \ln x = uv$$

so

$$u = x^2, \, v = \ln x$$

Then

$$\frac{du}{dx} = 2x, \quad \frac{dv}{dx} = \boxed{} \qquad\qquad\qquad \frac{1}{x}$$

Applying the product rule, we have

$$\frac{dy}{dx} = \frac{du}{dx}v + u\frac{dv}{dx}$$

$$= \boxed{} \qquad\qquad\qquad 2x \ln x + x$$

To obtain $\frac{d^2 y}{dx^2}$ we differentiate $\frac{dy}{dx}$. Hence we need to find $\frac{d}{dx}(2x \ln x + x)$. The derivative of x is simply 1 so let us examine $\frac{d}{dx}(2x \ln x)$.

To find $\frac{d}{dx}(2x \ln x)$ we use the product rule, with $u = 2x$, $v = \ln x$. Then

$$\frac{du}{dx} = 2, \quad \frac{dv}{dx} = \frac{1}{x}$$

and so

$$\frac{d}{dx}(2x \ln x) = \frac{du}{dx}v + u\frac{dv}{dx}$$

$$= 2 \ln x + 2x \left(\frac{1}{x}\right)$$

$$= 2 \ln x + 2$$

Finally

$$\frac{d^2y}{dx^2} = \frac{d}{dx}(2x \ln x + x)$$

$$=$$

$2 \ln x + 3$

Exercises

1 Find $\dfrac{dy}{dx}$ where y is given by

(a) $x \cos x$ (b) xe^x (c) $\sin x \cos 2x$ (d) $x^3 e^{2x}$
(e) $x^4 \sin 2x$

2 Calculate y' where y is given by

(a) $(t^2 + 1) \sin 4t$ (b) $(3t + 7)\,e^{-2t}$
(c) $(e^x + e^{-2x})(3x^2 - 2x)$ (d) $\sqrt{x}e^x$

(e) $\dfrac{t^2 + 1}{e^t}$

3 Find the second derivative of the functions in question 1.

Solutions

1 (a) $\cos x - x \sin x$ (b) $e^x(1 + x)$
(c) $\cos x \cos 2x - 2 \sin x \sin 2x$
(d) $x^2 e^{2x}(3 + 2x)$ (e) $4x^3 \sin 2x + 2x^4 \cos 2x$

2 (a) $2t \sin 4t + 4(t^2 + 1)(\cos 4t)$
(b) $-e^{-2t}(6t + 11)$
(c) $(e^x - 2e^{-2x})(3x^2 - 2x) + (e^x + e^{-2x})(6x - 2)$, which may be written as $e^x(3x^2 + 4x - 2) - e^{-2x}(6x^2 - 10x + 2)$

(d) $e^x\left(\dfrac{x^{-1/2}}{2} + x^{1/2}\right)$

(e) $-e^{-t}(t^2 - 2t + 1)$

3 (a) $-x \cos x - 2 \sin x$ (b) $e^x(x + 2)$
(c) $-5 \sin x \cos 2x - 4 \cos x \sin 2x$
(d) $2xe^{2x}(2x^2 + 6x + 3)$
(e) $16x^3 \cos 2x - 4x^2(x^2 - 3) \sin 2x$

The quotient rule

The quotient rule shows us how to differentiate a quotient of functions, for example

$$\frac{\sin x}{x}, \quad \frac{t^2 - 1}{t^2 + 1}, \quad \frac{e^z + z}{\cos z}$$

The quotient rule may be stated thus:

Key point

If

$$y(x) = \frac{u(x)}{v(x)}$$

then

$$\frac{dy}{dx} = \frac{v\dfrac{du}{dx} - u\dfrac{dv}{dx}}{v^2}$$

$$= \frac{vu' - uv'}{v^2}$$

Example 4.64 Find y' given $y = \dfrac{\sin x}{x}$.

Solution

We have

$$y = \frac{\sin x}{x} = \frac{u}{v}$$

so

$$u = \sin x, \ v = x$$

and so

$$\frac{du}{dx} = \cos x, \frac{dv}{dx} = 1$$

Applying the quotient rule gives

$$\frac{dy}{dx} = \frac{vu' - uv'}{v^2}$$

$$= \frac{x \cos x - \sin x \,(1)}{x^2}$$

$$= \frac{x \cos x - \sin x}{x^2}$$

Example 4.65 Find y' given $y = \dfrac{t^3}{t+1}$.

Solution

We have

$$y = \frac{t^3}{t+1} = \frac{u}{v}$$

and so

$$u = t^3, \quad v = t+1, \quad u' = 3t^2, \quad v' = 1$$

Applying the quotient rule gives

$$\frac{dy}{dt} = \frac{vu' - uv'}{v^2}$$

$$= \frac{(t+1)\,3t^2 - t^3\,(1)}{(t+1)^2}$$

which can be simplified to

$$\frac{dy}{dt} = \frac{t^2(2t+3)}{(t+1)^2}$$

Exercises

1 Find $\dfrac{dy}{dx}$ where y is given by

(a) $\dfrac{e^x}{x}$ (b) $\dfrac{x}{e^x + 1}$ (c) $\dfrac{\cos x}{\sin x}$ (d) $\dfrac{1 - x}{1 + x}$

(e) $\dfrac{\ln x}{x^2}$

2 Find y' when y is given by

(a) $\dfrac{t^2 - 1}{t^2 + 1}$ (b) $\dfrac{e^{2t} + t}{e^t - 1}$ (c) $\dfrac{\sin 3t}{\cos t + t}$

(d) $\dfrac{z + \sin z}{z + \cos z}$ (e) $\dfrac{1 + x + x^2}{1 + x^3}$

Solutions

1 (a) $\dfrac{e^x(x - 1)}{x^2}$ (b) $\dfrac{e^x + 1 - xe^x}{(e^x + 1)^2}$

(c) $-\mathrm{cosec}^2\, x$ (d) $\dfrac{-2}{(1 + x)^2}$ (e) $\dfrac{1 - 2\ln x}{x^3}$

2 (a) $\dfrac{4t}{(t^2 + 1)^2}$

(b) $\dfrac{(e^t - 1)(2e^{2t} + 1) - (e^{2t} + t)e^t}{(e^t - 1)^2}$

(c) $\dfrac{3(\cos t + t)\cos 3t - \sin 3t\,(-\sin t + 1)}{(\cos t + t)^2}$

(d) $\dfrac{(z + 1)\cos z + (z - 1)\sin z + 1}{(\cos z + z)^2}$

(e) $-\left(\dfrac{x^4 + 2x^3 + 3x^2 - 2x - 1}{(x^3 + 1)^2}\right)$

End of section exercises

1 Find the derivative of each of the following:

(a) $(x - 1)\sin 2x$ (b) $\dfrac{\sin 2x}{x - 1}$ (c) $\dfrac{x - 1}{\sin 2x}$

(d) $e^{2x}\sin 3x$ (e) $e^{-2x}\sin 3x$

2 Differentiate the following:

(a) $\dfrac{t^3 - t^2}{t^2 + 1}$ (b) $3\sin 2x\cos x$ (c) $\dfrac{3\cos x}{\sin 2x}$

(d) $\dfrac{e^{3r}}{e^{2r}}$ (e) $(r + 1)(r + \sin r)$

3 Find $\dfrac{dH}{dt}$ given

$H = e^{2t}t^2\sin t$

4 Find $\dfrac{dR}{dt}$ given

$R = \dfrac{e^{2t}\sin t}{t^2}$

Solutions

1 (a) $2(x - 1)\cos 2x + \sin 2x$

(b) $\dfrac{2(x - 1)\cos 2x - \sin 2x}{(x - 1)^2}$

(c) $\dfrac{\sin 2x - 2(x - 1)\cos 2x}{\sin^2 2x}$

(d) $e^{2x}(3\cos 3x + 2\sin 3x)$

(e) $e^{-2x}(3\cos 3x - 2\sin 3x)$

2 (a) $\dfrac{t(t^3 + 3t - 2)}{(t^2 + 1)^2}$

(b) $6\cos x\cos 2x - 3\sin x\sin 2x$

(c) $-3\left(\dfrac{\sin 2x\sin x + 2\cos x\cos 2x}{\sin^2 2x}\right)$

(d) e^r (e) $(r + 1)\cos r + \sin r + 2r + 1$

3 $e^{2t}[t^2\cos t + 2t(t + 1)\sin t]$

4 $\dfrac{e^{2t}[2t\sin t + t\cos t - 2\sin t]}{t^3}$

The chain rule

Introduction

In the previous section we saw how to differentiate products and quotients of functions. This block introduces the chain rule, which allows us to differentiate an additional class of functions.

The chain rule

Suppose y is a function of z, that is $y = y(z)$, and that z is a function of x, that is $z = z(x)$. So

$$y = y(z) = y(z(x))$$

Hence y may be considered to be a function of x. For example, if $y(z) = 2z^2 + 3z$ and $z = \cos 2x$ then

$$y = 2(\cos 2x)^2 + 3(\cos 2x)$$

Since y can be considered as a function of x, then $\frac{dy}{dx}$ may be found. The chain rule helps us to find $\frac{dy}{dx}$. The chain rule states

Key point

If $y = y(z)$ and $z = z(x)$, then

$$\frac{dy}{dx} = \frac{dy}{dz} \times \frac{dz}{dx}$$

Example 4.66

Given $y = z^4$ and $z = 3x + 6$, find $\frac{dy}{dx}$.

Solution

We have

$$y = z^4 = (3x + 6)^4$$

and we seek $\frac{dy}{dx}$. Now

$$y = z^4, \; z = 3x + 6$$

and so

$$\frac{dy}{dz} = 4z^3, \frac{dz}{dx} = 3$$

Using the chain rule we have

$$\frac{dy}{dx} = \frac{dy}{dz}\frac{dz}{dx}$$

$$= 4z^3(3)$$

$$= 12z^3$$

$$= 12(3x + 6)^3$$

Sometimes care must be taken to recognise the independent and dependent variables. Example 4.67 uses the chain rule, but it may look unfamiliar.

Example 4.67 Given $z(y) = y^3$ and $y(x) = 2x^2 - x$ find $\dfrac{\mathrm{d}z}{\mathrm{d}x}$.

Solution

We have

$$z(y) = y^3 \text{ so } \frac{\mathrm{d}z}{\mathrm{d}y} = 3y^2$$

and

$$y(x) = 2x^2 - x \text{ so } \frac{\mathrm{d}y}{\mathrm{d}x} = 4x - 1$$

The chain rule has the form

$$\frac{\mathrm{d}z}{\mathrm{d}x} = \frac{\mathrm{d}z}{\mathrm{d}y}\frac{\mathrm{d}y}{\mathrm{d}x}$$

$$= 3y^2(4x - 1)$$

$$= 3(2x^2 - x)^2(4x - 1)$$

Example 4.68 Given $y = (x^3 + x)^7$, find $\dfrac{\mathrm{d}y}{\mathrm{d}x}$.

Solution

We let $z = x^3 + x$ and so

$$y = (x^3 + x)^7 = z^7$$

Then $\dfrac{\mathrm{d}y}{\mathrm{d}z} = 7z^6$ and $\dfrac{\mathrm{d}z}{\mathrm{d}x} = 3x^2 + 1$. Applying the chain rule gives

$$\frac{\mathrm{d}y}{\mathrm{d}x} = \frac{\mathrm{d}y}{\mathrm{d}z}\frac{\mathrm{d}z}{\mathrm{d}x}$$

$$= (7z^6)(3x^2 + 1)$$

$$= 7(3x^2 + 1)(x^3 + x)^6$$

Example 4.69 Given $y = \sqrt{x^2 + 1}$ find $\dfrac{\mathrm{d}y}{\mathrm{d}x}$.

Solution

Let $z = x^2 + 1$ and then

$$y = \sqrt{x^2 + 1} = \boxed{} \qquad\qquad \sqrt{z}$$

Then

$$\frac{\mathrm{d}y}{\mathrm{d}z} = \boxed{} \quad , \quad \frac{\mathrm{d}z}{\mathrm{d}x} = \boxed{} \qquad \frac{1}{2}z^{-1/2}, 2x$$

and applying the chain rule gives

$$\frac{\mathrm{d}y}{\mathrm{d}x} = \frac{\mathrm{d}y}{\mathrm{d}z}\frac{\mathrm{d}z}{\mathrm{d}x}$$

$$= \boxed{} \qquad\qquad \frac{1}{2}z^{-1/2}(2x)$$

$$= \frac{x}{\sqrt{z}}$$

$$= \boxed{} \qquad\qquad \frac{x}{\sqrt{x^2+1}}$$

Example 4.70   Find $\dfrac{\mathrm{d}y}{\mathrm{d}x}$ given $y = \ln(x^2 + x + 1)$.

Solution

Let $z = x^2 + x + 1$ so that

$$y = \ln(x^2 + x + 1) = \boxed{} \qquad\qquad \ln z$$

Then

$$\frac{\mathrm{d}y}{\mathrm{d}z} = \boxed{}, \quad \frac{\mathrm{d}z}{\mathrm{d}x} = \boxed{} \qquad\qquad \frac{1}{z}, \; 2x+1$$

So

$$\frac{\mathrm{d}y}{\mathrm{d}x} = \frac{\mathrm{d}y}{\mathrm{d}z}\frac{\mathrm{d}z}{\mathrm{d}x}$$

$$= \boxed{} \qquad\qquad \frac{2x+1}{z}$$

$$= \frac{2x+1}{x^2 + x + 1}$$

We note that, in the final solution, the numerator is the derivative of the denominator. In general:

Key point

If $y = \ln f(x)$ then

$$\frac{\mathrm{d}y}{\mathrm{d}x} = \frac{f'}{f}$$

Example 4.71   Given $y = \ln(1 - x)$ find $\dfrac{\mathrm{d}y}{\mathrm{d}x}$.

Solution

Here $f(x) = 1 - x$ and $f'(x) = -1$. So

$$\frac{dy}{dx} = \frac{-1}{1-x}$$

which may be simplified to

$$\frac{dy}{dx} = \frac{1}{x-1}$$

Example 4.72 Given $y = 5\ln(2t - 1)$ find $\dfrac{dy}{dt}$.

Solution

Here $f(t) = 2t - 1$ and so $f'(t) = 2$. Hence

$$\frac{dy}{dt} = 5\left(\frac{2}{2t-1}\right)$$

$$= \frac{10}{2t-1}$$

Example 4.73 Given $y = \ln(e^x + \sin x)$ find $\dfrac{dy}{dx}$.

Solution

We have

$$y = \ln(e^x + \sin x)$$
$$= \ln f(x) \quad \text{where } f(x) = e^x + \sin x$$

So

$$\frac{dy}{dx} = \qquad\qquad \qquad\qquad \frac{f'}{f} = \frac{e^x + \cos x}{e^x + \sin x}$$

Exercises

1 Differentiate each of the following functions:

(a) $(x^3 + 2)^6$ (b) $\sqrt{\sin x}$ (c) $(e^x + 1)^7$
(d) $(\cos 2x)^5$ (e) $\ln(x + 1)$

2 Find $\dfrac{dy}{dt}$ where y is given by

(a) $e(3t^2)$ (b) $3e^{t^2}$ (c) $e^{\sin 2t}$ (d) $e^{2\sin t}$
(e) $2e^{\sin t}$

3 Find the rate of change of y at the specified point:

(a) $y = \ln(3t^2 + 5)$, $t = 1$
(b) $y = \sin(t^2)$, $t = 2$
(c) $y = \cos(t^3 + 1)$, $t = 1$
(d) $y = (t^3 - 1)^{2/3}$, $t = 2$
(e) $y = 4e^{\cos t}$, $t = \dfrac{\pi}{2}$

Solutions

1 (a) $18x^2(x^3 + 2)^5$ (b) $\dfrac{\cos x}{2\sqrt{\sin x}}$

(c) $7e^x(e^x + 1)^6$

(d) $-10 \sin 2x \cos^4 2x$ (e) $\dfrac{1}{x + 1}$

2 (a) $6te^{3t^2}$ (b) $6te^{t^2}$ (c) $2 \cos 2te^{\sin 2t}$

(d) $2 \cos te^{2 \sin t}$ (e) $2 \cos te^{\sin t}$

3 (a) 0.75 (b) -2.6146 (c) -2.7279

(d) 4.1821 (e) -4

End of section exercises

1 Use the chain rule to differentiate each of the following functions:

(a) $y = (6x^3 - x)^4$ (b) $h = (t^4 - 1)^{1/3}$

(c) $v = \sqrt{9 - 2t}$ (d) $i = \sin(y^3)$

(e) $R = \cos(\sqrt{r})$

2 Find the derivative of each function:

(a) $Y(t) = 5e^{\sin 2t}$ (b) $m(p) = 3 \ln(p^4 + 2)$

(c) $H(r) = 5 \sin(\pi r^2 + 1)$

(d) $x(t) = -3 \cos\left(\dfrac{1}{t}\right)$ (e) $Q(s) = \dfrac{1}{\ln s}$

3 Evaluate $\dfrac{dy}{dx}$ at the specified value of x.

(a) $y = \sqrt{x + \sin x}$, $x = 1$

(b) $y = \sin(x^2 + 1)$, $x = 0.5$

(c) $y = e^{\sqrt{x}}$, $x = 1$

(d) $y = 2 \cos\left(\dfrac{1}{x}\right)$, $x = 1$

(e) $y = \dfrac{1}{(3x^2 + 1)^4}$, $x = 0.5$

4 Differentiate the following functions where a, b and n are constants:

(a) $y = (at + b)^n$ (b) $y = e^{at+b}$

(c) $y = \sin(at + b)$

(d) $y = \cos(at + b)$ (e) $y = \ln(at + b)$

Solutions

1 (a) $4(18x^2 - 1)(6x^3 - x)^3$

(b) $\dfrac{4t^3(t^4 - 1)^{-2/3}}{3}$

(c) $-(9 - 2t)^{-1/2}$ (d) $3y^2 \cos(y^3)$

(e) $-\dfrac{1}{2}r^{-1/2} \sin\sqrt{r}$

2 (a) $10 \cos 2te^{\sin 2t}$ (b) $\dfrac{12p^3}{p^4 + 2}$

(c) $10\pi r \cos(\pi r^2 + 1)$

(d) $-\dfrac{3}{t^2} \sin\left(\dfrac{1}{t}\right)$ (e) $\dfrac{-1}{s (\ln s)^2}$

3 (a) 0.5675 (b) 0.3153

(c) 1.3591 (d) 1.6829

(e) -0.7311

4 (a) $an(at + b)^{n-1}$ (b) ae^{at+b}

(c) $a \cos(at + b)$ (d) $-a \sin(at + b)$

(e) $\dfrac{a}{at + b}$

Integration as differentiation in reverse

Introduction

The topic of **integration** can be approached in several different ways. Perhaps the simplest way of introducing it is to think of it as differentiation in reverse. In some applications we shall know the derivative of a function, but not the function from which it was derived. This is why we need knowledge of integration.

In this section we give a look-up table that you can use to integrate a wide range of functions, and we provide lots of opportunities for you to practise using it. Then rules are given that allow you to integrate a wider range of functions. In particular you will be able to integrate sums, differences and constant multiples of functions.

Differentiation in reverse

Suppose we differentiate the function $y = x^2$. We obtain $\frac{dy}{dx} = 2x$. Integration reverses this process, and we say that the integral of $2x$ is x^2. Pictorially we can regard this as shown in Fig. 4.28.

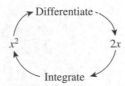

Fig. 4.28 Integration can be thought of as differentiation in reverse.

The situation is just a little more complicated because there are lots of functions we can differentiate to give $2x$. Here are some of them:

$$x^2 + 4, \quad x^2 - 15, \quad x^2 + 0.5$$

Example 4.74

Write down some more functions that have derivative $2x$.

Solution

e.g. $x^2 - 7$, $x^2 + 0.1$

All these functions have the same derivative, $2x$, because when we differentiate the constant term we obtain zero. Consequently, when we reverse the process, we have no idea what the original constant term might have been. Because of this we include in our answer an unknown constant, c say, called the **constant of integration**. We state that the integral of $2x$ is $x^2 + c$. There is nothing special about the letter c. We might use K for example, but we avoid using letters from the end of the alphabet like x, y and z, which are used for variables.

The symbol for integration is $\int$, known as an **integral sign**. Formally we write,

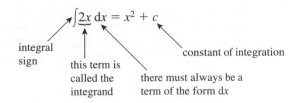

integral sign

this term is called the integrand

constant of integration

there must always be a term of the form dx

Note that along with the integral sign there is a term of the form dx, which must always be written, and which indicates the name of the variable involved, in this case x. The term dx must not be interpreted as a product of d and x. Rather it is a notation and as such you should think of dx as a single quantity.

We say that $2x$ is integrated *with respect to x* to give $x^2 + c$. The function being integrated is called the **integrand**. Technically, integrals of this sort are called **indefinite integrals,** to distinguish them from definite integrals, which are dealt with subsequently. When you find an indefinite integral your answer should always contain a constant of integration.

Exercises

1 (a) Write down the derivatives of each of

$$x^3, \quad x^3 + 17, \quad x^3 - 21$$

(b) Deduce that $\int 3x^2 dx = x^3 + c$.

2 Explain what is meant by the term 'integrand'.

3 Explain why, when finding indefinite integrals, a constant of integration is needed.

Solutions

1 (a) All have derivative $3x^2$.

A table of integrals

We could use a table of derivatives to find integrals, but the more common ones are usually found in a 'table of integrals' such as that shown in Table 4.10. You could check many of the entries in this table using your knowledge of differentiation. Try checking some of these for yourself.

When dealing with the trigonometrical functions the variable x must always be measured in radians and not degrees. Note that the fourth entry for integrating a power of x is valid whether n is positive, negative or fractional, but not when $n = -1$. If $n = -1$ use the fifth entry in the table. Various other conditions are detailed in the third column.

Example 4.75

(a) **Use the table of integrals to find $\int x^7 dx$.**
(b) **Check the result by differentiating the answer.**

Solution

(a) From the table note that

$$\int x^n dx = \frac{x^{n+1}}{n+1} + c$$

Table 4.10   Table of integrals.

Function $f(x)$	Indefinite integral $\int f(x)\,dx$	
constant, k	$kx + c$	
x	$\dfrac{x^2}{2} + c$	
x^2	$\dfrac{x^3}{3} + c$	
x^n	$\dfrac{x^{n+1}}{n+1} + c$	$n \neq -1$
$x^{-1} = \dfrac{1}{x}$	$\ln|x| + c$	
$\sin x$	$-\cos x + c$	
$\cos x$	$\sin x + c$	
$\sin kx$	$\dfrac{-\cos kx}{k} + c$	
$\cos kx$	$\dfrac{\sin kx}{k} + c$	
$\tan kx$	$\frac{1}{k}\ln|\sec kx| + c$	
$\sec kx$	$\frac{1}{k}\ln|\sec kx + \tan kx| + c$	
e^x	$e^x + c$	
e^{-x}	$-e^{-x} + c$	
e^{kx}	$\dfrac{e^{kx}}{k} + c$	
$\cosh kx$	$\frac{1}{k}\sinh kx + c$	
$\sinh kx$	$\frac{1}{k}\cosh kx + c$	
$\dfrac{1}{x^2 + a^2}$	$\frac{1}{a}\tan^{-1}\frac{x}{a} + c$	$a > 0$
$\dfrac{1}{x^2 - a^2}$	$\frac{1}{2a}\ln\dfrac{x-a}{x+a} + c$	$|x| > a > 0$
$\dfrac{1}{a^2 - x^2}$	$\frac{1}{2a}\ln\dfrac{a+x}{a-x} + c$	$|x| < a$
$\dfrac{1}{\sqrt{x^2 + a^2}}$	$\sinh^{-1}\left(\frac{x}{a}\right) + c$	$a > 0$
$\dfrac{1}{\sqrt{x^2 - a^2}}$	$\cosh^{-1}\left(\frac{x}{a}\right) + c$	$x \geq a > 0$
$\dfrac{1}{\sqrt{x^2 + k}}$	$\ln(x + \sqrt{x^2 + k}) + c$	
$\dfrac{1}{\sqrt{a^2 - x^2}}$	$\sin^{-1}\left(\frac{x}{a}\right) + c$	$-a \leq x \leq a$

In words, this states that to integrate a power of x, increase the power by one, and divide the result by the new power. You will find it helpful to remember this rule. With $n = 7$ we find

$$\int x^7 \mathrm{d}x = \frac{x^8}{8} + c$$

(b) The answer can be differentiated as a check.

$$\frac{\mathrm{d}}{\mathrm{d}x}\left(\frac{x^8}{8} + c\right) = \frac{1}{8}\frac{\mathrm{d}}{\mathrm{d}x}x^8$$

$$= \frac{1}{8} \times 8x^7$$

$$= x^7$$

The answer has been verified.

Example 4.76   Find $\int \cos 5x \, \mathrm{d}x$.

Solution

From the table note that

$$\int \cos kx \, \mathrm{d}x = \frac{\sin kx}{k} + c$$

With $k = 5$ we find

$$\int \cos 5x \, \mathrm{d}x = \frac{\sin 5x}{5} + c$$

Check this result for yourself by differentiating it.

In the table the independent variable is always given as x. However, with a little imagination you will be able to use it when other independent variables are involved.

Example 4.77   Find $\int \cos 5t \, \mathrm{d}t$.

Solution

We integrated $\cos 5x$ in the previous example. Now the independent variable is t, so simply use the table and read every x as a t. With $k = 5$ we find

$$\int \cos 5t \, \mathrm{d}t = \frac{\sin 5t}{5} + c$$

It follows immediately that, for example,

$$\int \cos 5\omega \, \mathrm{d}\omega = \frac{\sin 5\omega}{5} + c, \quad \int \cos 5u \, \mathrm{d}u = \frac{\sin 5u}{5} + c$$

and so on.

Example 4.78   Find $\displaystyle\int \sin \frac{x}{2}\, dx$.

Solution

Note that $\dfrac{x}{2}$ is equivalent to $\frac{1}{2}x$. Use the table of integrals with $k = \frac{1}{2}$.

$$\int \sin \frac{x}{2}\, dx = \qquad\qquad\qquad = -\frac{\cos \dfrac{x}{2}}{\frac{1}{2}} + c = -2\cos \frac{x}{2} + c$$

Example 4.79   Find $\displaystyle\int \sin \frac{2\pi t}{T}\, dt$ where T is a constant.

Solution

With respect to which variable is the integration being carried out?

The quantity $\dfrac{2\pi}{T}$ is a constant. Perform the integration:

$$\int \sin \frac{2\pi t}{T}\, dt =$$

$$= -\frac{\cos \dfrac{2\pi t}{T}}{\dfrac{2\pi}{T}} + c = -\frac{T}{2\pi}\cos \frac{2\pi t}{T} + c$$

Example 4.80   Find $\int 12\, dx$.

Solution

In this example we are integrating a constant, 12. Using the table we find

$$\int 12\, dx = 12x + c$$

Note that $\int 12\, dt$ would be $12t + c$ and so on. This shows the importance of including the term dx or dt in the integral.

Example 4.81   Find $\int dx$.

Solution

This example looks a little different from the earlier ones. But if we think of dx as $1\, dx$ then we are integrating a constant, 1. Using the table we find

$$\int 1\, dx = 1x + c \quad \text{or simply} \quad x + c$$

Note that $\int dx$ would be $t + c$.

Example 4.82   Find $\int e^{-3x} dx$.

Solution

Use the appropriate entry in the table with $k = -3$:

$$\int e^{-3x}\, dx = \frac{e^{-3x}}{-3} + c = -\frac{1}{3} e^{-3x} + c$$

Example 4.83   **Look for an entry in the table of integrals that will enable you to calculate**

$$\int \frac{1}{\sqrt{9 - t^2}}\, dt$$

Solution

Write down the appropriate entry.

$$\int \frac{1}{\sqrt{a^2 - x^2}}\, dx = \sin^{-1}\left(\frac{x}{a}\right) + c$$

Select an appropriate value for the constant a and hence find the integral.

Take $a = 3$, so that $a^2 = 9$. $\displaystyle\int \frac{1}{\sqrt{9 - t^2}}\, dt = \sin^{-1}\left(\frac{t}{3}\right) + c$

Exercises

1 Integrate each of the following functions with respect to x:

  (a) x^9 (b) $x^{1/2}$ (c) x^{-3} (d) $\dfrac{1}{x^4}$ (e) 4 (f) $\sqrt{x}$

  (g) e^{4x} (h) $\cos\dfrac{x}{2}$ (i) $\cos \pi x$

2 Find

  (a) $\int t^2\, dt$ (b) $\int 6\, dt$ (c) $\int \sin 3t\, dt$

  (d) $\int e^{7t}\, dt$ (e) $\displaystyle\int \cos\frac{2\pi t}{T}\, dt$ (f) $\displaystyle\int \frac{dz}{z}$

3 Find $\int e^t\, dt$.

4 Find

  (a) $\displaystyle\int \frac{1}{x^2 + 25}\, dx$ (b) $\displaystyle\int \frac{1}{\sqrt{t^2 - 4}}\, dt$

5 Find

  (a) $\int \sin \omega\, d\omega$
  (b) $\int \cos 3t\, dt$
  (c) $\int \tan \frac{1}{3} x\, dx$
  (d) $\int \tan \frac{x}{3}\, dx$
  (e) $\int \sinh 0.3x\, dx$
  (f) $\int \cos 0.01 \pi x\, dx$
  (g) $\int \cosh 0.01t\, dt$
  (h) $\int x^{7/2}\, dx$

Exercises continued

(i) $\displaystyle\int \frac{1}{\sqrt[3]{x}}\,dx$

(j) $\int x^{1/4}\,dx$

(k) $\int \sqrt[5]{t}\,dt$

(l) $\int e^{-0.7t}\,dt$

(m) $\displaystyle\int \frac{1}{64 - x^2}\,dx$

(n) $\displaystyle\int \frac{1}{\sqrt{64 - x^2}}\,dx$

(o) $\displaystyle\int \frac{1}{\sqrt{x^2 + 8}}\,dx$

6 Find

(a) $\dfrac{1}{5}\displaystyle\int \cos \dfrac{n\pi t}{5}\,dt,$ (b) $\dfrac{1}{5}\displaystyle\int \sin \dfrac{n\pi t}{5}\,dt.$

Solutions

1 (a) $\dfrac{x^{10}}{10} + c$ (b) $\dfrac{2x^{3/2}}{3} + c$ (c) $-\dfrac{1}{2}x^{-2} + c$

(d) $-\dfrac{1}{3}x^{-3} + c$ (e) $4x + c$ (f) same as (b)

(g) $\dfrac{e^{4x}}{4} + c$ (h) $2 \sin \dfrac{x}{2} + c$ (i) $\dfrac{\sin \pi x}{\pi} + c$

2 (a) $\dfrac{t^3}{3} + c$ (b) $6t + c$ (c) $-\dfrac{\cos 3t}{3} + c$

(d) $\dfrac{e^{7t}}{7} + c$ (e) $\dfrac{T}{2\pi}\sin \dfrac{2\pi t}{T} + c$ (f) $\ln|z| + c$

3 $e^t + c$

4 (a) $\dfrac{1}{5}\tan^{-1}\left(\dfrac{x}{5}\right) + c$ (b) $\cosh^{-1}\left(\dfrac{t}{2}\right) + c$

5 (a) $-\cos \omega + c$ (b) $\dfrac{1}{3}\sin 3t + c$

(c) $3 \ln|\sec\dfrac{x}{3}| + c$ (d) $3 \ln|\sec\dfrac{x}{3}| + c$

(e) $\dfrac{10}{3}\cosh 0.3x + c$ (f) $\dfrac{100}{\pi}\sin 0.01\pi x + c$

(g) $100 \sinh 0.01t + c$ (h) $\dfrac{2}{9}x^{9/2} + c$

(i) $\dfrac{3}{2}x^{2/3} + c$ (j) $\dfrac{4}{5}x^{5/4} + c$ (k) $\dfrac{5}{6}t^{6/5} + c$

(l) $-1.429e^{-0.7t} + c$ (m) $\dfrac{1}{16}\ln\dfrac{8 + x}{8 - x} + c$

(n) $\sin^{-1}\dfrac{x}{8} + c$ (o) $\ln(x + \sqrt{x^2 + 8}) + c$

6 (a) $\dfrac{1}{n\pi}\sin \dfrac{n\pi t}{5} + c$ (b) $-\dfrac{1}{n\pi}\cos \dfrac{n\pi t}{5} + c$

Some rules of integration

To enable us to find integrals of a wider range of functions than those normally given in a table of integrals we can make use of the following rules.

The integral of *k f*(*x*) where *k* is a constant

A constant factor in an integral can be moved outside the integral sign as follows

Key point

The integral of a constant multiple of a function

$$\int kf(x)\,dx = k\int f(x)\,dx$$

Example 4.84   Find $\int 11x^2 \, dx$.

Solution

$$\int 11x^2 \, dx = 11 \int x^2 \, dx$$

$$= 11 \left(\frac{x^3}{3} + c \right)$$

$$= \frac{11x^3}{3} + K$$

where K is a constant.

Example 4.85   Find $\int -5 \cos x \, dx$.

Solution

$$\int -5 \cos x \, dx = -5 \int \cos x \, dx$$

$$= -5(\sin x + c)$$

$$= -5 \sin x + K$$

where K is a constant.

Example 4.86   Find $\int \frac{14}{1 + s^2} ds$.

Solution

Use the result in the previous key point to extract the constant factor 14. Then use the table to complete the solution.

$$\int \frac{14}{1 + s^2} \, ds = \qquad\qquad\qquad\qquad\qquad 14 \int \frac{1}{1 + s^2} \, ds = 14 \tan^{-1} s + c$$

Example 4.87   Find $\int 2\pi m r^3 dr$.

Solution

In this example, integration is with respect to which variable?

r

The 2, π and m are all constant factors and can be written in front of the integral sign. Thus

$$\int 2\pi m r^3 \, dr = 2\pi m \int r^3 \, dr$$

$$= 2\pi m \left(\frac{r^4}{4}\right) + c$$

$$= \frac{\pi m r^4}{2} + c$$

The integral of $f(x) \pm g(x)$

When we wish to integrate the sum or difference of two functions, we integrate each term separately as follows:

Key point

The integral of a sum or difference of two functions

$$\int [f(x) \pm g(x)] \, dx = \int f(x) \, dx \pm \int g(x) \, dx$$

Example 4.88   Find $\int (x^3 + \sin x) dx$.

Solution

$$\int (x^3 + \sin x) \, dx = \int x^3 \, dx + \int \sin x \, dx$$

$$= \frac{x^4}{4} - \cos x + c$$

Note that only a single constant of integration is needed.

Example 4.89   Find $\int 3t^4 + \sqrt{t} \, dt$.

Solution

You will need to use both of the rules to deal with this integral.

$$\frac{3t^5}{5} + \frac{2t^{3/2}}{3} + c$$

Example 4.90   The hyperbolic sine and cosine functions, sinh x and cosh x, are defined as follows:

$$\sinh x = \frac{e^x - e^{-x}}{2} \quad \cosh x = \frac{e^x + e^{-x}}{2}$$

Note that they are simply combinations of the exponential functions e^x and e^{-x}. Find $\int \sinh x \, dx$ and $\int \cosh x \, dx$.

Solution

$$\int \sinh x \; dx = \int \left(\frac{e^x - e^{-x}}{2} \right) dx$$

$$= \qquad\qquad\qquad = \frac{1}{2}(e^x + e^{-x}) + c = \cosh x + c$$

$$\int \cosh x \; dx = \int \left(\frac{e^x + e^{-x}}{2} \right) dx$$

$$= \qquad\qquad\qquad = \sinh x + c$$

It is important that you are aware at this stage that the integral of a product of two functions is not the product of two separate integrals:

$$\int f(x) \times g(x) \; dx \neq \int f(x) \; dx \times \int g(x) \; dx$$

Exercises

1 Find $\int 2x - e^x \; dx$.

2 Find $\int 3e^{2x} \; dx$.

3 Find $\int \dfrac{x + \cos 2x}{3} \; dx$.

4 Find $\int 7x^{-2} \; dx$.

5 Find $\int (x + 3)^2 \; dx$ (be careful!).

6 Find $\int 3 \tan 2x + 2 \sin 3x \; dx$.

7 Find $\int \dfrac{8}{x^2 + 16} \; dx$.

8 Find $\int 3 \cos n\pi x \; dx$.

9 Find $\int 0.5 \sin n\pi x \; dx$.

10 Find $\int \dfrac{1}{2} \sin \dfrac{2\pi t}{T} \; dt$.

11 Find $\int \dfrac{\sin x + \cos x}{2} \; dx$.

Solutions

1 $x^2 - e^x + c$

2 $\dfrac{3e^{2x}}{2} + c$

3 $\dfrac{x^2}{6} + \dfrac{\sin 2x}{6} + c$

4 $-\dfrac{7}{x} + c$

5 $\dfrac{x^3}{3} + 3x^2 + 9x + c$

6 $\dfrac{3}{2}\ln|\sec 2x| - \dfrac{2}{3}\cos 3x + c$

7 $2 \tan^{-1}\left(\dfrac{x}{4}\right) + c$

8 $\dfrac{3}{n\pi} \sin n\pi x + c$

9 $-\dfrac{0.5}{n\pi} \cos n\pi x + c$

10 $-\dfrac{T}{4\pi} \cos \dfrac{2\pi t}{T} + c$

11 $\dfrac{-\cos x + \sin x}{2} + c$

End of section exercises

1 Integrate each of the following functions with respect to x:

(a) x^2 (b) x^{17} (c) 6 (d) $\sin 4x$ (e) e^{8x}

2 Integrate each of the following functions with respect to t:

(a) t^3 (b) 7 (c) e^{-3t} (d) e^{-t} (e) $\dfrac{1}{t}$

3 Find the following integrals:

(a) $\int 3t\,dt$ (b) $\int 3t^2\,dt$ (c) $\int 2t^4\,dt$
(d) $\int t + t^2\,dt$

4 Find the following integrals:

(a) $\int x^2 + 4x + 8\,dx$ (b) $\int 2x^2 - 4x + 7\,dx$
(c) $\int 6x^2 - x + 2\,dx$

5 Find $\displaystyle\int \sqrt{t} + \frac{1}{t^2}\,dt$.

6 Find $\int e^{-st}dt$ where s is a number.

7 Find $\displaystyle\int \frac{1}{s^2 + 0.5}\,ds$.

8 Find $\displaystyle\int \frac{1}{\sqrt{4 + t^2}}\,dt$.

9 Find $\displaystyle\int \frac{1}{\sqrt{25 - x^2}}\,dx$.

10 Find $\displaystyle\int \tan\frac{x}{5}\,dx$.

11 Find $\int \sin 100\pi t + \cos 100\pi t\,dt$.

12 Find $\int \cos(m + n)t\,dt$.

13 Find $\int mbx^2\,dx$.

14 Find (a) $\displaystyle\int \frac{1}{2}\theta\,d\theta$, (b) $\displaystyle\int 4\cos\frac{\theta}{2}\,d\theta$, (c) $\int \sqrt{2}\,d\theta$.

Solutions

1 (a) $\dfrac{x^3}{3} + c$ (b) $\dfrac{x^{18}}{18} + c$ (c) $6x + c$

(d) $-\dfrac{\cos 4x}{4} + c$ (e) $\dfrac{e^{8x}}{8} + c$

2 (a) $\dfrac{t^4}{4} + c$ (b) $7t + c$ (c) $-\dfrac{e^{-3t}}{3} + c$

(d) $-e^{-t} + c$ (e) $\ln|t| + c$

3 (a) $\dfrac{3t^2}{2} + c$ (b) $t^3 + c$

(c) $\dfrac{2t^5}{5} + c$ (d) $\dfrac{t^2}{2} + \dfrac{t^3}{3} + c$

4 (a) $\dfrac{x^3}{3} + 2x^2 + 8x + c$

(b) $\dfrac{2x^3}{3} - 2x^2 + 7x + c$

(c) $2x^3 - \dfrac{x^2}{2} + 2x + c$

5 $\dfrac{2t^{3/2}}{3} - \dfrac{1}{t} + c$

6 $-\dfrac{e^{-st}}{s} + c$

7 $\sqrt{2}\tan^{-1}(s\sqrt{2}) + c$

8 $\sinh^{-1}\left(\dfrac{t}{2}\right) + c$

9 $\sin^{-1}\left(\dfrac{x}{5}\right) + c$

10 $5\ln|\sec\dfrac{x}{5}| + c$

11 $-\dfrac{\cos 100\pi t}{100\pi} + \dfrac{\sin 100\pi t}{100\pi} + c$

12 $\dfrac{\sin(m + n)t}{(m + n)} + c$

13 $\dfrac{mbx^3}{3} + c$

14 (a) $\dfrac{\theta^2}{4} + c$ (b) $8\sin\dfrac{\theta}{2} + c$ (c) $\sqrt{2}\theta + c$

Definite integrals

Introduction

When integration was introduced as the reverse of differentiation in the previous section, the integrals you dealt with were *indefinite integrals*. The result of finding an indefinite integral is usually a function plus a constant of integration. In this section we introduce *definite integrals*, so called because the result will be a definite answer, usually a number, with no constant of integration. Definite integrals have many applications, for example in finding areas bounded by curves, and finding volumes of solids.

**Evaluating definite
integrals**

Definite integrals can be recognised by numbers written to the upper and lower right of the integral sign. The quantity

$$\int_a^b f(x)\,dx$$

is called the definite integral of $f(x)$ from a to b. The numbers a and b are known as the **lower** and **upper limits** of the integral. When you evaluate a definite integral the result will usually be a number. To see how to evaluate a definite integral consider the following example.

Example 4.91   Find $\int_1^4 x^2\,dx$.

Solution

First of all the integration of x^2 is performed in the normal way. However, to show we are dealing with a definite integral, the result is usually enclosed in square brackets and the limits of integration are written on the right bracket:

$$\int x^2\,dx = \frac{x^3}{3} + c \quad \text{so that} \quad \int_1^4 x^2\,dx = \left[\frac{x^3}{3} + c\right]_1^4$$

You should always use this convention. Then, the quantity in the square brackets is evaluated, first by letting x equal the value at the upper limit, then by letting x equal the value at the lower limit, and the difference between the resulting values is found:

$$\left[\frac{x^3}{3} + c\right]_1^4 = (\text{evaluate when } x \text{ equals upper limit})$$
$$- (\text{evaluate when } x \text{ equals lower limit})$$
$$= \left(\frac{4^3}{3} + c\right) - \left(\frac{1^3}{3} + c\right)$$
$$= \frac{64}{3} - \frac{1}{3}$$
$$= \frac{63}{3}$$
$$= 21$$

Note that the constants, c, cancel out. This will always happen, and so in future we can ignore them when we are evaluating definite integrals. So, the value of the definite integral $\int_1^4 x^2 \, \mathrm{d}x$ is 21.

Example 4.92   Find $\int_0^{\pi/2} \cos x \, \mathrm{d}x$.

Solution

Since $\int \cos x \, \mathrm{d}x = \sin x + c$ then

$$\int_0^{\pi/2} \cos x \, \mathrm{d}x = [\sin x]_0^{\pi/2}$$

$$= \sin\left(\frac{\pi}{2}\right) - \sin 0$$

$$= 1 - 0$$

$$= 1$$

Always remember that if you use a calculator to evaluate any trigonometrical functions, you must work in radian mode.

Example 4.93   Find $\int_1^2 (x^2 + 1) \, \mathrm{d}x$.

Solution

First perform the integration:

$$\left[\frac{x^3}{3} + x\right]_1^2$$

Now insert the limits of integration, the upper limit first, and hence find the value of the integral.

$$\left(\frac{8}{3} + 2\right) - \left(\frac{1}{3} + 1\right) = \frac{10}{3} \text{ or } 3.333 \text{ (3 d.p.)}$$

Example 4.94   This exercise is very similar to the previous one. Note the limits of integration have been interchanged.
Find $\int_2^1 (x^2 + 1) \, \mathrm{d}x$.

Solution

$$-\frac{10}{3}$$

Note from these two exercises that interchanging the limits of integration changes the sign of the answer.

Key point

If you interchange the limits, you must introduce a minus sign.

$$\int_a^b f(x)\,\mathrm{d}x = -\int_b^a f(x)\,\mathrm{d}x$$

Example 4.95

The average value of a function

If a function $f(t)$ is defined on the interval $a \le t \le b$ then the average value of the function over the interval is defined to be

$$\text{average value} = \frac{\int_a^b f(t)\,\mathrm{d}t}{b-a}$$

The average value of a function is found by evaluating a definite integral.

Find the average value of the function $f(t) = t^2$ across the interval $2 \le t \le 5$.

Solution

Apply the formula for finding the average value:

average value = $\dfrac{\int_2^5 t^2\,\mathrm{d}t}{5-2}$

Complete the integration to find this average value.

          $\dfrac{1}{3}\left[\dfrac{t^3}{3}\right]_2^5 = 13$

Exercises

1 Explain why a constant of integration is not needed when evaluating definite integrals.

2 Explain what happens to the value of a definite integral when the upper and lower limits are interchanged.

3 Evaluate

   (a) $\int_0^1 x^2\,\mathrm{d}x$ (b) $\displaystyle\int_2^3 \frac{1}{x^2}\,\mathrm{d}x$

4 Evaluate $\int_1^2 \mathrm{e}^x\,\mathrm{d}x$.

5 Evaluate $\int_{-1}^1 (1 + t^2)\,\mathrm{d}t$.

6 Find $\int_0^{\pi/3} \cos 2x\,\mathrm{d}x$.

7 Find $\int_0^\pi \sin x\,\mathrm{d}x$.

8 Find $\int_1^3 \mathrm{e}^{2t}\,\mathrm{d}t$.

9 Evaluate $\int_2^4 x^3\,\mathrm{d}x$. Show that

   $\int_2^4 x^3\,\mathrm{d}x = -\int_4^2 x^3\,\mathrm{d}x$.

10 Show that $\int_a^b \sin x\,\mathrm{d}x = \int_a^b \sin t\,\mathrm{d}t$.

11 Find $\int_0^k 2(kv^3 - v^4)\,\mathrm{d}v$.

12 Find $\int_0^{0.001} 100\,\mathrm{d}t$.

13 Find $100\int_0^{0.01} \sin 100\,n\pi t\,\mathrm{d}t$.

14 Find the average value of the function $f(t) = \sin t$ across the interval $0 \le t \le \dfrac{\pi}{2}$.

15 Find $\displaystyle\int_0^1 \frac{1}{\sqrt{9 - 4t^2}}\,\mathrm{d}t$.

16 Find $\int_0^a 2\pi m r^3\,\mathrm{d}r$.

Solutions

3 (a) $\frac{1}{3}$ (b) $\frac{1}{6}$

4 $e^2 - e^1 = 4.671$

5 2.667

6 $\frac{\sqrt{3}}{4} = 0.4330$

7 2

8 198

9 60

11 $\frac{k^5}{10}$

12 0.1

13 $-\frac{1}{n\pi}(\cos n\pi - 1)$

14 $\frac{2}{\pi}$

15 0.365

16 $\frac{m\pi a^4}{2}$

Further differentiation

Introduction

'Using a table of derivatives' (p. 501) showed how to calculate the derivative of a function using a table of derivatives. By differentiating the function, $y(x)$, we obtain the derivative, $\frac{dy}{dx}$.

The function, $\frac{dy}{dx}$, is more correctly called the **first derivative** of y. By differentiating the first derivative, we obtain the **second derivative**; by differentiating the second derivative we obtain the **third derivative** and so on. The second and subsequent derivatives are known as higher derivatives.

Example 4.96

Calculate the first, second and third derivatives of $y = e^{2x} + x^4$.

Solution

The first derivative is $\frac{dy}{dx}$.

$$\frac{dy}{dx} = 2e^{2x} + 4x^3$$

To obtain the second derivative we differentiate the first derivative:

$$\text{second derivative} = 4e^{2x} + 12x^2$$

The third derivative is found by differentiating the second derivative:

$$\text{third derivative} = 8e^{2x} + 24x$$

Notation

Just as there is a notation for the first derivative so there is a similar notation for higher derivatives.

Consider the function, $y(x)$. We know that the first derivative is denoted by $\frac{dy}{dx}$ or y'. The second derivative is calculated by differentiating the first derivative, that is

$$\text{second derivative} = \frac{d}{dx}\left(\frac{dy}{dx}\right)$$

So, the second derivative is denoted by $\frac{d^2y}{dx^2}$. This is often written more concisely as y''.

The third derivative is denoted by $\frac{d^3y}{dx^3}$ or y''' and so on. So, referring to Example 4.96 we could have written

$$\frac{dy}{dx} = 2e^{2x} + 4x^3$$

$$\frac{d^2y}{dx^2} = 4e^{2x} + 12x^2$$

$$\frac{d^3y}{dx^3} = 8e^{2x} + 24x$$

Key point

If $y = y(x)$

$$\text{first derivative} = \frac{dy}{dx}$$

$$\text{second derivative} = \frac{d^2y}{dx^2}$$

$$\text{third derivative} = \frac{d^3y}{dx^3}$$

Derivatives with respect to t are often indicated using a dot notation, so $\frac{dx}{dt}$ can be written as $\dot{x}$. Similarly, a second derivative with respect to t can be written as $\ddot{x}$, pronounced x double dot.

Example 4.97   Calculate $\dfrac{d^2y}{dt^2}$ and $\dfrac{d^3y}{dt^3}$ given $y = \sin t + \cos t$.

Solution

$$\frac{dy}{dt} = \cos t - \sin t$$

$$\frac{d^2y}{dt^2} = \boxed{} \qquad\qquad\qquad -\sin t - \cos t$$

$$\frac{d^3y}{dt^3} = \boxed{} \qquad\qquad\qquad -\cos t + \sin t$$

We could have used the dot notation and written $\dot{y} = \cos t - \sin t$, and $\ddot{y} = -\sin t - \cos t$.

We may need to evaluate higher derivatives at specific points. We use an obvious notation. The second derivative of $y(x)$, evaluated at, say, $x = 2$, is written as $\dfrac{d^2y}{dx^2}(2)$, or more simply as $y''(2)$. The third derivative evaluated at $x = -1$ is written as $\dfrac{d^3y}{dx^3}(-1)$ or $y'''(-1)$.

Example 4.98   Given

$$y(x) = 2\sin x + 3x^2$$

find (a) $y'(1)$ (b) $y''(-1)$ (c) $y'''(0)$

Solution

We have

$$y = 2\sin x + 3x^2$$

$$y' = 2\cos x + 6x$$

$$y'' = \boxed{} \qquad \boxed{-2\sin x + 6}$$

$$y''' = -2\cos x$$

(a) $y'(1) = 2\cos 1 + 6(1) = 7.0806.$

(b) $y''(-1) = \boxed{} \qquad \boxed{-2\sin(-1) + 6 = 7.6829}$

(c) $y'''(0) = -2\cos 0 = -2.$

Exercises

1 Find $\dfrac{d^2y}{dx^2}$ where $y(x)$ is defined by

   (a) $3x^2 - e^{2x}$ (b) $\sin 3x + \cos x$ (c) $\sqrt{x}$
   (d) $e^x + e^{-x}$ (e) $1 + x + x^2 + \ln x$

2 Find $\dfrac{d^3y}{dx^3}$ where y is given in question 1.

3 Calculate $y''(1)$ where $y(t)$ is given by

   (a) $t(t^2 + 1)$ (b) $\sin(-2t)$ (c) $2e^t + e^{2t}$
   (d) $\dfrac{1}{t}$ (e) $\cos\dfrac{t}{2}$

4 Calculate $y'''(-1)$ of the functions given in question 3.

Solutions

1 (a) $6 - 4e^{2x}$ (b) $-9\sin 3x - \cos x$
   (c) $-\dfrac{1}{4}x^{-3/2}$ (d) $e^x + e^{-x}$ (e) $2 - \dfrac{1}{x^2}$

2 (a) $-8e^{2x}$ (b) $-27\cos 3x + \sin x$ (c) $\dfrac{3}{8}x^{-5/2}$

   (d) $e^x - e^{-x}$ (e) $\dfrac{2}{x^3}$

3 (a) 6 (b) 3.6372 (c) 34.9928 (d) 2 (e) −0.2194

4 (a) 6 (b) −3.3292 (c) 1.8184 (d) −6 (e) −0.0599

End of section exercises

1 Calculate y'' where y is given by

   (a) $\cos 2t - \sin 2t$ (b) $e^{2x} - e^x$ (c) $2x^6 - 3x^7$
   (d) $-x^3 + 3x^2$ (e) $9 - \dfrac{9}{x}$

2 Find the fourth derivative of the following functions:

   (a) e^{3t} (b) e^{kt}, k constant (c) $\sin 2t$ (d) $\sin kt$,
   k constant (e) $\cos kt$, k constant

3 Show that $y = e^x + 2x$ satisfies the equation

$$y'' - y' - y = -2 - 2x - e^x$$

4 Evaluate $y'''(0)$ where y is given by

   (a) $\sin 3t + t^3$ (b) $2\cos t + \cos 2t$
   (c) $e^{-x}(e^x + 1)$ (d) $3 - 3t^4$ (e) $\dfrac{e^{2x} + 1}{e^x}$

5 The function $y(x)$ is defined by

$$y(x) = x^4 - 3x^3 + 3x^2 + 1$$

Calculate the values of x where $y'' = 0$.

Solutions

1 (a) $-4\cos 2t + 4\sin 2t$ (b) $4e^{2x} - e^x$
   (c) $60x^4 - 126x^5$ (d) $-6x + 6$ (e) $-18x^{-3}$

2 (a) $81e^{3t}$ (b) k^4e^{kt} (c) $16\sin 2t$ (d) $k^4\sin kt$
   (e) $k^4\cos kt$

4 (a) −21 (b) 0 (c) −1 (d) 0 (e) 0

5 $\dfrac{1}{2}$, 1

Further integration

Introduction

Often the technique of partial fractions can be used to write an algebraic fraction as the sum of simpler fractions. On occasions this means that we can then integrate a complicated algebraic fraction. We shall explore this approach in this section. A thorough understanding of the various forms that partial fractions can take is an essential prerequisite.

Integration using partial fractions

Sometimes expressions which at first sight look impossible to integrate using the techniques already met may in fact be integrated by first expressing them as simpler partial fractions, and then using the techniques described earlier in this chapter. Consider the following example.

Example 4.99 By expressing the integrand as the sum of its partial fractions find

$$\int \frac{2x + 11}{(x + 7)^2}\, dx$$

Solution

The denominator of the integrand contains a repeated linear factor $(x + 7)^2$. The appropriate form of partial fractions is

$$\frac{2x + 11}{(x + 7)^2} = \frac{A}{x + 7} + \frac{B}{(x + 7)^2}$$

Then

$$2x + 11 = A(x + 7) + B$$

from which, by letting $x = -7$, we find $-3 = B$. Equating coefficients of x, for example, gives $A = 2$. The integral becomes

$$\int \frac{2}{x + 7} - \frac{3}{(x + 7)^2}\, dx$$

The first integral is of the form $\int \dfrac{f'(x)}{f(x)}\, dx$ covered in Section 6.4. Thus

$$\int \frac{2}{x + 7}\, dx = 2 \ln |x + 7| + c$$

The second integral can be evaluated by making a substitution $u = x + 7$, $\dfrac{du}{dx} = 1$, to give

$$\int \frac{3}{(x + 7)^2}\, dx = \int \frac{3}{u^2}\, du$$

$$= -\frac{3}{u} + c$$

$$= -\frac{3}{x + 7} + c$$

Finally, putting both parts together we find

$$\int \frac{2x + 11}{(x + 7)^2} \, dx = 2 \ln|x + 7| + \frac{3}{x + 7} + K$$

Example 4.100   **Express**

$$\frac{23 - x}{(x - 5)(x + 4)}$$

as the sum of its partial fractions. Hence find

$$\int \frac{23 - x}{(x - 5)(x + 4)} \, dx$$

Solution

First produce the partial fractions (hint: write the fraction in the form $\frac{A}{x - 5} + \frac{B}{x + 4}$):

$$A = 2, \ B = -3$$

Then integrate each term separately.

$$2 \ln|x - 5| - 3 \ln|x + 4| + c$$

Exercises

By expressing the following in partial fractions evaluate the given integral. Remember to select the correct form for the partial fractions.

1 $\int \dfrac{1}{x^3 + x} \, dx$

2 $\int \dfrac{13x - 4}{6x^2 - x - 2} \, dx$

3 $\int \dfrac{1}{(x + 1)(x - 5)} \, dx$

4 $\int \dfrac{2x}{(x - 1)^2(x + 1)} \, dx$

5 $\int \dfrac{1}{x^2 - 2x - 1} \, dx$

Solutions

1 $\ln|x| - \dfrac{1}{2} \ln|x^2 + 1| + c$

2 $\dfrac{3}{2} \ln|2x + 1| + \dfrac{2}{3} \ln|3x - 2| + c$

3 $\dfrac{1}{6} \ln|x - 5| - \dfrac{1}{6} \ln|x + 1| + c$

4 $-\dfrac{1}{2} \ln|x + 1| + \dfrac{1}{2} \ln|x - 1| - \dfrac{1}{x - 1} + c$

5 $\dfrac{1}{2\sqrt{2}} \ln\left(\dfrac{x - 1 - \sqrt{2}}{x - 1 + \sqrt{2}} \right)$

End of section exercises

1 Find $\displaystyle\int \frac{3x - 17}{x^2 - 2x - 3}\, dx.$

2 Find $\displaystyle\int \frac{x + 3}{(x + 1)^2}\, dx.$

3 Find $\displaystyle\int \frac{t}{(t + 3)(t - 2)}\, dt.$

4 Find $\displaystyle\int \frac{3 - x}{(x - 2)^2(x + 1)}\, dx.$

5 Find $\displaystyle\int \frac{15x - 6}{(1 - 2x)(2 - x)}\, dx.$

6 Find $\displaystyle\int \frac{2dt}{(1 + t)(1 + 3t)}.$

7 Find $\displaystyle\int \frac{8 - x}{(x - 2)^2(x + 1)}\, dx.$

Solutions

1 $5\ln(x + 1) - 2\ln(x - 3) + c$

2 $\ln(x + 1) - \dfrac{2}{x + 1} + c$

3 $\dfrac{3}{5}\ln(t + 3) + \dfrac{2}{5}\ln(t - 2) + c$

4 $\dfrac{4}{9}\ln(x + 1) - \dfrac{4}{9}\ln(x - 2) - \dfrac{1}{3(x - 2)} + c$

5 $8\ln(x - 2) - \dfrac{\ln(2x - 1)}{2} + c$

6 $\ln(3t + 1) - \ln(t + 1) + c$

7 $\ln\dfrac{x + 1}{x - 2} - \dfrac{2}{x - 2} + c$

Applications of the calculus

Introduction

The maximum and minimum values of a function are often very important. For example, an engineer may need to know the value of the maximum power transferred from a voltage source to a load resistor. Maximum and minimum points are located by examining the derivative of a function, rather than the function itself.

Two tests are described that distinguish between maximum and minimum points. Finally, we explain what is meant by a point of inflexion and how such a point is located.

Maximum and minimum points

Consider Figs 4.29(a) and (b). The point A is a **local maximum**; the point B is a **local minimum**. Note that A is not the highest point on the graph. However, in the locality of A, A is the highest point. Use of the word 'local' stresses that A is a maximum only in its locality. Similarly B is a minimum in its locality but is not the lowest point on the entire graph.

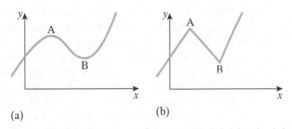

(a)   (b)

Fig. 4.29   (a), (b) A is a local maximum, B is a local minimum.

When moving away from A along the function, both to the left and to the right, the value of y decreases; when moving away from B along the function, the value of y increases.

It is useful to be able to locate points such as A and B. This is done by referring to the gradient of the function, rather than the function itself.

Locating maximum and minimum points

Consider Fig. 4.30, which shows the curve $y(x)$, together with some tangents. The tangents at A and B are parallel to the x axis, that is $\frac{dy}{dx} = 0$ at these points.

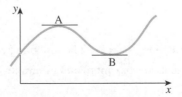

Fig. 4.30   At A and B, $\frac{dy}{dx} = 0$.

We now consider Fig. 4.29(b) again. At A and B it is impossible to draw tangents: that is, they do not exist. Hence at these points $\frac{dy}{dx}$ does not exist. In summary we have

Key point

> At maximum and minimum points, $\frac{dy}{dx} = 0$ or $\frac{dy}{dx}$ does not exist.

So, maximum and minimum points are located by looking for points where $\frac{dy}{dx} = 0$ or $\frac{dy}{dx}$ does not exist.

The first-derivative test

When given any function, $y(x)$, we can limit our search for maximum and minimum points to those points where $\frac{dy}{dx} = 0$ or $\frac{dy}{dx}$ does not exist. We also need to distinguish between a maximum point and a minimum point. To do this we consider y' on either side of the point.

Immediately to the left of a maximum point, such as A in Fig. 4.29, $y' > 0$, that is y is increasing. Immediately to the right of a maximum point, $y' < 0$, that is y is decreasing. Thus, in passing from left to right through a maximum point, y' changes from positive to negative.

Now consider a minimum point, such as B in Fig. 4.29. Immediately to the left of such a point, $y' < 0$, that is y is decreasing. Immediately to the right, $y' > 0$, that is y is increasing. So, in passing from left to right through a minimum point, y' changes from negative to positive.

This information is contained in the **first-derivative test**.

Key point

> - The first-derivative test distinguishes between maximum and minimum points.
> - To the left of a maximum point, $\frac{dy}{dx}$ is positive; to the right $\frac{dy}{dx}$ is negative.
> - To the left of a minimum point, $\frac{dy}{dx}$ is negative; to the right $\frac{dy}{dx}$ is positive.

Example 4.101

Determine the position of any maximum and minimum points of the function $y = x^2 + 1$.

Solution

By differentiation, $\frac{dy}{dx} = 2x$. The function $2x$ exists for all values of x. So, we need only look for maximum and minimum points by solving $y' = 0$. So

$$y' = 0$$
$$2x = 0$$

so

$$x = 0$$

At this stage, we know that the only place a maximum or a minimum point can be found is where $x = 0$. We now apply the first-derivative test.

To the left of $x = 0$, x is negative. So $2x$ is negative and hence y' is negative. To the right of $x = 0$, x is positive and so y' is positive. Since y' changes from negative to positive, there must be a minimum point at $x = 0$.

When $x = 0$, $y = 1$ so $(0, 1)$ is a minimum point. Fig. 4.31 illustrates this.

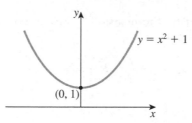

Fig. 4.31 There is a minimum point at $(0, 1)$.

| Example 4.102 | Determine the position of any maximum and minimum points of the function $y = 2x - x^2$. |

Solution

We see that $\dfrac{\mathrm{d}y}{\mathrm{d}x} = 2 - 2x$, which exists for all x. We look for maximum and minimum points by solving $\dfrac{\mathrm{d}y}{\mathrm{d}x} = 0$.

$$\frac{\mathrm{d}y}{\mathrm{d}x} = 0$$

$$2 - 2x = 0$$

$$2 = 2x$$

so

$$x = 1$$

Thus we examine the point where $x = 1$.

We examine the sign of $\frac{\mathrm{d}y}{\mathrm{d}x}$ to the left and to the right of $x = 1$. To determine the sign of $2 - 2x$ to the left and to the right of $x = 1$ we can use one of two techniques. We can sketch a graph of $2 - 2x$ and note the sign on both sides of $x = 1$. Another method is to evaluate $2 - 2x$ just to the left of $x = 1$, say $x = 0.9$, and then evaluate $2 - 2x$ just to the right of $x = 1$, say at $x = 1.1$. When $x = 0.9$, the value of $2 - 2x$ is 0.2; when $x = 1.1$ the value of $2 - 2x$ is -0.2. Since y' changes from positive to negative there must be a maximum at $x = 1$.

When $x = 1$, $y = 1$ and so $(1,1)$ is a maximum point. Fig. 4.32 illustrates this.

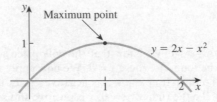

Fig. 4.32   There is a maximum point at (1,1).

| Example 4.103 | **Determine the position of any maximum and minimum points of the function** |

$$y = \frac{t^3}{3} - \frac{t^2}{2} - 2t + 3.$$

Solution

We have

$$\frac{dy}{dt} = t^2 - t - 2$$

Clearly, $\dfrac{dy}{dt}$ exists for all values of t. Solving $\dfrac{dy}{dt} = 0$ yields

$$t^2 - t - 2 = 0$$
$$(t - 2)(t + 1) = 0$$
$$t = -1, 2$$

We need to investigate the two points where $t = -1$ and $t = 2$.

$$t = -1$$

Consider a value just to the left of $t = -1$, say $t = -1.1$ Here

$$\frac{dy}{dt} = (-1.1)^2 - (-1.1) - 2$$
$$= 0.31$$

So, at $t = -1.1$, $\dfrac{dy}{dt}$ is positive.

Just to the right of $t = -1$, say at $t = -0.9$,

$$\frac{dy}{dt} = (-0.9)^2 - (-0.9) - 2$$
$$= -0.29$$

So, $\dfrac{dy}{dt}$ is negative. Since the derivative has changed from positive to negative there must be a maximum point at $t = -1$.

When $t = -1$, $y = \frac{25}{6}$ and so $(-1, \frac{25}{6})$ is a maximum point.

$t = 2$

By considering values just to the left and right of $t = 2$ we see that immediately to the left of $t = 2$, $\frac{dy}{dt}$ is negative; immediately to the right, $\frac{dy}{dt}$ is positive. Hence at $t = 2$ there is a minimum point.

When $t = 2$, $y = -\frac{1}{3}$ so $(2, -\frac{1}{3})$ is a minimum point. Fig. 4.33 illustrates a graph of the function.

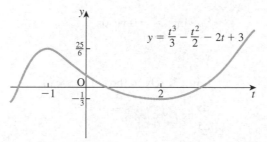

Fig. 4.33 There is a maximum point at $(-1, \frac{25}{6})$ and a minimum point at $(2, -\frac{1}{3})$.

Example 4.104   Determine the position of any maximum and minimum points of the function $y = |t|$.

Solution

Recall that

$$y = |t| = \begin{cases} -t, & t < 0 \\ t, & t \geq 0 \end{cases}$$

A graph of $y = |t|$ is shown in Fig. 4.34. Note that there is a corner at $t = 0$. Hence the derivative, $\frac{dy}{dt}$, does not exist at $t = 0$ and so this is a possible location of a maximum or minimum point. To the left of $t = 0$, $\frac{dy}{dt}$ is negative; to the right of $t = 0$, $\frac{dy}{dt}$ is positive and so there is a minimum at $t = 0$.

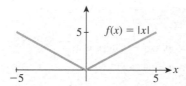

Fig. 4.34   Graph of the modulus function.

Example 4.105   Locate the maximum and minimum points of each of the following functions:

(a) $y = x^2 - 6x + 5$
(b) $y = x^3 - 3x$
(c) $y = x^{1/3}$

Solution

(a) Given $y = x^2 - 6x + 5$

$$\frac{dy}{dx} = \boxed{} \qquad\qquad 2x - 6$$

Solving $\dfrac{dy}{dx} = 0$ yields

$$x = \boxed{} \qquad\qquad 3$$

Immediately to the left of $x = 3$,

$$\frac{dy}{dx} \text{ is } \boxed{} \qquad\qquad \text{negative}$$

Immediately to the right of $x = 3$,

$$\frac{dy}{dx} \text{ is } \boxed{} \qquad\qquad \text{positive}$$

Hence at $x = 3$, there is a $\boxed{}$ minimum
When $x = 3$,

$$y = \boxed{} \qquad\qquad -4$$

Hence $(3, -4)$ is a minimum point.

(b) Given $y = x^3 - 3x$, here

$$y' = \boxed{} \qquad\qquad 3x^2 - 3$$

Solving $y' = 0$, yields

$$x = \boxed{} \qquad\qquad -1, 1$$

Consider $x = -1$.
Immediately to the left of $x = -1$,

$$y' \text{ is } \boxed{} \qquad\qquad \text{positive}$$

Immediately to the right of $x = -1$,

$$y' \text{ is } \boxed{} \qquad\qquad \text{negative}$$

Hence at $x = -1$ there is a $\boxed{}$ maximum
When $x = -1$,

$$y = \boxed{} \qquad\qquad 2$$

So $(-1, 2)$ is a maximum point.
We now consider $x = 1$.
Immediately to the left of $x = 1$,

y' is [ ] negative

Immediately to the right of $x = 1$,

y' is [ ] positive

Hence at $x = 1$ there is a [ ] minimum
When $x = 1$,

$y =$ [ ] -2

So $(1, -2)$ is a minimum point.

(c) Given $y = x^{1/3}$ then by differentiation we have

$$\frac{\mathrm{d}y}{\mathrm{d}x} = \boxed{} \qquad \frac{x^{-2/3}}{3} = \frac{1}{3x^{2/3}}$$

Note that at $x = 0$ the function $\dfrac{1}{3x^{2/3}}$ does not exist so there is no derivative at $x = 0$.
To the left of $x = 0$,

y' is [ ] positive

To the right of $x = 0$,

y' is [ ] positive

Since y' does not change sign we conclude there is neither a maximum nor a minimum at $x = 0$.

Example 4.106

Electrical Engineering – Maximum power transfer

Consider the circuit of Fig. 4.35 in which a non-ideal voltage source is connected to a variable load resistor with resistance R_L. The source voltage is V and its internal resistance is R_S. Calculate the value of R_L that results in the maximum power being transferred from the voltage source to the load resistor.

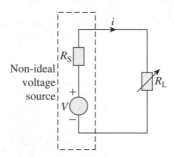

Fig. 4.35 Maximum power transfer occurs when $R_L = R_S$.

Solution

Let i be the current flowing in the circuit. Using Kirchhoff's voltage law and Ohm's law gives

$$V = i(R_S + R_L)$$

Let P be the power developed in the load resistor. Then

$$P = i^2 R_L$$

$$= \frac{V^2 R_L}{(R_S + R_L)^2}$$

Clearly P depends on the value of R_L. Differentiating we obtain

$$\frac{dP}{dR_L} = V^2 \frac{1(R_S + R_L)^2 - R_L\, 2(R_S + R_L)}{(R_S + R_L)^4}$$

$$= V^2 \frac{R_S - R_L}{(R_S + R_L)^3}$$

Equating $\dfrac{dP}{dR_L}$ to zero gives

$$V^2 \frac{R_S - R_L}{(R_S + R_L)^3} = 0$$

that is

$$R_L = R_S$$

We need to check whether this is a maximum point.

$$\frac{dP}{dR_L} = V^2 \frac{R_S - R_L}{(R_S + R_L)^3}$$

When R_L has a value just to the left of R_S, the derivative is positive. When R_L has a value just to the right of R_S, the derivative is negative. Hence there is a maximum when $R_L = R_S$. Therefore maximum power transfer occurs when the load resistance equals the source resistance.

Exercises

1 Determine the location of all maximum and minimum points of the following functions:

(a) $y = x^2 - 4x$

(b) $y = x^2 - 5x + 4$

(c) $y = 10 + 3x - x^2$

(d) $y = \dfrac{x^3}{3} - \dfrac{x^2}{2} + 1$

(e) $y = x^3 - 27x$

2 Determine the location of all maximum and minimum points of the following functions:

(a) $y = xe^x$

(b) $y = \dfrac{1}{1 + x^2}$

(c) $y = \dfrac{x^5}{5} - \dfrac{x^3}{3}$

(d) $y = \dfrac{x^4}{4} + x + 1$

(e) $y = (1 - \ln x)x$

Solutions

1 (a) $(2, -4)$ minimum

   (b) $(\frac{5}{2}, -\frac{9}{4})$ minimum

   (c) $(\frac{3}{2}, \frac{49}{4})$ maximum

   (d) $(0, 1)$ maximum, $(1, \frac{5}{6})$ minimum

   (e) $(-3, 54)$ maximum, $(3, -54)$ minimum

2 (a) $(-1, -0.3679)$ minimum

   (b) $(0, 1)$ maximum

   (c) $(-1, \frac{2}{15})$ maximum, $(1, -\frac{2}{15})$ minimum

   (d) $(-1, \frac{1}{4})$ minimum

   (e) $(1, 1)$ maximum

The second-derivative test

This is a test to distinguish between maximum and minimum points. Rather than examine the sign of y' on both sides of the points where $y' = 0$ we can instead consider the sign of the second derivative, y'', at these points.

On passing left to right through a maximum point, y' changes from positive to zero to negative. Hence, y' is decreasing and so the derivative of y' is negative, that is $y'' < 0$. Similarly, on passing left to right through a minimum point, y' changes from negative to zero to positive and so y' is increasing. Hence y'' is positive. The second-derivative test summarises this:

Key point

- If $y' = 0$ and $y'' < 0$ at a point, then the point is a maximum point.
- If $y' = 0$ and $y'' > 0$ at a point, then the point is a minimum point.
- If $y' = 0$ and $y'' = 0$ the second-derivative test fails and we must return to the first-derivative test.

Example 4.107

Use the second-derivative test to find all maximum and minimum points of

$$y = \frac{x^3}{3} - \frac{x^2}{2} - 6x + 2.$$

Solution

We see that

$$y' = x^2 - x - 6$$
$$= (x + 2)(x - 3)$$

Solving $y' = 0$ yields $x = -2, 3$. Now

$$y'' = 2x - 1$$

The sign of y'' is calculated at both $x = -2$ and $x = 3$.

When $x = -2$, $y'' = -5$. Since $y'' < 0$ then by the second-derivative test there is a maximum point at $x = -2$.

When $x = 3$, $y'' = -5$. Here $y'' > 0$ and so there is a minimum point at $x = 3$.

When $x = -2$, $y = \frac{28}{3}$. When $x = 3$, $y = -\frac{23}{2}$. So $(-2, \frac{28}{3})$ is a maximum point; $(3, -\frac{23}{2})$ is a minimum point.

Example 4.108

Determine the positions of all maximum and minimum points of $y = x^4$.

Solution

We have $y' = 4x^3$. Solving $y' = 0$ yields $x = 0$. Also we see

$$y'' = 12x^2$$

To apply the second-derivative test we evaluate y'' at $x = 0$. At $x = 0$, $y'' = 0$. Since $y'' = 0$ the second-derivative test fails. We return to the first-derivative test and examine the sign of y' to the left and to the right of $x = 0$.

Immediately to the left of $x = 0$, y' is negative. Immediately to the right of $x = 0$, y' is positive. Hence there is a minimum point at $x = 0$.

When $x = 0$, $y = 0$ and so $(0, 0)$ is a minimum point.

Example 4.109

Determine all maximum and minimum points of

$$y = \frac{x^5}{5} + \frac{x^2}{2} + 1$$

Solution

We have

$y' = $ ⬚ $x^4 + x$

Solving $y' = 0$, yields

$x = $ ⬚ $0, -1$

In order to use the second derivative test we calculate y''.

$y'' = $ ⬚ $4x^3 + 1$

The sign of y'' is calculated at each value of x.
When $x = -1$,

y'' is ⬚   negative

and so there is a ⬚ point at $x = -1$.   maximum
When $x = 0$,

y'' is ⬚   positive

and so there is a ⬚ point at $x = 0$.   minimum
When $x = -1$,

$y = $ ⬚ $\dfrac{13}{10}$

When $x = 0$,

$y = $ ⬚ 1

So $(-1, \frac{13}{10})$ is a maximum point; $(0, 1)$ is a minimum point.

Exercises

1 Determine the position of all maximum and minimum points using the second–derivative test.

(a) $y = \dfrac{x^2}{2} - x + 1$

(b) $y = 6 + 2x - \dfrac{3x^2}{2}$

(c) $y = \dfrac{x^3}{3} + \dfrac{3x^2}{2} - 1$

(d) $y = \dfrac{x^4}{4} - \dfrac{x^2}{2}$

Solutions

1 (a) $(1, \frac{1}{2})$, minimum

(b) $(\frac{2}{3}, \frac{20}{3})$, maximum

(c) $(0, -1)$, minimum; $(-3, \frac{7}{2})$, maximum

(d) $(0, 0)$, maximum; $(1, -\frac{1}{4})$, minimum; $(-1, -\frac{1}{4})$, minimum

OUTCOME 4

Tabular and Graphical Form

Data

Introduction

When a new engineering component is developed, there will be extensive testing at each stage. Much data will be gathered and analysed. It is useful to classify data as either **discrete** or **continuous**.

Discrete data

Sometimes a variable must take on a value from a specific set of numbers and no other values are possible. Such a variable is then called a **discrete variable**. Consider a quality control engineer who selects five silicon chips at random and tests each one to see whether it works or not. The engineer is interested in the number of chips that work. Let this variable be n. Then n must be a number from the set $\{0, 1, 2, 3, 4, 5\}$. It is impossible for n to have any other values.

As another example, consider the number of people living in a household. This could be 0, 1, 2, 3, . . . and so on. It is impossible to have 2.3 or 1.7 people living in a household.

These are just two examples of variables that are discrete. When a discrete variable is measured several times, the data so generated are called **discrete data**. Discrete data can have only a limited number of values. Other examples of discrete data are

* the number of cars produced in a factory in a week
* the shoe sizes of people in an office block
* the number of times a machine breaks down in 1 year.

Continuous data

Sometimes a variable can take on any value within a specified range. Such a variable is called **continuous**. For example, consider the weight of a pack of butter produced in a factory. A pack could have any weight between, say, 230 g and 270 g. The weight will be recorded to a particular accuracy, which depends upon the measuring device and the use to which the data will be put. However, the actual weight could be any value in the given range. When a continuous variable is measured several times the data generated are **continuous data**.

Examples of continuous data are

* the diameters of pistons produced in a factory
* the volume of gas produced in a chemical reaction
* the current in a branch of a circuit.

Exercises

1 Explain what is meant by (a) discrete data, (b) continuous data.

2 Give two examples of (a) discrete data, (b) continuous data.

3 Classify the following variables as discrete or continuous:

(a) the number of times a machine breaks down in 12 months

(b) the time between breakdowns of a machine

(c) the capacitance of a capacitor

(d) the amount of money in your pocket

(e) the number of hairs on your head.

Solutions

2 (a) number of employees of a firm, the number of cars passing a given point in 12 hours;

(b) the length of a metal bar, the volume of petrol used on a journey.

3 (a) discrete   (b) continuous   (c) continuous
(d) discrete   (e) discrete

End of section exercises

1 Classify the following variables as discrete or continuous:

(a) the distance travelled before a set of tyres needs replacing

(b) the intensity of light in a room

(c) the force needed to extend a spring by a set amount

(d) the number of bearings in a machine

(e) the percentage mark obtained in an examination.

2 Classify each of the following as discrete or continuous:

(a) the number of pages in a book

(b) the weight of a book

(c) the area of paper needed to make the pages of a book

(d) the price of a book

(e) the number of copies of a book that are sold.

Solutions

1 (a) continuous   (b) continuous   (c) continuous
(d) discrete   (e) discrete

2 (a) discrete   (b) continuous   (c) continuous
(d) discrete   (e) discrete

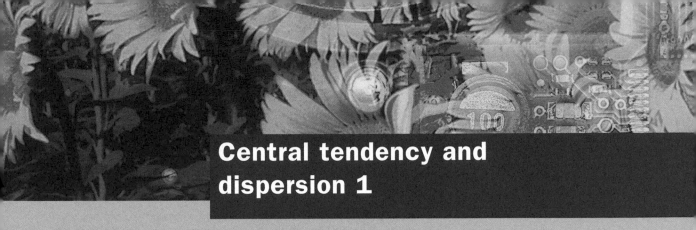

Central tendency and dispersion 1

Introduction

We are often presented with a large amount of data. It may be useful if we can look at a single number that typifies the data. For example, we measure the force at which a certain gauge of wire breaks. If this experiment is repeated many times the force required for breaking will vary: some values will be low, some will be high, and of course there will be some in between. We aim to find a single force that in some way summarises or typifies the measurements that we have made.

A value that typifies a set of data is called an **average**. In statistics there are three important averages: the arithmetic mean, the median and the mode.

The arithmetic mean

The arithmetic mean is also referred to simply as the **mean**. The mean is found by adding up all the data values and then dividing this total by the number of values:

Key point

$$\text{mean} = \frac{\text{sum of values}}{\text{number of values}}$$

Example 4.110

Mechanical Engineering – Breaking force

The force, in newtons, needed to break a wire was measured and the experiment repeated 10 times. The breaking forces are

26 19 17 23 25 20 23 18 20 21

Find the mean breaking force.

Solution

The sum of the values is 212. The number of values is 10. Thus

$$\text{mean} = \frac{\text{sum of values}}{\text{number of values}}$$

$$= \frac{212}{10}$$

$$= 21.2$$

To the nearest whole number, the mean breaking force is 21 newtons.

Example 4.111

The temperature, in °C, at which a liquid boils is measured several times. The results are

93.7 91.4 95.3 94.9 92.3 95.8

Find the mean temperature.

Solution

Sum of values =   563.4

Number of values =   6

Mean temperature = $\dfrac{563.4}{6} = 93.9$

A special notation is often used when calculating a mean. Suppose we have n values and we label these x_1, x_2, x_3, . . . , x_n. The sum of these values is denoted by $\sum_{i=1}^{n} x_i$, or more simply as $\sum x$. The mean is denoted by $\bar{x}$, pronounced 'x bar'. Hence

Key point

$$\text{mean} = \bar{x} = \frac{\sum_{i=1}^{n} x_i}{n}$$

Exercises

1 The diameters in mm of some ball bearings were measured; the results are

    5.1 4.9 5.0 5.2 5.1 4.8 5.2

Calculate the mean diameter, giving your answer to 1 d.p.

2 The current, in amps, in a wire was measured several times and the results noted as follows:

    13.1 12.9 13.1 12.8 12.7 12.6 13.2 13.1

Calculate the mean current, giving your answer to 1 d.p.

3 The temperature, in °C, at which a liquid froze was recorded several times. The results are

    −7   −4   −1   −6   −3   −2   −3   −4

Calculate the mean temperature at which the liquid freezes. Give your answer to the nearest integer.

Solutions

1 5.0 mm

2 12.9 amps

3 −4°C

Calculating the mean of a frequency distribution

The **frequency** of a value is the number of times it occurs. A set of numbers, together with their frequency, is called a **frequency distribution**. For example, suppose the force, in newtons, needed to break a wire is measured and the experiment repeated several times. The results are recorded in Table 4.11.

Table 4.11

Force (N)	Frequency, f
17	3
18	4
19	9
20	11
21	6
22	2

Thus a force of 17 N was recorded three times, a force of 18 N was recorded four times, and so on. Table 4.11 is an example of a frequency distribution. Note that the sum of the frequencies gives the total number of measurements made.

When data are presented in the form of a frequency distribution, the mean can still be calculated. Example 4.112 illustrates the method.

Example 4.112   Table 4.12 is a frequency distribution for the variable x.

Table 4.12

x	frequency, f
5	2
6	3
7	4
8	2
9	1

Calculate the mean of x: that is, $\bar{x}$.

Solution

The value 5 occurs twice and so contributes 5×2 to the sum of the x values. The value 6 occurs three times and so this contributes 6×3 to the sum of the x values. The remaining contributions are 7×4, 8×2 and 9×1. Hence

$$\text{sum of values} = (5 \times 2) + (6 \times 3) + (7 \times 4) + (8 \times 2) + (9 \times 1)$$
$$= 10 + 18 + 28 + 16 + 9$$
$$= 81$$

The number of values is $2 + 3 + 4 + 2 + 1 = 12$, that is the sum of the frequencies. Finally

$$\text{mean} = \bar{x} = \frac{\text{sum of values}}{\text{number of values}}$$
$$= \frac{81}{12}$$
$$= 6.75$$

The mean of the frequency distribution is 6.75.

By referring to Example 4.112 we see that the sum of the values is found by adding the products $x \times f$. The number of values is found by adding up all the frequencies. If the values are denoted by $x_1, x_2, \ldots, x_n$ and the corresponding frequencies by $f_1, f_2, \ldots, f_n$ then we see that

$$\text{Sum of values} = \sum_{i=1}^{n} x_i f_i$$

$$\text{Number of values} = \sum_{i=1}^{n} f_i$$

These are often written respectively in the more compact form as Σxf and Σf, where the limits are assumed.

The mean can now be stated:

Key point

$$\text{mean} = \frac{\sum_{i=1}^{n} x_i f_i}{\sum_{i=1}^{n} f_i}$$

$$= \frac{\sum xf}{\sum f}$$

When calculating the mean of the frequency distribution as given in Table 4.12 usually we would extend the table as follows:

x	f	xf
5	2	10
6	3	18
7	4	28
8	2	16
9	1	9
	$\Sigma f = 12$	$\Sigma xf = 81$

Example 4.113 Find the mean of the data given in Table 4.11.

Solution

The table is extended.

Force, x (N)	Frequency, f	xf
17	3	51
18	4	72
19	9	171
20	11	220
21	6	126
22	2	44
	$\Sigma f = 35$	$\Sigma xf = 684$

$$\text{mean} = \bar{x} = \frac{\sum xf}{\sum f}$$

$$= \frac{684}{35}$$

$$= 19.54$$

Exercises

1 Calculate the mean of the frequency distribution

x	f
17	4
18	11
19	14
20	9
21	5

2 The resistance, in ohms, of a certain type of resistor is measured many times. The results are

Resistance (Ω)	Frequency
4.7	6
4.8	11
4.9	4
5.0	8
5.1	3
5.2	7

Calculate the mean value of the resistance, giving your answer to 1 d.p.

3 The lifetimes of a set of components are measured to the nearest 100 hours. The results are

Lifetime (h)	Frequency
0	1
100	1
200	4
300	10
400	17
500	3
600	2
700	10

Calculate the mean lifetime.

4 The temperature of ignition of a certain mixture of gases is recorded to the nearest 10°C as follows:

Temperature (°C)	Frequency
170	2
180	11
190	10
200	6
210	1
220	2
230	1

Calculate the mean temperature of ignition.

Solutions

1 19

2 4.9 ohms

3 425 hours

4 190°C to the nearest 10°C

The median

The **median** of a set of numbers is found by listing all the numbers in ascending order and selecting the number that is half way along the list.

Example 4.114   **Find the median of the numbers**

$$6\ 8\ 3\ 11\ 10\ 12\ 7\ 9\ 7$$

Solution

The numbers are arranged in ascending order.

$$3\ 6\ 7\ 7\ 8\ 9\ 10\ 11\ 12$$

There are nine numbers in the list. The middle number is the fifth one, that is 8. Therefore, the median is 8.

When there is an even number of values in the list, the median is the mean of the two middle values.

Example 4.115   **Find the median of the following temperatures:**

$$49\ 50\ 40\ 38\ 41\ 57\ 56\ 52$$

Solution

The numbers are arranged in ascending order:

$$38\ 40\ 41\ 49\ 50\ 52\ 56\ 57$$

There are eight numbers in the list. The middle two values are 49 and 50. The mean of these is $\frac{49+50}{2} = 49.5$ and so the median temperature is 49.5.

Exercises

1 Calculate the median of each of the following sets of numbers:

(a) 63 47 51 59 56 50 61 55 58 61

(b) 10 12 16 11 14 11 10 7 13

(c) −4 0 −1 2 3 2 −3 −1

(d) 76 79 81 70 64 62 75 70 71 63 69

Solutions

1 (a) 57   (b) 11   (c) −0.5   (d) 70

The mode

The **mode** of a set of values is the value that occurs most often.

Example 4.116   **Find the mode of the set of numbers**

$$2\ 3\ 3\ 4\ 5\ 5\ 6\ 6\ 6\ 8\ 1\ 1$$

Solution

The number 6 occurs three times; this is more than any other number. Hence the mode is 6.

Example 4.117	**Find the mode of the set of numbers**

$$2\ 2\ 2\ 3\ 3\ 5\ 6\ 11\ 14\ 14\ 14\ 16$$

Solution

In this example there is no single number that occurs most frequently. The numbers 2 and 14 both occur three times. There are two modes. The data are said to be **bimodal**.

Exercises

1 State the mode of each of the following sets of data:

(a) 5 5 5 6 6 7 7 7 7 9 9 9 11 11

(b) 4 1 3 6 4 5 1 4 5 3 2

(c) 4 0 1 3 2 0 2 0 1 3 0 2

Solutions

1 (a) 7   (b) 4   (c) 0

End of section exercises

1 Find the mean, median and mode of each of the following sets of values:

(a) 6 9 5 7 6 8 10

(b) 0 −3 0 −2 1 2 −2 −1 −2 0

(c) 2 3 1 5 2 5 1 4 3 1 6

2 The resistance of several resistors was measured. The results are

Resistance (Ω)	Frequency
5.0	3
5.5	4
6.0	9
6.5	17
7.0	11
7.5	1

(a) Calculate the mean resistance.

(b) Calculate the median.

(c) Calculate the mode.

End of section exercises continued

3 The mean of the set of values

$$5\ 3\ X\ 10\ 2\ 11$$

is 8.3. Find X.

4 Find the mean of the data set

$$2\ 2\ 2\ 2\ 2\ 2\ 20$$

Explain why the mean does not represent the data adequately. Which average would have been more appropriate to use?

5 The force needed to buckle a support beam is measured several times. The results are tabulated thus

Force ($\times 10^3$ N)	Frequency
2.00	4
2.25	1
2.50	2
2.75	5
3.00	2
3.25	2

Calculate the mean buckling force.

Solutions

1 (a) 7.29, 7, 6   (b) −0.7, −0.5, −2 and 0 (bimodal)
(c) 3, 3, 1

2 (a) 6.36 Ω (b) 6.5 Ω (c) 6.5 Ω

3 18.8

4 Mean = 4.57. Mode would be more appropriate.

5 2.59×10^3 N

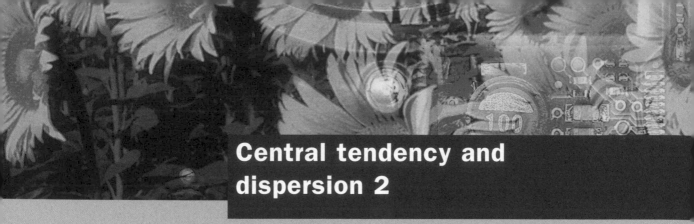

Central tendency and dispersion 2

Introduction

The previous section illustrated different ways of describing the central location of a data set. We now look at the variation in a data set.

Consider the mean of the two sets of data: 4 4 4 and 1 3 8. The means are

$$\frac{4+4+4}{3} = 4 \text{ and } \frac{1+3+8}{3} = 4$$

Both data sets have the same mean although the values in the first data set are all the same whereas those in the second set are spread widely. Clearly the mean value does not reflect the variability of the values in a data set. We need additional parameters to describe variability of data. These additional parameters are the **variance** and the **standard deviation**.

Variance and standard deviation

Both the variance and the standard deviation quantify the variation of a set of data values.

Suppose we have a set of n values: $x_1, x_2, x_3, \ldots, x_n$. The mean of these values is found and labelled as $\bar{x}$. Then the variance is given by

Key point

$$\text{variance} = \frac{\sum_{i=1}^{n}\left(x_i - \bar{x}\right)^2}{n}$$

Example 4.118

Find the variance of

(a) 4 4 4
(b) 1 3 8

Solution

(a) We have $x_1 = 4$, $x_2 = 4$, $x_3 = 4$. The mean, $\bar{x}$, is calculated to be 4. So

$$x_1 - \bar{x} = 0, \ x_2 - \bar{x} = 0, \ x_3 - \bar{x} = 0$$

and so

$$\begin{aligned}
\text{variance} &= \frac{\sum_{i=1}^{3}\left(x_i - \bar{x}\right)^2}{3} \\
&= \frac{0^2 + 0^2 + 0^2}{3} \\
&= 0
\end{aligned}$$

The variance is zero. Since there is no variation in the data values it is not surprising that the variance is zero.

(b) Here we have $x_1 = 1$, $x_2 = 3$, $x_3 = 8$ and $\bar{x} = 4$. Then

$$x_1 - \bar{x} = -3, \ x_2 - \bar{x} = -1, \ x_3 - \bar{x} = 4$$

and so

$$\text{variance} = \frac{\sum_{i=1}^{3}\left(x_i - \bar{x}\right)^2}{3}$$

$$= \frac{(-3)^2 + (-1)^2 + 4^2}{3}$$

$$= \frac{26}{3}$$

$$= 8.67$$

The variance is 8.67.

The **standard deviation** is found from

$$\text{standard deviation} = \sqrt{\text{variance}}$$

Note that the standard deviation has the same units as the given data, and as such is a useful measure of variation.

From Example 4.118 we see that the standard deviation of 4, 4, 4 is $\sqrt{0} = 0$. The standard deviation of 1, 3, 8 is $\sqrt{8.67} = 2.94$.

Example 4.119 Calculate the variance and standard deviation of

11 6 9.6 10.2

Solution

$$\text{mean} = \frac{11 + 6 + 9.6 + 10.2}{4}$$

$$= 9.2$$

The calculation of the variance is given in Table 4.13.

Table 4.13

x_i	$x_i - \bar{x}$	$(x_i - \bar{x})^2$
11	$11 - 9.2 = .8$	$(1.8)^2 = 3.24$
6	$6 - 9.2 = -3.2$	$(-3.2)^2 = 10.24$
9.6	$9.6 - 9.2 = 0.4$	$(0.4)^2 = 0.16$
10.2	$10.2 - 9.2 = 1.0$	$1.0^2 = 1.00$
		$\sum(x_i - \bar{x})^2 = 14.64$

$$\text{variance} = \frac{\sum(x_i - \bar{x})^2}{n}$$

$$= \frac{14.64}{4}$$

$$= 3.66$$

$$\text{standard deviation} = \sqrt{\text{variance}}$$
$$= \sqrt{3.66}$$
$$= 1.91$$

Example 4.120 Calculate the variance and standard deviation of

0 2 3 6 6 10

Solution

mean = [ ]   4.5

Complete the calculation started in Table 4.14.

Table 4.14

x_i	$x_i - \bar{x}$	$(x_i - \bar{x})^2$
0		
2		
3		
6		
6		
10		

−4.5,	20.25
−2.5,	6.25
−1.5,	2.25
1.5,	2.25
1.5,	2.25
5.5,	30.25

$\sum (x_i - \bar{x})^2 =$ [ ]   63.5

variance = [ ] $\dfrac{63.5}{6} = 10.58$

standard deviation = [ ] $\sqrt{10.58} = 3.25$

When data are presented in the form of a frequency distribution the variance and standard deviation can still be found. Example 4.121 illustrates this.

Example 4.121 The number of hardware faults for each computer in a laboratory containing 30 computers is recorded over a 12 month period. The results, in the form of a frequency distribution, are given in Table 4.15.

Table 4.15

Number of faults, x	Frequency, f
0	11
1	4
2	3
3	7
4	5

So 11 of the computers had no faults during the 12 month period, 4 had one fault, 3 had two faults and so on. Note that the sum of the frequencies gives the total number of computers, that is 30.

Calculate the variance and standard deviation.

Solution

The mean, $\bar{x}$, is found to be 1.7. The remainder of the calculation is set out in Table 4.16.

Table 4.16

x_i	f_i	$x_i - \bar{x}$	$(x_i - \bar{x})^2$	$f_i(x_i - \bar{x})^2$
0	11	−1.7	2.89	31.79
1	4	−0.7	0.49	1.96
2	3	0.3	0.09	0.27
3	7	1.3	1.69	11.83
4	5	2.3	5.29	26.45
	$\Sigma f_i = 30$			$\Sigma f_i(x_i - \bar{x})^2 = 72.3$

Then

$$\text{variance} = \frac{\Sigma f_i(x_i - \bar{x})^2}{n}$$

$$= \frac{72.3}{30}$$

$$= 2.41$$

and

$$\text{standard deviation} = \sqrt{\text{variance}}$$

$$= 1.55$$

Example 4.121 illustrates the formula for calculating the variance of a frequency distribution.

Key point

$$\text{variance} = \frac{\Sigma f_i(x_i - \bar{x})^2}{n}$$

End of section exercises

1 Find the variance and standard deviation of the following sets of data:

(a) 6 11 10 9 7 8 9
(b) 5.3 7.2 9.1 8.6 5.9 7.3
(c) −6 −6 −5 −1 0 2 1 0 −2

Which set has the greatest variation?

2 Find the variance and standard deviation of the following frequency distribution:

x	f
6	7
7	3
8	2
9	4
10	2

3 The resistances of 50 resistors are measured and the results recorded as follows:

Resistance (Ω)	Frequency
5.0	17
5.5	12
6.0	10
6.5	6
7.0	5

Calculate the standard deviation of the measurements.

4 The standard deviation of the values $x_1, x_2, x_3, \ldots, x_n$ is σ. Calculate the standard deviation of the values $kx_1, kx_2, kx_3, \ldots, kx_n$ where k is a constant.

5 Calculate the variance and standard deviation of the values

−6 −11 4 0 1 −5 6 3

Solutions

1 (a) variance = 2.53, standard deviation = 1.59
(b) 1.81, 1.35 (c) 8.32, 2.88. Set (c) has the greatest variation.

2 variance = 2.14, standard deviation = 1.46

3 variance = 0.44, standard deviation = 0.66

4 $k\sigma$

5 variance = 29.50, standard deviation = 5.43

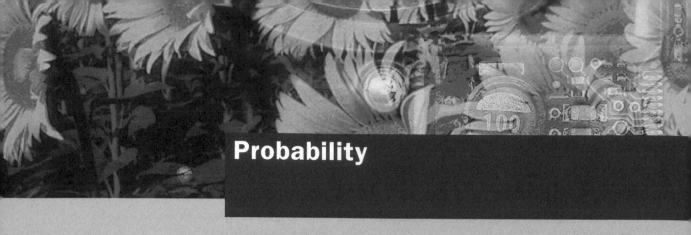

Probability

Introduction

When an event is impossible we say the probability of it happening is 0. When an event is certain, we say the probability of it happening is 1. For example, it is impossible to live without oxygen and so the probability of doing this is 0. It is certain that a metal bar will sink when placed in water and so the probability of this happening is 1.

Most events are neither impossible nor certain. They have varying degrees of likelihood. The probability of such events lies between 0 and 1. Events that are likely to happen have probabilities close to 1; events that are unlikely to happen have probabilities close to 0. An event that is as likely to happen as not has a probability of 0.5. For example, the probability of throwing a head with a fair coin is 0.5.

Experimental and theoretical probabilities

We introduce the notation used in probability theory and calculations.

We let E denote an event and $P(E)$ denote the probability of the event E happening. For example, suppose E is the event 'A 4 is obtained on throwing a die'. The probability of this is $\frac{1}{6}$. We would write this as $P(E) = \frac{1}{6}$.

Since all probabilities lie between 0 and 1 we know that for any event, E, $0 \le P(E) \le 1$.

Key point

For any event, E

$$0 \le P(E) \le 1$$

There are two ways in which we ascertain the probability of a particular event: theoretically and experimentally.

To calculate a theoretical probability we need to have knowledge of the event. For example, suppose we toss a fair coin and let H be the event that it lands with the head facing uppermost. Clearly $P(H) = 0.5$. Similarly suppose we roll a fair die and E is the event that a 4 is obtained; then $P(E) = \frac{1}{6}$. These probabilities have been calculated from knowledge of the physical situation. When any experiment is carried out there are usually several possible outcomes, or **events** as we call them. For example, when throwing a coin there are two possible events: the coin lands with the tail uppermost or lands with the head uppermost. Often the possible events have equal probabilities. In the case of throwing a coin, there are two equally likely events. So if

H: the coin lands with the head uppermost
T: the coin lands with the tail uppermost

then clearly

$$P(H) = P(T) = 0.5$$

Example 4.122 **A die is rolled. Calculate the probability that a 4 is uppermost.**

Solution

When a die is rolled there are six possible events: a 1 is uppermost, a 2 is uppermost and so on. Each of the six events is equally likely to happen and so the probability of each event is $\frac{1}{6}$. In particular, the probability that a 4 is uppermost is $\frac{1}{6}$.

In some circumstances we do not have sufficient information to calculate a theoretical probability. We know that if a coin is unbiased the probability of obtaining a head is $\frac{1}{2}$. However, suppose the coin is biased so that it is more likely to land with the head uppermost than with its tail uppermost. We can experiment by tossing the coin a large number of times and counting the number of heads obtained. Suppose we toss the coin 1000 times and obtain 650 heads. We can estimate the probability of obtaining a head as $\frac{650}{1000} = 0.65$. Such a probability is known as an **experimental probability**. It is accurate only if a large number of experiments have been performed.

Example 4.123

A biased die is thrown 1000 times and a 6 is obtained on 330 occasions. Calculate the probability of obtaining a 6 on a single throw of the die.

Solution

$$\text{probability of throwing a } 6 = \frac{330}{1000}$$

$$= 0.33$$

Exercises

1 A company manufactures precision bearings. On an inspection three batches out of 500 were rejected. Calculate the probability that a batch is rejected.

2 A pack of 52 cards is shuffled and a single card is drawn. Calculate the probability that it is the queen of hearts.

3 A television manufacturer sold 36 000 TV sets of which 297 were returned within 12 months with faults.

   (a) Calculate the probability that a TV set, chosen at random, is returned within 12 months.

   (b) A store buys 500 TV sets from the manufacturer. How many can be expected to develop faults within 12 months?

Solutions

1 0.006

2 $\frac{1}{52}$

3 (a) 0.00825 (b) 4.125, that is four sets.

Compound events

Suppose we roll a fair die and we wish to calculate the probability that the number showing is 3 or higher. To obtain a score of 3 or more, we could throw a 3, 4, 5 or 6: that is, there are four ways of obtaining such a score. When the die is rolled there are six possible outcomes, of which four result in a score of 3 or more. So

$$P \text{ (obtaining a score of 3 or more)} = \frac{4}{6}$$

$$= \frac{2}{3}$$

An event such as 'score 3 or higher' is an example of a **compound event**. When all the outcomes of an experiment are equally likely then we can calculate the probability of a compound event, E, using

Key point

$$P(E) = \frac{\text{number of ways that } E \text{ can happen}}{\text{total number of possible outcomes}}$$

Example 4.124   **A fair die is rolled. Calculate the probability of obtaining an odd score.**

Solution

The chosen event is throwing an odd score: that is, a 1, 3 or 5. Thus there are three ways in which the chosen event can occur out of a total of six equally likely outcomes. So

$$P \text{ (odd score)} = \frac{3}{6}$$

$$= \frac{1}{2}$$

Example 4.125   **Two fair coins are tossed.**

(a) Write down all the possible outcomes.
(b) Calculate the probability of obtaining one or more heads.

Solution

(a) Letting H stand for head and T for tail, the possible outcomes are

   HH HT TH TT

All outcomes are equally likely.

(b)

number of ways of obtaining one or more heads = 3

total number of possible outcomes = 4

probability of obtaining one or more heads = $\frac{3}{4}$

Exercises

1 A pack of 52 cards is shuffled and a card is selected. Calculate the probability that the card is

(a) black
(b) red
(c) a club
(d) a jack
(e) a red queen

2 Three fair coins are tossed.
(a) List the eight possible outcomes.
(b) Calculate the probability of obtaining
(i) exactly two heads, (ii) at least two heads, (iii) no heads.

3 A fair die is rolled. Calculate the probability that the number showing is

(a) odd
(b) 2 or more
(c) less than 4

4 Two fair dice are thrown. Calculate the probability that the total is
(a) 6   (b) 8   (c) more than 10

Solutions

1 (a) $\frac{1}{2}$ (b) $\frac{1}{2}$ (c) $\frac{1}{4}$ (d) $\frac{1}{13}$ (e) $\frac{1}{26}$

2 (a) HHH, HHT, HTH, HTT, THH, THT, TTH, TTT

(b) (i) $\frac{3}{8}$ (ii) $\frac{1}{2}$ (iii) $\frac{1}{8}$

3 (a) $\frac{1}{2}$ (b) $\frac{5}{6}$ (c) $\frac{1}{2}$

4 (a) $\frac{5}{36}$ (b) $\frac{5}{36}$ (c) $\frac{1}{12}$

Complementary events

Consider the following situation. A component is tested. Either it works or it does not work, so there are two possible events. When the component is tested one of these events must happen. In addition, each event excludes the other. We say that the two events are **complementary**.

In general, two events are complementary if one of them must happen and, when it does, the other event cannot happen. If A is an event, then the corresponding complementary event is denoted by $\bar{A}$. The sum of probabilities of two complementary events is always one. For example, if the probability that the component works is 0.92, then the probability that it does not work is $1 - 0.92 = 0.08$.

Example 4.126

The events A and B are defined by

    A: a score of 5 is rolled with a fair die
    B: the box contains more than 10 components

State the complementary events, $\bar{A}$ and $\bar{B}$.

Solution

$\bar{A}$ is the event: a score other than 5 is obtained when the die is rolled.
$\bar{B}$ is the event: the box contains 10 or fewer components.

Exercises

1 State the complement of the following events:

(a) the component is reliable
(b) the digit is greater than 7
(c) the volume is less than or equal to 1 litre
(d) the machine is not working
(e) all components have been tested
(f) at least four components from the batch are unreliable.

Solutions

1 (a) the component is not reliable
(b) the digit is 7 or less
(c) the volume is more than 1 litre
(d) the machine is working
(e) some components have not been tested
(f) three or fewer components from the batch are unreliable.

Use of tree diagrams to calculate probabilities

When a problem involving probabilities is complex, it is sometimes useful to introduce a **tree diagram**. Tree diagrams enable information to be presented in a clear way and aid understanding.

Example 4.127

Reliability Engineering

Machines A and B make components. Of those made by machine A, 95% are reliable; of those made by machine B, 92% are reliable. Machine A makes 70% of the components with machine B making the rest. Calculate the probability that a component picked at random is

(a) made by machine B
(b) made by machine A and is reliable
(c) made by machine B and is unreliable
(d) reliable.

Solution

(a) Since machine A makes 70% of the components then machine B makes the remaining 30%. Hence the probability that a component is made by machine B is 0.3.

To answer (b), (c) and (d) we introduce the tree diagram.

Consider 100 components: 70 are made by machine A and 30 are made by machine B. This is represented as in Fig. 4.36.

Consider the 70 components made by machine A: 95% of these are reliable and so 5% are unreliable. Now 95% of 70 = 66.5, 5% of 70 = 3.5, and this information is represented by Fig. 4.37.

Similarly, of the 30 components made by machine B, 92% are reliable and so 8% are unreliable. We know that 92% of 30 = 27.6 and 8% of 30 = 2.4. This information is represented by Fig. 4.38.

Putting together Figs 4.36, 4.37, and 4.38 we obtain the tree diagram shown in Fig. 4.39.

We use Fig. 4.39 to answer (b), (c) and (d).

Fig. 4.36   Fig. 4.37

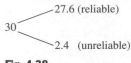

Fig. 4.38

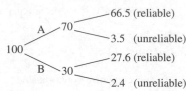

Fig. 4.39

(b) We see that there are 66.5 components made by machine A that are reliable from the original 100 components. So

$$P(\text{component is made by A and is reliable}) = \frac{66.5}{100}$$

$$= 0.665$$

(c) We see from Fig. 4.39 that there are 2.4 components made by machine B that are unreliable.

$$P(\text{component made by B and is unreliable}) = \frac{2.4}{100}$$

$$= 0.024$$

(d) There are $66.5 + 27.6 = 94.1$ reliable components from the original 100. So

$$P(\text{component is reliable}) = \frac{94.1}{100}$$

$$= 0.941$$

Example 4.128   **Reliability Engineering**

Machines A, B and C make components. Machine A makes 30% of the components, machine B makes 50% of the components, and machine C makes the remainder. Of those components made by machine A, 93% are reliable, of those made by machine B, 89% are reliable, and of those made by machine C, 96% are reliable.

A component is picked at random. Calculate the probability that it is

(a) made by machine C
(b) made by machine B and is unreliable
(c) made by either machine A or machine B
(d) reliable.

Solution

Consider 100 components. A tree diagram that illustrates the information is shown in Fig. 4.40.

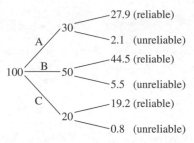

Fig. 4.40

(a) Machine A makes 30% of the components, machine B makes 50% of the components and so machine C makes $(100 - 30 - 50)\% = 20\%$ of the components. So

$$P(\text{component is made by machine C}) = 0.20$$

(b) From Fig. 4.40, the number of components made by machine B that are unreliable is

5.5

So

$$P(\text{component is made by B and is unreliable}) = \quad \frac{5.5}{100} = 0.055$$

(c) Out of 100 components, machine A makes 30 and machine B makes 50. So

$$P(\text{component is made by either A or B}) = \quad \frac{30 + 50}{100} = 0.8$$

(d) Out of 100 components there are   91.6   reliable ones.

So

$$P(\text{component is reliable}) = \quad \frac{91.6}{100} = 0.916$$

Exercises

1 Components are made by machines A and B. Machine A makes twice as many components as machine B. When made by machine A, 3% of the components are faulty; when made by machine B, 5% are faulty. Calculate the probability that a component picked at random is

(a) made by machine B
(b) made by machine A and is faulty
(c) made by machine B and is not faulty
(d) faulty.

2 Silicon chips are manufactured by four machines, A, B, C and D. Machines A, B, C and D manufacture 20%, 25%, 35% and 20% of the components respectively. Of those silicon chips manufactured by machine A, 2.1% are faulty. The respective figures for machines B, C and

Exercises continued

D are 3%, 1.6% and 2.5%. A silicon chip is selected at random. Calculate the probability that it is

(a) made by machine C and is faulty
(b) made by machine A and is not faulty
(c) faulty.

3 Precision components are made by machines A, B and C. Machines A and C each make 30% of the components with machine B making the rest. The probability that a

component is acceptable is 0.91 when made by machine A, 0.95 when made by machine B and 0.88 when made by machine C.

(a) Calculate the probability that a component selected at random is acceptable.
(b) A batch of 2000 components is examined. Calculate the number of components you expect are not acceptable.

Solutions

1 (a) 0.3333   (b) 0.02   (c) 0.3167   (d) 0.0367

2 (a) 0.0056   (b) 0.1958   (c) 0.0223

3 (a) 0.917   (b) 166

End of section exercises

1 Which of the following numbers cannot represent probabilities?

$$\frac{2}{3}, \frac{1}{11}, -\frac{2}{3}, \frac{3}{7}, \frac{9}{7}, \frac{7}{9},$$

0.000, 1.010, 1

2 A company manufactures resistors. During a quality control check, 36 out of 2500 resistors failed to perform to the required standard.

(a) Calculate the probability that a resistor picked at random will fail to perform to the required standard.
(b) In a batch of 700 resistors how many would you expect to fail?

3 Resistors are manufactured by machines A and B. Machine A makes 60% of the resistors with machine B making the rest. When made by machine A, 3% of the resistors are faulty; when made by machine B, 7% are faulty.

A resistor is picked at random. Calculate the probability it is

(a) made by machine B
(b) made by machine A and is not faulty
(c) made by machine B and is faulty
(d) faulty.

4 The probability of throwing a '6' with a fair die is $\frac{1}{6}$. A student makes the following argument.

If I throw the die once, the probability of obtaining a '6' is $\frac{1}{6}$. So if I throw the die twice, then the probability of throwing a '6' must be $2 \times \frac{1}{6} = \frac{1}{3}$. If I throw the die three times then the probability of throwing a '6' must be $3 \times \frac{1}{6} = \frac{1}{2}$ and so on.

Is the argument sound? If not, why not?

5 Components are made by machines A, B and C. Machines A and B each make 36% of the components with machine C making the rest. For machine A, 2% of the components made are faulty, for machine B, 6% are faulty, and for machine C, 7% are faulty.

A component is picked at random. Calculate the probability that it is

(a) faulty and made by machine C
(b) not faulty.

6 State the complement of the events:

(a) the machine is ready
(b) the assignment was delivered on time
(c) both printers are working
(d) at least one person is absent today.

Solutions

1 $-\dfrac{2}{3}, \dfrac{9}{7}, 1.010$

2 (a) 0.0144 (b) 10

3 (a) 0.4   (b) 0.582   (c) 0.028   (d) 0.046

4 The argument is unsound. Using this argument, when the die is thrown seven times, the probability of throwing a '6' is $7 \times \frac{1}{6} = \frac{7}{6}$, which is clearly nonsense.

5 (a) 0.0196   (b) 0.9516

6 (a) the machine is not ready
(b) the assignment was not delivered on time
(c) at least one of the printers is not working
(d) no one is absent today.

Probability distributions

Introduction

There are usually several possible outcomes for any given experiment. For example, when a component is tested it may be classified as substandard, satisfactory or first class. Here there are three possible outcomes. The outcome is a discrete variable. As another example, consider measuring the diameter of a piston. It may be 10.101 cm, 10.093 cm, 10.102 cm and so on. Here the outcome is a continuous variable, which can have any value within a specified range.

Probability distributions are used to assign probabilities to the various possible outcomes of an experiment. If the variable is discrete we use a probability distribution; if the variable is continuous we use a modified form of a distribution, called a **probability density function** (p.d.f.).

Probability distributions

Key point

The probability distribution of a discrete variable, X, gives the probabilities of all the possible values of X.

Example 4.129

Components produced in a factory are graded as substandard, satisfactory or first class. The percentage of each is 10%, 85% and 5% respectively. Thus the probability distribution is as follows:

Component description	Probability
Substandard	0.10
Satisfactory	0.85
First class	0.05

Example 4.130

A service engineer records the number of calls received in an 8 hour period for 300 similar periods. The results are given as:

Number of calls	Frequency
0	2
1	7
2	26
3	97
4	101
5	53
6	14

Construct a probability distribution for the number of calls.

Solution

Let X be the number of calls received. Note that X is a discrete variable that takes on values 0, 1, 2, . . . , 6. The probability of each different value of X occurring is calculated.

$$P(X = 0) = \frac{2}{300}$$

$$= 0.0067$$

$$P(X = 1) = \frac{7}{300}$$

$$= 0.0233$$

$$P(X = 2) = \qquad\qquad \frac{26}{300} = 0.0867$$

$$P(X = 3) = \qquad\qquad \frac{97}{300} = 0.3233$$

$$P(X = 4) = \qquad\qquad \frac{101}{300} = 0.3367$$

$$P(X = 5) = \qquad\qquad \frac{53}{300} = 0.1767$$

$$P(X = 6) = \qquad\qquad \frac{4}{300} = 0.0467$$

The probability distribution is

Number of calls, X	Probability
0	0.0067
1	0.0233
2	0.0867
3	0.3233
4	0.3367
5	0.1767
6	0.0467

A probability distribution may be represented graphically in the form of a **bar chart**. Fig. 4.41 is a bar chart that represents the probability distribution of Example 4.130.

Note that when all the possible values of a variable have been considered, then the sum of the probabilities is 1.

To find the probability of several outcomes, the individual probabilities are added. Example 4.131 illustrates this.

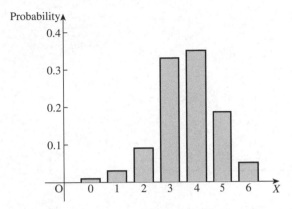

Fig. 4.41   Bar chart for probability distribution of Example 6.2.

Example 4.131   Using the data from Example 4.130, calculate the probability that the service engineer receives five or six calls in an 8 hour period.

Solution

The individual probabilities are noted: $P(X = 5) = 0.1767$, $P(X = 6) = 0.0467$.

So adding the probabilities we find the probability of receiving five or six calls.

$$P(X = 5 \text{ or } 6) = P(X = 5) + P(X = 6)$$

$$= 0.1767 + 0.0467$$

$$= 0.2234$$

Exercises

1 Explain what is meant by a probability distribution.

2 The number of employees absent each day in a particular firm is recorded over a 200 day period. The results are as follows:

Number absent	Frequency
2	12
3	36
4	81
5	10
6	15
7	46

(a) Calculate the corresponding probability distribution.

(b) Calculate the probability there are five or more absent employees on a day chosen at random.

Solutions

2 (a)

Number absent	Probability
2	0.06
3	0.18
4	0.405
5	0.05
6	0.075
7	0.23

(b) 0.355.

Probability density functions

Consider a continuous variable, X, which can take on any value between some prescribed limits. The probability that X lies somewhere between values, say, a and b is found from a **probability density function (p.d.f.)**, $f(x)$.

Key point

> The probability that the continuous variable, X, lies between a and b, that is $P(a < X < b)$, is given by
>
> $$P(a < X < b) = \int_a^b f(x)\mathrm{d}x$$
>
> where $f(x)$ is the probability density function of X.

Thus the area under the p.d.f. between $x = a$ and $x = b$ gives the probability that the variable X lies between a and b. Fig. 4.42 illustrates this.

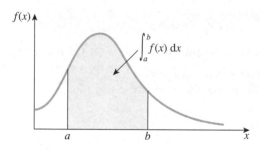

Fig. 4.42 $P(a < X < b) = \int_a^b f(x)\,\mathrm{d}x$

For a function to be a valid p.d.f. it must

1. never be negative
2. have a total area under the curve of 1, representing total probability.

Example 4.132 Given that X is a continuous variable, interpret the following expressions.

(a) $P(15 < X < 20)$
(b) $P(X < 1.7)$
(c) $P(X > 9.6)$
(d) $P(X = 2.6)$

Solution

(a) This represents the probability that X lies between 15 and 20.
(b) This is the probability that X is less than 1.7.
(c) This is the probability that X is greater that 9.6.
(d) $P(X = 2.6)$ is not a valid statement for a continuous variable. Probability statements for continuous variables must always be in terms of intervals. We could calculate $P(2.59 < X < 2.61)$ for example, but not $P(X = 2.6)$.

Example 4.133 A p.d.f. for the continuous variable X is given by

$$f(x) = 2x \quad 0 < x < 1$$

(a) Check that $f(x)$ is a valid p.d.f.
(b) Calculate $P(0.1 < X < 0.7)$.

Solution

(a) The function, $f(x)$, is defined only on the interval $0 < x < 1$ and on this interval it is never negative. Also

$$\int_0^1 f(x)\, dx = \int_0^1 2x\, dx$$

$$= [x^2]_0^1$$

$$= 1$$

and so the total area under $f(x)$ is 1. Hence $f(x)$ is a valid p.d.f.

(b) $P(0.1 < X < 0.7) = \displaystyle\int_{0.1}^{0.7} 2x\, dx$

$$= [x^2]_{0.1}^{0.7}$$

$$= 0.48$$

The probability that X lies between 0.1 and 0.7 is 0.48.

Example 4.134 A p.d.f., $f(x)$, for a continuous variable X is given by

$$f(x) = \frac{3}{16}(4 - x^2) \quad 0 < x < 2$$

Calculate

(a) $P(0.5 < X < 1.5)$ (b) $P(X < 1)$ (c) $P(X = 1.6)$

Solution

(a) $P(0.5 < X < 1.5) =$

$$\frac{3}{16}\int_{0.5}^{1.5} 4 - x^2 \mathrm{d}x = 0.5469$$

(b) $P(X < 1) =$

$$\frac{3}{16}\int_{0}^{1} 4 - x^2 \mathrm{d}x = 0.6875$$

(c) $P(X = 1.6)$ is not a meaningful statement for a continuous variable.

Exercises

1 Explain what is meant by a probability density function.

2 State two properties that a function must have in order to be a probability density function.

3 A p.d.f., $f(x)$, for a continuous variable X is given by

$$f(x) = \frac{3}{10}(x^2 + 1) \quad 1 < x < 2$$

(a) Verify that $f(x)$ can be a p.d.f.

(b) Find $P(1.7 < X < 2)$.
(c) Find $P(X < 1.5)$.
(d) Find $P(X > 1.25)$.

4 A p.d.f. for a continuous variable X is given by

$$f(x) = e^x \quad x < 0$$

Calculate

(a) $P(-1 < X < 0)$
(b) $P(-3.5 < X < -3)$
(c) $P(X < -1)$
(d) $P(X > -2)$

5 A p.d.f. for the continuous variable X is given by

$$f(x) = e^{-x} \quad x > 0$$

If $P(0 < X < \alpha) = 0.5$, find α.

Solutions

3 (b) 0.3987   (c) 0.3875   (d) 0.8297

4 (a) 0.6321   (b) 0.0196   (c) 0.3679   (d) 0.8647

5 0.6931

End of section exercises

1 A p.d.f., $f(x)$, has the form

$$f(x) = \alpha(x + 1) \quad 0 < x < 1$$

Calculate α.

2 Table 4.17 is a probability distribution.

Table 4.17

x	$P(x)$
6.0	0.13
6.5	0.10
7.0	0.09
7.5	0.02
8.0	0.23
8.5	0.43

End of section exercises continued

Find

(a) $P(x \geq 7.0)$ (b) $P(x > 7.5)$

(c) $P(x \leq 8.0)$ (d) $P(x < 7.5)$

(e) $P(6.5 < x \leq 8.0)$

3 The number of reject components in each of 700 boxes is counted and recorded in Table 4.18.

(a) Construct a frequency distribution from the given data.

(b) Calculate the probability that the number of reject components is between 1 and 4 inclusive.

Table 4.18

Number of rejects per box	Frequency
0	117
1	123
2	236
3	147
4	63
5	14

4 A p.d.f. for the continuous variable X is given by

$$f(x) = \frac{x^2}{21} \quad 1 < x < 4$$

Calculate

(a) $P(2 < X < 3)$ (b) $P(X > 2.5)$

(c) $P(X < 3.5)$

5 A p.d.f. for the continuous variable X is given by

$$f(x) = 2e^{-2x} \quad x > 0$$

Calculate

(a) $P(1 < X < 5)$

(b) $P(X > 1)$

(c) $P(X < 2)$

(d) the value of α such that 90% of the X values are less than α.

Solutions

1 $\frac{2}{3}$

2 (a) 0.77 (b) 0.66 (c) 0.57 (d) 0.32 (e) 0.34

3 (a)

Number of rejects per box	$P(x)$
0	0.1671
1	0.1757
2	0.3371
3	0.2100
4	0.0900
5	0.0200

(b) 0.813

4 (a) 0.3016 (b) 0.7679 (c) 0.6647

5 (a) 0.1353 (b) 0.1353 (c) 0.9871 (d) 1.1513